...cy Pendleton

5103 Roland Avenue

323-4813

3277.

1.50

Voice Science

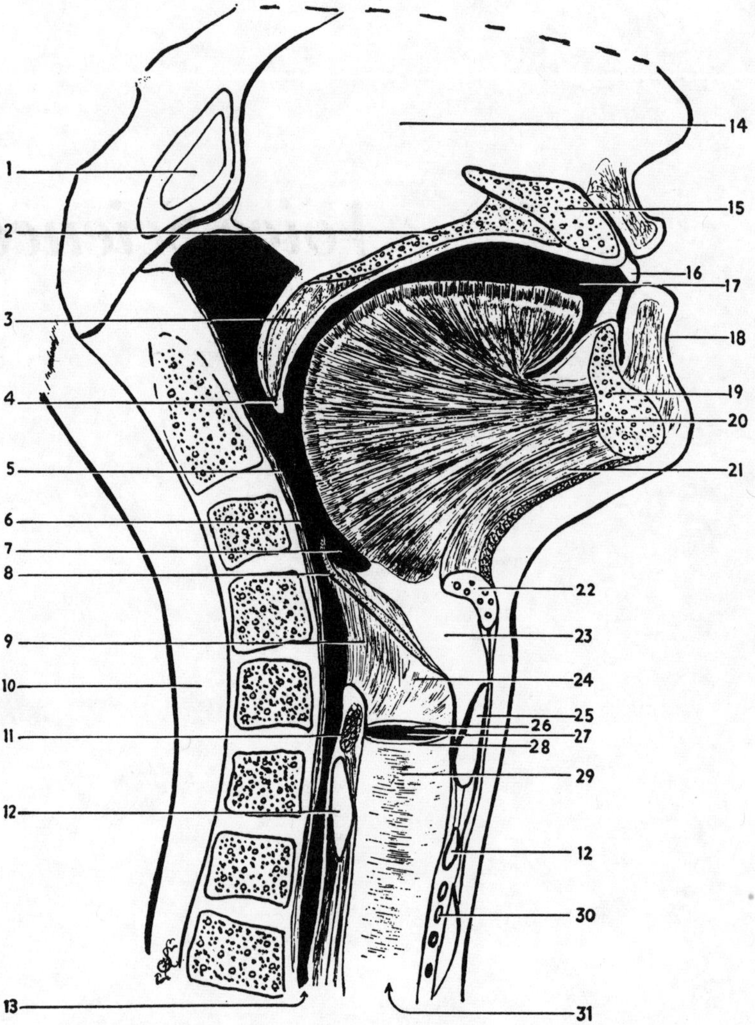

FRONTISPIECE. Median Sagittal Section Through the Head and Neck.

1. Sphenoidal sinus; 2. hard palate; 3. soft palate; 4. uvula; 5. superior pharyngeal constrictor; 6. middle pharyngeal constrictor; 7. vallecula; 8. epiglottis; 9. aditus laryngis; 10. vertebral canal; 11. arytenoidei; 12. cricoid cartilage; 13. esophagus; 14. nasal cavity; 15. maxilla; 16. teeth; 17. oral cavity; 18. lip; 19. mandible; 20. genioglossus; 21. geniohyoid; 22. hyoid bone; 23. adipose tissue; 24. hyperglottal cavity; 25. thyroid cartilage; 26. superior ventricular folds; 27. glottis; 28. vocal folds; 29. hypoglottal cavity; 30. tracheal cartilages; 31. trachea.

Voice Science

SECOND EDITION

LYMAN S. V. JUDSON

Winona State College

AND

ANDREW THOMAS WEAVER

University of Wisconsin

NEW YORK

APPLETON–CENTURY–CROFTS

Division of Meredith Publishing Company

637-10

Library of Congress Card Number: 65–12033

PRINTED IN THE UNITED STATES OF AMERICA
E 49265

In memory of

Ellen M. Judson, B.S., M.A., M.S. (in Library Science), who was co-author of the first edition, even though her name did not appear on the title page, and who bore the same relationship to this revision.

Preface

The definitive attribute of Man is his speech—together with the thinking and communication it makes possible. Such communication, by implication, assumes hearing.

The study of how speech is produced and of how we hear should have a place, therefore, in the life of any person who is interested in himself and those about him. The more one studies the normal mechanisms of speech and hearing the more assuredly he is amazed at the complexity, and even the beauty, of their organization and function. In the normal development of these mechanisms from fertilized ovum to mature adult there is further evidence of coordination of a highly complex order. Such considerations are in themselves sufficient reason to study the normal mechanisms responsible for speech and hearing.

For anyone who plans to spend his professional life in one of the fields of communications, for example, speech, drama, languages, telephony, radio or television, a study of the speech and hearing mechanisms is imperative. And for specialists dedicated to aiding those millions handicapped by defective speech or hearing, or both, a basic knowledge of what is the *normal* logically precedes studies of the abnormal. Only in contrast to the normal is the abnormal meaningful.

In this revision the normal mechanisms of speech and hearing are considered in relation to the integrated human organism. Admittedly, in the normal individual the mechanisms that make it possible for him to produce speech and to hear are separate and distinct. Yet, at the same time, the mechanisms are so complex and inter-coordinated that any stimulus affecting any one must inevitably affect the others—if not, indeed, the entire organism.

Even though we may study one part in isolation in order to simplify its function and thereby make it easier to understand, we must never forget that the entire body may be and often is involved when any one mechanism or part is affected. Indeed, it is the vital relation of speech and hearing to human life that raises to such a high level of importance this interaction between speech-thought and bodily well-being, between hearing and bodily safety and comfort, and, conversely, between the physiological condition of the body and the ability to produce normal speech or to hear normally.

While the content of this book is based on known scientific fact and accepted experimentation, we can still say after nearly a quarter of a century of pioneering in the field of voice science that there is challenge in the realization that so much is still unknown about the mechanisms of speech and hearing.

Although teaching methods vary, this volume can probably best be used in connection with a course in which, outside class periods, the student spends his time as follows: approximately one-half his preparation-for-class time on the basic textbook; from one-sixth to one-third of his time in the laboratory; the remainder in enriching his background by independent study or by assigned library readings in reference books and representative journals. It is largely for this last function that the *Bibliography* was compiled.

To hasten the student's growing familiarity with articles in periodicals, the teacher may wish to make a definite assignment each day of a chronological section of the *Bibliography and Chronicle* and to suggest that the student select and read one article that has some special appeal to him. In assigning sections covering the last ten years, the student may also be asked to recommend any additional references or current references that, in his opinion, would be valuable additions to the present selective bibliography.

Throughout this textbook the figures are lettered or numbered to indicate clearly the structures shown. Further value may be obtained from them if students are asked to label the drawings and color the various parts with different crayons or inks. The book may then be turned in to the instructor as a laboratory manual.

Exercises and Questions are placed at the ends of most chapters. The exercises, so numerous that no student should be required to do them all, will have to be selected, in some measure, on the basis of the apparatus and equipment available. Supplemental questions on the material in each chapter are found in the *Additional Exercises and Questions* in the Appendix. Most of the questions here constitute a means of survey and review with an opportunity for the student to test his knowledge while material just studied is still before him. Some of the augmented exercises and questions are designed to force the student to go beyond the textbook and to think about the broader, philosophical aspects of speech and hearing.

We have included a new section on *Metric Equivalents* since students are usually amazed to learn how minute, even microscopic, are so many of the functional parts of the normal speech and hearing mechanisms. Invariably, a student is interested when he compares the dimensions of cells, nerves and other anatomical structures with those of a printed comma or period.

The inherent limitations of space and budget will determine the laboratory resources a given college or university can provide. In the section on *Laboratory Equipment* we have indicated some of the models, charts, and other equipment useful to students, particularly in giving them an opportunity to see the tri-dimensional relationships of some of the parts of mechanisms.

During the academic year 1962–63, the first author was Lecturer in Speech at the University of Wisconsin where some sixty graduate and undergraduate students in his classes in *Anatomy and Physiology of Speech and Hearing* provided inspiration throughout the early stages of preparing this revision. This special opportunity was made possible thanks to Dr. Frederick W. Haberman, Professor of Speech and Chairman of the Department of Speech, and to Dr. John V. Irwin, Professor of Speech and Director of the Speech and Hearing Clinics, at the University of Wisconsin.

In this revised edition we continue to recognize our debt to those authorities whose assistance we so much appreciated while preparing the first edition: Dr. Claude E. Kantner, Professor and Director of the School of Dramatic Art and Speech, Ohio University [*Phonetics*]; Dr. John Hornbeck, Professor of Physics, Kalamazoo College [*The Physics of Sound*]; Dr. T. H. Bast, late Professor of Anatomy, University of Wisconsin [*The Ear and Hearing*]; Dr. Frederick D. Geist, Professor of Anatomy, University of Wisconsin [*Neurology*]; Dr. H. W. Mossman, Professor of Anatomy, University of Wisconsin [*Embryology*]; Dr. Walter E. Sullivan, Emeritus Professor of Anatomy, University of Wisconsin [*Anatomy*]; and Dr. Lester W. Paul, Professor of Radiology, University of Wisconsin [*Roentgenographs*]. Dr. Kantner's orginal material has been retained in this edition.

Dr. Otto A. Mortenson, Professor and Chairman of the Department of Anatomy, and Associate Dean of the Medical School, University of Wisconsin, has also aided us during this revision. For assistance in the field of Audiometry we thank Mr. Clark F. Edwards, Audiologist, University of Wisconsin Speech and Hearing Rehabilitation Center.

In acknowledging the aid and counsel we received on many specific points from the scholars mentioned above, we assume full responsibility for any errors that may still remain in the text. Dr. Lorna Seabury Lengfeld, Associate Professor of Spech, Stout State College, helped in preparation of some of the illustrations. We greatly appreciate her assistance and that of personnel at the University of Wisconsin who supplied X-ray films, photographs, and photomicrographs. We thank the librarians of the Memorial Library, the Mathematics and Physics Library, and of the libraries of the College of Medicine and of the College of Engineering, all of the University of Wisconsin, for their assistance.

L.S.V.J.
A.T.W.

Table of Contents

Table of Figures

Introduction

It may prove helpful to think of this book as divided into four parts, plus an *Appendix*. While the parts are necessarily inter-related, each covers its own special area of information.

The first part includes the initial five chapters. It deals in considerable detail with the production of English speech sounds. Although the five chapters as a group treat these sounds as isolated phenomena, the fifth chapter recognizes them as elements within continuous, dynamic speech.

The second part includes one chapter, the sixth. Its purpose is to present a simplified yet comprehensive story of the embryological and fetal development of the human being, with special emphasis on those parts of the organism that will become the normal mechanisms of speech and hearing.

The third part, also, includes one chapter, the seventh. The presentation of neurology here serves two purposes: (1) the nervous system is shown to be the coordinating network that makes possible the smoothly integrated functioning of the great number of structures working together to produce speech, and (2) the nervous system is presented as the partner of the ear in making hearing possible.

The fourth part includes the final two chapters. Chapter VIII considers two aspects of the physics and psychology of sound: (1) as the physical material constituting speech and (2) as the stimulus that impinges on the eardrum and, thus, makes normal hearing possible. The ninth chapter describes how the ear works, discusses the theories of hearing, and builds on the previously studied neurological material in considering the highest concepts of hearing. There is a discussion of the important role of hearing in making possible the learning of speech, in helping to control the production of speech, and in channeling the over-all processes of communication.

The Mechanisms Involved in the Production of Normal Speech Sounds

The term *speech sounds* covers a wide area. Although much of what we will have to say applies to speech sounds in general, we have limited ourselves nevertheless to discussion of English speech sounds. We explain their production by a coordinated series of progressive and dynamic processes that may be grouped under the headings of Respiration, Phonation, Resonance, and Articulation.

Briefly, by *respiration* we mean inhalation and exhalation of air from the lungs. By *phonation* we mean production of tone by the laryngeal generator (vibrating vocal folds). By *resonance* we mean sympathetic or forced vibration of the air in cavities below, above, in front of, or behind the source of the sound. By *articulation* we mean breaking up or interrupting of the phonated or non-phonated breath stream. Inasmuch as the description of each of these processes requires an entire chapter, the preceding definitions are necessarily not only brief, but rather general.

We differentiate between voice and speech. *Voice* is laryngeal vibration (phonation), plus resonance; it may be involuntary or purposive. If purposive, it may be utilized as speech sounds with or without further modification. Usually when we use the term *voice* in this text we mean purposive voice.

A *speech sound* may be produced by phonation or articulation or both, plus resonance. A speech sound, therefore, may be either voiced or voiceless. In other words, a speech sound may be the result of:

(1) Phonation + Resonance (e.g., [ɑ]),
(2) Phonation + Resonance + Articulation + Resonance (e.g., [d]), or
(3) Articulation + Resonance (e.g., [t]).

To help you understand these relationships more clearly, consider phonation as a type of articulation. If articulation be defined as a breaking up of the forcibly exhaled stream (breath) of air particles into sound wave patterns, then a speech sound wave is the result of articulation. This breaking up or interrupting of the air stream may occur *at any place* in the air tract where there is a structure to cause such stoppage and/or later release. This condition is fulfilled: (a) at the level of the larynx, and (b) at the level of the mouth. If we accept such a definition of articulation, the phenomena called phonation, which occur at the level of the larynx, could be considered as articulatory in nature. If articulation were so defined, it would be possible to distinguish two types: primary articulation and secondary articulation. **Primary articulation** would result from interruption, for the *first time,* of the exhaled air stream to form sound waves. Thus, primary articulation could take place at the level of the larynx (e.g., [ɑ]) or at the level of the mouth (e.g., [t]). **Secondary articulation** would result from the interruption, for the *second time,* of the forcibly exhaled air column by an articulatory effector at the level of the mouth (e.g., [d]). More precisely, secondary articulation would be the interruption of the sound waves produced in the process of primary articulation so as to change the nature of the complexity of the sound waves. The acceptance of such an approach would broaden the significance of the term *articulation* and would eliminate the term *phonation* as now used.

The Production of Speech Sounds a Superimposed Function

The processes of respiration, phonation, resonance, and articulation make use of a vegetative tract including all of the physiological airway and parts of the physiological foodway. This tract is a series of cavities: the nose, the nasopharynx, the mouth, the oropharynx, the laryngopharynx, the larynx, the trachea, and the lungs. (Other cavities, also used in eating, do not directly concern us here.) All of the cavities listed above may be used in breathing and are regularly so used during speaking. In *normal* breathing for vital purposes, the mouth is not used. On the other hand, in swallowing, the nasopharynx and the nasal cavity (used in breathing) are closed off from the other cavities by the velar-pharyngeal musculature, and the protective mechanism of the larynx operates to close off the laryngeal cavity, trachea, and lungs from the pharynx.

The fact that animals breathe and eat even though they make little or no use of voice indicates that, when we deal with human speech, we are studying a function which has been superimposed upon vegetative mechanisms that have not been developed especially and exclusively for the production of speech sounds. At any given moment these mechanisms may have all they can do to operate properly without assuming any extra duties; they always revert to their basic functions when the biological situation demands. For example, when his body needs oxygen the speaker must pause long enough to breathe. But these mechanisms usually fulfill their "overlaid" functions surprisingly well. The only real refinements in them for producing speech sounds effectively are, in the widely accepted view, neurological. Man's evolution, however, may have produced muscles adapted specifically to the purposes of speech.

While it is true that the physiological airway and foodway systems return to their normal or vital positions when speech sounds are not being produced, this does not mean that after the production of every speech sound a complete return to some no-speech-sound state occurs. Speech is not the result of a discrete series of completed movements from normal-to-speech-to-normal positions. Rather, speech is produced by seriate muscle movements resulting from time-ordered nerve impulses. Each movement is evolved from the previous movement and modified by the subsequent movement. Because of the great number of muscles and other structures involved, the mathematical possibilities for different movements or combinations of movements within the system are practically infinite. In the production of speech sounds, therefore, it is probable that no two apparently identical sounds are ever—unless accidentally—exactly alike. If one produces the "same" sound a number of times, for example [t], on no two occasions will the sounds be identical, except by accident. However, for all practical purposes and within limits, any normal [t] is heard as [t]. The ear is not keen enough to detect the minute differences. All that is necessary for intelligibility is that a given sound be within the limits of the family or phoneme of the sound.

The Influence of Changing from a No-Speech-Sound State to a Speech-Sound Condition

If the speech mechanisms are in a *no-speech condition* (i.e., are not producing any resonated speech sound, voiced or unvoiced, articulated or unarticulated), specific movements and adjustments of the mechanisms must be made prior to the production of any speech sound. We may say, for convenience, that the movement from the no-speech state is a movement from a neutral position or from a normal breathing position. This movement, itself, may produce sound (speech or non-speech sound) before the first purposeful movements of the mechanisms produce speech sounds. A good example is the uttering of "ah's" (non-purposeful) as an initial response to a difficult or embarrassing question prior to verbalizing an answer (purposeful). Furthermore, *such pre-sound will condition any immediately subsequent sound.*

Reversing the process, if the mechanisms are in a *speech-sound condition* (i.e., are producing speech sounds), specific adjustments and movements of the mechanisms (phonative, articulatory, resonant) must be made as the production of speech sounds ceases and there is a return to the no-speech-sound state. These movements, too, may produce sound. In any case, they will have their effect upon the final speech sounds produced.

Moving out of or into a no-speech-sound state has detectable acoustical effects upon any adjacent speech-sound state.

In addition, moving out of or into any adjacent speech-sound state from another speech-sound state affects both the connected and the connecting speech sounds.

All of these movements play their part in the production of connected English speech.

The Ear and the Hearing of Speech Sounds

The mechanisms effecting the production of speech have their counterparts in neurological mechanisms serving the ear. Hearing plays roles in the human organism that are superimposed upon the more strictly biological ones, *e.g.*, those valuable to the primeval animals in terms of food-getting, mating, and protection.

Human hearing is a pre-condition for normal human speech. Speech provides the symbols of communication that make human societies possible; hearing confirms the symbols.

The Spirit of Inquiry

Much more research must be done in the fields of speech and hearing, two of the most important areas of human life, before we can have all the correct answers. We are aware that it is disconcerting to some students to proceed in the study of a subject before all the evidence is in. Yet in the following pages—and, specifically, in the questions—we have tried deliberately to approach our subject in the spirit of open query. We sincerely hope that students, fired with this same spirit, will set themselves to seek more definitive answers.

Voice Science

Chapter I

RESPIRATION

I. External Respiration for Vegetative Purposes
  A. Inhalation
    1. The Physio-anatomical System
      a. The Bony and Cartilaginous Framework of the Thorax
      b. The Trachea and the Lungs
    2. The Mechanism of Inhalation
      a. Quiet Inhalation
      b. Forced Inhalation
  B. Exhalation: an active plus a passive phenomenon
    1. Active Factors
    2. Passive Factors
II. Vital Capacity
    The Measurement of Vital Capacity
III. The Air Column Requirements for the Production of Speech Sounds
    A Comparison of Normal Breathing and Breathing for Speech
    1. For Speech Purposes Inhalation is Deeper and/or More Rapid
    2. In Speech Exhalation is More Forceful
    3. Control of Volume Varies
    4. The Rate and Rhythm Vary
Exercises and Questions

We are interested in the physical nature of respiration because normal speech sounds, voiced or unvoiced, depend for their production upon an exhaled stream of air. However, we may better understand this superimposed service function of respiration if, first, we know something about the more important vital or vegetative function of respiration.

Every living thing requires oxygen for its vital processes. Carbon dioxide is always an end product of these processes (metabolism). Respiration is the provision of Nature in all living things to make possible such a gaseous interchange between the organism and its environment that oxygen may be absorbed and carbon dioxide eliminated. In lower animals such as the amoeba, the interchange may take place through the exterior surface of the organism. In man, a circulating blood stream bathes, directly or indirectly, all the tissues of the body. Oxygen from the air is absorbed by the blood in the lungs and carried to the living cells; carbon dioxide is absorbed by the blood from the cells and carried to the lungs, where it is eliminated.

Our immediate interest in this chapter is in what is known as external respiration. *External respiration* [1] involves the inhalation of air; the absorption of oxygen through the walls of the alveoli by the blood in the lung capillaries; the elimination of carbon dioxide from the blood to the alveoli; [2] and the exhalation of air from the lungs.

EXTERNAL RESPIRATION FOR VEGETATIVE PURPOSES

At sea level, the air which we breathe is under a pressure of 760 mm. Hg. (approximately 15 lbs. per square inch). Differences of pressure between the outside air and the air within the respiratory tract produce, upon inhalation, a flow of air into the lungs and, upon exhalation, a flow of air out of the lungs. During inhalation, the pressure of the air outside the lungs is greater than that inside and, during exhalation, the converse is true.

The relation of the lungs to and within the thoracic cage is such that any movement of the cage is followed by a corresponding movement of the lungs. If the thoracic cavity be enlarged by movements of the ribs, cartilages, and diaphragm there is a consequent increase in the capacity of the pleural cavity. This reduces the pressure on the pleural surface of the lungs, and hence the lungs expand and increase their capacity. With this increase in capacity comes a lowering of the air pressure in the respiratory tract and a resultant inrush of air from the outside. This is *inhalation*. If the capacity of the thorax and hence of the lungs is decreased, the air within the lungs is put under pressure and expelled.[3] This is *exhalation*.

It is usually said that, in quiet respiration, inhalation is the result of an active mechanism while exhalation is the result of a passive mechanism;

[1] *Internal respiration* involves the gaseous exchange which takes place during the flow of the blood from the lung capillaries to the body tissues, and from the body tissues to the lung capillaries.

[2] The passage of oxygen into the blood and carbon dioxide out of the blood in the lungs is a physical process called *diffusion*. The oxygen pressure in venous blood is lower than that in the air in the alveoli of the lungs, the carbon dioxide pressure is higher than that of the alveolar carbon dioxide.

In venous blood, the oxygen is under a pressure of about 37 mm. Hg., and the CO_2 is under a pressure of 42 mm. Hg. In the air of the alveoli of the lungs, oxygen is under a pressure of 100 mm. Hg., and CO_2 is under a pressure of from 35 to 40 mm. Hg. The physical relations of pressure between alveolar air and the gases in the venous blood brings about diffusion in the direction indicated by the arrows:

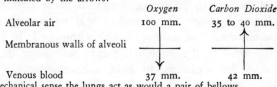

	Oxygen	*Carbon Dioxide*
Alveolar air	100 mm.	35 to 40 mm. ↑
Membranous walls of alveoli	↓	↑
Venous blood	↓ 37 mm.	42 mm.

[3] In the mechanical sense the lungs act as would a pair of bellows.

and that in forced breathing, both inhalation and exhalation employ active mechanisms. We are inclined to believe, on the basis of fluoroscopic study, that normal exhalation is not entirely passive; that it, too, at least in part, is active.

A. Inhalation

1. THE PHYSIO-ANATOMICAL SYSTEM

We have defined the physiological airway and foodway as made up of a series of cavities through which we may inhale and exhale air. These cavities include those of the nose, the nasopharynx, the oral cavity, the oropharynx, the laryngopharynx, the larynx, the trachea, and the lungs. In its *normal* condition for quiet breathing it may be described as follows:

(1) The nasal cavity is patent. Its structure is such that normally it always remains open.

(2) The nasopharynx, oropharynx, and laryngopharynx present a single patent tubelike cavity. The structure of this tube is such that its cavity can be obstructed only by the combined action of the velarpharyngeal musculature.

(3) The laryngeal cavity is unrestricted at the glottis. The vocal folds are separated so that the air stream is relatively unimpeded.

(4) The trachea and lung passageways are open.

(5) The oral cavity is practically obliterated by the comparatively relaxed tongue; the lips are closed lightly.

The musculature of the entire system is in a state of normal tonus, except for the alternate active participation of the muscles involved in inhalation and exhalation. Some slight corresponding balanced activity takes place at the glottis, i. e., laryngoscopic investigation shows that upon inhalation the glottis is widened somewhat, while upon exhalation it is not quite so wide.

a. The Bony and Cartilaginous Framework of the Thorax

The chest cage, called the *thorax,* is made up of a skeleton of cartilage and bone. Its boundaries are as follows:

The sternum and costal cartilages, in front;

The twelve ribs (costae), on each side;

The twelve thoracic vertebrae and the posterior (i. e., necks and heads) parts of the ribs, behind.

The *sternum* (breast bone) forms the central portion of the anterior thoracic wall. Cephalically it supports the clavicles; its margins articulate with the cartilages of ribs 1–7, inclusive. Its consists of three parts: manubrium, body (gladiolus), and xiphoid process. Its average length is 17 cm.

In the fetus the *ribs* are formed at right angles to the axis of the body, but later change their angle. This is brought about gradually by the necessity of the ribs' assuming that angle which will permit them to function most efficiently in breathing. The change helps to explain why although babies breathe in a predominantly abdominal manner, adults may not. It is also a clue as to why, when reclining, easy breathing, even in the adult, becomes more abdominal. The change of relationship of the angle between the ribs and axis of the body is illustrated by the fact that in the fetus and at birth it is 90°; at the age of 4, 82°; and in the adult, 64°. These figures probably vary somewhat with the build of the individual. Not all ribs in the adult are at the same angle; the angle of the lower ribs away from the long axis of the body is less than that for the upper ribs. Between the ribs are the intercostal spaces. The internal and external intercostal muscles bridge the eleven intercostal spaces.

The thorax has three diameters, vertical, transverse, and antero-posterior. If we consider the thorax as a skeletal framework, the cavity enclosed has the shape of a truncated cone. In the thoracic cavity are the two pleural cavities with the enveloped lungs, one on either side, separated by the heart and other structures. The diaphragm, to be described later, forms the floor of the thorax. Intimately associated with the thorax is the shoulder girdle consisting of the scapulae and clavicles.

To these thoracic bones and cartilages, and to a few others, are attached the muscles which move some or all of them during respiration.

b. The Trachea and the Lungs

The *trachea* (windpipe) is a cartilaginous and membranous tube, extending from the subglottic larynx (about level with the sixth cervical vertebra), to its division into the two bronchi, one for each lung, at about the level of the fifth thoracic vertebra. Variations in length are found, but in women it is about 10 cm. and in men about 11.5 cm.; the diameter varies from 1.0 to 2.0 cm. in the living subject and from 2.5 to 3.5 cm. in the dead subject. Approximately one-half (5 cm.) of its extent is above the level of the top of the sternum.

Each cartilage (there are approximately 18) of the trachea forms two-thirds of a ring; the one-third of the circumference behind (dorsal) being completed by fibro-elastic tissue and smooth muscle fibers. The longitudinal fibers [4] are superficial and the transverse fibers (trachealis muscle) deep. Such construction permits the tracheal tissue to give inward when a large bolus of food passes down the adjacent esophagus, and at the same time the tonus of the trachealis muscle prevents the esophagus from collapsing the trachea when at rest. It also makes possible maximal distension during forced respiration.

[4] The trachea may be shortened as much as 1.25 cm.

Trachealis muscle (tunica muscularis)

Origin and Insertion: A transverse layer of unstriped fibers in the dorsal portion of the trachea connecting the posterior ends of the tracheal rings.

Innervation: Recurrent branch of X and sympathetics.

Action: The contraction of the trachealis muscle diminishes the caliber of the trachea transversely but increases it anteroposteriorly.

The *tracheal cartilages* have an inherent elasticity which is opposed by the trachealis muscle which by its contraction decreases the caliber of the trachea. The muscle needs no opponent because when relaxed, the elasticity of the cartilages comes into play. The trachealis muscle relaxes, upon inspiration, and the lumen of the treachea is enlarged. During expiration, and, particularly during forced expiration, the lumen of the tube decreases in size, i. e., the muscle contracts.

The mucous membrane lining of the trachea is continuous above and below with that of the larynx and bronchi, respectively.

At the *bifurcation of the trachea,* there is a change in the area of the cross section of the respiratory tract. Our composite measurements of numerous specimens provide material for a comparison of the cross-section areas of the trachea and the bronchi.

Area trachea, 312 sq. mm.; area left bronchus, 150 sq. mm.; area right bronchus, 216 sq. mm. Combined cross-section area of bronchi is 54 sq. mm. greater than the cross-section area of the trachea.

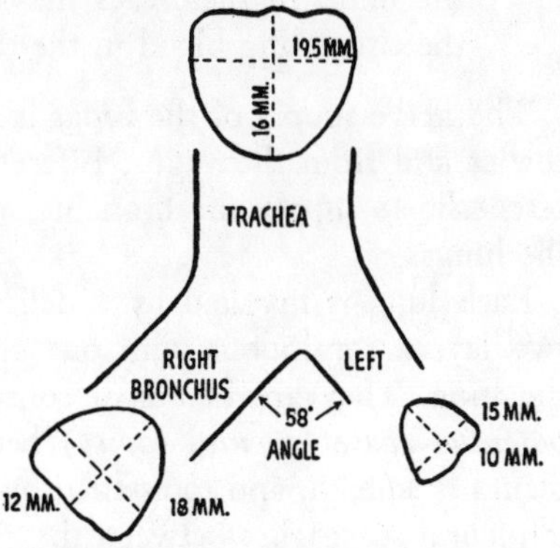

FIG. 1. Specimen to Illustrate that the Combined Cross-section Area of the Bronchi Exceeds that of Trachea.

Air entering the trachea encounters progressively decreasing resistance because of the constantly increasing cross-sectional area of the divisions of the pulmonary tree. The first of these divisions is at the bifurcation of the trachea.

Conversely, air flowing out of the lungs must encounter increasing resistance due to the decrease in cross section of the tubes through which it passes.

Of the two bronchi, the right one is shorter (2–3 cm. in length; 6–8 cartilages) than the left (4–5 cm. in length; 9–12 cartilages). It has a greater cross-sectional area, however.

Each *bronchus* leads to a *lung* (pulmone). The left lung is divided into two lobes; the right lung is divided into three lobes.

The lungs are of a light, porous, spongy texture; they are highly elastic. This latter quality is a significant characteristic.

The lung structure is divided and subdivided, but no matter how small the subsequent divisions, the combined cross-sectional area of any subdivision is always greater than the cross-sectional area of the parent division. To make clear the numerous subdivisions, we give the following tabulation. The divisions denoted by asterisks (*) altogether constitute what is called a primary lobule.

Trachea, divides to form
Bronchi, which subdivide to form primary, secondary, and tertiary bronchi.[5] These subdivide to form
Bronchioles, which subdivide to form
* *Respiratory bronchioles.* Finally, there are the
* *Alveolar ducts,* each of which terminates in
* *Atria.* These open out into a number of
* *Alveolar air sacs.* These *alveoli* are the ultimate limits of division in the lung. In these sacs the air is brought into close proximity to the circulating blood in the delicately walled lung capillaries.

The nerve supply of the lungs is brought by branches from the sympathetics and from the vagus. Efferent fibers supply the lung muscles; afferent fibers supply the bronchial mucous membrane and the alveoli of the lungs.

Each lung is invested by a delicate membrane, the *pleura.* There are two layers, continuous with one another around and below the root of the lung. They are in actual contact with one another, but there is a *potential space* (*pleural cavity*) between them. The free surface of the pleura is smooth, and moistened by a serous fluid. The *mediastinum* (interpleural space) lies between the right and left pleurae; it extends from the sternum to the vertebral column, and contains all the thoracic viscera excepting the lungs.

Because of the extreme elasticity of the lung tissue, and because of the differential in air pressure outside the thorax and inside, the lungs always entirely fill the thoracic lung cavity (pleural cavities) no matter what its volume. If the dimensions of the thoracic cavity are enlarged by muscular action, the lungs are likewise expanded and contain more

[5] In the bronchi, the musculature is complete, whereas in the trachea it is found only in the posterior third of the circumference of the tube.

air. When the volume of the thoracic cavity is decreased, the volume of the lungs is decreased and they contain less air. In other words, the relation of lungs to thoracic cavity is such that any change in the volume of the cavity is at once accompanied by a related change in the volume of the lungs.

If one side of the thorax be punctured as by a wound, the air can enter by the wound and so the air pressure in the lung on that side is equal to that outside. That lung will collapse and will be useless for breathing. Sometimes, for the treatment of tuberculosis, one lung is made to collapse so that it may rest and recover.

2. THE MECHANISM OF INHALATION

To produce inhalation the air pressure within the lungs must be decreased in comparison with that outside the body, thus causing air to flow into the lungs. This can be done only by increasing the volume of the lungs. Inasmuch as the lungs always entirely occupy all of the possible space within the thoracic cage, the only way the lungs can occupy more space—i. e., be increased in their capacity—is for the pleural space within the thorax to be increased.

The active process of inhalation is brought about by muscular contraction, due to the fact that at rather definite intervals efferent impulses from the respiratory center[6] go out to the muscles which directly or indirectly act to increase the size of the thoracic cavity. Real work is done in filling the highly elastic lungs with air, just as work is done in filling an elastic rubber balloon with air.

The bony and cartilaginous framework of the thorax with its various tissue coverings is movable, permitting the three diameters of the cage to be varied. Increasing any one of these somewhat increases the volume of the thorax. Increasing all of them together causes a considerable increase in capacity. The *antero-posterior diameter* and the *transverse diameter* are increased by the elevation of the ribs. The *vertical diameter* is increased chiefly by the descent of the diaphragm. All of these variations in chest capacity are brought about by the action of the numerous muscles which are attached to the skeleton of the thorax.

After studying the attachments of the muscles involved in the act of breathing the student may come to the conclusion that the muscles having attachment to the thorax at a lower level may be controlled for more

[6] *p*H and the respiratory center: The degree of alkalinity or acidity of the blood is considered in terms of hydrogen-ion concentration, the symbol of which is *p*H. The *p*H of the blood has a direct and marked influence upon the activity of the respiratory center, which is located in the medulla oblongata. The normal stimulus of the respiratory center is the H-ion concentration of the blood. If the blood supplying the center becomes more venous—that is, more acid, or of a lower *p*H—the respirations are increased in force (depth) or rate, or both. If the blood supplying the center is more arterialized than normal—that is, more alkaline, or of a higher *p*H—the center acts more feebly.

delicate movements than can the muscles having higher attachments. This may lead to the conclusion that diaphragmatic-abdominal breathing is superior to clavicular-costal breathing.

In increasing the antero-posterior and the transverse diameters of the chest cage, the muscles of inhalation must do work to overcome the force of gravity. In raising the thorax, these muscles are placed under tension. We shall see later that, when the muscles relax, the elasticity of the skeletal parts of the thoracic cage will tend to aid gravity in lowering the heavy bony cage. As the thoracic cage is lifted and as the ribs are raised

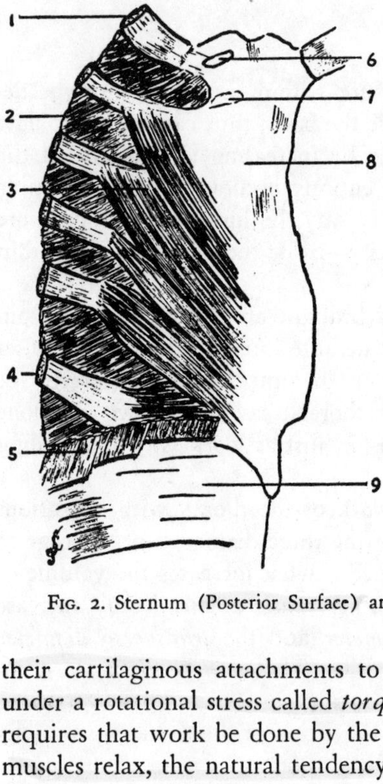

1. 1st costal cartilage; 2. internal intercostal; 3. transversus thoracis; 4. 6th costal cartilage; 5. cut edge of diaphragm; 6. attachment of sternohyoideus; 7. attachment of sternothyreoideus; 8. sternum; 9. transversus abdominus.

FIG. 2. Sternum (Posterior Surface) and Attached Costal Cartilages and Muscles.

their cartilaginous attachments to the sternum are rotated and placed under a rotational stress called *torque*. To rotate the cartilages of the ribs requires that work be done by the muscles of inhalation. As soon as the muscles relax, the natural tendency of the cartilages is to untorque. This phenomenon of torquing may be demonstrated with a wet towel. Twist it as though wringing out the water. This requires the expenditure of considerable energy. Stop wringing the towel and it will untwist or untorque.

a. Quiet Inhalation

The muscles ordinarily utilized in *quiet inhalation* are as follows:

Diaphragm
External intercostals

Scaleni (anterior, medius, posterior)
Levatores costarum

Diaphragm (diaphragma; midriff)

Origin: Ensiform and costal cartilages, 6 or 7 lower ribs, ligamental arcuata and lumbar vertebrae.
Insertion: Central tendon.
Innervation:[7] C 3, 4, 5 (phrenic nerve)
Action: Inspiration and abdominal expulsive acts. The chief muscle of inhalation. Later in this chapter, the action of the diaphragm will be treated at length.

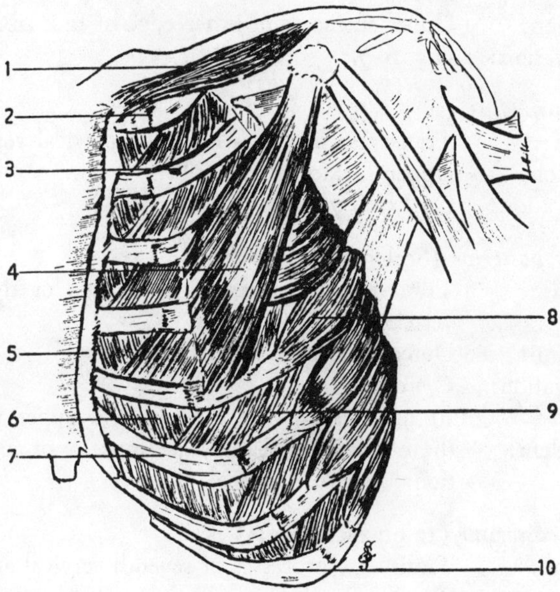

FIG. 3. Thoracic Cage and Deep Chest Muscles Associated in Breathing.

1. Subclavius; 2. 1st rib and cartilage; 3. 2nd rib; 4. pectoralis minor; 5. cut edge of pectoralis major; 6. internal intercostal muscle; 7. cartilage of 6th rib; 8. serratus anterior; 9. external intercostal muscle; 10. 8th rib and cartilage.

External intercostals (Intercostales externi) (11 on each side).

Origin: Inferior border of ribs.
Insertion: Superior border of rib below.
Innervation:[7] T 1–12
Action: Elevate ribs in inhalation.

Authorities disagree as to the action of the external and internal intercostal muscles. Some believe that the

[7] C indicates Cervical; T, Thoracic; L, Lumbar; S, Sacral.

external intercostals are muscles of inhalation and that the internal intercostals are muscles of exhalation. Some believe that both are muscles of inhalation. Still other observers hold that the external intercostal and internal intercostal muscles contract simultaneously thus providing a curtain which prevents excessive in and out movement at the intercostal spaces during the respiratory phases.

Scalenus anterior (Scalenus anticus)

Origin:	Transverse processes of third to sixth cervical vertebrae.
Insertion:	Upper surface and inner edge of first rib.
Innervation:	C 5, 6, 7.

Scalenus medius

Origin:	Transverse processes lower six cervical vertebrae.
Insertion:	Upper surface of first rib.
Innervation:	C 4, 5, 6, 7, 8.

Scalenus posterior (Scalenus posticus)

Origin:	Transverse processes of lower two or three cervical vertebrae.
Insertion:	Outer surface of second rib.
Innervation:	C 7 or 8.
Action of Scaleni:	In quiet inhalation they fix the upper two ribs. If the neck be fixed, they are muscles of forced inhalation.

Levatores costarum (12 on each side)

Origin:	Transverse processes of seventh cervical and 11 upper thoracic vertebrae.
Insertion:	Each to next two ribs below.
Innervation:	C 8; T 1–11.
Action:	Lift ribs in inhalation. Probably the effect of contraction of the muscles is slight because the levatores are inserted so close to the fulcra of the ribs.

The most important muscle of inhalation is the diaphragm.[8] For a basic understanding of breathing one might consider that the chest has a fixed and immovable wall and that most of the phenomena associated with the mechanism of respiration are the result of the action of the

[8] Its importance is overestimated, according to R. Fick, *Handbuch der Anatomie und Mechanik der Gelenke unter Berücksichtigung der bewegenden Muskeln* (in von Bardeleben's *Handbuch*).

diaphragm. Then later, one might add those modifications which are due to the mobility of the skeletal structure.

The diaphragm is a convex-concave musculofibrous partition between the thoracic and abdominal cavities; it is attached to the entire lower circumference of the framework of the thorax. Its convex or cephalic side is the floor of the thorax; its concave or caudal side is the roof of the abdominal cavity. Due to the constant state of tonus of the walls of the abdomen, the abdominal viscera press up against the diaphragm forcing the diaphragm upward and giving it the shape of a dome. Actually, the diaphragm presents two domes—the one on the right side being higher. Contraction of the diaphragm shortens every diameter of it and consequently increases the space within the thorax by depressing its convex floor. The range of movement of the diaphragm may vary ordinarily between 12 and 28 mm. (See Figs. 4 and 5.)

The action of this dome-shaped chief muscle of inhalation is as follows: The lower ribs being fixed, or rendered relatively stationary by the action of their attached muscles, the musclar fibers of the diaphragm contract to draw the central tendinous portion downward and forward. The whole dome moves down upon and compresses the abdominal viscera, but at first the curvature of the concavity is not greatly altered—i. e., all its parts move about equally. The descent of the diaphragm increases the depth of the thorax. This descent of the diaphragm and abdominal viscera is made possible by the elasticity of the abdominal wall. When the limits of elasticity are reached, however, the descent of the viscera is stopped; the viscera now act as a fulcrum for the central tendon and, with slight additional contraction of its muscle fibers, the diaphragm pushes the thoracic cage, particularly the lower ribs, outward.

Obviously, as the convex diaphragm straightens out and becomes less convex it must push down more and more upon the viscera in the abdominal cavity. That is, the gain in the size of the thoracic cavity is at the expense of the size of the abdominal cavity. It would be more nearly so if the walls of the abdomen were simply forced outward by the force of the viscera just so long as pressure continued to be applied to the viscera by the diaphragm. The walls of the abdominal cavity, however, are made up of muscles which by their contraction prevent a too great outward excursion of themselves. In short, the downthrust of the diaphragm places the viscera under pressure from which, aided by the elasticity of the muscular walls of the abdomen, they seek to escape. The tonicity or contraction of the following muscles aids in the fixation of the viscera: levator ani, coccygeus, rectus abdominis, transversus abdominis, obliquus externus abdominis, obliquus internus abdominis. Given the opportunity, the viscera and the walls will recoil and force the diaphragm back into position. The greater the original descent of the

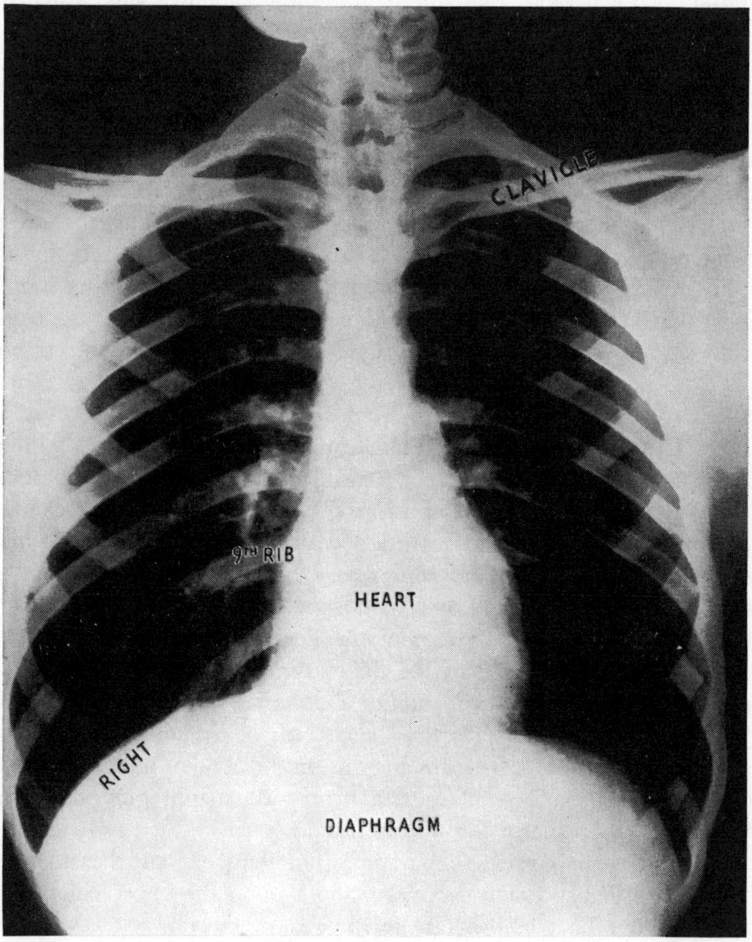

FIG. 4. X-ray Photograph of the Thoracic Cage during Deep Inhalation.

Compare this with the X-ray photograph of the same subject during deep exhalation (Fig. 5). Note: (*a*) the curve of the domes of the diaphragm; (*b*) the size of the heart; (*c*) the angle of the ribs to the long axis of the body; (*d*) the distance of the movement of the diaphragm as related to the ribs; (*e*) the relation of clavicle and ribs.

In this figure the 10th rib is seen above the right dome of the diaphragm. In Fig. 5 the 9th rib is seen above the right dome. The actual maximum excursion of the diaphragm for this subject was: left dome, 49 mm.; right dome, 46 mm. The increase in the size of the chest wall on each side is 15 mm. or a total increase of 30 mm.

diaphragm, the greater the potential force stored up to push it back upward.

The muscular-tendinous tissue of the diaphragm is quite elastic. When relaxed after contraction, its natural tendency is to return to its normal tonic state.

The relative position of the diaphragm depends upon the position of

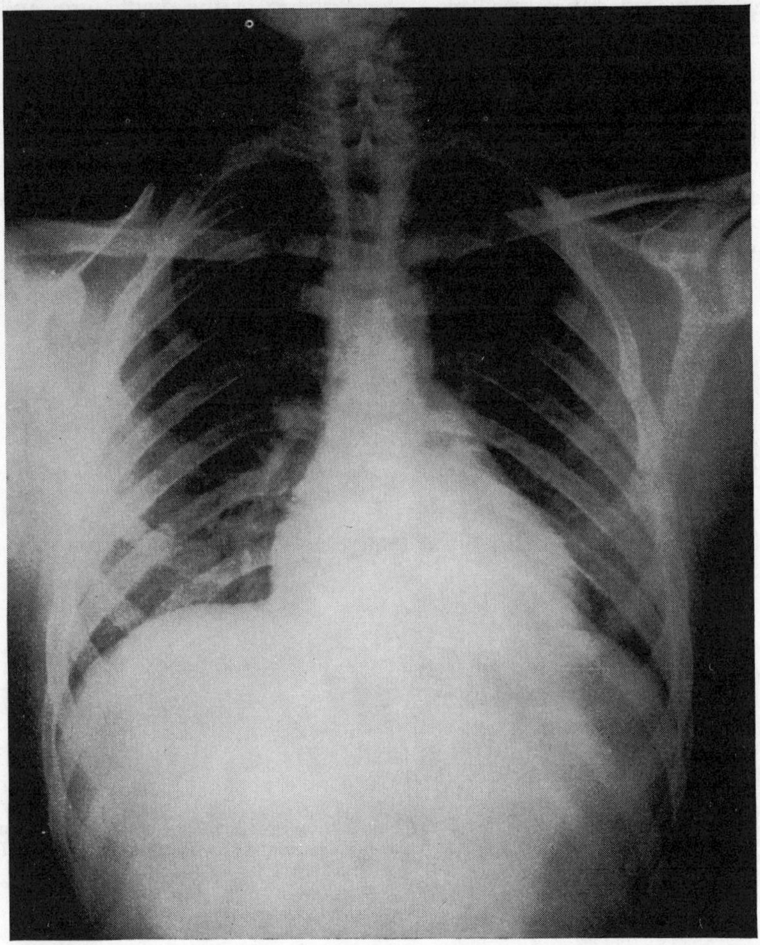

FIG. 5. X-ray Photograph of the Thoracic Cage during Deep Exhalation. Same Subject as in Fig. 4.

the body; it is related to the tendency of the lung tissue to contract and hence to draw up the diaphragm, and to the pressure of the viscera, due to the state of contraction of the abdominal musculature. If the heavy bony thoracic cage expands in all diameters during inhalation, the force of gravity will be operative in reducing its diameter no matter what position the body assumes. If the body be in the prone or supine position the effect of the force of gravity will not be as great as if the body were in an upright position, but usually, as in sleeping, the supine position is associated with a less energetic type of breathing.

Aside from its function in inhalation, the diaphragm contracts forcefully during such vegetative functions as sneezing, coughing, and laughing. A hiccup is produced by a clonic spasm of the diaphragm, and is probably caused by irritation of the phrenic nerve.

b. Forced Inhalation

In deep respiration, all of the movements of quiet respiration are greater in extent. In *forced inhalation,*[9] the previously listed muscles of quiet inhalation plus several others may be employed. Depending upon the degree of depth and rapidity of inhalation, some or any of the following additional muscles are involved directly.

Serratus anterior
Serratus posterior superior
Serratus posterior inferior
Pectoralis major
Pectoralis minor
Latissimus dorsi
Subclavius
Sternocleidomastoid

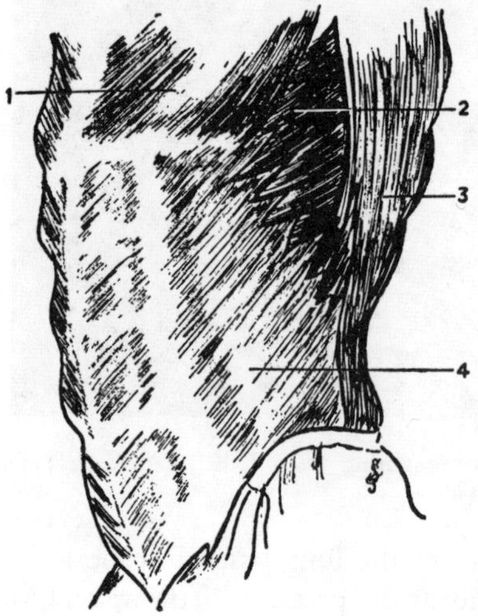

1. Pectoralis major; 2. serratus anterior; 3. latissimus dorsi; 4. obliquus externus abdominis.

FIG. 6. Superficial Abdominal Musculature.

Serratus anterior (Serratus magnus)
Origin: Angles and dorsal (ventral) border of scapula.

[9] The following figures represent the changes which occur during the deepest possible inhalation. The manubrium sterni moves 30 mm. in an upward and 14 mm. in a forward direction; the width of the subcostal angle, at a level of 30 mm. below the articulation between the body of the sternum and the xiphoid process, is increased by 26 mm.; the umbilicus is retracted and drawn upward for a distance of 13 mm.

Insertion: Eight or nine upper ribs; intercostal aponeuroses.
Innervation: C 5, 6, 7.
Action: If shoulders are fixed, may assist in raising ribs and aiding, somewhat, in forced inhalation.

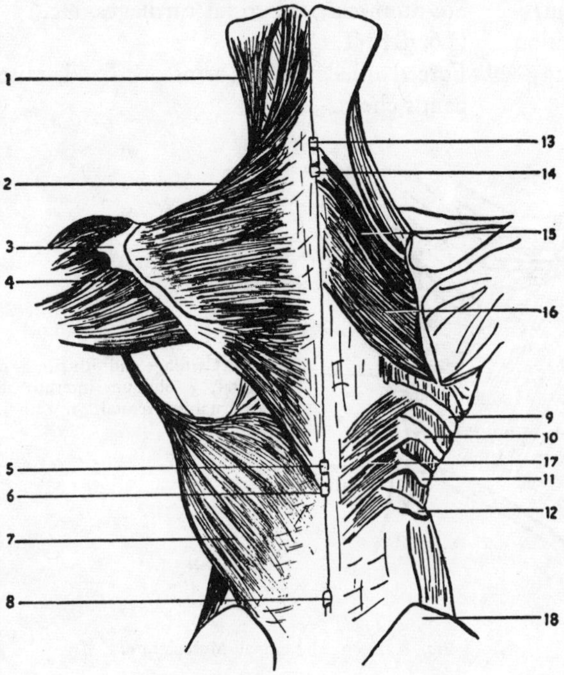

FIG. 7. Muscles of Back Involved in Breathing.

1. Sternocleidomastoideus; 2. trapezius; 3. scapula; 4. deltoideus; 5. 12th thoracic vertebra; 6. 1st lumbar vertebra; 7. latissimus dorsi; 8. 1st sacral vertebra; 9. 9th rib; 10. 10th rib; 11. 11th rib; 12. 12th rib; 13. 7th cervical vertebra; 14. 1st thoracic vertebra; 15. rhomboideus minor; 16. rhomboideus major; 17. serratus posterior inferior; 18. ilium.

Serratus posterior superior (Serratus posticus superior)
Origin: Spinous processes of seventh cervical and upper two or three thoracic vertebrae.
Insertion: Upper borders of the second to fifth ribs.
Innervation: T 1, 2, 3, 4.
Action: Inhalation. Raises ribs, enlarges thorax.

Serratus posterior inferior (Serratus posticus inferior)
Origin: Spines of lower two thoracic and upper two or three lumbar vertebrae.
Insertion: Lower border of four lower ribs.
Innervation: T 9, 10, 11.

Action: Inhalation. Pulls lower ribs down and out to enlarge thorax.

Pectoralis major

Origin: Anterior bicipital ridge of humerus.
Insertion: Sternum, clavicle, costal cartilages, etc.
Innervation: C 6, 7, 8; T 1.
Action: Forced inhalation. If arms are fixed, raises ribs; expands chest.

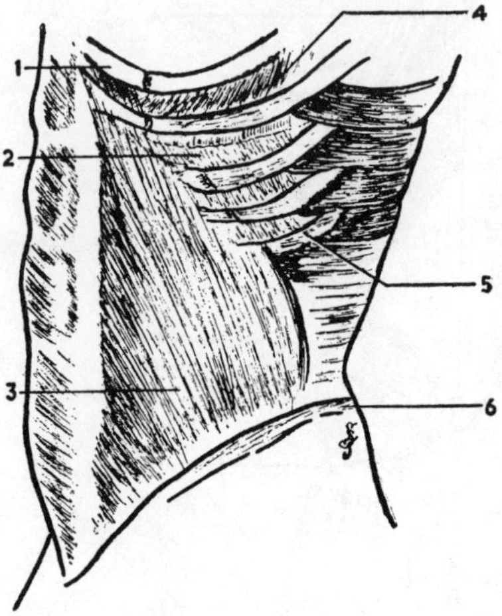

1. Cartilage and 8th rib; 2. internal intercostal; 3. obliquus internus abdominus; 4. external intercostal; 5. 12th rib; 6. ilium.

FIG. 8. Deep Abdominal Musculature.

Pectoralis minor

Origin: Coracoid process of scapula.
Insertion: Second, third, fourth, and fifth ribs by aponeurosis.
Innervation: C 7, 8.
Action: Forced inhalation. Scapula is fixed, raises ribs; expands chest.

Latissimus dorsi

Origin: Bicipital groove of humerus.
Insertion: Spinous processes of lower 6 thoracic vertebrae, and lumbar and sacral vertebrae, crest of ilium, and 4 lowest ribs.
Innervation: C 6, 7, 8.
Action: Forced inhalation. Raises lower ribs if arms are fixed. According to some authorities this muscle is used in exhalation to fix the lower ribs.

Subclavius

Origin: Lower surface of clavicle.
Insertion: First rib and its cartilage.
Innervation: C 5, 6.
Action: Forced inhalation, if clavicle is fixed.

Sternoclavicularis.

Origin: An occasional slip from the subclavius, from upper part of sternum.
Insertion: Clavicle beneath pectoralis minor.

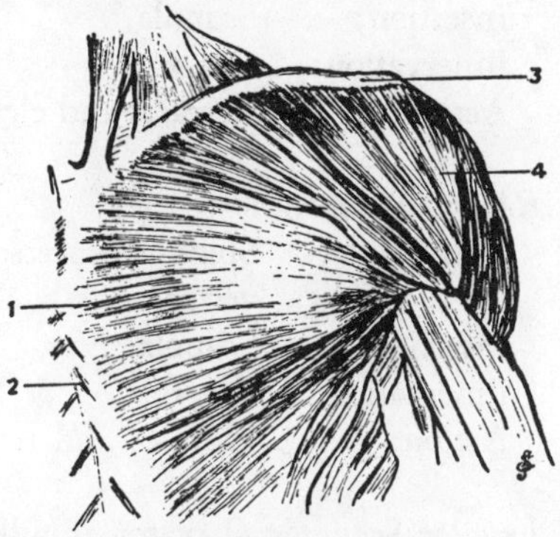

1. Pectoralis major; 2. sternum; 3. clavicle; 4. deltoideus.

FIG. 9. Superficial Muscles of Chest Used in Breathing.

Sternocleidomastoideus

Origin: By two heads, one from the sternum; the other from the clavicle.
Insertion: Mastoid process and outer portion of superior oblique line of occipital bone.
Innervation: XIth cranial nerve.
Action: Elevates thorax when head is fixed.

Cleidomastoideus. A portion of the sternocleidomastoideus.

Whereas the preceding muscles act directly on the ribs in inhalation, there is an additional group of muscles which act upon the shoulder girdle to fix it and thus aid indirectly in forced inhalation. These muscles are as follows:

Trapezius
Rhomboideus major
Rhomboideus minor
Levator scapulae
Deltoideus

Trapezius (Cucullarius)

Origin:	Superior curved line of occipital bone, ligamentum nuchae, spinous processes of last cervical, and all thoracic vertebrae.
Insertion:	Clavicle, spine of scapula, and acromion.
Innervation:	XIth cranial nerve, and cervical plexus (C 3, 4).
Action:	Retracts and fixes clavicle and scapula.

Rhomboideus major

Origin:	Spinous processes of 2, 3, 4, 5 thoracic vertebrae.
Insertion:	Scapula.
Innervation:	C 5, 6.
Action:	Retracts and elevates scapula; depresses shoulder.

Rhomboideus minor

Origin:	Spinous processes of seventh cervical and first thoracic vertebrae.
Insertion:	Scapula.
Innervation:	C 5, 6.
Action:	Elevates and retracts scapula; depresses shoulder.

Levator Scapulae (Levator anguli scapulae)

Origin:	Transverse processes upper 4 cervical vertebrae.
Insertion:	Vertebral (posterior) border scapula.
Innervation:	C 3, 4.
Action:	Raises upper angle of scapula.

Deltoideus

Origin:	Clavicle, acromion, and spine of scapula.
Insertion:	Middle of outer side of shaft of humerus.
Innervation:	C 5, 6.
Action:	Aids in fixing clavicle if arm is fixed.

In forced inhalation, the shoulders and the vertebral borders of the scapulae are fixed and the limb muscles, trapezius, serratus anterior, pectorales, and latissimus dorsi, are called into play. The scaleni are in strong action, and the sternocleidomastoidei also assist when the head is fixed by drawing up the sternum and by fixing the clavicles. The first rib is therefore no longer stationary, but, with the sternum, is raised, and, with it, all the other ribs except the last are raised to a higher level. In conjunction with the increased descent of the diaphragm this action provides for a considerable increase of all the thoracic diameters. The anterior abdominal muscles come into action so that the umbilicus is drawn upward and backward, but this allows the diaphragm to exert a more powerful influence on the lower ribs; the transverse diameter of the upper part of the abdomen is greatly increased and the subcostal angle opened out. The deeper muscles of the back—e.g., the serrati posteriores superiores and the sacrospinales and their continuations, are also brought into action; the thoracic curve of the vertebral column is partially straightened, and the whole column, above the lower lumbar vertebrae, drawn backward. This action increases the antero-posterior diameters of the thorax and upper part of the abdomen and widens the intercostal spaces.

B. Exhalation: An Active Plus a Passive Phenomenon

Exhalation results when any or all of the diameters of the thoracic cage are decreased, placing the air in the lungs under greater pressure than that of the outer air. To establish an equilibrium, air continues to be forced out of the lungs until the pressure inside the lungs is equal to that outside. Although it is agreed that inhalation is an active process involving work and dependent on the contraction of numerous muscles, it is usually assumed that exhalation is primarily a passive process which comes about as an undoing of some of the things done to produce inhalation.

Whereas, heretofore, the passive factors of exhalation have been considered of primary importance, we place importance on the active contraction of the muscles associated with exhalation and relegate the passive factors to a secondary, if important, place.

1. ACTIVE FACTORS

On the basis of fluoroscopic observations and anatomical evidence we list these *active factors* in exhalation: (*a*) the muscles of the abdominal cavity wall contract, (*b*) certain muscles of minor value contract, and (*c*) the pelvic diaphragm regains its state of tonic contraction.

(*a*) Contraction of these muscles:

Transversus thoracis
Rectus abdominis
Transversus abdominis
Internal oblique
External oblique

Transversus thoracis (Triangularis sterni)

Origin:	Back of xiphoid process and lower portion of sternum.
Insertion:	Costal cartilages of second to sixth ribs.
Innervation:	T 2, 3, 4, 5, 6.
Action:	Exhalation. Depresses the ribs.

Rectus abdominis

Origin:	Cartilages of ribs 5 to 7 and xiphoid process.
Insertion:	Crest of pubes and ligamentous tissues at symphysis.
Innervation:	T 7, 8, 9, 10, 11.
Action:	Compresses abdominal contents; depresses thorax.

Transversus abdominis (Transversalis abdominis)

Origin:	Poupart's ligament, crest of ilium, lower six costal cartilages, lumbar fascia, interdigitating with the diaphragm.
Insertion:	Most of the fibers of the muscle pass transversely inward terminating near the outer border of the rectus muscle in an aponeurosis by which it is inserted into the linea alba and the crest of the pubis.
Innervation:	T 7, 8, 9, 10, 11, 12; L 1.
Action:	Compresses the viscera; contracts thorax.

Obliquus internus abdominis (Internal oblique; ascending oblique)

Origin:	Crest of ilium, inguinal ligament, and lumbar fascia.
Insertion:	A few fibers, conjointly with the fibers of the transversus, insert into the crest of the pubis; some end in the linea alba; others by aponeuroses to the seventh, eighth, and ninth costal cartilages, and to costal cartilages of the three lower ribs in continuity with the internal intercostal muscles.
Innervation:	T 9, 10, 11, 12; L 1.
Action:	Depresses thorax.

Obliquus externus abdominis (External oblique; descending oblique)

Origin:	Crest of ilium, inguinal and lacunar ligaments, linea alba by aponeurotic fibers, crest of pubes.
Insertion:	Lower eight ribs by interdigitations between corresponding processes of the anterior serrati (upper five) and the latissimus dorsi (lower three).
Innervation:	T 5, 6, 7, 8, 9, 10, 11, 12; L 1.
Action:	Compresses abdomen; depresses thorax; aids in expulsive acts.

These are the muscles of the abdominal cavity wall. Their active contraction co-ordinated with the relaxation of the diaphragm elevates the abdominal viscera, with the aid of the levatores ani and coccygei, thus pushing up the domes of the diaphragm into the thoracic cavity and decreasing the volume of the thoracic cavity and hence of the lungs. In forced exhalation, the degree of activity of these muscles is increased.

(*b*) The following muscles, although relatively not so important, contract:

Subcostals
Quadratus lumborum
Internal intercostals

Subcostals (Subcostales; Infracostales) (10 on each side)

Origin:	Inconstant; inner surface of ribs.
Insertion:	Inner surface of first, second, or third rib below.
Innervation:	Related intercostal nerve.
Action:	Depresses ribs; contracts thorax.

Quadratus lumborum

Origin:	Crest of ilium; transverse processes of third, fourth, and fifth lumbar vertebrae.
Insertion:	Twelfth rib.
Innervation:[7]	L 1, 2, 3, 4.
Action:	Exhalation: fixes origin of diaphragm.

Internal intercostals (Intercostales interni) (11 on each side)

Origin:	Inferior border of ribs and costal cartilages.
Insertion:	Upper border of rib and costal cartilage below.
Innervation:	T 1–12.
Action:	Expiration; depresses ribs. See note after external intercostal muscle.

(*c*) The pelvic diaphragm regains its state of tonic contraction. The levatores ani and coccygei unite to form the muscular pelvic diaphragm which like a sling supports the pelvic viscera. The pelvic viscera are not separated from the abdominal viscera. When the diaphragm presses down on the abdominal contents all of the viscera are compressed and the pelvic diaphragm is pushed down and the muscles give somewhat under the pressure. When the pressure is released the muscles of the pelvic diaphragm regain their normal tonic state, thus pushing up the viscera.

Levator ani

Origin:	Body and ramus of pubes, white line of obturator, spine of ischium.
Insertion:	Coccyx and median raphe, rectum and central point of perineum.
Innervation:[7]	S 4.
Action:	Normally supports viscera so that it acts as a fulcrum

[7] C indicates Cervical; T, Thoracic; L, Lumbar; S, Sacral.

A Summary Table of the Muscles Involved in Respiration Arranged According to Their Innervation

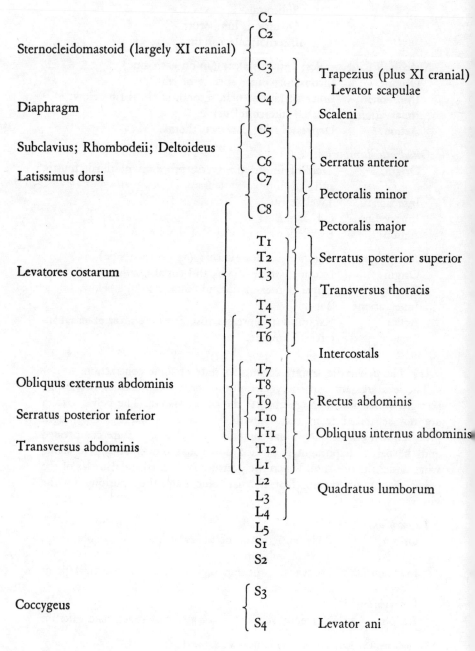

	C1	
	C2	
Sternocleidomastoid (largely XI cranial)		
	C3	Trapezius (plus XI cranial)
		Levator scapulae
Diaphragm	C4	Scaleni
	C5	
Subclavius; Rhombodeii; Deltoideus		
	C6	Serratus anterior
Latissimus dorsi	C7	
		Pectoralis minor
	C8	
		Pectoralis major
	T1	
	T2	Serratus posterior superior
Levatores costarum	T3	
		Transversus thoracis
	T4	
	T5	
	T6	
		Intercostals
	T7	
Obliquus externus abdominis	T8	
	T9	Rectus abdominis
Serratus posterior inferior	T10	
	T11	Obliquus internus abdominis
Transversus abdominis	T12	
	L1	
	L2	Quadratus lumborum
	L3	
	L4	
	L5	
	S1	
	S2	
	S3	
Coccygeus		
	S4	Levator ani

for the diaphragm. Of even greater aid in forced exhalation.

Coccygeus (Ischiococcygeus)

Origin: Ischial spine and lesser sacrosciatic ligament.
Insertion: Coccyx and sacrum.
Innervation: S 3, 4.
Action: Normally supports viscera so that it may be used as a fulcrum by the diaphragm.

2. PASSIVE FACTORS

Operating in a co-ordinated manner with the active factors, so-called *passive factors* are involved in exhalation. Concerning these there seems to be no disagreement. They may be listed as follows:

(*a*) Gravity. Upon relaxation of the muscles used in inhalation, the sheer weight of the bony cage will cause it to fall, thus reducing its diameters and decreasing its volume. Inasmuch as a change in the volume of the cage is followed by a similar change in the volume of the lungs, the lung volume will be decreased and air will be expelled when the thorax decreases its volume.

(*b*) Elastic recoil of the skeletal elements of the thoracic cage. The natural elasticity of the ribs and costal cartilages of the thorax is such that when the muscles attached to them relax they tend to recoil to their state of rest.

(*c*) Untorquing of the costal cartilages. This phenomenon of torquing and untorquing is explained on page 8.

(*d*) Elastic recoil of the lung tissue. As has been pointed out, it requires energy to fill the highly elastic lungs with air. When the thoracic cage decreases its diameters, as in exhalation, the same thing tends to happen to air in the lungs that happens to air in a balloon if we open the aperture —the air is expelled by the elastic recoil of the wall of the container.

(*e*) Elastic recoil of the viscera underlying the diaphragm. The natural tendency of the viscera when released from pressure is to return to a normal position. This recoil aids in moving the diaphragm upward, thus reducing the volume of the thorax and forcing the air from the lungs.

VITAL CAPACITY

Vital capacity is the maximum volume of air which may be expired, following a maximal inspiration. It varies with sex, age, stature, etc.

In quiet respiration only about 360 cc. of the 500 cc. of inhaled or *tidal air* actually reaches the alveoli of the lungs; the remaining 140 cc. fill the upper air passages and bronchi. Because the air in the trachea and all parts of the lungs except in the alveoli is unable to give up its oxygen or take on carbon dioxide from the body, it is not useful in respiration. Hence the space occupied by such air is known as *dead space*. It is somewhat variable—from 140 cc. to 200 cc.

Forced inspiration may add to the tidal air 1600 cc. of *complemental air*. Forced expiration may, in addition to the tidal air, result in the breathing out of 1600 cc. of *supplemental air*. The vital capacity is the sum of the tidal, complemental, and supplemental air—an average of approximately 3700 cc.

Ordinarily, of the 2600 cc. of *reserve air* in the lungs, 1000 cc. (the *residual air*) cannot be voluntarily expired, but would escape upon opening the thorax and permitting the lungs to collapse. That is, the residual air is what remains in the lungs after the fullest possible expiration. A small volume, the *minimal air,* would be imprisoned in the lung tissues by the collapse.

VITAL CAPACITY 3700 cc.	COMPLEMENTAL (forced inspiration) 1600 cc.
	TIDAL (dead space, 140 cc.; into alveoli, 360 cc.) 500 cc.
	SUPPLEMENTAL (forced expiration) 1600 cc.
RESERVE 2600 cc. plus	SUPPLEMENTAL (forced expiration) 1600 cc.
	RESIDUAL (escapes with opening of thorax) 1000 cc.
	MINIMAL-IMPRISONED AIR

THE MEASUREMENT OF VITAL CAPACITY

A *spirometer* is used in measuring vital capacity. It consists of an air-tight dome, over water (temperature of 37° C.), to which is connected a tube (from the mouth) through which air is blown. The air causes the dome to rise and move a pointer on a graduated scale which indicates in cubic inches or cubic centimeters the volume of air exhaled. The principle of the spirometer is that of the familiar gas storage tank of commercial gas companies.

Because measurements of vital capacity give us information about the amount of air an individual exhales and because the volume and force of the exhaled air stream determine the pitch and intensity of the voice, the first and second experiments placed at the end of this chapter should prove of interest.

THE AIR COLUMN REQUIREMENTS FOR THE PRODUCTION OF SPEECH SOUNDS

The efficiency of the respiratory mechanism for speech purposes is determined by its ability to deliver an adequate total volume of air at a pressure which is constantly under control—a pressure which is high enough to meet all the requirements for the production of speech sounds.

That individual displays a high degree of breath control who is capable of:

inhaling, at any desirable rate of intake, any required volume of air up to his maximum capacity;

exhaling, at any desirable rate, any required volume of air up to his maximum capacity;

exhaling with economy while speaking;

inhaling and exhaling unobtrusively while speaking;

carrying on inhalation and exhalation in such a manner as to coordinate—even artistically—the speech processes.

A Comparison of Normal Breathing and Breathing for Speech

There are several differences between the use of the physiological airway for vital purposes and for speech purposes.

1. For speech purposes inhalation is deeper and/or more rapid

In ordinary breathing as well as in breathing during speaking, the contraction of the diaphragm is responsible chiefly for the enlargement of the thorax and the resultant expansion of the lungs. The excursion of the diaphragm is greater during speaking than during ordinary breathing. Also, during speaking, the descent of the diaphragm is more rapid than during normal breathing. In order to enable (*a*) a greater volume of air to enter the lungs in (*b*) a shorter period of time, an individual invariably breathes through his mouth while speaking. This gulping of air is particularly noticeable to the listener if the speaker is broadcasting. When not speaking, the same person breathes through his nose.

2. In speech exhalation is more forceful

To be useful in the production of speech sounds, exhalation must be more *forceful* and *controlled* than it is in ordinary quiet breathing. Two factors act to produce such exhalation.

First, the physical structure of the lungs is such that there is a tendency for exhaled air to be put under pressure. Second, the passive factors and the contraction of the muscles involved in exhalation during speaking produce an air column which is forceful as well as controlled. The outrush of air is more forceful than in normal breathing because muscles are more actively contracting to reduce the thoracic diameters. Even the passive factors of exhalation operate, during speaking, to a greater degree than they do in normal breathing. For example, there is still the factor of gravity, but if the heavy chest has been raised higher it has farther to fall. If a deeper breath has been taken in, the costal cartilages have been put under greater potential force to untorque. If a deeper inspiration has drawn more air into and greatly expanded the lungs, the elastic recoil of the lung tissues will be greater.

The exhaled air column during speaking is more controlled than it is during normal breathing. Kymograph records of respiration in speech, for example, show that there is not a steady continuous contraction lasting until the end of exhalation, but that the contractions show gradations as well as continuity of activity. It is like pulling up the anchor of a boat; there is a continuous pull to maintain the rope already taken in, but in addition there is the steady inch-by-inch gain as the rope comes in hand over hand.

Most writers in the field of voice science are emphatic in pointing out that when one talks he is not heard because he is powerfully emitting and projecting an actual column of air, likened to a sizable stream of water issuing from the mouth of a statue in a fountain. Actually the air stream, issuing from the mouth, affects the air for no great distance in front of the speaker.[10] It is the sound-energy vibration which travels, not the air blast.

We should like to add that the actual, moving breath stream within the air tract has an influence on the quality of the sound wave which is finally emitted from the lips and nostrils. We believe that there is a relation between the rate of transmission of the sound wave and the rate of movement of the exhaled air which may be a contributing factor in the production of a distinguishing quality for the various sounds. The phenomenon may be particularly important at the region of the larynx, for from here the sound waves progress up through the pharynx and down the trachea at one and the same time. During this same period, the exhaled air itself is moving only in the one direction, although there may be an element of discontinuity to its gross movement.

3. CONTROL OF VOLUME VARIES

In the production of speech sounds, the expenditure of air bears a definite relation to the intensity of the sound produced; an increase in intensity means a greater escape of air due to the great excursions of the vocal folds. Scripture gives Roudet (1900) as authority for these expenditures of air per second when [ɑ] was produced at a pitch of about C_2: feeble intensity utilized 11 cc.; medium intensity accounted for 17 cc.; strong intensity used 24 cc.

[10] The most sensitive test of the distance is one devised by bacteriologists to discover how far bacteria may be expelled by the breath stream. Sterile nutrient agar plates are placed at various distances in front of the speaker. After an incubation period, numerous bacteria cultures will appear on the plates nearest to the speaker, and fewer and fewer cultures on the plates farther and farther away, until at a distance of a few yards the plates will show no cultures.

There is a psychological as well as a physiological basis for the control of the breath expended in producing sounds. There is probably a fairly definite rate of expenditure of air associated with the production of each sound under certain conditions.

If [ɑ] is phonated at a constant intensity at successive pitches corresponding to C_2, E_2, G_2, and C_3, it appears that less and less air per unit of time is used as the pitch increases.

Further, if [ɑ] be phonated at a pitch corresponding to C_2 and with constant intensity for periods of 1, 2, and 3 seconds, the volume of air used is approximately 14 cc., 16 cc., and 18 cc., respectively. Or the per second consumption of air is 14 cc., 8 cc., and 6 cc., respectively.

The volume of air expended in the production of speech sounds varies, depending on the sound, its position in the word, the position of the body, the health of the body, age, etc. In general, more air is required for fricatives than for plosives; for voiceless fricatives than voiced fricatives; for voiceless plosives than their corresponding nasals. While the fricative has a greater total expenditure than a plosive, the average expenditure (total volume divided by time) is less. That is, the plosive uses up its volume of air more rapidly. In each of the following pairs, the greater volume of air is expended by the first member: [fɑ], [pɑ]; [fɑ], [vɑ]; [pɑ], [mɑ]; [ɑs], [ɑt]; [ɑf], [ɑp]; [zɑ], [dɑ]; [sɑ], [zɑ].

Elsewhere, we have pointed out that voice and speech are continuously dynamic. We emphasize this again because the account would be incomplete if we omitted reference to the fact that much of the force and control of the exhaled air column is a result of correlated activity in the laryngeal region. In fact, as we shall see in Chapter II, the control exercised at the larynx is of fine degree, while that exercised by the breathing musculature is relatively crude.

4. THE RATE AND RHYTHM VARY

The average number of respirations of normal depth in the resting adult varies for individuals from 14 to 17 per minute. The rate is influenced, however, by various conditions of the body, and also by sex and age. The frequency and/or depth of breathing is increased by any muscular effort and by psychical activity. To a certain extent, the rate is under the control of the will, although, normally, breathing is carried out without any special act of volition.

The rate is under the control of the medulla, while the chemical (*p*H) condition of the blood regulates the depth of breathing. Every sensory gate is open to the alteration of the breathing cycle; a dash of cold water anywhere on the body, a cracker crumb in the larynx, a fiery oration, a high diver, all have their effect on respiration.

In normal breathing, the time occupied by each inhalation phase is approximately equal to the time occupied by each exhalation phase. We may estimate between 3 and 4 seconds for each complete respiration; that is, approximately 1¾ seconds for inhalation and 1¾ seconds for exhalation.

During speaking, the time relationships of the phases of inhalation and exhalation are greatly altered. The time expended in inhalation is only about one-quarter to one-half of a second, while the time occupied for exhalation is increased to from 3 to 4 seconds or even longer.[11] During speaking, therefore, the individual may not breathe so many times each minute. Speaking is such a strenuous occupation, calling into play, as it does, so many muscles, that the body's demands for oxygen are increased. To meet these demands, if there are fewer inhalations per minute, there is an automatic adjustment of the respiratory mechanism so that the depth of inspiration is increased and more air is taken in with each breath than during normal breathing. Thus, even with fewer inhalations per minute, a greater volume of air may be taken in during speaking than in an equal interval of time during normal breathing.[12] In some individuals, the rate remains normal and the depth changes; in others both rate and depth are increased.

During speaking a person exercises some degree of control over his breathing. For example, if he wishes to finish a long sentence before stopping to inhale he may do so. Or he may speak to be heard by one person, a hundred people, or a thousand people. Such factors produce a complex situation, neurologically. During normal breathing when there is no thought involved in the process, respiration is carried on under the control of the medulla oblongata. The fact that certain rudimentary sound combinations in speech may be under the control of the medulla oblongata only indicates that originally they were simply vocal accompaniments to breathing, because breathing is under the control of the medulla oblongata. Purposeful breathing must be under the control of the cerebral cortex. For man to be able to carry on this rapid shift of control from low to high levels in the nervous system is indicative of a tremendously complex development which must appear truly remarkable to the philosophically minded student.

[11] The ratio of time of inspiration to time of expiration is 5 to 5 (1.0) during normal breathing, and 0.4 to 5 (0.08) or 0.3 to 5 (0.06) during speaking. Most emotions, according to Feleky (1916), have less influence on respiration: Laughter, 0.30; hate, 0.50; disgust, 1.05; pleasure, 1.10; anger, 1.40; pain, 1.50; wonder, 2.50; fear, 2.65.

[12] Not only does the speaker's speech alter his own respiratory cycle, but his speech also alters the respiratory cycle of the listener. The effects are related and similar. (See Judson, 1932.)

EXERCISES AND QUESTIONS

I. The Measurement of Vital Capacity.

Insert a new wooden mouthpiece or a sterilized glass one in the end of the rubber tube of the spirometer. Take a maximum inspiration (just at the end make a sudden extra effort) and then blow all the air possible into the spirometer (just at the end make a sudden extra effort). Make three trials. Record your best trial on the form provided. Remove and sterilize or dispose of the mouthpiece.

Fill in the blanks on the accompanying form and record the vital capacity of each member of the class in relation to height or weight. In the ruled spaces draw lines connecting the figures thus set down—females, dots; males, dashes; both sexes, solid lines. With colored crayon indicate your own position on the graph.

1. (*a*) What is the average vital capacity of the members of the class? (*b*) How does this compare with the average of 3700 cc.? (*c*) Explain your deviation, if any, from the average.

2. With practice could you better your spirometer record? Explain.

3. Is there a high degree of correlation between vital capacity and sex? height? weight? age? athletic training? or any other factor? Explain.

II. An Experiment to Determine the Relation of Vital Capacity to Speech and Voice Production.

Two students working together: one observer, one subject.

A. Using a stop watch, determine the length of time S can continue the normal—according to O's judgment—production of each of the following sounds, after a maximal inspiration: [i], [ɪ], [ɛ], [æ], [ɑ], [ɔ], [u], [ʌ], [m], [n], [ŋ], [l], [f], [v], [θ], [s], [z], [ʃ].

B. After a maximal inspiration determine, by counting, the number of each of the following normal sounds that can be made on expiration: [p], [b], [t], [d], [k]. Time each trial.

Questions on the data

1. Using the figure obtained for S's vital capacity, determine the per second consumption of air for each of the experimental sounds.

2. Arrange the sounds in a list in order of their *economy* in the use of air.

3. Compare your list with those of others in the class. Are there any sex differences? Would you expect to find any differences on the basis of the vital-capacity figures previously obtained in class?

4. If you were inventing an efficient language, what sounds would you utilize? Could you entirely do away with the use of the less efficient sounds?

5. We are used to hearing people talk who have vital capacities similar to our own. What would be our reaction to a Martian who spoke our language, but who had a vital capacity 5, 10, or 20 times our own; to one having a vital capacity 1/5, 1/10, 1/20 of ours? Explain.

Vital Capacity Data

*Name*____________________ *Vital Capacity*__________

*Sex*__________ *Age*__________ *Weight*__________ *Height*__________

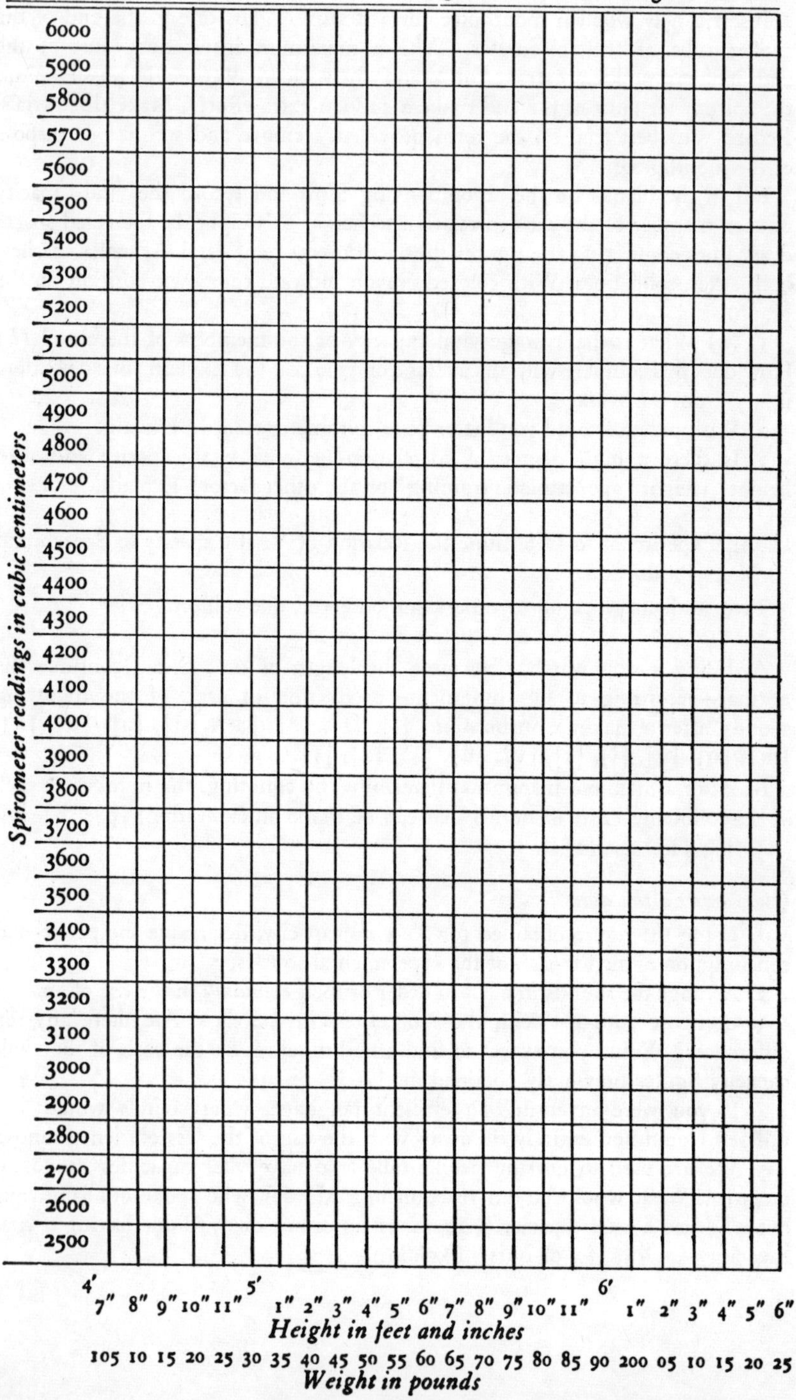

6. Summarize the *indirect* and the *direct* effects of vital capacity on speech. How could you apply your findings to the improvement of your own speech?

III. An Experiment to Determine the Control of Exhalation.

Close valve *C*. Open valve *B*. Turn valve *E* so that air escapes from *G* rather than *F*. Blow into the tube *A* until the mercury in the manometer is at the

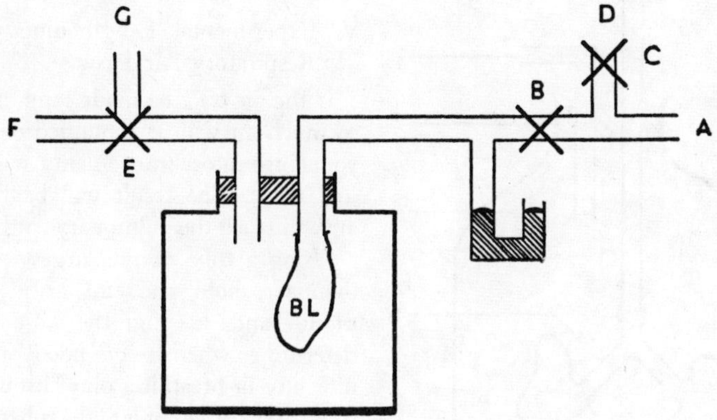

FIG. 10. Apparatus Used in the Experimental Study of the Degree of Steadiness and Control of Exhalation.

level indicated by the instructor, and the balloon be expanded. Close the valve *B* to prevent the escape of the air.

Fasten a second balloon over the outlet at *F*. Turn the valve *E* so that air flows into the balloon at *F* rather than escaping at *G*.

Having opened the valves *B* and *C*, blow through tube *A* with just sufficient force and control to overcome the loss of air through the tube *D* and to keep the volume of air in the balloon, *BL*, constant. Continue for 10 to 20 seconds. Any movement of the second balloon at *F*, due to its being inflated, will indicate your lack of control. Close the valve *B* after each trial without letting any air escape. With the valve *E*, equalize the pressure. Try using tubes of different diameters at *A* and at *D*.

If you permit the second balloon to become inflated to a definite extent, the test then becomes one of maintaining that exact degree of inflation.

(1) Can you accomplish the same results by watching the degree of inflation of *BL*, *G* and *F* remaining closed? Explain.

(2) How accurate is your control? Does it improve with practice?

IV. The Construction of a Laboratory Model to Illustrate Breathing.

Set up apparatus as shown below in Fig. 11. There are two methods of operation:

(1) Withdraw air through L-tube, while shutting off top of thistle tube. The "diaphragm" will rise. Why? Now place finger over mouth of L-tube, and open thistle tube. The air will rush in to expand the balloons.

(2) By means of the thread attached at the center, pull down the "diaphragm," the L-tube being closed. The balloons will expand. Why?

Complete the labeling of the sketch by indicating what parts of the apparatus are comparable to the *mouth, larynx, thoracic cage, trachea, bronchi, lungs,* and *diaphragm*. What are the deficiencies of the model? How would you improve it?

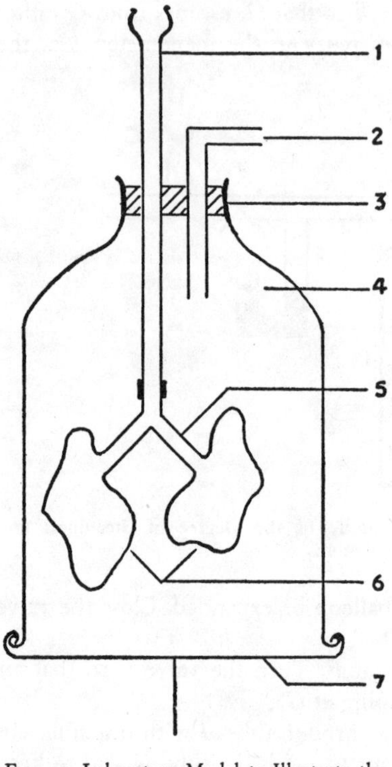

FIG. 11. Laboratory Model to Illustrate the Mechanism of Inhalation and Exhalation.

1. Thistle tube; 2. L-tube; 3. cork or rubber stopper; 4. bell jar; 5. glass Y-tube; 6. rubber balloons; 7. rubber dam closing bottom of bell jar.

V. Experimental Lengthening of the Respiratory Air Passage.

If the air tract be made long enough, so much air will be contained in it that your inspiratory movements will only just fill it. The result will be that no air will reach the pulmonary epithelium.

Using a tube of the largest possible diameter, hold one end of it in the mouth and, keeping the nose closed, determine whether or not you have difficulty in breathing only through the tube. Try different-length tubes, until you find one which is just too long to be of service to you in breathing. Fill this "just too long" tube with water and empty the water into a graduated container. What is the volume of the tube in cubic centimeters?

How do you account for your results? Is there any relation between this experiment and the fact that approximately 140 cc. of the average individual's vital capacity is wasted in the dead space of the air passages. Is all dead-space air or any dead-space air an advantage or a disadvantage to the organism?

VI. The Pneumograph.

Variations in the external circumference of the thorax or abdomen may be measured by a *pneumograph*. There are several types of this instrument, operating either with air systems or with electrical systems. The majority are of the former classification.

The pneumograph is strapped or tied about the thorax in such a manner that with each inspiration (inhalation) the air within the pneumograph-tube-tambour system is under decreased pressure. This results in a downward movement of the writing lever which is recorded on a revolving drum. Exhalation brings about an increase in air pressure within the system and a consequent upward movement of the recording lever.

VII. Experiment on Auscultation.

Three students working together: two observers, one subject.

Auscultation—the act of listening for sounds within the body. *Mediate auscultation* is auscultation performed by the aid of an instrument interposed between the ear and the body.

With colored chalk, lipstick, or ink outline on S's chest and back the approximate position of the lungs and heart. With a *stethoscope* explore the chest surface within the boundaries given to the lungs. Each inhalation is accompanied by a fine rustling sound, the "vesicular murmur," probably caused by the sudden dilatation of the lung vesicles, or by eddy currents as the air passes from the narrow bronchioles into the wider infundibula. A much louder sound is heard over the larger air passages, i. e., the larynx, trachea, and bronchi. It accompanies both inhalation and exhalation; it resembles a sharp whispered *hah*. This is the "bronchial murmur." In other parts of the thorax the healthy lung prevents the propagation of sound to the thoracic cage wall.

On chest and back auscultate in the regions of the outline of the heart. Two heart sounds may be distinguished. One has a deeper pitch and is longer in duration than the other (*lubb-dup*). Let one O count the heartbeats while the other O notes the rate of breathing. The O who counts the number of breaths per time unit will hold a stop watch. At the end of one minute, from the signal of "go," the two observers will note the number of breaths and the number of heartbeats. Make three trials. Make one three-minute trial. What is the average of the two rates, and what is the breathing rate–heart rate ratio?

Let S run in place for 30 seconds. Take his heartbeat and respiratory rate during the next 60 seconds.

Let S take a deep breath and exhale through a rubber tube. O place the stethoscope on the tube. Does the heartbeat have any influence on the expiratory stream? Explain.

Chapter II

PHONATION

I. Introduction
II. The Laryngeal Cavity
III. The Anatomy of the Laryngeal Region
  A. The Cartilaginous Framework of the Larynx
  B. The Ligaments and Membranes of the Larynx
IV. The Laryngeal Generator
  A. The Muscles Used in Phonation
    1. Intrinsic Muscles
    2. Infrahyoid Muscles
  B. The A, B, C, D Positions of the Vocal Folds
    1. Position A—Closed
    2. Position B—Open as in Phonation
    3. Position C—Open as in Whispering
    4. Position D—Open as in Breathing
V. Phonation
  A. The Mechanism of Phonation
  B. Voice: Age and Sex Differences
  C. Controversies as to the Nature of Phonation
    1. The Probability of the Folds Vibrating in Phase
    2. The Possibility of the Folds Vibrating in Opposite Phase
    3. Complete Versus Segmental Vibration
  D. The Mechanism of the Falsetto
  E. Pitch and Amplitude Factors at the Glottis
    1. The Effect of Altering the Level of the Glottis
    2. Voluntary Control of Pitch and Intensity
    3. Voice Pitch Changes at Puberty
  F. The Physical Effect of the Reflected Air Stream on Vocal Folds
  G. The Function of the Ventricular Folds
  H. The Significance of the Epiglottis
  I. The Artificial Larynx
  J. Esophageal Speech
  K. Speech during Inhalation
Exercises and Questions

INTRODUCTION

In this chapter we shall study what happens to the moving column of exhaled air when it reaches the larynx at the top of the trachea. Before we take up the detailed study of the larynx, however, it will prove instructive to look briefly at the evolutionary development of the larynx. Incidentally, it is probably true that the evolution of the structure of the pharynx and mouth of man and the relation of the epiglottis and tongue to the soft palate have been at least as important in the development of voice and speech as has the larynx.

When life began to emerge from an aquatic (hydrosphere) environment, and when lungs were evolved to make possible the breathing of air (atmosphere), the framework of the larynx, particularly the cricoid and thyroid cartilages, was developed to keep the air tract patent. It was essential that there be some method of preventing the entrance of food or water into the lungs, and, therefore, at the pharyngeal orifice of the pulmonary outgrowth a protective valve—the larynx—was developed. Thus, the simple larynx is a valve in the air passageway; it is not primarily an organ of voice. There are a half-dozen or more primitive functions of the larynx—including the prevention of the entrance of foreign material into the lungs, the establishing of the Hering-Breuer reflex, the fixation of the thorax so that it may act as a cushion-fulcrum for the bony levers of the body in efforts of lifting, swinging suspended by the arms, etc. Difficult manual labor, such as lifting, may result in a temporary condition of hoarseness due to the strenuous closing of the glottis. After total laryngectomy, the absence of the laryngeal valve prevents fixation of the thorax.

One of the most notable differences which distinguishes the larynx of man from that of most other animals involves the ratio which exists between the cartilaginous (arytenoid) boundaries of the glottis and the soft boundaries (thyroarytenoid folds); the ratio between the glottis respiratoria and the glottis vocalis. Birds, for example, have a primitive type of larynx. The cartilages are long; the thyroarytenoid folds are short. The cartilages are not well adapted to rapid vibratory movements and, even if they were, could not be controlled within fine limits. Furthermore, it requires an extremely high breath pressure to set the cartilages into vibration. Birds have need of an adequate fixating mechanism for flying, and hence nearly all of them have developed a specialized sound-producing organ, the *syrinx,* located at the bifurcation of the trachea.[1] For most sounds, the bird uses the syrinx, although it uses the larynx for the pro-

[1] How the sounds get out from the syrinx through the larynx which supposedly is closed for thoracic fixation or, if the larynx is open to permit the emission of the sound, why the syrinx has been evolved, apparently are at present unanswered questions.

duction of certain sounds, such as hissing. Song birds have relatively elaborate syringes and use them in the production of their complex melodies.

The larynx best suited for phonation has vocal folds which are long and which have round, but not too round, freely moving edges; smooth but not too smooth; and with free, but not too free, margins which can come into contact along their entire length. Further, the tension of the folds should be variable grossly and segmentally. Again, the vocal processes of the arytenoid cartilages should not be too long. Man happens to possess such a phonative organ [2] because he is not a fast runner, does not eat herbage, and because his "valvular heritage" from an arboreal past has degenerated. Some other animals possess phonative mechanisms similar to that of man, yet are silent.

To say that the larynx of man was not "designed" primarily for voice production is not to imply, as do some writers, that the larynx is not an essential organ of speech. Even if one agrees that the vowel sounds may be due to the resonance characteristics of the vocal cavities; that vowels may be produced by blowing air across the open mouth, while the breath is held and the larynx remains inoperative—provided, of course, that the mouth be shaped for the pronunciation of the various vowels—this is not to agree that such a means of producing sounds constitutes *normal* speech. Normal speech and voice necessitate the normal functioning of the phonatory mechanism.

Negus's work on the larynx in no sense lends support to a narrow interpretation of the "superimposed speech" dogma. Rather, his study should lead us to assume a questioning attitude about the speech mechanism. He does not show that man has *the* superior valvular mechanism. On the other hand, he does show that although man has a laryngeal valve similar to the laryngeal valve of certain other animals, nevertheless, man's valve shows a development toward the voluntary type of musculature and a neurological association that for simple biological uses of the valve are not only unnecessary, but in some cases even detrimental.

The bald statement, narrowly interpreted, that speech is an overlaid function or, better, that it is a superimposed activity, has for many years acted as a brake on the scientific study of the relation of the end-product speech to the speech-producing mechanism. By too many, the statement is taken as an assumption that even though speech or voice had never developed in man, nevertheless, he would now have the identical muscular and neurological speech-producing combination. In other words, the respiratory, masticatory, lifting, etc., demands in man are such that, even if

[2] Man's relatively sharp inferior vocal folds are not explained by the requirements of voice. These structures are present in many animals which are usually silent, and are absent in some animals which are noisy. Usually, inferior folds are found in animals which have the independent use of the fore limbs. Such association is found more highly correlative than is that of phonation and the presence of vocal folds.

there were no speech, every muscle and nerve combination now existing would exist wholly because of these vegetative demands; that even though there were no speech or voice, the many voluntary and involuntary connections, now existing in the central nervous system—and now utilized in speech—would still be in existence. Such dogma rules out any correlation between the development of speech in man, and the development of the cortical and sub-cortical brain centers. Surely, the field of speech is in need of experimental research which will answer this question: "What anatomical, neurological, and physiological differences distinguish the speech mechanism from the vegetative mechanism?"

THE LARYNGEAL CAVITY

At the top of the trachea the exhaled breath stream enters the *laryngeal cavity* (cavum laryngis). A natural dividing line at the level of the rima glottidis subdivides the cavity into two parts, each of which contains important structures.

Cavities of the larynx and their landmarks:
- Hyperglottal cavity (vestibule; vestibulum laryngis)
  - Ventricular folds (false vocal folds)
  - Ventricles
    - Appendix
  - Vocal folds
- Hypoglottal cavity (sub-vestibule)

The single cavity, when the glottis is open, or the two cavities, when the glottis is closed, of the larynx extend from its upper laryngeal entrance (*aditus laryngis*) to the lower border of the cricoid cartilage where it is continuous with the cavity of the trachea. For our study, it may be said to be divided into upper and lower parts by the projecting vocal folds. These two parts are continuous through the rima glottidis. (See Frontispiece.) The upper part of the cavity, above the vocal folds, is the *vestibule*.[3] In its inferior part it is markedly compressed laterally. It diminishes in width from above downward. Because the inlet is oblique, its vertical height is greater in front than behind. Anteriorly, it is bounded by the posterior surface of the epiglottis, i.e., its mucous-membrane-covered surface. Because of the leaflike shape of the epiglottis, the cavity narrows below as it approaches the anterior ends of the vestibular folds. The epiglottis presents a convex posterior surface above, below which is a slight concavity. Below this, and appearing conspicuously in a laryngoscopic examination, is a protuberance over the superior part of the thyro-

[3] The aditus laryngis is much more accessible than is usually thought. If the tongue be drawn far forward, the epiglottis may be seen. The laryngeal opening can be felt if a finger be inserted into the oral cavity.

epiglottic ligament. This bulge is the epiglottic tubercle or cushion of the epiglottis. The medial surface of the respective aryepiglottic fold forms the smooth and slightly concave side wall of the vestibule. The posterior wall of the vestibule is the interval between the upper parts of the arytenoids. Its width, which depends upon the position of the arytenoids, is variable. When the posterior wall is narrow due to the drawing together of the cartilages, the mucous membrane covering the wall is thrown into longitudinal folds.

The vestibule is continuous above with the pharynx and is roughly triangular in outline. Its base is directed anteriorly. There is a slight antero-posterior slope to the aperture. Its boundaries are: anterior—the epiglottis; lateral—the arytenoepiglottic folds and cuneiform cartilages; posterior—arytenoid and corniculate cartilages. The free border of the epiglottis provides its anterior or basal part. The narrow apex of the triangle, lower than its base, occupies the interval between the arytenoid cartilages. The lateral boundaries are formed by the aryepiglottic folds, two folds of mucous membrane stretching between the lateral margins of the epiglottis (anterior) and the arytenoid cartilages (posterior). Between the layers of mucous membrane which compose the folds is: some areolar tissue; the sphincteric muscular fibers of the aryepiglottic muscles; and, behind, the cuneiform and corniculate cartilages. These latter produce the bulbous prominences called, respectively, the *cuneiform* and *corniculate tubercles.* The tubercles assist the epiglottic tubercle in closing the aditus laryngis when the aryepiglottic sphincter is in action.

Moving pictures of the vocal folds often show, on each side of the laryngeal opening, a small pharyngeal pit called the *piriform fossa.* This depression is part of the lateral food trough which leads from the oropharynx behind and at the base of the tongue around the aditus laryngis to the entrance of the esophagus. The pocket is bounded medially by the arytenoid cartilage and the aryepiglottic fold, and laterally by the epithelial lining of the thyroid lamina and thyrohyoid membrane. Sometimes foreign bodies are caught in the fossa.

The vestibule contains, from above down: the ventricular folds, the ventricles of the larynx, and the vocal folds.

The *ventricular folds* or *vestibular folds* (plicae ventriculares; superior, ventricular, or false vocal folds) of mucous membrane enclose the ventricular ligaments. Anteriorly these are attached at the junction angle of the laminae of the thyroid cartilage, below the attachment of the stem of the epiglottis. Behind they are attached to the arytenoid cartilages or just below the superimposed cuneiform cartilages. The inferior border of each ligament, with its mucous membrane envelope, forms the upper boundary of the ventricle of the larynx. The histological make-up of the vestibular folds is shown in Fig. 13. Increasingly deep to the mucous membrane are the supporting vestibular ligament, glandular tissue, and scattered muscle fibers.

Although numerous writers say that the ventricular folds constitute part of the valvular protective mechanism of the airway and that their closure normally aids in preventing the entrance of foreign substances into the lungs, it is not clear from histological study how the folds can be closed. Certainly, it is difficult to identify the muscle systems responsible for such closure. Because the *rima vestibuli* (false glottis; glottis spuria) is wider than the underlying rima glottidis, the vocal folds as well as the ventricular folds are easily seen in laryngoscopic investigations.[4]

The *ventricle of the larynx* (ventricle of Morgagni; ventriculus laryngis; the *sinus of the larynx*) is a spindle-shaped cavity—a lateral diverticulum situated between the ventricular and vocal folds, the former making up

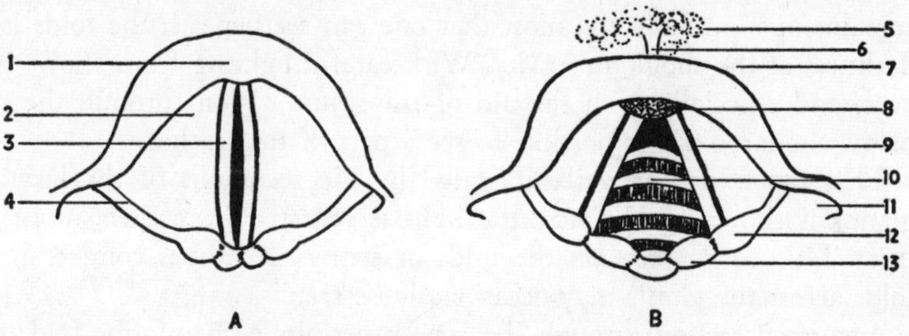

FIG. 12. Laryngoscopic Views of Cavity of Larynx.

A. Rima glottidis almost completely closed.
B. Rima glottidis open.

1. Epiglottis; 2. vestibular fold; 3. vocal fold; 4. aryepiglottic fold; 5. dorsum of tongue; 6. glossoepiglottic fold; 7. vallecula; 8. cushion or tubercle of epiglottis; 9. sinus of larynx; 10. trachea; 11. piriform fossa; 12. cuneiform tubercle; 13. corniculate tubercle.

the roof of the ventricle, the latter the floor. Its approximate dimensions are: 12 to 20 mm. long and 4 to 8 mm. high; it is almost twice as large in the male as in the female. Anteriorly the ventricle opens into a pouch, the appendix.

The *appendix of the laryngeal ventricle* (appendix ventriculi laryngis; laryngeal saccule) is a blind sac which projects rostrally from each ventricle and onto the membranous surface of which open many mucous glands. This sac is enclosed by delicate muscular fasciculi which compress it and express the mucous secretion it contains upon the vocal folds, as a lubricant.

The *vocal folds* (vocal cords; vocal bands; vocal lips; vocal ledges; vocal cushions; voice lips; inferior ventricular folds; etc.) are attached anteriorly to the angle of the thyroid cartilage, and posteriorly to the vocal processes

[4] Well supplied with sensory nerve endings, this region is extremely sensitive. A strong cough reflex results if the area be stimulated by a foreign substance.

of the arytenoids. The vocal folds are the thickened upper portion of the conus elasticus. The lower border of each fold is continuous with the lateral portion of the conus elasticus; the upper border is the lower boundary of the ventricle.

Viewed from above, as in laryngoscopy, the larynx presents in the mid-line: the tubercle or cushion of the epiglottis, which is a round elevation covered with mucous membrane of pink or reddish color; on either side, the arched superior thyroarytenoid fold whose downward-directed concavity forms the roof of the ventricles; and, below, the vocal folds,[5] which may be seen stretching in a postero-anterior direction across the laryngeal cavity from their respective attachments. The folds have a pearly white appearance. During phonation their median edges may be seen, if one uses stroboscopy or high-speed moving pictures, alternately approaching and retreating from the mid-line. During quiet breathing, when the glottis remains open, usually the most that one can see beneath the folds is the darkness of the subglottal cavity. With careful lighting from above, however, and especially with the aid of transillumination through the neck below the larynx, it is possible to see a part of the trachea.

That the folds are well lubricated by the secretions of the laryngeal glands is shown by the way the light is reflected from their moist surfaces. Mucous droplets on the folds or strings of mucus connecting the folds across the glottis may occasionally be seen.

A coronal section through the larynx permits each inferior fold to be seen in its cross section. Figure 13 shows clearly that the thyroarytenoid muscle lies relatively deep within the fold, covered by successive layers of glandular tissue, elastic tissue and, finally, mucous membrane. Notice how the difference in function of the various areas of the fold is represented by a difference in histological structure. Most important is the fact that where the vocal folds are more active and come into forcible contact with one another the mucous membrane of that area consists of a flat pavement or *stratified squamous epithelium,*[6] whereas, elsewhere, its structure is that of *columnar epithelium*. Also, there is no glandular tissue beneath the *striking edges* of the fold and between those margins and the muscular tissue. Above and below that area, however, there is an abundance of glandular tissue.

A sex difference in the structure of the vocal folds is apparent when they are studied in coronal section. The male folds are more massive and more rounded than those of the female.

The upper margin of each inferior vocal fold forms a relatively flat ledge, the floor of the ventricle, over which hangs the ventricular fold.

[5] During two periods, namely year 0–1 and 14–16, the vocal folds show their greatest growth.

[6] Only in man and the higher anthropoids are the true vocal folds covered with stratified epithelium.

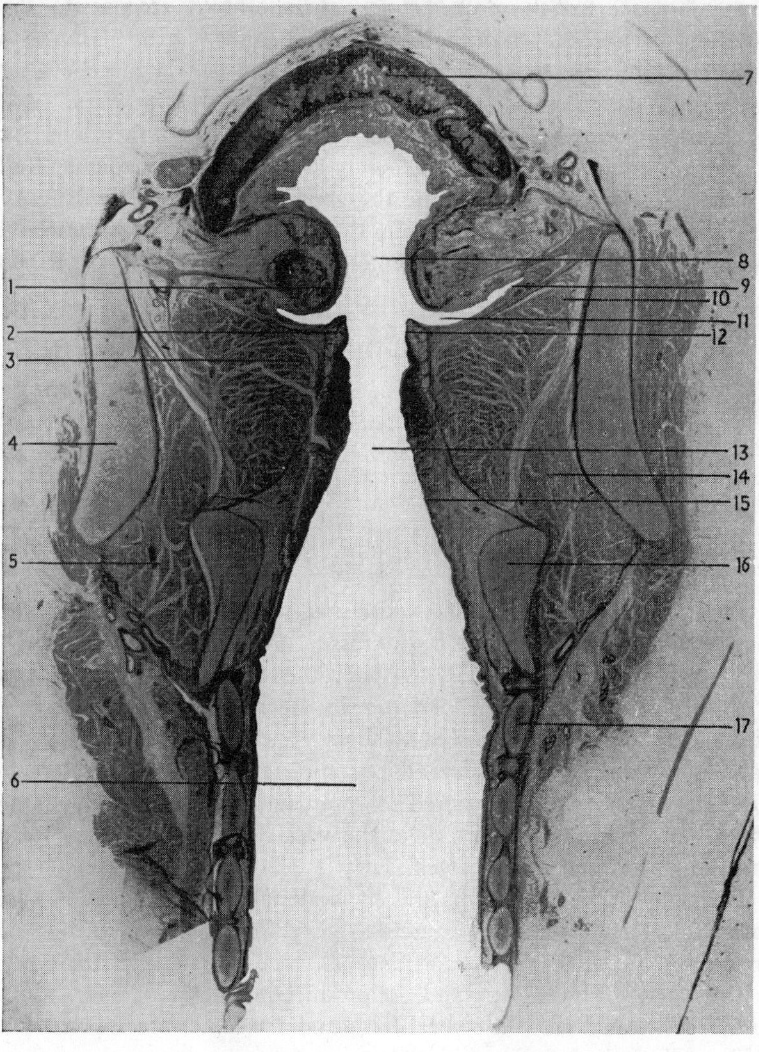

FIG. 13. Photomicrograph of Coronal Section through Larynx.

1. Vestibular fold; 2. vocal fold; 3. thyroarytenoid muscle; 4. thyroid cartilage; 5. cricothyroid muscle; 6. cavity of trachea; 7. epiglottis; 8. hyperglottal cavity; 9. appendix of laryngeal ventricle; 10. aryepiglottic muscle; 11. ventricle of larynx; 12. stratified squamous epithelium; 13. hypoglottal cavity; 14. lateral cricoarytenoid muscle; 15. columnar epithelium; 16. cricoid cartilage; 17. tracheal cartilage.

The *rima glottidis* (true glottis, glottis vera) is the elliptical opening [7] (aperture, fissure, chink) between the vocal folds anteriorly and the vocal processes and bodies of the arytenoids posteriorly. The portion (pars in-

[7] Length: in the male, approximately 20 to 24 mm.
in the female, 14 to 17 mm.
Width: at the widest part between the vocal processes, approximately 8 mm.

termembranacea) of the glottis between the vocal folds accounts for three-fifths of the entire length of the glottis, and is known as the *glottis vocalis*. The remaining two-fifths of the glottis lies between the arytenoid cartilages and is called the pars intercartilaginea or *glottis respiratoria*.

Although there are wide individual variations in the dimensions of the vocal folds and the glottis, the following averages will be enlightening. It is interesting to note that, despite the great differences in the lengths of vocal folds of the male and female, there is but little sex difference between the ratios of length to the antero-posterior diameter of the glottis.

Sex	*Antero-posterior diameter of glottis*	*Length of of vocal cords*	*Ratios of diameter of glottis to length of cords*	*Width of glottis between vocal processes*
Male	24 mm.	18 mm.	1.33 to 1	14 mm.
Female	15 mm.	11 mm.	1.36 to 1	12 mm.

The rima glottidis is the most constricted portion of the air tract in the larynx. The open glottis provides a cross-section area of approximately 50 to 70 sq. mm. Above and below this point the airway presents an increased cross section of 200 sq. mm. or more. In other words, at the glottis, the physiological airway is narrowed by about 75 per cent, thus forming a partial dam to the air stream. To produce complete closure of the glottal aperture the vocal folds are required to complete only the small remaining 25 per cent of the task. This gives the vocal folds a great factor of advantage and a high degree of efficiency.

Through the rima glottidis the hyperglottal and hypoglottal cavities communicate. The glottic aperture assumes different shapes during: quiet breathing, whispering, the production of a tone of low pitch, the production of a tone of high pitch, and the production of falsetto voice. The fissure is obliterated when the vocal folds and arytenoids are approximated.

The *sub-vestibule,* or *hypoglottal* cavity, is bounded above by the vocal folds; thus, its superior aperture may be opened or closed by the vocal folds. When not closed it is somewhat compressed laterally. Below, the cavity is continuous with the trachea at the cricotracheal junction. The circular inferior aperture of the sub-vestibule is of greater area than its restricted superior aperture at the glottis. The walls of the cavity are formed by the cricoid cartilage and the cricothyroid ligament.[8] The mucous membrane lining of the entire laryngeal cavity is continuous here with that of the trachea.

[8] Through this surgical entrance is gained in cases of laryngotomy.

THE ANATOMY OF THE LARYNGEAL REGION [9]

Either the breath stream passes, as in normal breathing, without great hindrance, through the region just described, or it is subjected to active vibratory interference by the laryngeal mechanism. We are interested in the latter phenomenon, which is known as *phonation*. That is, we are to consider the larynx as a generator of sound waves, although we know quite well that it is only one of Nature's planned accidents which enables man to utilize for speech purposes a mechanism which was not originally, and is not now primarily, developed for purposes of phonation.

The *larynx,* a valve at the upper end of the pulmonary air tract, is situated between the trachea and the root of the tongue, at the upper and forepart of the neck, where it projects in the mid-line. It forms the lower part of the anterior wall of the pharynx, and is covered behind by the mucous lining of that cavity. Its vertical extent corresponds to the height of the 4th, 5th, and 6th cervical vertebrae.

Any movement of the head or neck alters the position of the larynx. The larynx is elevated by the backward movement of the head and by swallowing; it is depressed by lowering the jaw toward the chest. X-ray photographs show that when vowel sounds are produced there are accompanying alterations in the pharyngeal cavity and, concurrently, alterations in the position of the larynx and of its parts relative to one another.

The larynx is composed of three single cartilages and three pairs of cartilages which are connected by ligaments and moved by numerous muscles. It is lined by mucous membrane, continuous above with that of the pharynx and below with that of the trachea.

A. The Cartilaginous Framework of the Larynx

Cartilages of Larynx: [10]

- Cricoid
- Thyroid
- Arytenoid (two)
- Corniculate (two)
- Cuneiform (two)
- Epiglottis

The following measurements will be helpful in visualizing the size of the larynx. Distance from superior border of epiglottis to inferior border of cricoid cartilage: male, 7.0 cm.; female, 5.0 cm. Transverse diameter of

[9] At this point the monumental volume on *The Mechanism of the Larynx,* by V. E. Negus, may be consulted with profit.

[10] With advancing age (25–65), the cricoid, thyroid, and the bases of the arytenoids progressively ossify. See X-ray pictures, Figs. 17 and 18.

larynx: male, 4.0 cm.; female, 3.5 cm. Sagittal diameter of larynx: male, 4.0 cm.; female, 3.5 cm.

The Cricoid Cartilage

The cricoid (signet ring) cartilage [11] surmounts the trachea and may, indeed, be considered as the differentiated uppermost cartilage of the trachea. Its inferior border is attached to the first ring of the trachea by the same kind of fibrous membrane that connects the tracheal rings. The cricoid provides the articulating foundation of the laryngeal framework. The smooth inner surface of the cricoid cartilage is covered with mucous membrane continuous with that of the trachea, below, and the laryngeal cavity, above. The lumen of the ring is elliptical (Fig. 14) above, more nearly circular below.

The signet portion of the cartilage is at the back (posterior), and is called the *posterior quadrate lamina.* It is 20–30mm in height in the male. On its superior border, laterally, are two articulating facets on which rest the bases of the arytenoid cartilages. This border provides attachment for the lateral cricothyroid muscle and the cricothyroid membrane. In depressions on each side of the mid-line the posterior cricoarytenoid muscles find attachment.

The narrow *anterior arch* (5–8mm high) of the cricoid provides origin for the cricothyroid muscles. Behind are attached some fibers of the inferior constrictor. On each side, an articular depression at the junction of lamina and arch receives the corresponding inferior horn (*cornu;* plural, *cornua*) of the thyroid cartilage.

The Thyroid Cartilage

The thyroid (shield-shaped) cartilage makes up most of the anterior and lateral walls of the framework of the larynx. It is the largest of the laryngeal cartilages. Although, in the adult, the cartilage appears to be a single structure, it is composed of two laminae or wings (alae) fused along their anterior borders in the mid-line. The angle of junction of the thyroid laminae in the child and the adult female is approximately 120–130 degrees; in the male after puberty the angle is about 90–100 degrees.[12] The prominent superior portion of this angle of junction is called the Adam's apple (pomum Adami) because it is more pronounced in the male. On either side pass the sternohyoid muscles. Directly above the prominence is the easily located superior thyroid notch (incisura thyroideae). Not far above this the hyoid bone may be felt. Internally, the alae at their angle of junction, and on each side of the mid-line, give attachment to

[11] Of hyaline cartilage.

[12] The change which takes place in the larynx of the male permits the larynx to be rated as a secondary sex characteristic.

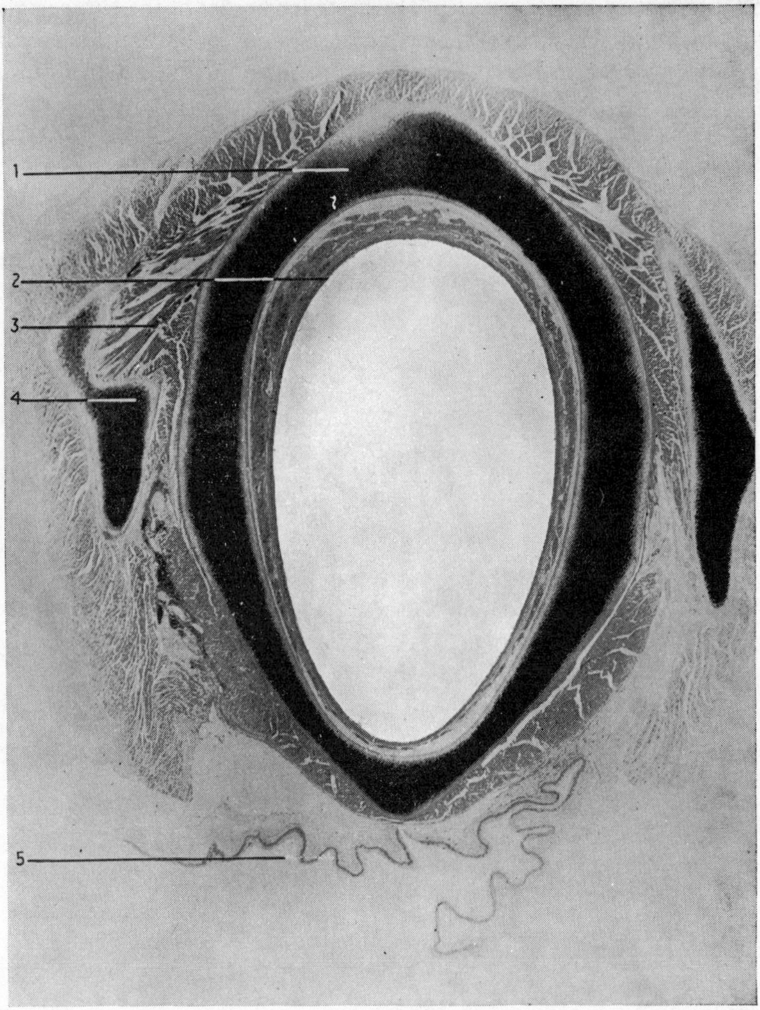

FIG. 14. Photomicrograph of Cricoid Cartilage. Cross Section below Level of Arytenoid Cartilage.

1. Cricoid cartilage; 2. mucous membrane lining; 3. cricothyroid muscle; 4. **thyroid** cartilage; 5. esophagus.

the ventricular folds and to the vocal folds. The alae present an upper border giving attachment to the hyothyroid membrane. These borders terminate posteriorly in the superior cornua, which are attached to the greater cornua of the hyoid bone by the thyrohyoid ligaments. To the lower border, terminating in the inferior cornua, is attached the central portion of the cricothyroid membrane. The inferior cornua articulate with the cricoid cartilage to which firm attachment is made by capsular ligaments. The inferior cornua provide attachment for the cricothyroid and inferior constrictor muscles. The posterior border of the laminae gives attachment to the pharyngeal aponeurosis, and to the palatopharyngei and stylopharyngei. The oblique line presented to the external surface

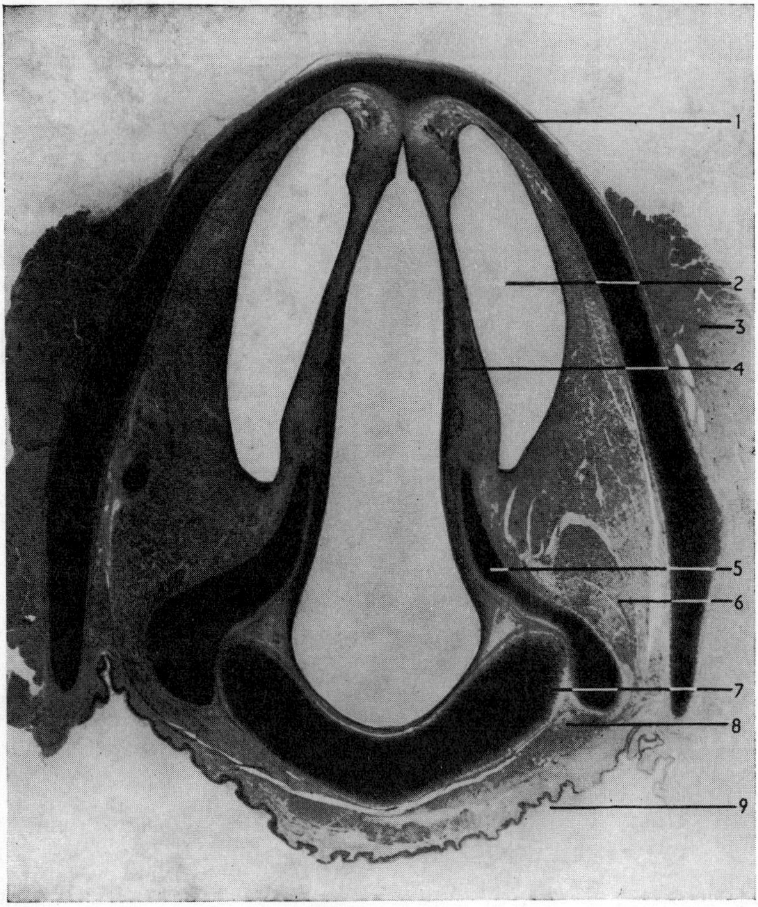

FIG. 15. Photomicrograph Showing Thyroid, Cricoid, and Arytenoid Cartilages.

1. Thyroid cartilage; 2. sinus of the larynx; 3. sternothyroid muscle; 4. thyroarytenoid ligament; 5. arytenoid cartilage; 6. lateral cricoarytenoid muscle; 7. cricoid cartilage; 8. arytenoid muscles; 9. esophagus.

of each lamina gives attachment to the sternothyroid, thyrohyoid, and inferior constrictor of its own side. The inner surface of the laminae at the angle of their fusion, gives attachment to the epiglottis, thyroarytenoid, and thyroepiglottic muscles.

The inferior horns of the thyroid cartilage articulate with the lateral facets on the cricoid cartilage, providing a variety of relational movements significant in the control of adjustments of muscles used in phonation.

The Arytenoid Cartilages

The arytenoid (ladle-shaped) cartilages [13] (two) are set on the posterior and superior border of the lamina of the cricoid cartilage. They are ir-

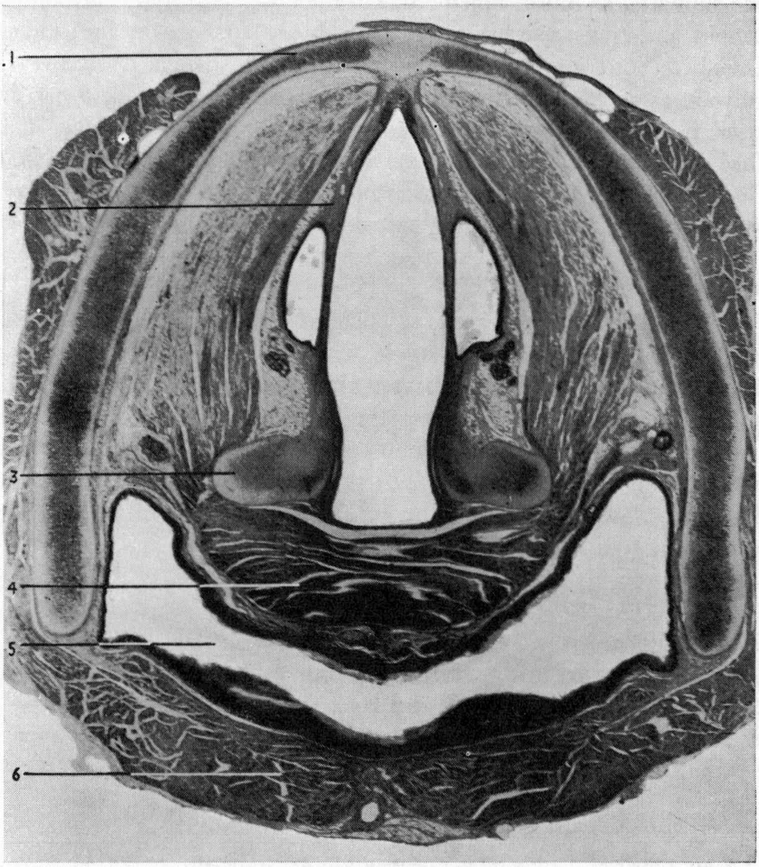

FIG. 16. Photomicrograph of Arytenoid and Thyroid Cartilages. Taken at a Level Higher Than That Shown in Fig. 15.

1. Thyroid cartilage; 2. thyroarytenoid muscle; 3. arytenoid cartilage; 4. lateral and oblique arytenoid muscles; 5. esophagus; 6. inferior constrictor of pharynx.

regularly pyramidal in form. The apex of each cartilage curves somewhat backward and medially and supports its respective corniculate cartilage. The triangular base of each cartilage provides a concave facet which articulates with the superior border of the lamina of the cricoid cartilage. Each base, also, provides a lateral and posterior projection, the muscular process, giving attachment, behind, to the posterior cricoarytenoid and in

[13] Composed of hyaline cartilage, except the apices which are of yellow elastic tissue.

front, to the lateral cricoarytenoid, and a small, sharp-pointed anterior projection, the vocal process, which gives attachment to the inferior thyroarytenoid ligament. The antero-lateral surface of each cartilage gives attachment to the thyroarytenoid muscle, and the thyroarytenoid ligament which supports the mucous membrane of the false vocal fold. The oblique arytenoid and transverse arytenoid muscles are attached to the smooth and concave posterior surface of the cartilage. The medial surface is triangular in shape and its smooth, vertical extent is separated by a narrow interval from the corresponding surface of the opposite cartilage. This surface is covered by the continued mucous membrane of larynx and trachea. Separating the three surfaces of the arytenoid cartilage are three borders—anterior, posterior, and lateral.

The Corniculate Cartilages

The corniculate (corn-shaped) cartilages[14] (cartilages of Santorini) are roughly pyramidal and articulate with the apices of the arytenoid cartilages, serving to extend the arytenoids medially and posteriorly. For phonation the cartilaginous part of the glottis, between the arytenoids, must be closed so that the air current can be directed through the membranous portion of the glottis. The corniculates aid the arytenoids in making the closure complete. The corniculates are located in the arytenoepiglottic folds.

The Cuneiform Cartilages

The cuneiform (wedge-shaped) cartilages[14] (cartilages of Wrisberg) are, likewise, situated in the arytenoepiglottic folds. Each is anterior and lateral of its respective arytenoid cartilage.

(Viewed from above the corniculate and cuneiform cartilages appear to be small swellings in the arytenoepiglottic folds.)

The Epiglottis

The epiglottis[14] looks like a leaf with its stalk directed downward. By means of the thyroepiglottic ligament the base of the stalk is attached to the inner surface of the angle of the thyroid cartilage. The upper, leaf-like part of the epiglottis is free and curves upward behind the base of the tongue. Most of the base of the tongue overhangs the epiglottis.

Except for a portion just below the center, the epiglottis presents a concave—i.e., from side to side—postero-inferior surface toward the laryngeal cavity. The entire surface is covered with mucous membrane. The portion excepted above is a convexity or slight eminence called the *cushion* or *tubercle of the epiglottis*. The antero-superior surface of the epiglottis is convex from side to side. It faces the base of the tongue to

[14] Of yellow elastic tissue.

which it is attached by three glossoepiglottic folds containing three glossoepiglottic ligaments. It is attached to the hyoid bone by the hypoglossal membrane or hyoepiglottic ligament. The lateral margins of the epiglottis curve backward. Along their extent, the arytenoepiglottic folds are attached and the thyroepiglottic and aryepiglottic muscles find insertion. These two muscles act to depress the epiglottis.

As viewed through the laryngo-periskop, the epiglottis may be seen to occlude the superior aperture of the larynx when the larynx is elevated. During swallowing, the epiglottis moves backward and the larynx rises so that the expanded tubercle portion of the epiglottis occludes the superior aperture of the larynx when they meet. During breathing and ordinary phonation the geniohyoglossus, geniohyoid, and mylohyoid muscles keep the epiglottis drawn forward and in a vertical position.

The X-ray laterals of the neck region (Figs. 17 and 18) show the relation of the laryngeal structures to the cervical vertebrae. Roentgenograms taken during quiet respiration show that ordinarily the tip of the epiglottis is at about the level of the superior border of the 3d cervical vertebra. The level of the top of the arytenoid cartilages is opposite the intervertebral space between the 4th and 5th cervical vertebrae; the inferior border of the cricoid cartilage is on a level with the inferior border of the 5th cervical vertebra. Thus, in general, the vertical extent of the larynx corresponds to the distance between the superior border of the 3d and the inferior border of the 5th cervical vertebrae. During phonation, the position of the hyoid bone and of the laryngeal structures is changed in relation to the cervical vertebrae.

Anteriorly, the thyroid cartilage is separated from the outer air by the skin and two layers of fascia. Posteriorly, the larynx is separated from the vertebral column by the pharyngeal cavity, the posterior wall of the pharynx, and the prevertebral fascia.

B. The Ligaments and the Membranes of the Larynx

The *capsule* and the *posterior cricoarytenoid ligament* connect each arytenoid to the cricoid.

Between the thyroid articular surface on the cricoid cartilage and the articular surface on the inferior cornu of the thyroid cartilage is a joint which has a synovial membrane. It is strengthened by a *capsular ligament.* The cricothyroid articulation permits the approximation of the anterior portions of the two cartilages by a revolving movement on a transverse axis of the joint. Some gliding backward and forward probably is also possible at the joint.

The *cricotracheal ligament* connects the cricoid cartilage with the upper ring of the trachea.

From the middle of the anterior surface of the epiglottis the *glossoepi-*

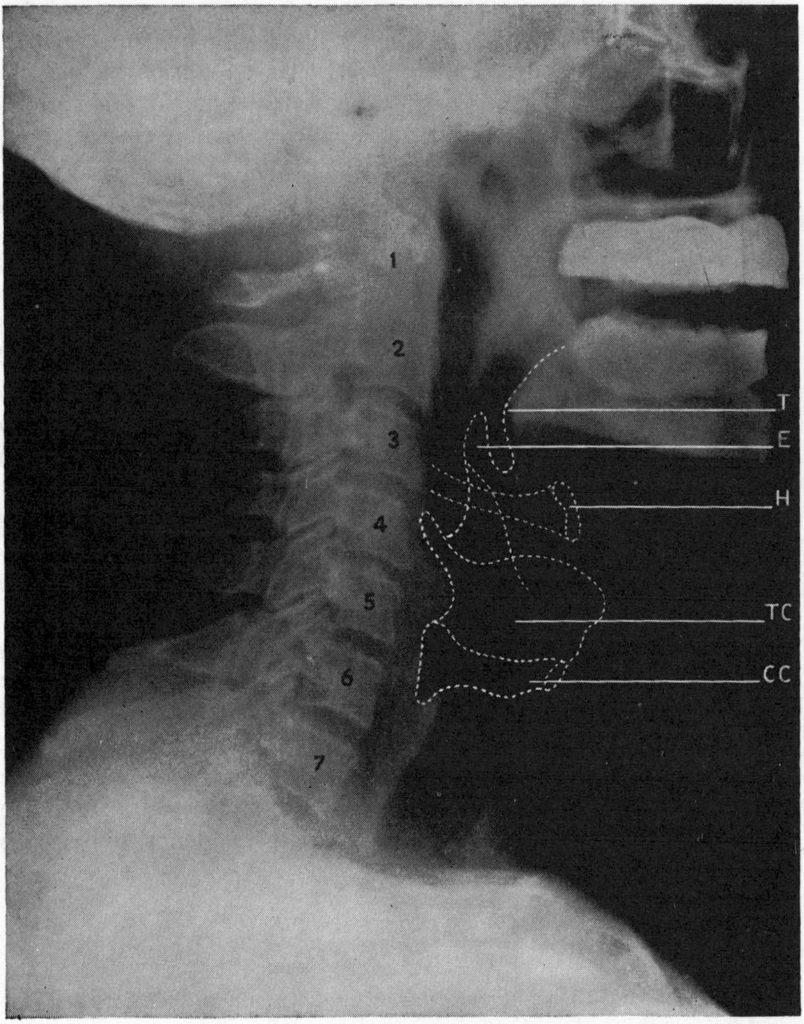

FIG. 17. X-ray Lateral of the Neck during Respiration.

1–7. Cervical vertebrae; T. base of tongue; E. epiglottis; H. hyoid bone; TC. thyroid cartilage; CC. cricoid cartilage. Notice the relation of the structures to the cervical vertebrae and compare with Fig. 18.

glottic fold extends to the back of the tongue. From the lateral margins of the epiglottis the *pharyngoepiglottic folds* extend to the pharyngeal walls on either side of the tongue. On either side, the glossoepiglottic fold and the pharyngoepiglottic fold form elevations bounding a depression known as the *vallecula*. From the lateral margins of the epiglottis, there also extend out the *aryepiglottic folds,* but to the arytenoid cartilages. The aryepiglottic folds constitute the margins of the laryngeal inlet; within

extrinsic - connect larynx to body
intrinsic - connect cartilages to each other

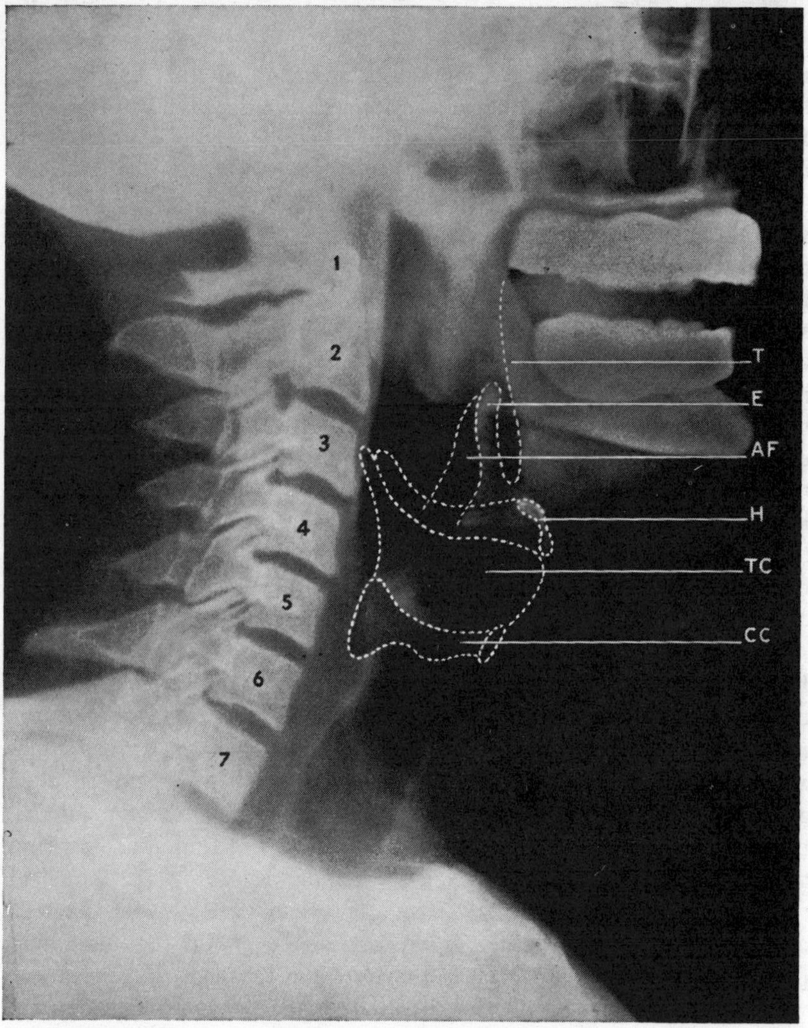

FIG. 18. X-ray Lateral of Neck during Phonation.

1–7. Cervical vertebrae; T. base of tongue; E. epiglottis; AF. aryepiglottic folds; H. hyoid bone; TC. thyroid cartilage; CC. cricoid cartilage. [Here, and in Fig. 17, dotted lines have been used to clarify the relation of the structures.]

the folds are the corniculate and cuneiform cartilages and the aryepiglottic muscles.

The *thyroepiglottic ligament* connects the epiglottis at its stem to the angle of the thyroid just under the superior thyroid notch, and above the attachment of the ventricular ligament.

The *hyoepiglottic ligament* extends from the superior border of the body of the hyoid bone to the anterior surface of the epiglottis.

The *ventricular ligament,* giving form and support to the ventricular fold, has its anterior attachment between the thyroid laminae above that of the vocal ligament, and its posterior insertion on the antero-lateral surface of the arytenoid cartilage at a level higher than the vocal process. Its fibro-elastic tissue is continuous with that of the aryepiglottic fold. It is invested with a loose covering of mucous membrane.

The *hyothyroid membrane* (thyrohyoid membrane) extends from the superior border of the thyroid cartilage and the front of its superior cornua to the upper margin of the posterior surface of the body and greater cornua of the hyoid bone. The *middle hyothyroid ligament* constitutes the thickened central portion of the hyothyroid membrane. Below, it is attached to the margins of the V-shaped thyroid notch. Above, it is attached to the hyoid. Lateral to the ligament, the hyothyroid membrane is loose and thin. Behind the middle hyothyroid ligament is the epiglottis, from which it is separated by a small amount of loose areolar tissue. On each side a thickened *lateral hyothyroid ligament* forms the lateral border of the hyothyroid membrane. On either side they pass from the tip of the superior cornu of the thyroid cartilage to the extremity of the greater cornu of the hyoid bone. They often contain a nodule of cartilage (cartilago triticea) which may be ossified.

The *cricothyroid membrane* or *conus elasticus*[14] consists of middle and lateral portions. The superior border of the arch of the cricoid between the arytenoid facets provides the inferior attachment (U-shaped) of the membrane, which extends upward. The thickened *anterior part* or *middle cricothyroid ligament,*[15] somewhat triangular in shape, is attached at the junction of the laminae of the thyroid cartilage on the inferior border. The two *lateral portions* extend upward and find attachment on the medial aspect of the laminae. The membranes narrow the lumen of the larynx. The free upper border of each membrane (attached, anteriorly, to about the inferior $\frac{1}{3}$ of the thyroid lamina at the angle and, posteriorly, to the vocal process of the arytenoid cartilage) constitutes the vocal ligament. At their anterior ends the vocal ligaments are in contact; they diverge posteriorly.

The *vocal ligaments* or *inferior thyroarytenoid ligaments*[14] (Chordae vocales of Ferrein) extend horizontally from the angle of the thyroid cartilage to the vocal processes of the arytenoids. Their inner, free edges invested with a layer of mucous membrane are thin; their outer borders are continuous with the cricothyroid membrane, and in contact with the thyroarytenoid muscles. These elastic cords form the groundwork of the vocal folds.

[14] Of yellow elastic tissue.
[15] Laryngotomy is performed through the lower border of this membrane.

THE LARYNGEAL GENERATOR

There is no disagreement on the point, and we may accept it as a fact, that voice is initiated in that part of the air tract known as the larynx. At least as far back as the time of Galen (175 A.D.), it was recognized that the edges of the glottis were an essential factor in the production of voice. Views concerning the manner in which the vocal folds function have progressed through three stages: First, the vocal "cord" was thought of (Rayleigh, 1894) as a string having its mass concentrated at its center between its two points of attachment. Such a conception makes it easy to explain the production of fundamentals and partials. In the second place, the vocal "bands" have been considered as membranous bands stretched across the air channel. Finally, the vocal "lips" may be treated as elastic cushions (Ewald, 1897; Scripture, 1901) which yield under compression.

Our modern knowledge of the entire laryngeal cavity makes it easy for us to reduce to two the possible *useful* obstructions to the exhaled air stream in the larynx, namely: the vocal folds and the ventricular folds. Of these, it has long been known that the vocal folds are the voice-producing mechanism of the larynx.[16] Therefore, we shall proceed at once to a consideration of the production of voice by the vocal folds. Later, we shall have something to say about the ventricular folds which, although they are not useful normally in producing voice, on occasion may be so used or, at least, may give rise to auxiliary sounds.

A. The Muscles Used in Phonation

The delicate intrinsic muscles of the larynx, except the cricothyroid, are well protected by the thyroid cartilage. Their functions are primarily sphincteric and are directed toward protective closure of the airway and, thus, to fixation of the thorax.

The summary chart on page 67 shows the function of the laryngeal muscles important in voice production, namely, (*a*) opening and closing the glottis, and (*b*) determining the amount of tension of the vocal cords. Additional information indicates the importance of the muscles in altering the level of the glottis and in the sphincteric action which closes the superior laryngeal opening.

1. THE INTRINSIC MUSCLES OF THE LARYNX

With the exception of the cricothyroid muscles which are innervated by the *superior laryngeal* (Xth Cranial) nerve,[17] the muscles in this group

[16] Only recently has the mode of operation been understood, and that must still await the confirmatory evidence which more refined research techniques will make available.

[17] Lower motor neurone paralysis in the superior laryngeal (X) nerve supply to the cricothyroid, thus preventing contraction of this muscle, would permit approximation of the thy-

extrinsic muscles attach to thorax, mandible, head etc
sling-like move larynx up or down back or forth

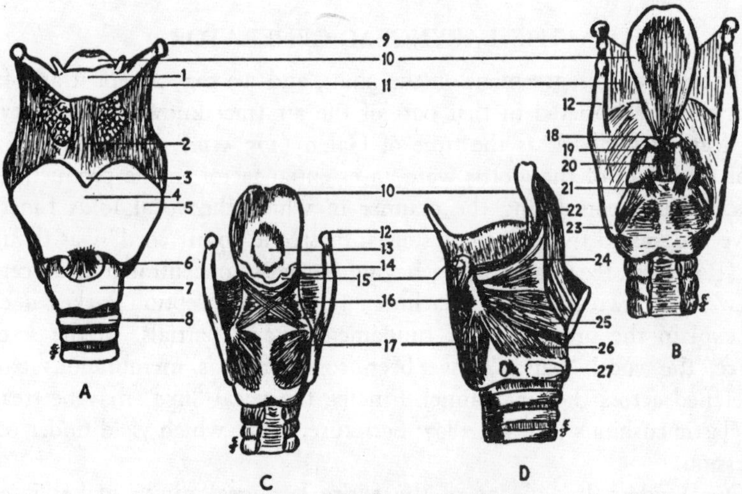

FIG. 19. Muscles and Ligaments of the Larynx.
A. Anterior View of Ligaments of Larynx.
B. Posterior View of Ligaments of Larynx.
C. Posterior View of Muscles of Larynx.
D. Side View of Muscles of Larynx; Right Half of Thyroid Cartilage Removed.

1. Body of hyoid bone; 2. middle thyrohyoid membrane; 3. thyroid notch; 4. laryngeal prominence; 5. thyroid cartilage; 6. cricovocal membrane; 7. cricoid cartilage; 8. tracheal cartilage; 9. greater horn of hyoid bone; 10. epiglottis; 11. thyrohyoid membrane; 12. superior horn of thyroid cartilage; 13. tubercle of epiglottis; 14. cuneiform cartilage; 15. corniculate cartilage; 16. arytenoid muscles, transverse and oblique; 17. posterior cricoarytenoid muscle; 18. corniculate cartilage; 19. arytenoid cartilage; 20. thyroepiglottic ligament; 21. posterior cricoarytenoid ligament; 22. thyroepiglottic muscle; 23. articulation of inferior horn of thyroid cartilage with cricoid cartilage; 24. aryepiglottic muscle; 25. thyroarytenoid muscle; 26. lateral cricoarytenoid muscle; 27. point of attachment of cricothyroid muscle.

are innervated by the *recurrent laryngeal* (Xth Cranial) nerve.[18] The superior laryngeal nerve supplies sensory fibers to the mucous membrane of the larynx.

Cricothyroid
Posterior cricoarytenoid
Lateral cricoarytenoid
Oblique arytenoid
Transverse arytenoid
Thyroarytenoid

---

roid and arytenoid cartilages with the resultant shortening of the inferior folds and their consequent loss of elasticity. Effective phonation would be impossible. In one-sided paralysis of this nature, laryngoscopic observations would show the inferior fold of the affected side to be shorter and lower than that of the unaffected side.

[18] Lower motor neurone paralysis of the recurrent laryngeal nerve supply to the posterior cricoarytenoid prevents abduction of the arytenoid cartilage; at the same time, the unopposed thyroarytenoid tilts the arytenoid forward and down. Laryngoscopic observation reveals the vocal fold of the affected side to be shorter and lower than its fellow.

Cricothyroid [19] (m. cricothyreoideus)

Origin: Front and side of the cricoid cartilage.

Insertion: *Pars obliqua* (lower fibers running backward and lateralward)—anterior border of the inferior cornu of the thyroid cartilage; *Pars recta* (fibers running upward, backward, and lateralward)—posterior part of the lower border lamina of the thyroid cartilage. (The *middle cricothyroid ligament* occupies the space between the medial borders of the two muscles.)

Action: Depresses lamina and elevates arch of cricoid cartilage. Draws thyroid cartilage forward and down. Combined action increases the distance between the vocal processes of the arytenoid cartilages on the lamina of the cricoid and the angle of the thyroid; elongates vocal folds and renders them tense, providing the arytenoids remain fixed.

Posterior cricoarytenoid (m. cricoarytænoideus posterior)

Origin: Posterior surface of lamina of the cricoid cartilage.

Insertion: (Upper fibers horizontal; middle, oblique; lowest, vertical.) Muscular processes of arytenoid cartilages.

Action: Pars recta: elevates arch of cricoid cartilage; concurrently depresses lamina with attached arytenoid cartilages thus increasing distance between the posterior attachment (to vocal process) of each vocal fold and its anterior commissure. Pars obliqua: depresses dorsal portion of cricoid; may slide the cartilage posteriorly. Combined action, providing the arytenoids are fixed, is to lengthen or stretch vocal folds, thus increasing their tension.

Ceratocricoid (m. ceratocricoideus) A slip of the posterior cricoarytenoid. A fasciculus from the cricoid is inserted into the inferior cornu of the thyroid cartilage.

Lateral cricoarytenoid (m. cricoarytænoideus lateralis)

Origin: Upper border of each side of the cricoid cartilage.

Insertion: (Fibers pass obliquely upward and backward.) Muscular processes of the arytenoid cartilages.

Action: Pulls arytenoid cartilage forward, tenses vocal ligament. Rotates arytenoid cartilage inward so that the

[19] Covered laterally by the sternothyroid and sternohyoid muscles, the cricothyroid may be considered continuous with the inferior pharyngeal constrictor.

[20] The cricothyroids and posterior cricoarytenoids, in providing a firm attachment for the thyroarytenoids, enable their fibers to control the degree of elasticity of the glottic ledges.

vocal processes are moved toward the mid-line; approximates vocal folds; closes rima glottidis.

Oblique arytenoid (m. arytænoideus obliquus)

Origin: Base of posterior surface of one cartilage.

Insertion: Apex of posterior surface of other cartilage. The crossing of the oblique fibers from side to side form an X.

Action: Draws together the arytenoid cartilages, closes rima glottidis, especially the cartilaginous portion. A few fibers pass around the apex of the arytenoid cartilage to join the aryepiglottic muscle to form sphincter for superior aperture of the larynx.

Aryepiglottic (m. aryepiglotticus; arytenoepiglottideus)

Origin: Apex and anterior border of arytenoid cartilage.

Insertion: Upper fibers: mucous membrane at margin of arytenoepiglottic fold.

Lower fibers: side of epiglottis. (It is joined by some fibers of the oblique arytenoid muscle, which pass around to insert into the apex of the opposite arytenoid cartilage.)

Action: Pulls epiglottis backward and compresses laryngeal pouch. With arytenoid acts as sphincter of superior aperture of larynx.

Transverse Arytenoid.[21] (m. arytænoideus transversus) (Crosses transversely between the two cartilages)

Origin: Base of posterior surface and outer border of arytenoid cartilage.

Insertion: Apex of posterior surface of other arytenoid cartilage.

Action: Draws together the arytenoid cartilages, closes rima glottidis, especially the cartilaginous portion. If many fibers extend around the edges of the arytenoids and are inserted on the lateral surface, their pull would approximate the cartilages but cause the vocal processes to toe out, thus opening the membranous glottis. This tendency is offset by the lateral cricoarytenoid and the thyroarytenoid muscles.

Thyroarytenoid [22] (m. thyreoarytænoideus externus)

Origin: Angle of the thyroid cartilage and middle cricothyroid ligament.

[21] Some fibers may be continued around the cartilage and intermingle with those of the thyroarytenoid.

[22] Its inferior border is adjacent to the lateral cricoarytenoid; its superior border extends higher than the level of the vocal fold and is adjacent to the thyroepiglottic.

Insertion: Base and anterior surface of arytenoid cartilages.

Vocalis (m. thyreoarytænoideus internus; vocal muscle)
The deeper fibers of the thyroarytenoid, differentiated as a triangular band closely related to the lateral aspect of the vocal ligament, insert into the vocal processes of the arytenoid cartilages.

1. Superior horn of thyroid cartilage; 2. lateral cricoarytenoid muscle; 3. thyroarytenoid muscle; 4. superior margin of thyroid cartilage; 5. posterior cricoarytenoid muscle; 6. cricoid cartilage; 7. arytenoid muscle; 8. arytenoid cartilage; 9. rima glottidis; 10. vocal ligament.

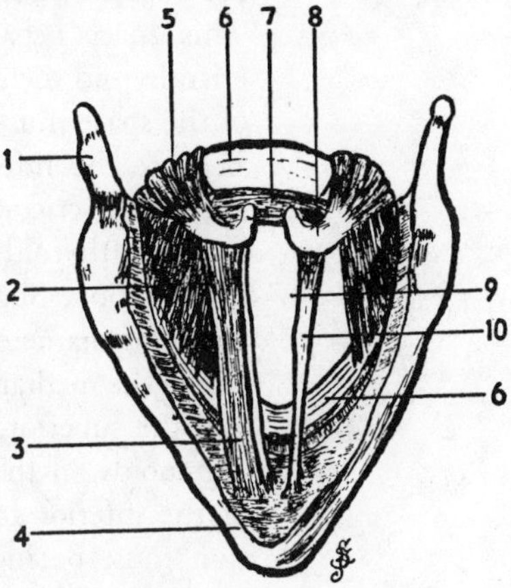

FIG. 20. Muscles of the Larynx. Superior View.

Aryvocalis. The deeper fibers of the vocalis attached to the vocal ligament.

Action: Relaxes and shortens vocal ligament by drawing arytenoid cartilages forward; when the arytenoids are fixed by the action of the cricoarytenoids and the transverse arytenoid muscles, approximates vocal folds by drawing vocal processes downward and inward. A portion of the vocal fold may be tensed while the remainder is relaxed, by contraction of some of the fibers of the aryvocalis muscle.

If it acted alone the muscle would approximate the thyroid and arytenoid cartilages; however, when it contracts the arytenoid cartilages are fixed by the cricoarytenoids and transverse arytenoids, so that the thyroarytenoids function as vestibular sphincters to close the vestibule by bringing the vestibular folds together.

The vocalis muscle tenses and makes adjustments of the tension of the vocal ligament and, hence, of the vocal fold. Acting with the transverse arytenoid muscles, the vocalis muscles approximate the vocal folds, bringing them together for purposes of thoracic fixation or phonation.

Contraction of the cricothyroid approximates the inferior, anterior border of the thyroid cartilage and the superior, anterior border of the cricoid cartilage. This space between the cartilages is closed by the cricothyroid membrane. Decreasing the vertical extent of the space must lessen the tension on the membrane. Because the inferior pharyngeal constrictor tends to anchor the cricoid cartilage, the cricoid moves slightly and the thyroid relatively greatly to make the approximation. Such a movement increases the antero-posterior diameter of the larynx, i. e., the distance between the median junction angle of the thyroid lamina and the superior, posterior border of the cricoid. The arytenoids on the cricoid remaining fixed, the length of the inferior folds must be increased, or their tension must be increased, or both. The degree of the tension may be further increased if the thyroarytenoid muscle contracts at the same time that the cricothyroid is contracting. In this case, probably, there will be no resulting movement of the thyroid cartilage, but there will be increased precision in the control of the degree of elasticity of the glottic lips.

Thyroepiglottic (m. thyreoepiglotticus)

Composed of a few fibers of the thyroarytenoid which are prolonged into the aryepiglottic fold to the epiglottis. They aid in depressing the epiglottis, thus acting as a sphincter of the laryngeal inlet.

Depressor epiglotticus

Origin: A portion of the thyroepiglottic muscle.

Insertion: Epiglottis.

Action: Depresses epiglottis.

Ventricularis (m. ventricularis)

Composed of a few fibers of the thyroarytenoid extending along the wall of the ventricle to the side of the epiglottis. The fibers may pass into the structure of the ventricular fold.

2. THE INFRAHYOID MUSCLES

Sternohyoid
Sternothyroid

Thyrohyoid
Omohyoid

(Innervation of the infrahyoid muscles: Branches from 1st, 2d, and 3d cervical nerves.)

The infrahyoid muscles constitute a great part of the extrinsic musculature of the larynx. The importance of the *extrinsic* muscles of the larynx lies in the indirect but needed assistance which they give to the intrinsic muscles during phonation. They give greatest aid during the production of tones of high pitch. It may be observed that in producing such tones the larynx and the hyoid bone are approximated, with the larynx being the prime mover. Assisting in raising the hyoid or in fixing it from above are these muscles: geniohyoid, hyoglossus, geniohyoglossus, mylohyoid, stylohyoid, and the middle pharyngeal constrictor. Fixing it from below are the sternohyoid and omohyoid muscles. Assisting in raising the larynx are the thyrohyoid muscles exerting a vertical pull, and the palatopharyngei, salpingopharyngei and inferior pharyngeal constrictors exerting an oblique but upward pull. Opposing the contractions of these muscles, which tend to raise the larynx in the neck, is the contraction of the sternothyroid pair, which serve to anchor the whole larynx. Some slight drag, also, is given by the dead weight of the trachea. More considerable drag is provided by the attachment of the esophagus to the cricoid and corniculate cartilages. Because the esophagus is anchored to the diaphragm it cannot rise as does the freer trachea, hence, if the larynx tends to rise the corniculate cartilages become effectively anchored. But the corniculates are quite intimately bound to the arytenoid cartilages. So, if the larynx rises, the corniculate and arytenoid cartilages are anchored—at least at their posterior attachments—to the esophagus. The result is that the cartilages are tipped downward and tend to slide backward on their facets. The vocal processes, as part of the arytenoid cartilages, are, of course, pulled backward. This assists the cricothyroids and posterior arytenoid muscles in fixing to the arytenoid cartilages so that they will not be pulled forward by the contraction of the thyroarytenoid muscles during the production of tones of high pitch.

Sternohyoid (Sternohyoideus)
Origin: Manubrium sterni and clavicle.
Insertion: Body of hyoid bone, lower border.
Action: Depresses the hyoid and larynx.

Sternothyroid (Sternothyreoideus)
Origin: Sternum and cartilage of first rib.
Insertion: Ala of thyroid cartilage.

Action: Depresses the larynx; draws thyroid cartilage downward; assists cricothyroid in tensing vocal folds by drawing thyroid cartilage downward and forward.

Thyrohyoid (Thyreohyoideus)

Origin: Oblique line side of thyroid cartilage.

Insertion: Greater horn of hyoid.

Action: Raises thyroid cartilage toward hyoid bone. Acting with the sternothyroid, it depresses the hyoid and larynx.

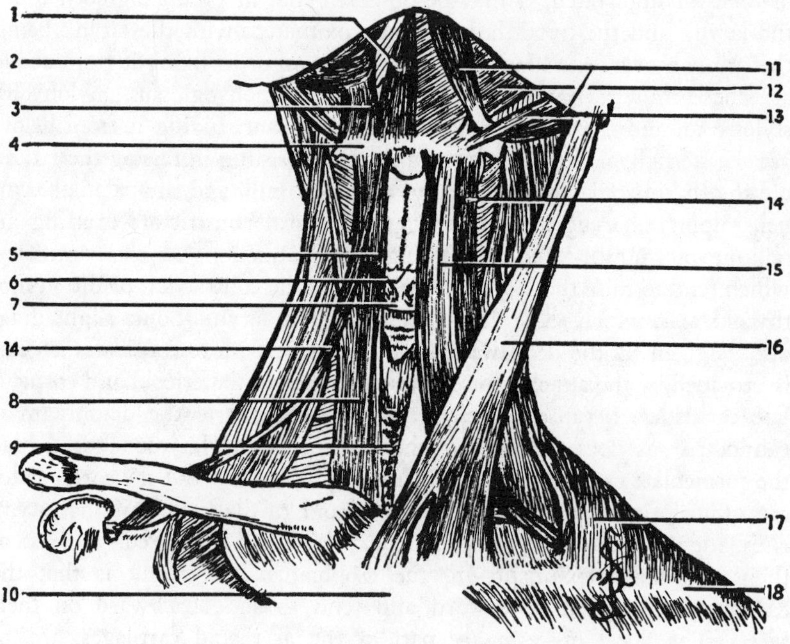

FIG. 21. Neck Muscles. Anterior View.

1. Geniohyoid; 2. styloglossus; 3. hyoglossus; 4. hyoid bone; 5. thyrohyoid; 6. thyroid cartilage; 7. cricoid cartilage; 8. sternothyroid; 9. trachea; 10. sternum; 11. digastric; 12. mylohyoid; 13. stylohyoid; 14. omohyoid; 15. sternohyoid; 16. sternocleidomastoid; 17. trapezius; 18. clavicle.

Omohyoid (Omohyoideus)

Origin: Two bellies united by central tendon:

Anterior: Lower border of body of hyoid bone.

Posterior: Superior border of scapula.

Insertion: Both bellies are inserted into an intervening tendon on a level with the cricoid cartilage. The tendon is bound by fascia to the clavicle and first rib.

Action: Retracts and depresses hyoid.

SUMMARY OF FUNCTIONS AND INNERVATION OF INFRAHYOID MUSCLES

Muscle	*Function*	*Innervation*
Sternohyoid	Depresses hyoid bone.	C 1, 2, 3
Sternothyroid	Depresses larynx by its pull on the thyroid cartilage.	C 1, 2, 3
Thyrohyoid	Elevates larynx if hyoid bone be fixed or is being elevated. Otherwise depresses hyoid bone.	C 1, 2, 3
Omohyoid	Acting together, depress and retract hyoid bone. Either one acting alone depresses and retracts corresponding side of hyoid bone.	C 1, 2, 3

B. The A, B, C, D Positions of the Vocal Folds

An open and fairly unimpeded air tract is essential in normal breathing. Therefore, during quiet breathing the glottis is open. As long as the glottis remains patent the air stream is not set into vibration; no sound is made, and breathing takes place quite silently. It should be said that in breathing the glottis is larger—i. e., the vocal folds are more widely separated—during inhalation than during exhalation.

To produce sound at the glottis, or, in fact, at any portion of the air tract, there must be presented to the air stream some constriction less than complete closure. Closure would mean, of course, no air flow and no sound. The nature and degree of obstruction and the force of the current of exhaled air determine the character of the sound generated.

The positions of the glottic lips determine the type of sound which they may produce. The glottic lips may be *closed* or *open*. There may be numerous degrees of *openness* of the glottis, only three of which need concern us.[23]

1. POSITION A—CLOSED

Of course, if the glottis be closed no sound is produced, but if the pressure of air builds up so that the vocal folds are forced open suddenly there is produced a glottal explosion, known as a glottal catch or glottal attack. It is but infrequently used in English.

2. POSITION B—OPEN AS IN PHONATION

First, the glottis may be open to a range of positions at which phonation—the production of tone—results.

[23] Of the muscles that act upon the larynx, the same muscles must determine every degree of adjustment of the glottis from completely open, through all stages of partially open, to complete closure.

3. POSITION C—OPEN AS IN WHISPERING

Second, the glottis may be open to such a degree that it presents some frictional hindrance to the passage of the air stream. This produces frictional sounds. Such sounds from the partly closed, partly opened glottis are utilized in *whispering*. English, it has been said, is based on whispered speech; phonation is but an auxiliary. Certainly if one were to determine a basis for speech which would necessitate a minimum expenditure of energy, a minimum of alteration in the function of the air-food-getting mechanism, it would be whispering.

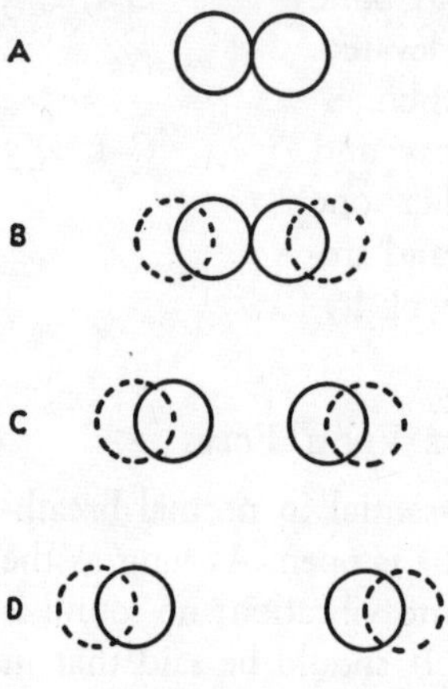

FIG. 22. The *A, B, C, D* Positions of the Glottis.
See text for description.

In the case of a whisper, the vocal folds are not adjusted so as to permit of a definite musical vibration. The obstruction presented by the glottis to the air results in a rustling sound. In whispering, the form of the glottis is variable. In some cases only the cartilaginous portion is open. The degree of approximation of the vocal folds depends on the force of the whisper, increasing with increasing strength of the whisper.

Within anatomical and physiological limits, the acoustic effects produced by whispering are constant and invariable; there is always the same articulatory mold to the cavities. Whispered speech cannot be inflected and its quality cannot be changed; however, it may be produced with variations in emphasis, and in rate. Because whispering involves but a small expenditure of energy, its carrying power is limited; the range of audibility of whispering is slight compared with that of phonated speech. For example, the loudest (spoken without shouting) voiced sounds can be heard from five to twenty times as far as sounds can be heard when whispered in as loud a manner as possible. Whispering also is uneconomical in the use of the exhaled air stream; the relatively large glottis permits such a waste of air that the efficiency of whispering is low. Only a few words may be whispered before another breath must be taken. For these reasons whispering would provide a relatively ineffective basis for speech.

4. POSITION D—OPEN AS IN BREATHING

Third, the glottis may be open so wide that the air stream, for all practical purposes, passes in or out without hindrance. The margins of the aperture do not interfere with the flow. Therefore little or no sound is produced. This is the condition existing during normal breathing and during forced inhalation for speech.[24]

In Fig. 22, in *B, C,* and *D* each diagram represents a range of movement. In each case, one blends into the next; *B* into *A* and *C*; *C* into *B* and *D*. Among them, there are zones—a glottal no man's land—in which some overlapping takes place. If the degree of overlapping is great, the individual may, theoretically, pass from one glottal function to another by degrees indistinguishable to the listener. In homorganic sounds such as [f] and [v], for example, if [f] is being produced and while it is being produced there is a shift from the *D* to the *B* position of the glottis, phonation changes the [f] to [v].

In *D,* for normal breathing, the laryngeal musculature displays a balanced relaxation, only the ordinary muscle tonus being present. For forced breathing at the widest aperture (dotted lines) there is a muscular imbalance, with the abductors contracted and the adductors correspondingly relaxed.

In *C* and *B* there is a balanced contraction of the musculature, the degree of contraction and the exactness of balance being greater in *B* than in *C*.

In *A* there is represented an unbalanced condition, with the adductors contracted and the abductors correspondingly relaxed.

The position of the glottic lips, or the degree of opening of the glottis, is due to the balance which is maintained between the antagonistic abductor and adductor muscles of the larynx. This balance is being disturbed constantly: slowly, during normal breathing; more rapidly during phonation.

No vocal adjustment is ever completely stable; there is a continuously varying degree of muscular contraction. Some of these variations the ear may detect, but even if the ear cannot detect them, delicate oscillograph records prove their presence. Furthermore, the greater the intensity of the stimulation, and, hence, of the tones produced, the greater its instability. Oscillograph records prove that tones of little intensity are more stable, although themselves variable, than are loud tones. The physical and emotional condition of the body has an effect on the neural stimulation of the vocal mechanism and hence on the accuracy of its control. A person who is upset emotionally has lessened control of his voice. A person who is ill or fatigued reveals his condition in his voice. Many general medical practitioners rely upon the sound of the patient's voice as one diagnostic sign.

[24] In forced breathing friction noises may be produced, but they are probably due to such obstacles as the teeth and the limiting boundaries of an airway which is momentarily inadequate to accommodate the flow of air.

PHONATION

Sound waves are made up of a successive series of condensations or pressures and rarefactions or lack of pressures. The disk siren is a device for permitting successive puffs of air under pressure to escape through holes; each pressure-puff is separated from the following by an interval in which no air can escape until another hole is presented. This disk siren, therefore, produces sound waves.

If a Seebeck siren (see Chapter 8 for description) be rotated slowly, a series of puffs will be heard. If the disk be rotated more rapidly, the individual character of the puffs will disappear; they will blend, with the resulting formation of a tone. If, for example, the disk be revolved so that, at regular intervals, the jet of air will pass through 256 holes each second, the tone produced will be that designated as middle C or as C_1 on the physical scale. Doubling the speed of rotation, so that 512 pressure-puffs will escape each second, causes the tone to rise an octave in pitch.

Now, if instead of passing a series of holes rapidly before the air stream, the aperture of the hole be made to open and close rapidly—somewhat like the action of the shutter of a camera—so that each time it opens a puff of air escapes, and each time it closes the air is dammed up and builds up pressure, then the result will be, as with the disk siren, the production of tones, the pitch of which will depend upon the rapidity of the opening and closing of the aperture. In addition to the fundamental tone, overtones will be produced, probably because of the shape and nature of the surfaces of the openings. In the production of voice, the air stream is the forcibly exhaled air column; the aperture, which opens and closes, is the glottis.

In the case of the tone produced by a siren it should not be overlooked that variations in the holes of the revolving disk—e. g., round, square, triangular—result in tones having different characteristics. It seems reasonable that we should be able to apply this observation to the production of tones at the glottic aperture according to the pressure-puff theory. If so, we should not overlook the possibility of accounting in part, at least, for the distinguishing differences in persons' voices on a basis of the shape or form of the puffs released by glottic apertures of different shapes.

A. The Mechanism of Phonation

The rapidity of the movements of the larynx during voice production emphasizes the dynamic nature of the mechanism. To reduce phonation to a series of static pictures robs the process of its essential nature. But only in this way can a conception of what is taking place be gained. In the following steps, in which we attempt to explain the effect of each muscle contraction in isolation, we are but studying the shadow background of a living, continuing process. It is to be hoped that once the fundamental concepts have been established, the student will be able to carry them over to the functional whole.

(1) The arytenoid cartilages are approximated so that their medial surfaces come into contact, thus closing the glottis respiratorio.

Muscles involved: arytenoids.

(2) Accompanying this approximation, the vocal processes are rotated and meet at the mid-line, thus approximating the vocal folds and closing the glottis vocalis. Moving-picture studies of the vocal folds show that they come together first posteriorly and then proceed progressively forward from this posterior point.

Muscles involved: lateral cricoarytenoid.

(3) The arytenoid cartilages are fixed so that they will not glide or slide on their facets.

Muscles involved: cricoarytenoids.

(4) The elasticity of the vocal folds is increased.

Muscles involved: cricothyroid; thyroarytenoid, if the arytenoid and thyroid cartilages be fixed.

A study of the cricothyroid muscles in relation to their opponents, the thyroarytenoid muscles, will show that if the opposing contractions of these are balanced there need be no forward or depressing movement of the thyroid cartilage, nor need there be a shortening of the vocal folds. That is, the opposing contractions may produce a sensitive regulative mechanism by which the elasticity of the vocal folds may be adjusted by extremely fine degrees.

(5) When a sufficient and controlled pressure has been built up beneath the glottic lips by the air stream forcibly emitted from the lungs, the lips are blown apart,[25] thus releasing a puff of air and reducing the air pressure in the sub-vestibule and trachea.[26] This act produces sound waves.

The accurate approximation or meeting of the adjoining edges of the glottic lips, under tension, holds the air back in the trachea until rising intratracheal air pressure is just great enough to force the folds apart. A single puff of air escapes. If the approximation is only partial, some air will escape through the glottis, so that a greatly increased air pressure useful for voice must be built up by the respiratory mechanism.

(6) The elasticity of the glottic lips is such that as soon as the air pressure is reduced they recoil or snap back into their position of approximation or near approximation.

(7) The pressure builds up again and, thus, repeatedly, the glottis is

[25] The movement may be imitated by blowing out the lightly approximated lips (orbicularis oris) as in a modified Bronx cheer.

[26] For their initial movement, the glottic lips need not close the glottis completely; they only need block the air sufficiently to be blown apart.

opened and closed; the rapidity of its alternate openings and closings—and of the consequent release of puffs of air—depends on the air pressure and the degree of contraction of the laryngeal musculature. The number of puffs of air released per second determines the pitch of the sounds produced.

(8) The larynx is tilted best to conform to the shape assumed by the pharynx for the production of the sound in question. Almost instantaneous related adjustments of form and tensions, differing for different sounds, are made by the larynx and pharynx.

Muscles involved: cricothyroids.

The laryngeal sounds are not produced by vibrations of the vocal folds themselves, but by the pressure puffs which they permit to escape rhythmically. We do not deny that a tenable theory of voice production may be built upon the idea of each vocal fold being vibrated in part or as a whole. In fact, as explained elsewhere, we believe that for certain high-frequency notes some such auxiliary phenomenon, involving the tense thin vocal folds, may occur.

In the mechanism just described it is sometimes overlooked that (*a*) the puff of air released at the glottis seeks escape through the mouth or nose, and that (*b*) the sound wave complex produced by the vibrator also follows the same channels before its propagation in the outer air. The velocity of the air puff is small, indeed, when compared with the velocity (approximately 1100 feet per second) of the sound wave.

So far we have described phonation as due to an *active* muscular process of closing the glottis and a *passive* process of opening the glottis under the influence of air pressure. This is not quite the whole story unless we are unwilling to assign to the posterior cricoarytenoids an active part in phonation—a tenable hypothesis. We prefer to take the stand that there is an alternation of stimuli which produces a diadochokinesis between the abductor and adductor muscles of the glottis.[27] That is to say, the opening of the glottis need not be dependent entirely on pressure from the exhaled air column; the opening may be due in part to the action of the posterior cricoarytenoids, thus necessitating a somewhat reduced air pressure for effective phonation. Our belief that such a mechanism is operative in phonation need in no way alter the description of the action of the vocal folds previously given.

At this point arises the question of how many nerve impulses may be transmitted along a nerve in a second? Also, how many times may a muscle contract and relax in a second? It is obvious that if we carry the role of the posterior cricoarytenoids too far—that is, to the point of making them active participants in phonation—we must find evidence to sup-

[27] If the cricothyroid be paralyzed because of loss of its innervation, the thyroarytenoid will undergo atrophy because of disuse against its antagonist.

port the contracting and relaxing of the muscles and of their antagonists from 100 to 300 times per second, so that that many puffs of air may escape per second to produce fundamental tones. Anatomical support is lacking for such high rates of muscle contraction, even if it were neurologically possible.

The role that must be assigned to these agonist-antagonist phonative muscles is one of such a fine degree of balanced opposition that the optimum air pressure may be held at a minimum.

The sounds produced by the laryngeal vibrator do not of themselves constitute voice. The *laryngeal tone, cord tone,* or *voice complex* generated by this laryngeal mechanism (which has just been described) consists of a fundamental tone and a rich supply of overtones. Presumably, the laryngeal tone is weak, of poor quality, and of little carrying power. Only as it is influenced by the resonators below and above the rima glottidis and as

SUMMARY OF ACTION OF INTRINSIC MUSCLES OF LARYNX

Muscle	*Effect on level of glottis*	*Effect on aperture of glottis*	*Effect on elasticity of glottis*	*Sphincteric action to close superior laryngeal opening*
posterior cricoarytenoid	raises level	opens glottis (abduction)	tenses vocal folds	
lateral cricoarytenoid	raises level	closes membranous glottis (adduction)	tenses vocal folds	
cricoarytenoid	Acting together, they fix the arytenoid cartilages so that the other intrinsic muscles may produce finer adjustments of the glottic margins.			
transverse arytenoid	lowers level	closes glottis (adduction)	tenses vocal folds	sphincter
oblique arytenoid		closes cartilaginous glottis (adduction)		sphincter
thyroarytenoid	lowers level	closes glottis (adduction)	relaxes vocal folds	sphincter
cricothyroid			tenses vocal folds	
				(the aryepiglottic muscle also aids)

its various partials are resonated, as will be explained in Chapter III, does it become, upon issuing from the mouth and nose, the human voice so useful in communication. This implies hearing; that is, phonation (plus resonance) produces an acoustic phenomenon called voice.

B. Voice: Age and Sex Differences

From early childhood to about age fourteen, there is an increase in the pitch range of the voice of children. In old age, the range decreases, the loss being mainly in the high notes. Sopranos become mezzo-sopranos; tenors frequently become baritones. In advancing age, the voice changes come on gradually. They are due to the loss of elasticity of the muscles and the calcification of the cartilages of the larynx. In addition to the decrease in range, there is a decrease in resonance. Often the voice becomes tremulous on account of the reduced integrity of the nervous system.

The vocal folds of the female are about one-third shorter than those of the male. Also, their cross-section structure (muscle, fat, tissue) is less. Presumably, therefore, the female vocal folds may be vibrated more rapidly than those of the male; therefore, they produce the higher-pitched voice of the female.

C. Controversies as to the Nature of Phonation

Until this point we have proceeded on the assumption that there is little or no disagreement as to the exact nature of phonation. Now that the student has a background for understanding them, we may say that there are several schools of thought concerning what really happens during phonation. These divergences of opinion arise out of the difficulties inherent in studying the living, normally functioning mechanism. Furthermore, these differences of opinion are based on the available experimental evidence as it is seen by the experimenters. To charge the experimenters with stirring up a controversy for the sake of attendant publicity or to charge them with gross mishandling of the experimental evidence with resulting erroneous conclusions in no way settles the various questions. We do not feel that a mere review of the opposing points of view will resolve the problem. Our belief is that no one school of thought need necessarily have a monopoly on all the right answers. Ultimately the facts may reveal that some part of each seemingly opposed point of view may become vital in the total and correct picture. But until more accurate and objective experimental equipment—electronic, acoustic, photographic—is widely available we must wait patiently for the authoritatively final word on the exact nature of the process of phonation.

1. THE PROBABILITY OF THE FOLDS VIBRATING IN PHASE

Because it has been longest held and is still held by the great majority of the careful students of phonation, we may begin by observing that, in all probability, the vocal folds are displaced synchronously. When the right one moves up, so does the left. Such vibrations in phase are due to the carefully balanced tensions of the musculo-fibrous vocal folds and to the alternate upward and downward forces exerted by the air column.

In Fig. 23*A* we represent the synchronous action of the vocal folds as they are forced apart by the air blast and then return to their original

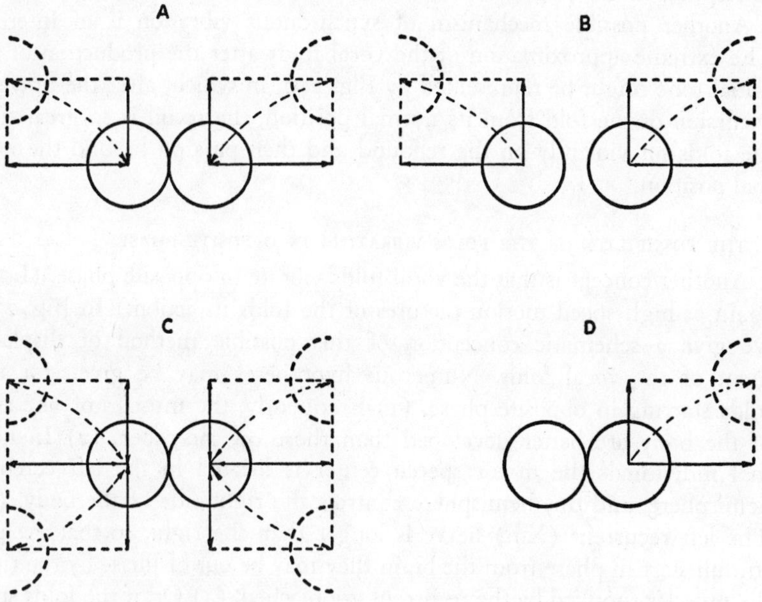

FIG. 23. Schema to Show Mode of Vibration of Vocal Folds.

A. From the completely closed position the folds (solid lines) are blown up (solid arrow) and laterally (solid arrow) to the position represented by the broken half circle. Resolving the two forces produces movements in the actual direction indicated by the broken arrow. Upon rebound the folds are assumed to return to their original position.

B. Same as *A*, except that the initial position of the folds is somewhat open.

C. Same as *A*, except that upon the rebound it is assumed that the vocal folds do not stop at their initial position but instead continue down and laterally as indicated, after which the return is made to the original position. Air is released on both the uprising and down-swing of the vocal folds. If the ratio of the period during which it is open on the down-swing (original-down-original) is anything other than one to one, the mechanism may provide a distinct quality factor.

D. Same as *A*, except only one vocal fold is represented as displaced by the air pressure. The other fold may be displaced upon the return of the first to its initial position. This would provide alternate displacement of the vocal folds. Or the one fold may continue to be displaced rhythmically while the other remains relatively immovable. Or, again, one fold may be displaced the full distance while the other is displaced only, say, half the distance, and not in rhythm with its fellow. This would produce a complex range of pitches.

position. Assume that the circles represent return to their original position, and that the circles represent a coronal section through the vocal folds. Actually, of course, the cords are more wedge-shaped, as shown in the photomicrograph (Fig. 13).

In the diagrams and descriptions of the approximation of the glottic folds the impression has been given that closure must be complete. This need not be true in all cases. We see no reason why once the vocal folds are set into vibration they need be entirely closed at their position of "rest." In fact, the higher the pitch and the greater the amplitude, the less is the need for a position of absolute closure of the glottic lips after each release of a puff of air. The schematic drawing in Fig. 23*B* shows our conception of the possible mechanism.

Another possible mechanism of synchronous vibration is of interest. The extreme approximation of the vocal folds after the production of an initial tone might be represented by Fig. 23*C,* in which, after the upward excursion of the fold from its normal position, the recoil is so great that the folds hit violently on the rebound and then pass on beyond the normal position.

2. THE POSSIBILITY OF THE FOLDS VIBRATING IN OPPOSITE PHASE

Another concept is that the vocal folds vibrate in opposite phase. (Look again at high speed motion pictures of the folds in action.) In Fig. 23*D* we give a schematic conception of this possible method of displacement of the vocal folds. Numerous hypotheses may be given for the folds starting in opposite phase. (1) Frequently, the muscles of one side of the body are better developed than those on the other. (2) In normal individuals the motor speech center is located in the left cerebral hemisphere, and this hemisphere controls the right side of the body. (3) The left recurrent (Xth) nerve is longer than the right, so that even if stimuli start in phase from the brain they may be out of phase by the time the muscles supplied by the recurrent are reached. (4) Or, if the folds start in phase, they may be thrown out of phase at once by the eddy currents set up by the air stream as it rushes through the restricted glottis.

One reason assigned for believing that the folds vibrate alternately is that, because of structural or physiological differences, one fold will be weaker than the other and will give way first under pressure of the air. Once this fold gives way, the air pressure is released and the fold is returned toward its original position by its own elasticity. In returning to its position (it may be argued), there will be a pressing upon the air which is still trying to escape, thus so increasing the pressure below the glottis that now the second fold will be pushed up. On its return, the first fold will again give way, and so on; first one and then the other fold will go through its cycle in alternate fashion.

If we go back to the original premise upon which this explanation stands, that of the inherent weakness of the muscles of one fold, it becomes difficult to believe that the alternating phenomena would take place. Rather, it would seem that either the weaker fold will be blown upward more frequently than the stronger or that it will be blown upward farther than the stronger. Or, the weaker fold will be the only one blown upward because the other one is always able to withstand the pressure of the exhaled air column.

3. COMPLETE VERSUS SEGMENTAL VIBRATION

In addition to the problem of whether the folds are displaced alternately or synchronously, there is the question of whether all or part of each glottic lip is involved in the vibration. Does the whole fold take part in phonation, or is the vibration segmental—i. e., characterized by nodes, as in the case of certain vibrating strings (Fig. 24*A* or *B*)? Or is some combination of movement present? On anatomical grounds, at least, it is quite probable that the vocal folds may demonstrate a segmental type of vibration. Some fibers of the marginal portion of each thyroarytenoid muscle do not run the entire length of the glottis, from the thyroid angle to the arytenoid cartilage. They are short fibers which arise from the elastic tissue of the cricothyroid membrane and their insertion is the vocal process of the arytenoid cartilage. These short internal fibers constitute what is known as the aryvocalis muscle. The shortest, inmost fibers of the aryvocalis muscle are so short that they do not extend to the vocal process; not only do they arise from the conus, but they are also inserted in the elastic tissue by attachments posterior to their points of origin. If these short fibers contract, the overlying epithelial covering and, hence, the medial margins of the glottal lip will be thrown into crescentic shapes, even though the fold, as a whole, will not be altered in shape.

Even if we accept the histological evidence that the fibers of the aryvocalis muscle lie at such an angle to the vocal ligament and the thyroarytenoid muscle that their contraction would in all likelihood put the conus elasticus and vocal ligament under tension in this or that segment of its length depending on what group of fibers were innervated, what conclusion should be drawn? That the segment contracted would vibrate? That the segment not under contraction would vibrate? For example, in Fig. 24*A* if we assume that segments *A* and *C* are under tension due to contraction of the aryvocalis fibers, and that segment *B* is not under tension, will *A* and *C* vibrate? Or will *B?* In Fig. 24*B,* will the same answers apply as applied to Fig. 24*A?*

In favor of *A* and *C's* (Fig. 24*A*) vibrating in the air blast is the tension and drawing out of the striking edge of the vocal fold to a thin tissue. Once it is started, its greater elasticity would permit it to recoil easily.

In favor of *B*'s vibrating is the fact that the tension of segments *A* and *C* will hold them in opposition to movement while *B* will give freely before the pneumatic assault. Segment *B* will act passively. Both possibilities derive support from the histological evidence, but such evidence alone is insufficient for our needs.

A further question arises which cannot be satisfactorily answered on simple histological grounds. If the muscle fibers underlying the segment *B* contract, will segment *B* of the conus elasticus be tensed or the opposite?

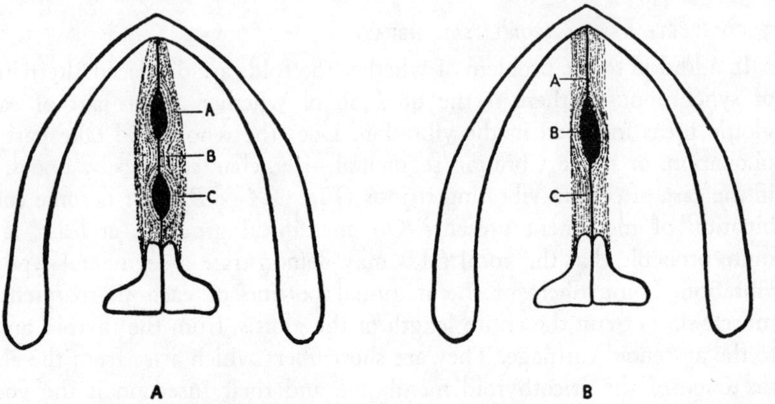

FIG. 24. Schema to Show Segmental Vibration of Vocal Folds.

A. Type of segmental vibration showing two glottic apertures.
B. Type of segmental vibration usually associated with the production of falsetto voice.

The answer must depend upon the intimacy of the binding together of muscle fibers, connective tissue, and epithelium. If they are bound together so that when the muscle contracts the other tissues are placed under tension, then segment *B* will be tensed when the fibers contract. But if the tissues are not so intimately connected, the contraction of the muscle fibers will cause a loosening of the overlying tissues and segment *B* will not be under tension.

Any attempt to establish a segmental type of vibration runs into the difficulty of establishing a neurological control, under the guidance of the ear, which will permit the total number of a group of fibers in one segment to be innervated while on either side of the segment the fibers are not being innervated or are innervating one segment on each side of a non-innervated segment. Before seeking a complicated neurological explanation for such a phenomenon, it would be well to ask whether the same result might appear from other causes.

There is another hypothesis concerning the action of the vocal folds which appears to be somewhat supported by ultra-high-speed pictures of the folds in action. It utilizes the contraction of the thyroarytenoid muscles, as do most hypotheses, but from a diametrically opposite point of view. The more the thyroarytenoid contracts, the looser becomes the overcoating of tissue and squamous epithelium; the less the contraction of the muscle, the more taut the overlying tissue layers. In the production of low tones —especially those of greater intensity—the muscle contracts strongly and the tissue is free to move and vibrate with a considerable degree of amplitude. The tissue is rolled up in a wavelike action resembling that of water. The wavelike activity moves from just beneath the most medial portion of the vocal fold, and passes up and over this fold in a lateral direction. This type of action permits a large arc-segment of the fold to be thrown into use. In the production of tones of higher pitches, the amount and extent of such movement is decreased. The more limited movements are much more rapid, on account of the increased tenseness of the tissue involved—and, in turn, on account of the relaxation of the thyroarytenoids and associated muscles.

Segmental vibration has been offered by some as the explanation of upper partials. Figure 24*A* assumes that the glottis is vibrating as a whole. In such a case, presumably the greatest energy of the complex tone will be contained in the fundamental. But, also, in Fig. 24*A*, segmental vibration is represented as taking place. At the nodes or non-vibrating portions of the glottis the opposing vocal folds are in contact. But it is apparent that in the open phase of glottal vibration the nodes, also, are separated. Those puffs of air escape as a whole to be set into vibration, but at the same time the smaller vibrating segments also place their stamp upon the voice complex. For the thinking of those who eschew any explanation which apparently likens the vocal folds to vibrating strings, it may be added that the mechanism of segmental vibration might produce a series of upper partials because the friction which such segments would offer to the breath stream would produce friction sounds of high pitch.

D. The Mechanism of the Falsetto

Although it is not a normal mechanism, some knowledge of the production of falsetto voice is helpful, by way of contrast, in a thorough understanding of phonation.

The production of *falsetto* tones at the larynx is brought about by these adjustments:

(1) The more external fibers of the thyroarytenoid muscles relax. (Quite the opposite of normal phonation.)

(2) The more internal fibers of the thyroarytenoid muscles contract strongly.

(3) The contraction of the posterior cricoarytenoid and cricothyroid muscles slightly increases the antero-posterior diameter of the glottis. This

approximates the superior margin of the cricoid and inferior margin of the thyroid cartilage ventrally.

(4) The air pressure blows apart the glottic lips which remain apart to form what appears to the observer to be a small elliptical opening in the middle or anterior one-third of the length of the vocal folds. It may be argued that the opening is not constant; that it merely appears to be present because in the falsetto the period of closure is so rapid in comparison with the slow open period. In either case, the excessive opening time will produce the same results.

(5) Because of the elliptical glottic opening there is a constant escape of air. Herein lies the greatest difference between the falsetto and normal phonation.

(6) When they are forced apart by the air stream and set into vibration, the upward displacement of the glottic lips appears to be greater than the lateral, whereas in ordinary phonation the lateral displacement is greater.

(7) The edges of the vocal folds are drawn out thin.

(8) Friction noises are produced as the air forces past the thin glottic lips.

In summary, we may say that the falsetto apparently is much more dependent upon air pressure than upon the increased elasticity of the vocal folds. Because of the constant glottal opening, the mechanism is not an efficient one.

E. Pitch and Amplitude Factors at the Glottis

Thus far we have said little about the pitch, intensity, and quality of the tone produced by the vocal folds. Our experience tells us that voices vary greatly. What is the laryngeal mechanism of such variations?

The anatomical structure of the laryngeal valve at the top of the pulmonary outgrowth readily lends itself to the idea that the pitch produced at the glottic level is a resultant of either or both of these operative factors:

(1) If the elasticity of the margins of the vocal folds remains constant, an increase in the intra-tracheal air pressure will increase the pitch (and amplitude) of the laryngeal tone.

(2) If the intra-tracheal air pressure beneath the vocal folds remains constant, an increase in the elasticity of the margins of the vocal folds will result in an increase in pitch.

In the case of the increase in air pressure, the elasticity factor remaining constant, the vocal folds will be blown open wider—that is, the amplitude will be increased at the same time the pitch is increased, and more air will be used per unit of time. On the other hand, in the case of an increase in the elasticity factor, the pressure remaining constant, the excursion of the glottic lips will be decreased, there will be a decrease in amplitude and a rise in pitch, and less air will be used per unit of time. If pitch *and* amplitude are to increase together, greater air pressure is required.

The intensity of the tone heard by the ear depends upon the amplitude of the laryngeal vibration which, in turn, depends upon the intra-tracheal air pressure. The amount of pressure available depends upon the vital capacity and the degree of contraction of the muscles used in forced exhalation. The greater the amplitude, the greater the volume of air expended. For maximum efficiency, the volume of air used should be small in comparison with the intensity heard. This efficiency varies for different sounds, so that we may say that, from the point of view of intensity, certain sounds are more economical than others. To produce certain sounds consumes more air per unit of time than to produce certain other sounds. If a given tone is to be produced for a period of time at a constant intensity, a high degree of control over the entire vocal mechanism is required. A continuous series of readjustments must be made to maintain such a tone.

More than once, we shall point out that there may be made an infinite number of sounds; that no one ever reproduces exactly any sound he has made; that only the ear's sensitiveness limits us in detecting and giving symbolic value to all sounds. Analysis of the *acoustic spectra* (see Fletcher, 1929) of some vowels reveals that from twenty to forty partials may be identified. Inasmuch as a vowel may be characterized if only two or three frequency areas are reinforced, it seems to be a logical mathematical deduction to say that the possible number of permutations and combinations that can be obtained from forty factors, varying in pitch and/or intensity is, for all practical purposes, infinite.

Ample evidence is available from numerous studies on the intact larynges of patients with tracheotomy openings and researches with the excised larynges of baboons to prove that when air under pressure is introduced beneath the vocal folds the frequency of vibration of the folds increases, within limits, with an increase in air pressure. In numerous cases where wounds have left a tracheal fistula, attempts have been made to measure the pressure of the air stream which normally would be directed against the vocal folds but which in the case of a tracheal fistula escapes into the outer air without passing through the larynx. In such cases a tube from the fistula is led to a water manometer and readings are taken at three pitches. Several experiments show fair agreement on these figures:

Pressure while producing tones of low pitch, 100 mm. H_2O
Pressure while producing tones of medium pitch, 160–200 mm. H_2O
Pressure while producing tones of high pitch, 800–900 mm. H_2O

As early as 1741, Ferrein carried on experiments with the excised larynges of dogs. He and later experimenters connected a bellows to the trachea and with threads and weights on the arytenoid cartilages and in other ways adjusted the glottic aperture so as to produce tones of varying pitches while maintaining a constant air pressure. Air pressure was measured with a manometer. With no change in tension on the cords and with constant air pressure, the pitch could be raised by bringing the vocal folds together. If the tension of the folds was increased, increases in pitch resulted. With increases in air pressure further increases in pitch were produced.

Johannes Müller (1839) was perhaps the first to construct an artificial larynx in an attempt to solve the secrets of the laryngeal mechanism.

Presumably, to raise the pitch of the tone produced at the glottis the thyroarytenoid muscles are contracted to a greater degree. This tensing of the muscles would pull the arytenoid cartilages toward the angle of the thyroid, thus tending to relax the vocal folds, if it were not for the automatic adjustment of the antagonistic muscles which increase their degree of contraction to fix the arytenoid cartilage in relation to the thyroid cartilage. At least three conditions present themselves to complicate the picture. (1) The contraction of the thyroarytenoid muscle fibers may be offset by other forces so that there is neither shortening nor lengthening of the vocal fold. Laryngo-periskopic observations tend to point to this as the normal mechanism. This permits the finest type of glottic lip adjustment, because other muscles produce a state of near-equilibrium for the thyroarytenoid muscles, so that they need not function to produce gross movement, but may function solely to regulate the degree of tension of the vocal folds. (2) The contraction of the thyroarytenoid muscle fibers may tend to shorten the vocal folds because no opposing forces act in opposition. This would reduce the size of the glottis. But the air pressure, which is as great as before, now acts against a reduced area, and hence in respect to the glottis is an increased air pressure and will act against the vocal folds with greater force. (3) The contraction of the fibers of the thyroarytenoids may call forth increased contraction of opposing muscles. If the opponents overbalance the pull of the thyroarytenoids, thus lengthening the vocal folds, even while the folds increase their tension, there will be presented to the air stream a greater area of glottic margin. Thus, while the pitch is increased the amplitude would be decreased.

If it were possible to detach the larynx from its external connections we could see that if the intrinsic muscles of the larynx produced a tight approximation of the vocal folds, a rise in air pressure in the trachea would produce an upward movement of the whole larynx. As a matter of fact, some rise of the larynx may be seen or felt when one raises the pitch and volume of a tone. Part of this rise may be due to air pressure, but in the main it is a product of muscle contraction. The extrinsic laryngeal muscles come into action, particularly, during the production of high pitches. When the larynx rises, its anterior portion rises higher than its posterior portion. This is because of the anchoring effect of the esophagus, which is attached to the posterior part of the cricoid cartilage and to the tips of the corniculate cartilages. The anchoring effect of the esophagus is passed on from the corniculate to the arytenoid cartilages so that their apices are tipped back, and at the same time the vocal processes are raised and tipped backward. This movement of the arytenoids on their axes aids the cricothyroid and posterior cricoarytenoid muscles in opposing the contraction of the thyroarytenoid muscles during the production of tones of high frequency.

Consult Fig. 13 again and note the relation of the overlying tissue and epithelial investment of the thyroarytenoid muscle. Does it not seem plausible that if the muscle contracts greatly, the relatively nonelastic epithelium may be correspondingly loosened? If this actually occurs—as seems probable from fairly extensive experimental evidence—then when the thyroarytenoid greatly contracts, as it does when high pitches are being generated at the glottis, there should be presented to the air column an extremely thin and mobile glottic margin capable of rapid alternations of low amplitude. In our opinion, this vibratory mechanism operates in the production of fundamental notes of high pitch or in the production of high-frequency tones, harmonic or inharmonic to the fundamental.

So far we have considered increased air pressure and the increased elasticity of the vocal folds as separate factors, either one of which acting alone is capable of producing a rise of pitch. Normally, both factors operate together, with the result that only a small increase of each is capable of producing a considerable increase in pitch. Also, in increasing the intensity of a tone the same two factors are operative.

The following conclusions may be given:

A rise of pitch may be due to

(*a*) an increase in the elasticity of the vocal folds,
(*b*) an increase in the tracheal air pressure, or
(*c*) a combination of the above.

An increase in intensity may be due to

(*a*) a decrease in the elasticity of the vocal folds,
(*b*) an increase in the tracheal air pressure, or
(*c*) a combination of the above.

I. THE EFFECT OF ALTERING THE LEVEL OF THE GLOTTIS

Depression of the vocal processes produces a consequent lowering of the level of the glottis. Elevation of the vocal processes raises the level of the glottis. As the level of the glottis is raised, the angle at which the vocal folds meet in or near the mid-line becomes more acute. Consult the photomicrograph (Fig. 13). When the level of the glottis is lowered, more of the mass of the folds opposes the exhaled air stream. When the level of the glottis is raised less of the mass of the folds is affected because the shape of the sub-glottic cavity is such as to aid more readily in the escape of the air. In the raised glottis the air stream encounters less resistance. If the folds are tense, little tissue will be vibrated. The escape of the puffs of air will be more rapid and the pitch will be raised.[28]

2. VOLUNTARY CONTROL OF PITCH AND INTENSITY [29]

Kinesthetic sensations play a part in our control of the speech mechanism. Because one seldom tries to raise such sensations to a conscious level, they usually give one but little information as to what is taking place in the larynx. By concentrating, one can begin to draw some information from these sensations. Try, for example, a series of light glottal implosions on slight inhalation. Probably, with practice one could raise this region into a higher degree of consciousness. However, even though one may be unconscious of the kinesthetic sensations arising from the larynx, this does not mean that they play no part in the fineness of the adjustments made there. Their place in the neural scheme below consciousness may even imply that their function is so important as to require unconscious control at all times.

All speech and voice is, fundamentally, a result of muscular contraction or muscle tension. For the teacher of voice to instruct the student to "relax the throat" is a doubtful procedure. What is really meant is, "strive for a more perfectly balanced agonist-antagonist musculature." As this balance is attained in greater accuracy, the tone quality and tone control are improved in like degree. Then the fingers, guided by the ear or kinesthetic sensations, may "report" that the laryngeal region "feels more relaxed."

Pitch discrepancies in the voice when striking or maintaining a tone are due to defects in the control of the laryngeal musculature. The defect may be primary or secondary. To produce a tone, corresponding to a given tone, the ear mechanism (primary) is first called into activity; then the laryngeal muscles (secondary) are adjusted for its production. The ear (primary) compares the two tones, and, if necessary, further laryngeal adjustments are made. The maintenance of the tone depends on the integrity of the ear-larynx circuit, and particularly on the maintenance of the correct tensions of the laryngeal muscles. To recapitulate: the discrepancies in pitch in reproducing a note will depend upon the individual's ability to distinguish pitches (primary), and upon the error in movements of the laryngeal muscles (secondary). Inability, on the part of the ear, to detect gross differences in tones will result in large, unconscious variations in the voice. Large errors of movement in the muscular mechanism will also cause varia-

[28] On the other hand, the raised position of the glottis offers more resistance to inhalation than does the lowered or level position. Does this explain why it is difficult to produce high tones on inhalation, but not so hard to produce low tones?

[29] Opposed to voluntary control, is the psychic control of speech. It may be simply demonstrated in a number of ways. As far back as 1894, Vietor found that the force of the expired air stream varies in speaking *the same word* as an assertion, as a question, as in irritation, or as a warning. His procedure was to insert a tube into the corner of the mouth. This led to a recording tambour; the main body of air was permitted to escape.

tions; the subject may be either conscious or unconscious of the variations. He may, therefore, be either able or unable to correct his errors.

Each individual has certain auditory habits. These auditory habits are bound up with his speech habits. The ear does not automatically and without training receive speech sounds as such. The speech sounds that will be perceived by the ear will depend on the sensitiveness to those differences which distinguish speech sounds, and on the experience of the listener with familiar sounds. Fine discrimination in the perception of speech sounds is increased when the listener produces those sounds with his own voice and speech equipment.

3. VOICE PITCH CHANGES AT PUBERTY

The above explanation accounts for the difficulty experienced by the male at the time of puberty. At this time he loses control of his voice, and it is said to "break." The reason for the loss of control may be explained briefly.

During childhood and until puberty there is little difference in the sizes of male and female larynges and, hence, in the measurements of their respective vocal folds. There is no great difference in the pitch of the voices. For the first ten to sixteen years of life the boy has accustomed himself to the control of his laryngeal mechanism. Then, for about a year, changes over which he has no control take place in his larynx. He continues to attempt to control his larynx in speaking as he has done in the past, but now the effort which formerly produced an acceptable result may not do so. The boy does not know what sound will be produced at the next effort. He is about as certain of his control over this changing mechanism as is the blindfolded victim who must pin a tail on a drawing of a donkey—the drawing in the meantime being moved about the room by the other guests!

It takes about a year for him to learn or, rather, to relearn to control the more massive [30] laryngeal mechanism, in which the average pitch of the voice is now one octave below that of the childhood voice. The sudden change in the dimensions of the male larynx at puberty is considered to be a secondary sex characteristic. That this viewpoint has a physio-chemical foundation is evidenced by eunuchs, whose lack of sexual development is correlated with a female-like, high-pitched voice. The larynx of the eunuch is only slightly larger than that of the female.

F. The Physical Effect of the Reflected Air Stream on the Vocal Folds

We now come to a question which has bothered investigators for many years. If the air pressure beneath the glottal level is so important, must we not consider, also, the effect of pressure above the glottal level? In producing certain tones, the ventricular folds, or the epiglottis—particularly

30 At puberty the larynx of the male increases in size almost a third.

the tubercle of the epiglottis—move toward the mid-line. Thus, when a blast of air passes the vocal folds it may be directed against some superior structure and be reflected against the upper surface of the vocal folds so as to force those structures down. This reflection may exercise some influence on the pitch or amplitude of tones produced by the vocal lips.

Our opinion on this question is that alterations do occur in the cavities immediately above the vocal folds, and that although the reflected air stream may have some influence on the folds, the main effect is obtained not because the air is reflected onto the folds, but because the alterations produce variations in the tension of the vibrating glottic lips and, even more important, in the size, shape, and tension of the resonators of the physiological airway and foodway systems. The cricothyroid and external laryngeal muscles tilt the larynx to correlate its position with these various adjustments. The vocal folds and the resonators (Chapter III) of the air tract probably take different positions for the production of various sounds because of the integrative action of the nervous system according to the stereotyped patterns of habitual speech movements.

G. The Function of the Ventricular Folds

We have stated that there is no doubt but that voice is produced by the vocal folds. This should not, however, lead us to neglect any other possible or auxiliary sound-producing or sound-altering mechanisms inherent in the laryngeal structure. Next to the vocal folds, the most obvious possible phonative system is to be found in the ventricular folds or so-called false vocal cords. Each ventricular fold is formed of elastic connective tissue, a few fat cells, and some muscle fibers from the thyroarytenoid muscle of the same side. Great individual differences exist in the abundance of muscle fibers. The mucous membrane covering is continuous with that of the aryepiglottic folds, laterally; the base of the epiglottis, anteriorly; and the anterior surface of the arytenoid swelling, posteriorly. The median, free border of each ventricular fold is much thinner than the rest of the fold and is sometimes called the ventricular ligament. The inferior surfaces of the folds constitute the roof of the ventricles.

Although normally the ventricular folds are not responsible for and probably do not affect phonation, they may function in some persons as secondary vocal folds. That is, under certain conditions the vocal folds may be operating to set the air into vibration and at the same time the ventricular folds may approach toward the mid-line and themselves be blown apart by the air blast, thus adding a tone complex of their own. This so-called double voice (diplophonia) tone is in harmony with the tone produced by the vocal folds. When the ventricular folds function in this manner it is difficult, if not impossible, to see the vocal folds beneath them.

By their approximation toward the mid-line, the ventricular folds alter the form of the vestibule and thus its resonance characteristics. Undoubtedly this would alter the character of the vibrations of the vocal folds and hence of the tone produced. Whether the ventricular folds might act as dampers by actual contact with the vocal folds is doubtful.

In trained voices, the ventricular folds may play more of a part in the production of the individual quality of voice than is the case in average voices. On the other hand, a rough, hoarse voice, especially after the loss of voice through the failure of the vocal folds, may result if the ventricular folds function instead of the true vocal folds. [31] If the voice was hoarse originally, after practice in the use of the ventricular folds it is almost impossible to distinguish the substitution.

H. The Significance of the Epiglottis

Some workers in the field of Voice Science place great importance on the epiglottis—especially on the tubercle of the epiglottis. We know that it may be active in the production of high-pitched tones of some intensity, but its action is probably related to an alteration in the laryngeal cavity size and hence is a factor in resonance, primarily.

Upon laryngoscopic investigation the tubercle of the epiglottis appears to bulge outward in a posterior direction and descend slightly toward the vibrating vocal folds during the production of many higher pitches and falsetto tones. Much of the movement of the tubercle in respect to the glottic margins is relative, however; depending in part, also, upon movements of the arytenoid cartilages. The cushion of the epiglottis is lowered and at the same time protruded toward the arytenoid cartilages by the combined action of the aryepiglottic and the thyroepiglottic muscles. Whether this is the correct explanation of the phenomenon which we see in the laryngoscope mirror, we do not know. The histology of the region in question makes it difficult to give any definite explanation of the muscles involved. In fact, it may be that the tubercle of the posterior surface of the epiglottis moves down and protrudes only because the base of the tongue forces itself against the anterior surface of the epiglottis so as to bulge out the posterior surface. In any case, even if we knew the anatomical mechanism involved, the question of exactly what effect the epiglottis has on voice is still open.

I. The Artificial Larynx

In cases where, because of laryngectomy or otherwise, an individual is deprived of the use of his larynx for purposes of phonation he may substitute an artificial larynx for the normal vibrator mechanism.

The operation of an early type could be described as follows:

(*a*) Air comes from the lungs via a tracheal cannula or from a bellows or pump operated by the patient. In any case, the range of pressures avail-

[31] This ventricular form of phonation occurs in 4 per cent of the cases of hoarseness.

able are not so great or so controlled as in normal speech.

(*b*) A reed vibrated by the air stream produces tones within the normal voice range. Usually the artificially produced tones do not display the degree of flexibility of the normal voice tones.

(*c*) Tone is conducted by a tube into the mouth or nose.

(*d*) The patient uses his own articulating and resonating organs to form the vibrating air stream into useful speech sounds.

The reed vibrator of the improved type of artificial larynx gives the user a range of tones of about an octave and the frequency of the tones produced may be altered by simply turning a screw which regulates the tension of the reed.

A modern artificial larynx provides an electrically-driven generator to produce a fundamental and partials. This synthetic voice complex is resonated and articulated by users to produce speech sounds.

J. Esophageal Speech [32]

In the case of an individual upon whom total laryngectomy has been performed, esophageal voice may be substituted for laryngeal voice. This requires considerable practice. Briefly, the procedure involved is developing substitutes for the vibrating vocal folds and for the respiratory tract. The usual substitutes are the sphincteric muscular orifice of the esophagus and the upper portion of the esophagus. Ordinarily, the orifice or lumen of the esophagus is kept closed by the tonic activity of the cricopharyngeus musculature—the lower portion of the inferior pharyngeal constrictor. The moving column of air which is necessary to force open the orifice in a rhythmical manner comes from the esophagus and not from the lungs and trachea. Air is swallowed by the individual and then expelled under control of the will. The difficulty is in learning to emit a steady stream of air rather than a spasmodic eructation. The esophagiated air column is set into vibration at almost the same level as if it were phonated by the larynx, and hence it is subject to resonator and articulatory modifications in the cavities above just as if it had been produced in the larynx. The speech sounds produced are easily understandable; they suffer, however, in quality and in the range of pitch available to the user.

K. Speech During Inhalation

Little practice is needed to make it possible for one to control the approximation of his vocal folds to just the right degree so that he may speak on inhalation. However, inhalation must be more rapid than normally, and fewer words may be read while inhaling once than may be read while exhaling once.

[32] First record of pseudovoice in patient of Czermak (1859).

Summary Statement

The laryngeal generator is essential in setting up sound waves in the production of the great majority of all normal speech sounds: [b], [d], [g]; [v], [z], [ʒ], [ð]; vowels [l], [r], [w], [j]; [m], [n], [ŋ]; [h].

Those sound waves which result when the air stream is set into vibration at the larynx must be reinforced or otherwise acted upon by the resonators of the physiological airway and foodway systems, or subjected to articulatory modifications at the level of the mouth, or both, before they become useful for speech purposes. To such further refinements by resonance we are now prepared to give attention.

EXERCISES AND QUESTIONS

Sensory Approaches to the Study of the Larynx

The three main senses of the student will aid him in learning something about the larynx. *Sight* discloses the gross movements of the larynx externally and the more intrinsic movements internally. For the latter he must apply the laryngoscopic technique. *Touch* will indicate the gross movements; and *hearing*, correlated with the other two, will enable him to work out cause and effect relationships concerning this valvular mechanism.

I. Laryngeal Observations.[33]

Two students. O and S should engage in a few preliminary practices so that each, acting as O, may gain skill in the proper manipulation of the mirror, and so that each one acting as S may accustom himself to the mirror in his throat. (The gag reflex which will be tripped off when the mirror touches the fauces may be brought under partial voluntary control with practice. Every time the student brushes his teeth he should gently brush the fauces a few times. In a few days the gag reflex will be well under control for laryngoscopy.)

Equipment: light source; head-mirror; sterilized guttural mirror; tongue depressors. The mirror should be boiled before use and then cooled.

With O and S seated, O, facing the light source, will adjust the head-mirror over his left eye, shading the right, so it reflects the light along his line of vision (left eye). S opens his mouth. O focuses the light therein and introduces the sterilized guttural mirror which has been wiped dry and the temperature of which is approximately that of S's lip, against which the mirror may be touched. With his right hand, O holds the shank of the mirror almost in contact with the upper incisor teeth. The left hand is free to manipulate a tongue depressor, if one be necessary. The back of the mirror should make contact with the velum. The insertion and handling of the mirror and depressor should be done with an air of confidence so as to inspire the Subject with faith in the ability of the Observer. This makes it possible for S to relax. If S cannot relax so that the larynx may be plainly seen, he may produce the vowel sound

[33] The original laryngoscope was made by Manuel Garcia (1854), a famous singing-master.

[ɛ]. Variations in pitch may be helpful. Glottal attacks and releases may help in disclosing the glottis. Or, while pressing down on the tongue, have S try to make any of the so-called front vowels. O should note the relation of the epiglottis to the glottis, i. e., does it appear at the base or the apex of the triangular form? What is the relation of the mirror image of the glottis to the real image? Explain. What are the colors of the parts? What is the condition of the vocal folds?

It is interesting to carry on laryngoscopic observations of the vocal folds in a darkened room when the source of light comes from beneath the glottis by means of *transillumination.*

II. The Laryngo-periskop.

To enable an individual to study his own glottic movements, Dr. G. Oscar Russell has invented the Laryngo-periskop. In this instrument a minute light bulb which is attached to and inserted with the guttural mirror, illuminates the region to be investigated. The reflection in the guttural mirror is carried out of the mouth through a metal tube and is reflected, from an adjustable mirror, to the eye. Essentially, the instrument is a self-illuminating laryngoscopic mirror plus a periscope.

III. Laryngoscopy With Stroboscope.[34]

Stroboscopy makes use of the so-called positive after-image. If an object be lighted and then if the light be interrupted the retina still continues to receive an impression of the image for from 1/7 to 1/5 of a second after the object be no longer lighted. If the light to an object be interrupted 2, 3, or 4 times per second the eye will have the impression of light flickering on the object. If, however, the light to an object or between the object and the eye be interrupted 20 or more times per second the object will appear to be constantly lighted and there will appear to be no time at which the object is not lighted. The separate stimuli are no longer sensed as separate.

If there is available a perforated disk (holes equidistant from each other and from the center) which may be revolved at a carefully regulated speed between the light source and the head mirror of O, he will be in a position to apply the principle of the stroboscope to his investigations. If we assume that the folds are producing, e. g., a pitch of 100 d.v. per second, then each vocal fold will be blown away from its center position during 1/200 of a second, but immediately returning, due to its elasticity, during the next 1/200 of a second. If, now, the revolving disk interrupts the light 100 times per second, then only the outward or the inward phase of vocal fold movement will be seen in the mirror; the folds will appear stationary. By operating the disk out of phase with the vibrations of the vocal folds it is possible to see a slow-motion view of their opening and closing.

One of the most recent ideas is that of affixing a small microphone to the guttural mirror so that the condensation waves from the larynx will impinge upon it and operate a neon lamp. The lamp remains lighted only during the

[34] Oertel first employed intermittent illumination, using Mach's stroboscopic disk.

condensation wave and hence only illuminates the field of vision of such periods. This gives a stroboscopic impression of the glottal movements.

During phonation, the folds are seen to have their greatest movement—amount of separation—at a point midway between their anterior (thyroid cartilage) attachment and their insertion into the vocal processes of the arytenoid cartilages. We would expect that this mid-point would represent the area, on the respective cords, of greatest friction. If the impact of the cords at this point were great enough, we would expect it to be the location of submucous haemorrhage with the resultant formation of a small nodule (singer's node). Further, without rest treatment, we would expect this small node, because of continued buffeting, to enlarge. This is what actually happens.

The presence of singer's nodes (or growths such as papilloma and epithelioma) may be detected auditorially because they permit, with each vibration, the escape of extra, inharmonic puffs of air or fricative sounds. Nodes prevent the holding of long-sustained tones; the result is a husky voice which easily fatigues.

IV. Palpation of the Throat Region.

Apply only slight pressure with your fingers in your manipulations.

Using the superior thyroid notch as a point of departure, locate the following:

Hyoid bone
Superior border of the thyroid cartilage
Inferior border of the thyroid cartilage
Cricoid cartilage
Trachea

NOTE: (1) The possible movements of the thyroid and of other laryngeal structures, and

(2) The relation of the parts to each other, while

(*a*) Breathing through the nose
(*b*) Breathing through the mouth
(*c*) Swallowing
(*d*) Chewing gum (opening and closing jaws)
(*e*) Singing [i] from your lowest to your highest pitch
(*f*) Vocalizing [ɑ], [ɛ], [i], [ɔ], [u].

V. Constructing a Model of the Larynx.

Students working in pairs.

Materials: white or yellow, red, and green modeling clay.

1. One student will model the *left half* of the larynx (including ½ cricoid, ½ thyroid, [½ trachea] 1 arytenoid); the partner will model the *right half*. Use white or yellow clay.

2. Each student will place in proper position on his model, the muscles (red) and membranes (green) of the larynx. Notice specifically the size and relation of the parts of the larynx.

VI. To determine the effect upon the pitch of a sustained vowel of slight pressure at various levels of the neck region.

Two students.

Let the Observer mark lightly in ink points at the following levels of the neck: hyoid bone, hyothyroid membrane, thyroid notch, cricothyroid space, cricoid cartilage, trachea.

The Subject will sustain the vowel [ʌ] and the observer will press lightly with his fingers at one of the levels marked. Repeat for each level. Using the vowels [i], [u], [ɔ], [ɑ], repeat the experiment.

Is there any change in the pitch of the vowel tone when the pressure is applied? If so, is it the same at all levels? For all vowels? Does abruptly applied pressure give different results from steadily applied pressure? What is your explanation of the cause of the observed results? Compare your results with those of Dodd (1926).

VII. Secure an artificial larynx and a bellows. Pump air through the artificial larynx and direct the tone into the corner of the mouth. Practice producing various simple sentences, beginning with one such as "Mary, I love you."

VIII. To determine the range of audibility of whispered and phonated sounds outdoors on a level field on a still day.

Two students.

Let the experimenter whisper the following sounds as loudly as possible: [f], [v],[θ], [ð], [s], [z], [ʃ], [ʒ], [ɑ], [i], [u]. In each case, what is the maximum distance each sound can be heard by the Observer? Repeat the experiment, adding voice to the voiced sounds. In each case what is the maximum distance each sound can be heard by the Observer? Prepare a comparative chart to show your results.

IX. If, in exhalation, the control of the vocal folds for phonation is more delicately balanced than is the case in inhalation, is it due to

(*a*) The fact that structurally the folds and the airway are better designed for phonation on exhalation?

(*b*) Or is it only a matter or practice? That is, if fifty per cent of all phonation were done on inhalation and fifty per cent on exhalation, would there be any superiority of exhalatory phonation over inhalatory phonation?

X. Some Related Questions.

1. What part might the rise in intra-tracheal air pressure, during high-pitch phonation, have upon the elevation of the larynx?

2. If with the raising of the larynx and the contraction of the inferior pharyngeal constrictor, the pharynx as a resonating cavity is made smaller, would you conclude that such elevation of the larynx is a faulty vocal mechanism?

3. The glottal attack is made by closure of the glottis followed by sudden opening. Practice substituting the glottal catch for such sounds as [p] and [k]. Would you expect to find such substitution in the infant speech of normal

children? Under what conditions might you expect to find the glottal catch used in normal adult speech? Make a list of illustrative words in the English language. Does the place of the glottal catch in speech show an evolutionary advance or regression?

4. In laryngoscopy, why may it be poor technique to ask the subject to say "ah"?

5. If the esophagus were freely movable instead of being fastened to the diaphragm, what changes in the muscular mechanism controlling the ascent of the larynx would be necessary to effect the same end result which now obtains from the mechanical anchoring of the gullet?

Chapter III

RESONANCE

I. The Nature of Resonance and the Human Resonators
  A. The Nature of Resonance
    1. Relation Between Generator and Resonator
    2. Air as a Sounding Body
    3. Properties of Cavities as Resonators
    4. Types of Resonators
    5. Coupling
    6. The Damping Factor
    7. Tubes
  B. Resonance Factors Applied to the Human Resonators
    1. Volume of the Cavity
    2. Area of the Aperture
    3. Surface of the Cavity
    4. Coupling Factors
    5. Sources of Vibration Used in Speech Sounds
  C. The Potential Human Resonators
    1. Tracheo-bronchial Tree
    2. Laryngeal Cavities
    3. Pharyngeal Cavity
    4. Oral Cavity
    5. Nose
II. Vowels the Basis of Speech
  A. Some Theories of Vowel Production
    1. The Harmonic Theory of Vowel Production
    2. The Cavity-Tone Theory of Vowel Production
    3. A Comparison of the Theories of Vowel Production
  B. Vowels—General Considerations
  C. The Production of Vowel Sounds
    1. The Front Vowels
    2. The Back Vowels
    3. The Central Vowels
  D. The Duration of Vowels
  E. Resonators and Frequency Areas
III. Experimental Evidence Supporting Resonance Theories

THE NATURE OF RESONANCE AND THE HUMAN RESONATORS

In great part, resonance determines the final form of any speech sound. This is true whether the sound be produced as a result of the vibrating mechanism at the larynx, as has just been described; whether it be produced by the action of articulatory organs, as we shall explain in Chapter IV; or whether it be the end product of phonation and articulation combined. In this chapter we are interested primarily in the influence of resonance upon the sounds which may be produced at the larynx. Before going further, however, we must understand what is meant by resonance.

A. The Nature of Resonance

1. RELATION BETWEEN GENERATOR AND RESONATOR

The period at which a vibrating body vibrates with the greatest ease is known as its *natural period* or *free period*. Once the body is set into vibration, even though the source of energy originally causing it to vibrate be withdrawn, it will continue to vibrate in its natural period for some time—depending upon its mass and the other damping factors involved. For example, pluck a violin string, strike a key of the piano, or shout into a canyon.

A body is set into vibration by an *exciting cause*. The exciting cause, called a *generator*, dissipates energy when it sets the body into vibration. All other things being equal, the greater the energy released, the greater the strength of the resulting vibrations. The number of vibrations of a generator in a unit of time (second) determines the frequency of the generator. Thus, a generator passing through 256 complete vibrations per second may be said to have a frequency of 256 cycles.

If the generator is of a frequency equal to that of the natural frequency of a second body which is being set into vibration, the two may be said to be in *resonance* or in *tune*. If the response of the body being set into vibration is maximal, the tuning is said to be *sharp*. If the frequency of the generator differs from the natural period of the vibrating body, the two are not sharply tuned, and the greater the difference in frequency, the less sharp the tuning. If the generator and vibrating body are greatly out of tune, there can be but little resonance.

A body which vibrates in resonance to the generator is a *resonator*. Examples of generators and their related resonators are: piano strings and piano soundboard; oboe reeds and the conical body of the instrument. If, for example, a piano string be removed from the sounding board of the piano and struck, its tone will be weak. But with the sounding board acting as a resonator, the string when struck produces a loud tone. The stroke imparts a certain amount of energy to the wire; with the sounding board the energy is dissipated more rapidly, and hence the tone sounds louder. The board itself adds no energy. On the other hand, without the board, the string would continue to vibrate longer after being struck than it does with the sounding board.

A resonator gives out no tones unless they be received from the generator. Further, a resonator may not give out all the tones received. In a system where there is a generator and one or more resonators, no tone except that produced by the generator and also reproduced by one or more of the resonators may be heard. It is important to remember that not only can *no tones be emitted from a resonator unless they be received from the generator,* but that in many cases, rather than being reinforced by the resonator, the tones will be diminished or will not be given out at all by the resonator. In the latter case, it will be as though the generator had not produced them. The resonator, therefore, may amplify, damp out, or destroy tones. The degree of tuning existing between resonator and generator establishes not only the pitch and intensity, but also the quality of a resultant tone.

2. AIR AS A SOUNDING BODY

Air possesses properties of elasticity and mass. Therefore, the term "body" may be applied to a volume of air. When enclosed in a cavity—e. g., a bottle—and disturbed in any way, the air pulsates in and out of the aperture of the cavity. If it were visible it might be likened to a jack-in-the-box. Filling a cavity with a heavy smoke and setting it into vibration will illustrate the phenomenon. It will be seen that at first the smoky air will "protrude" out of the container, then it will "recede" into the cavity even below the level of the neck. In terms of pressure, the former means greater pressure inside the container than outside it; the latter means greater pressure outside the cavity than within it. As long as any difference of pressure exists between the air inside and the air outside, the pulsations will continue. Further, the mass of the air itself will continue it in vibration. It is rather like the phenomenon that we see if a lawn swing be displaced from its position of rest. It does not stop, when, upon release, it comes to its neutral or rest position, but swings on past to the opposite side and so continues to oscillate back and forth for some time—the length of time depending largely upon its mass. With each oscillation (vibration), the amplitude of the swing (surge) decreases (damps out). The rate of the surgings (per second) of the air in and out of the cavity depends mainly upon the volume of the cavity and the size of the aperture of the cavity.

3. PROPERTIES OF CAVITIES AS RESONATORS

(1) The greater the volume of the cavity, the longer the time required for pressure differences to equalize themselves, and the greater the mass of the air involved. *The larger the cavity, the slower the rate of pulsations or vibrations.*

For a given aperture or mouth, it is the volume of the resonator that is important rather than the shape of the cavity. All that is essential is that no dimension of the cavity be such as to permit much difference in pressure in different parts of the cavity. If every dimension be considerably less than a quarter of the wave length, the pitches obtained from resonators of divers shapes are the same, provided, further, that the apertures are similar and not too large, and that the volumes of the resonators are equal.

(2) A large opening permits more rapid surgings, and hence a more rapid equalization of pressure. Other factors being equal, *the larger the opening, the more rapid the pulsations or vibrations.*

Given two resonators just alike, except for the size of their apertures, the one with the larger aperture will have the higher natural frequency.

(3) There is a third factor, namely, the length of the neck of the orifice, which is usually considered in resonance experiments. In the human resonance mechanism it is probably not an important element.

(4) Finally, the surface of the wall of the resonator is important in determining its properties. This will be discussed later in some detail.

4. TYPES OF RESONATORS

As has been pointed out, a sounding body—e. g., a resonator—has one or more natural periods in which it vibrates easily. A body vibrating in tune or with the frequency of the generator is said to be in *sympathetic vibration.* If the body is set into sympathetic vibration by the generator, and if the generator then be withdrawn, the body will continue to vibrate in its natural free period.

Even if a resonator is not naturally in tune with the generator, it may be forced by the generator to vibrate—*forced vibration.* In the case of forced vibration, because of lack of tuning between the generator and resonator, the generator is not vibrating in its natural frequency and the resonator is not vibrating in its natural frequency. The frequency of the forced vibration is somewhere between the two natural frequencies. In other words, the natural frequency of the resonator plus the natural frequency of the generator may result in a common forced frequency unnatural to either body. In this case, the generator influences the resonator, but the resonator also influences the generator. In general, it may be stated that the influence of generator upon resonator is greater than that of resonator upon generator.

There are many degrees of sharpness of tuning between the extremes of sympathetic vibration and forced vibration.

Because there are these two general types of vibration, there are two general types of resonators. One possesses its own more or less definite natural period and, because of its selectivity, will reproduce only sounds of definite pitch and quality. Such a resonator responds not only to pitches corresponding to its fundamental frequency, but also to those in tune with its overtones. A *Helmholtz resonator,* spherical and made of brass, is such a tuned resonator. The other type, having no particular natural frequency of its own, may respond to tones of any frequency or to complex tones made up of several frequencies; it will reproduce many gradations of tone quality.

5. COUPLING

A vibrating system which consists of two or more parts—e. g., a generator and a resonator, or several resonators—that could vibrate independently if the parts were not connected is known as a *coupled system.*

If any part of a coupled system be set into vibration it will act to exert a periodic force on another part which, in turn, will execute a sympathetic or a forced vibration. This, in turn, produces a reacting force on the first part, altering its pattern of vibration. A *loosely coupled system* is one in which the force that one part of the system exerts on another is small. In such a system the normal vibration frequency of the system approaches the natural vibration frequencies of the several components. A closely or *tightly coupled system* is one in which the force that one part of the system exerts on another is large.

A coupled system may execute free vibrations if any part of the system is left to itself. Or a coupled system may execute forced vibrations if any part of the system be subjected to a periodic force.

The possible variations which may be obtained from coupling together two or more resonators is a function of the relative sizes of their cavities and of their apertures. To some extent these variables may be treated mathematically. Other factors more difficult of treatment also may enter into consideration—e. g., the types of surfaces of the cavities and the shape of the cavities.

6. THE DAMPING FACTOR

If a tuning fork—of, say, 128 d.v./sec.—be struck it will vibrate and will continue to vibrate and emit a weak tone for x seconds. The listener will be able to hear the tone only if the fork be held close to his ear. If a resonator, tuned to the pitch of the fork, be held near the struck fork so as to resonate the tone, the tone can now be heard at some distance. Also, the fork will not vibrate for so long a period as it did in the first case. It will continue to vibrate for x seconds minus a rather constant factor for the particular resonator used. The reason the tone is louder is that the resonator is absorbing and radiating energy from the generator (in this case, the fork). The amplitude of the vibrations of the fork are damped out more rapidly than would be the case if there were no resonator. Every resonator may be said to have this damping effect on the generator. The greater the damping, the more rapid the dissipation of energy. By knowing this damping factor, it is possible to figure how much louder the sound will be as well as how much shorter will be its duration.

7. TUBES

A *tube closed at one end* is a cavity whose length is greater than its diameter, and whose diameter is maintained right to its mouth. (See Fig. 25.)

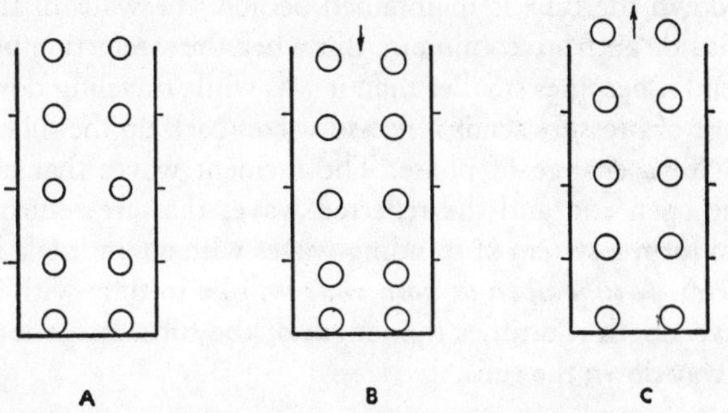

FIG. 25. Fictitious Schema of Behavior of "Layers" of Molecules in a Tube Closed at One End.
A. Normal distribution of molecules, that is, equilibrium.
B. Compressional disturbance transmitted to successive "layers" of molecules.
C. Molecules released from pressure.

The molecules of air in this tube may be diagrammed (*a*) under no pressure, (*b*) under pressure, and (*c*) after release of pressure.

The "layers" of molecules can be compressed, and because of elasticity will return to (and beyond) their "normal" position. Pressure (positive—in, or negative—out) applied to the first layer, at the aperture, is transmitted to succeeding layers as an incident wave until it reaches the layer at the closed end of the tube. This last layer cannot move down the tube but can only be compressed. The wave is said to stand at this point. Hence, the compression wave must be reflected back up the tube as a reflected wave. When it reaches the mouth the air at that point has then performed half a complete vibration.

The time taken by the wave to traverse the tube twice (down and up) is a function of the length of the tube; it does not depend on the diameter or the volume of the cavity.

The resonator period of a closed-end tube depends only on the length of the tube. Such a tube will be in tune with a frequency whose wave length is 4 times the length of the tube ("In" + "Out" = ½ cycle × 2 = 1 complete cycle). Because the surface at the end of the tube is rigid there is almost no loss of energy or intensity in the reflected wave. The wave is reflected with no change in phase. The incident waves and the reflected waves in a tube closed at one end combine to form a system of standing waves in which a node is situated at the "bottom" or closed end of the tube.

In a tube of which both ends are open, the walls keep the compressed layer of air of a compression wave from spreading sideways as it progresses down the tube, but at the far end of the tube the air expands outward freely and, thus, the degree of compression at that end of the tube becomes less than it was while traveling in the tube. Because of this decrease in pressure, reflected waves travel backward up the tube. In the same way, a rarefaction traveling down the tube is maintained because the walls of the tube prevent the outside air from coming in. But when the rarefaction phase reaches the open end it becomes smaller than it was while traveling down the tube. This change of pressure sends reflected waves back up the tube. Waves are reflected with a change of phase. The incident waves that are traveling toward the open end and the reflected waves that are returning from it combine to form a system of standing waves with an antinode located near the open end. A *tube open at both ends* will be in tune with a frequency whose wave-length is 2 times the length of the tube. Its node will be at a point halfway down the tube.

B. Resonance Factors Applied to the Human Resonators

Now that we have a background of information concerning the general nature of resonance, we are ready to apply it specifically in considering the human resonators involved in the production of speech sounds.

1. VOLUME OF THE CAVITY

In the first place, we know that the volume of a cavity is one factor which aids in determining its resonance characteristics. A glance at the frontispiece will be sufficient to indicate that there are several potential resonating cavities in the speech mechanism. Each is unique in its shape and dimensions. If the volume of a resonator remains constant, all other factors being unchanged, we know that the natural period of the resonator also remains constant. This information is quite helpful in the case of a fixed spherical resonator, for example. But in the case of the human resonators which are constantly varying in their volume, it is apparent that, at best, one can but approximate and relate volume and pitch. The musculature of all these resonators is so co-ordinated that for every individual sound produced there are numerous alterations and related adjustments made in each of the several cavities—adjustments which probably vary greatly at the beginning, middle, and termination of each sound.

Approximate Volumes of the Human Resonators		
Bronchi and trachea		60 cc.
Trachea alone	35 cc.	
Larynx		25 cc.
Pharynx		80 cc.
Laryngopharynx	20 cc.	
Oropharynx	30 cc.	
Nasopharynx	30 cc.	
Mouth		100 cc.
Nose		60 cc.
Nasal sinuses		125 cc.
2 Maxillary	50 cc.	
2 Frontal	40 cc.	
2 Sphenoidal	20 cc.	
6 Ethmoidal	15 cc.	
	Total	450 cc.

Related to the capacity of a resonator is its shape. Many of the resonating chambers that we are to study may be classified as irregular. This means small wall irregularities, not such major ones as would of themselves form cul de sacs or distinct cavities. Moreover, because the cavities are constantly changing, the irregularities are constantly fluctuating.

2. AREA OF THE APERTURE

The area of its aperture or apertures is another factor determining the frequency characteristics of a cavity. Some of the human resonators have multiple apertures, as is shown in the chart on page 97.

3. SURFACE OF THE CAVITY

All of us have had experiences with echoes in rooms with hard walls which make excellent reflecting surfaces. Under these conditions one characterizes the sounds heard as brilliant, metallic, hard, brittle, crisp, etc. High-frequency tones are accentuated. Also, most of us have visited the acoustically treated rooms of a broadcasting station, in which, when one speaks, one's normal voice quality seems to be altered or "absorbed" by the walls. Such a studio sounds "dead," we say. Under these conditions, one characterizes the sounds heard as dead, mellow, subdued, soft, mushy, etc. High-frequency tones are suppressed. Such experiences as these indicate that the character of the surfaces of a cavity in great part determine its resonance characteristics. It is not difficult to understand that if the containing walls are smooth—e. g., as in a tube or sphere—the pattern of reflections of energy transmission of the vibrating molecules will be simple as compared to the pattern which may be expected if the walls are rough. In our own vocal resonating cavities there is a wide variety of surfaces, many of which are subject to radical and almost instantaneous changes. At one extreme is the hard surface of the teeth; at the other, the spongelike consistency of the lung. Intermediately, such structures as the tongue and velum may vary their surfaces from a degree of laxness to one of tenseness.

The principles of resonance which apply to metal resonators are not the same as those which apply to cavities with soft walls. A metal resonator responds well only if the generator is in tune with the resonator. Soft-wall resonators—for example, resonators with walls of tissue—are responsive to a wide range of pitches. Within limits, the softer the wall of the resonator, the wider the range of frequencies to which it will respond.

To demonstrate the change which takes place in such a resonator as the mouth cavity, vary the size of the aperture at the lips, vary the volume of the cavity, vary the tension of the cheek walls—while tapping the cheeks with a pencil.

4. COUPLING FACTORS

It is not enough that each resonator demonstrate its own variations of volume, area of aperture, and surfaces. If two resonators are coupled together the characteristics of each undergo change. For example, if two resonators are coupled together their frequency characteristics are lowered. If several resonators are coupled together, as in the case of those being studied, the range of frequencies covered is limited only by the individual adjustments of which each part of the coupled system is capable. And as these are numerous, the frequency range of the system must be well suited to aid in the production of speech sounds. The apertures of this complexly coupled system are particularly subject to changes in their dimensions. Often, an aperture of a cavity may be entirely eliminated for a brief period.

Further, we must remember that these resonators have a damping influence on the sound generator. If the resonator cavity volume and the orifices are changed, the damping factors likewise fluctuate.

5. SOURCES OF VIBRATIONS USED IN SPEECH SOUNDS

If we recall that the air in a cavity is set into vibration when energy is transmitted to it by a generator, we may now ask, By what means is the air in the human resonating cavities set into vibration? In the production of speech sounds three methods are used: phonation, e.g., [i]; frictional factors, e.g., [s]; limited implosion-explosion factors as, for example, in the sound [p]. In the main, in this chapter, we shall concern ourselves with resonance and phonation.

Before we consider the human resonators as they are related to these generative sources of vibrations, we must point out that the air in the resonators

Coupling Relations of the Human Resonators

Cavity	*Number of Orifices*	*Size of Orifices Relative to Size of Cavity*	*Possible Alterations of Orifices*	*Alterations Creating Two Cavities from One*
Nasal	2 external nares	large	normally patent	none
	2 maxillary sinuses	minute	" "	"
	2 frontal "	"	" "	"
	6 ethmoidal "	"	" "	"
	2 sphenoidal "	"	" "	"
	2 choanae	large	" "	"
Maxillary sinuses	1 each	small	normally patent	none
Frontal "	1 each	"	" "	"
Ethmoidal "	1 each	"	" "	"
Sphenoidal "	1 each	"	" "	"
Oral	lips	large	all degrees of adjustment from closed to wide open.	Tongue may divide oral cavity into two cavities: anterior and posterior. Either may be larger than the other depending on position of the tongue
	oropharynx	large	normally patent	
Nasopharynx	nasal cavity	large	normally patent	none
	oropharynx	"	*normally closed in the production of all speech sounds except [m] [n], [ŋ] when it is open. There may be any degree of velar-pharyngeal closure, however.	"
Oropharynx	nasopharynx	large	See * above.	none
	oral cavity	"	May be obliterated by tongue.	"
	laryngopharynx	"	Normally patent	"
Laryngopharynx	esophagus	NOT OF INTEREST IN NORMAL SPEECH		
	larynx	large	Normally patent	none
	oropharynx	"	" "	"
Larynx	laryngopharynx	large	Normally patent	none
	trachea	"	" "	May be divided into 2 cavities by vocal cords.
Trachea	larynx	large	Normally patent	none
	bronchi	"	" "	"
Bronchi	trachea	large	Normally patent	none
	subdivisions of lungs	"	" "	"

may be energized either (1) directly through the open apertures, or (2) indirectly through the cavity walls.

(1-*a*) In the first case, we may illustrate by saying that the air of the laryngeal cavity is set into vibration by the phonative mechanism and that the energy is transmitted through the aperture between the laryngeal and pharyngeal cavities thus setting into sympathetic vibration the air in the pharynx which, for the moment, we shall assume is tuned to one of the frequencies emitted by the generator.

(1-*b*) Or again, the puffs of air, without reference to their frequency of emission or, simply, a steady stream of air—provided the air passes over the edge of the aperture of the cavity so as to provide a friction noise—may set into free or even forced vibration the air in the cavity. In such a case the resonated tone is that of the natural period of the cavity.

(2) Finally, we may illustrate by saying that if the velar-pharyngeal closure is complete, then the energy of the vibration in the oral cavity may set the hard palate into vibration, the palate, in turn, setting into vibration the air of the nasal cavity.

C. The Potential Human Resonators

In this chapter we are proceeding on the assumption that any or some or all of the cavities of the physiological airway and foodway systems may act as resonators. Further, if they do act as resonators, they will have some influence on voice and speech. At the outset, let it be said that we do not know exactly how all the human resonators respond and that there exist differences of opinion as to whether some cavities actually are important from the viewpoint of speech and voice, and, if important, as to their mode of operation.

Any cavity coupled directly or indirectly to that in which the laryngeal generator (vocal folds) is located may be considered a *potential* resonator. The resonators associated with the human speech mechanism are listed below and will be considered at this time.

1. Tracheo-bronchial tree
   a. Lungs
   b. Trachea and bronchi
2. Laryngeal cavities
   a. Infraglottal
   b. Supraglottal
3. Pharyngeal cavity
   a. Nasopharynx
   b. Oropharynx
   c. Laryngopharynx
4. Oral cavity

5. Nose
   a. Nasal fossae
   b. Nasal sinuses

1. TRACHEO-BRONCHIAL TREE [1]

In our opinion, the tracheo-bronchial tree below the bifurcation of the trachea has little if any effect on sound waves generated at the larynx. Any effect that it does have is due to the absorption of tones—probably of all frequencies—by the spongelike tissue of the lungs. That, for some pitches, sound transmitted to the entire tracheo-bronchial tree and thence to the chest proper may cause the thorax to act as a sounding board giving off vibrations to the outside air which mix with those emerging from the mouth and nose, we believe is possible, but even if so, can have little significance in the sound complex which eventually reaches the ears of a listener.

We are inclined to the opinion that the trachea acts as a resonator, probably for pitches of approximately 128 and 256 d.v./sec., although at the same time we admit that the whole question is debatable. On strictly physical grounds, there is every reason to believe that sound waves generated at the larynx may as readily travel down the airway as up the airway. It is usually believed that the sound waves can travel up the air tract with the outrushing stream of air. The question in the minds of some is, Can the sound wave travel down the trachea against the air stream? Sound waves have a velocity of 1100 feet per second. The exhaled air stream may have a velocity of from 5 to 30 feet per second. Comparison of these velocities would seem to indicate that the velocity of the sound wave is so great that it may almost as easily oppose as accompany the air current.

It is interesting to hypothesize that if a sound impulse of a given frequency be originated by the laryngeal generator, a portion of the wave (*a*) will pass upward at $1100 + x$ feet per second, while another portion (*b*) will pass downwards at $1100 - x$ feet per second. (x is the velocity of the air column.) Reflected back up the airway, the sound wave (*b*) will issue from the mouth in an out-of-phase relation dependent on the velocity of x and the distance actually traversed by (*b*) down the trachea and up. The frequency assumed to be reinforced will depend upon whether the distance measured is from the lips to the tracheo-bronchial tree or from the glottis to the tracheo-bronchial tree. It should be recalled that a tube closed at one end and having a length of about one foot will respond to a sound having a wave length of approximately four feet (256 cycles). Such a sound is near the range of the fundamental of the female voice and the first overtone of the male voice.

[1] The anatomy of this region has been discussed in Chapter I. If necessary, it may be reviewed at this time.

It is a common experience in walking along an ocean beach during a storm to find that it is impossible to shout to someone a few feet away. The wind seems to blow your words back into your mouth. A companion cannot hear what you say. But this is not due to wind velocity alone—the chief difficulty is that the noises of the storm mask out the speech sounds, making it impossible to hear either with or against the wind.

During phonation the lungs are emptying and the trachea is undergoing a progressive series of decreases in volume due to shortening. At first glance, this may lead one to conclude that the trachea cannot reinforce any one pitch, that any reinforcement would have to be of a progressive series of pitches directly related to the progressive series of volume changes of the cavity.

The cartilaginous framework of the trachea, as well as its length, give it the necessary qualities of an effective resonator. Relative to what has been said above about the shortening of the trachea, it is to be noted that this takes place upon exhalation because of (*a*) a rise of the lung root and (*b*) the ascent of the diaphragm. During inhalation, with the descent of the lung root, the trachea, bronchi, and bronchioles are lengthened.

As we have stated previously, two main factors determine the pitch of a resonator: the volume of the cavity and the size of the aperture. Applying this information to the trachea, we find that, as the volume of the cavity decreases—if the aperture remains constant—the cavity will respond to progressively higher pitches. Also, if the aperture of the trachea decreases—assuming the volume to remain constant—the cavity will respond to progressively lower pitches. Now, therefore, if the volume decreases while, concomitantly, the aperture decreases, the cavity should always respond to a single pitch. Obviously, the question that arises concerns the possibility of decreasing the aperture of the trachea. In our discussion of the lungs and trachea in the chapter on Respiration (Chapter I) we pointed out that the trachealis muscle may constrict the trachea. Hence, our conclusion is that the trachea is capable of reinforcing a tone of a given frequency. That tone is probably at about the range of the speaker's fundamental voice tone or within the range of the first or second overtone.

2. LARYNGEAL CAVITIES [2]

Whether or not the laryngeal cavities themselves act as resonators seems to be a debatable question.

Our observations with the laryngo-periskop lead us to agree with Scripture, Paget, and Russell that the laryngeal cavity prepares for the production of each vowel by assuming such a variation of form, in conjunction with the vocal cords, as will result in producing not only the note to be

[2] The anatomy of this region has been discussed in Chapter II. If necessary, it may be reviewed at this time.

intoned, but also a particular selection of overtones or "partials." Probably, the overtones produced are those which are suitable for setting up resonance in the cavities which are simultaneously formed in the mouth and throat. The larynx, small as it is, may be divided into two major parts. Each one will now be presented in an attempt to determine its importance as a resonator.

The *infra-glottic larynx* is that portion of the larynx bounded below by the superior end of the trachea—i. e., the level of the trachea-cricoid union

Figure 26 shows the foundation of an interesting hypothesis, an hypothesis regarding ventricular resonance. Let us assume that in the adult male the ventricle is well developed. Assuming that fold *A* is blown upward, the air blast will be blown into or across the opposite ventricle. A powerfully resonated tone will characterize the sound wave. Now, fold *B* is blown upward, in turn, and the opposite ventricle functions as a resonator. If both folds are blown upward at the same time, as we believe, the two ventricular resonators will be influenced at once. For all low pitches and in falsetto voice due to the activity of the ventricular folds, the ventricles are obliterated and the tone produced by the vocal folds is no longer resonated by the ventricles but only above the larynx in single mid-line cavities. Thus might sound waves of high pitches be differentiated from those of low pitches in the adult male. A further assumption is helpful: that in the male before puberty and in the female before and after puberty, the ventricles are extremely shallow or practically nonexistent. We repeat, this is merely an interesting hypothesis at present.

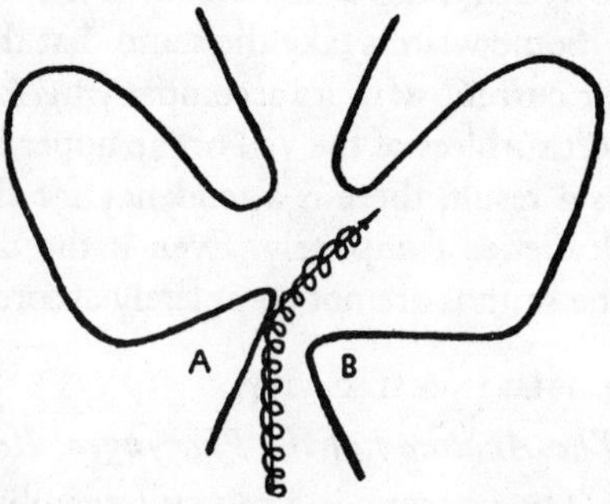

FIG. 26. Sketch to Illustrate an Hypothesis of Ventricular Resonance.

—and, above, by the glottic lips. Except for the fact that the cavity at this point tapers toward its upper limits there is little to differentiate it from the trachea, with which it is continuous. This cavity, therefore, will act with and as a part—a neck—of the cavity of the trachea.

The *supra-glottic larynx* extends from the glottic lips below to the hyoid bone above. We may recognize two divisions of this cavity:

(*a*) Between the glottic lips and the superior or false folds there are, first of all, the ventricles. As long as the superior thyroarytenoid folds are relaxed the ventricles are practically nonexistent. Probably the ventricles are not important as resonators under these conditions. However, if the superior folds are approximated—and it can be demonstrated with the laryngoperiskop that this occurs in the production of certain sounds—the ventricles will be at their maximum size. Under these conditions, some slight distension may result from the pressure of the air stream. In such a case, we might agree with Russell that the ventricles could act as resonators giving a harsh quality to the voice.

(*b*) Another cavity may be produced between the glottic lips and the epiglottis. At a somewhat higher level than the anterior attachments of the ventricular folds is the tubercle of the epiglottis. This structural prominence is often active at the same time that the ventricular folds are active. On account of the angle of the epiglottis it is easy to see how, when there is a general constrictor action in this region, the tubercle and the corniculate cartilage will be drawn together, aiding the ventricular folds in partially pinching off this section of the larynx. The superior portion of the epiglottis may move into a position which will draw it toward the back wall of the pharynx. By this constriction, the upper neck of the laryngeal cavity is narrowed and the wall surfaces of the cavity tensed.

Some writers take the stand that the epiglottis serves to deflect the issuing air current with its accompanying sound vibrations up into the enmeshing soft surfaces of the veil of the upper back throat (palatine arches), and that, as a result, there is a tendency for the sounds to be mellowed, and finally deadened completely. Even if the deflection occurs, it is our opinion that the sounds are not completely absorbed.

3. PHARYNGEAL CAVITY

The Anatomy of the Pharyngeal Region

The pharynx is a musculo-membranous conic tube—11 cm. in length in the male—extending from the base of the skull to the upper border of the sixth cervical vertebra. At the level of the inferior border of the cricoid cartilage, the pharynx opens into the esophagus. The pharynx has three divisions from above downward: a nasal part, the nasopharynx; an oral part, the oropharynx; and a laryngeal part, the laryngopharynx. The tube is broader in the transverse than in the antero-posterior diameter. Seven cavities communicate with it: posterior nares (two), Eustachian tubes (two), mouth, larynx, and esophagus. The mucous membrane of the pharynx is continuous with that of the cavities connected with it.

The top of the pharynx is attached to the base of the skull. At this superior portion its width is 3 cm.; its depth (antero-posterior) is 2 cm.[3] Lower down, where the pharynx is connected with the inner circumference of the hyoid bone, its width is 3 cm. and its depth is from 2 to 3 cm. These dimensions may be altered by movements of the muscular walls and adjoining structures. Beneath this framework the larynx is suspended. Below the hyoid bone the diameter of the tubular structure decreases rapidly until it is obliterated in the contracted walls of the esophagus. In general, the curve of the vertebral column establishes the conformation of the posterior

[3] From the posterior edge of the nasal septum to the vertebral column. The edge of the septum is at once the posterior limit of the nasal cavities and the anterior limit of the pharynx.

wall of the pharynx. There is a decided curve forward opposite the hindermost part of the tongue. These two factors narrow the pharynx in this region to a mere slit.

The *nasopharynx* is behind the nose, above the level of the soft palate. Its cavity always remains patent. It communicates with the nasal cavities through the choanae. On its posterior wall is a mass of lymphoid tissue—the pharyngeal tonsil or adenoids. The two posterior nares (choanae) mark the highest point of the anterior wall of the pharynx. They are separated from each other by the posterior margin of the nasal septum. With a mirror behind the soft palate, as in posterior rhinoscopy, the superior, middle, and inferior turbinates can be seen. Between the nasal cavities and the larynx, the nasopharynx and the oropharynx complete the respiratory tract.

The *Eustachian tubes* may be seen in posterior rhinoscopy as trumpet-shaped pharyngeal orifices on each side of the nasopharynx about opposite the inferior turbinates. Running upward, backward, and outward, each tube opens into the anterior wall of the middle ear, behind the tympanic membrane. It is narrowest at the middle of its extent. The walls are osseous near the tympanum, and cartilaginous toward the pharynx. Its length is 4 cm.; the cartilaginous pharyngeal portion being 2.5 cm. long while the superior bony part is 1.5 cm. long. The mucous membrane lining of the pharynx is continuous with that of the tube and tympanum. In the normal Eustachian tube, air has free access to the middle ear; e. g., in swallowing. This may be demonstrated by holding the nostrils closed while swallowing.

The *oropharynx* extends from the soft palate to the level of the hyoid bone. It opens through the isthmus faucium into the oral cavity. In its lateral wall is the palatine tonsil.

The *laryngopharynx* extends from the hyoid bone to the inferior border of the cricoid where it becomes continuous with the esophagus. The transverse diameter of the pharynx is greater than its antero-posterior diameter. Its widest point is opposite the greater cornua of the hyoid; its narrowest is at the junction with the esophagus.

The *hyoid* or *lingual bone* (os hyoides) somewhat resembles the mandible in that it is horseshoe-shaped with its open portion directed posteriorly. The hyoid bone [4] is situated between the larynx and the tongue, serving as an area of attachment for the muscles of the tongue. It consists of a body and four horns or processes; two *greater cornua* and two *lesser cornua.* It is suspended above the larynx from the styloid processes of the temporal bones by the stylohyoid ligaments. All movements or changes of position of the hyoid bone are imparted to the larynx which is suspended, in turn, from the hyoid bone. The anterior surface of the bone is convex; the posterior surface is concave, corresponding to the shape of the epiglottis.

[4] With your fingers, locate this bone below and about one and one-half inches posterior to the symphysis of the mandible.

The thyrohyoid membrane proceeds from the superior border of the thyroid cartilage to the superior and posterior part of the hyoid bone. The stronger central portion of the membrane is known as the anterior thyrohyoid membrane or ligament. The lateral thyrohyoid membranes, one on each side, extend between the superior cornua of the thyroid cartilage and the greater cornua of the hyoid bone. The small cartilaginous nodule in each membrane is the cartilago triticea.

Because it is not directly attached to any other part of the skeletal structure of the body, the hyoid bone is free to move or to tilt in any direction—i. e., up, down, forward, backward, to the right, to the left, or in any combination of these directions. Such freedom of motion makes the hyoid bone an important factor in vegetative and voice processes. Furthermore, the attachments of the hyoid bone to other structures means that its movements and their movements will influence each other. The hyoid bone attachments are as follows: to the larynx by the thyrohyoid muscle, membrane, and ligament; to the mandible by the digastric (anterior belly), geniohyoid, mylohyoid, and genioglossus muscles; to the tongue by the genioglossus and hyoglossus muscles and the hyoglossal membrane; to the temporal bone (immovable) by the digastric (posterior belly) and stylohyoid muscles, and the stylohyoid ligament; to the pharynx by the middle pharyngeal constrictor; to the sternum (relatively immovable) by the sternohyoid muscle; to the scapula (relatively immovable) by the omohyoid muscle.

THE SUPRAHYOID MUSCLES

Digastric
Stylohyoid
Mylohyoid
Geniohyoid

Digastric (digastricus), anterior belly

Origin:	Inner surface of mandible near symphysis.
Insertion:	Intermediate tendon and hyoid bone.
Innervation:	Mylohyoid branch of inferior alveolar (V).
Action:	The action of the anterior bellies, with the mandible fixed, is to pull the hyoid bone (and tongue) up and forward. The action of the anterior bellies, with the hyoid bone fixed, is to depress the mandible. (See also posterior belly, to which the anterior belly is united by a round tendon.)

posterior belly

Origin:	Mastoid notch of temporal bone.
Insertion:	Hyoid bone and intermediate tendon.

Innervation: Facial (VII).
Action: Elevates and retracts hyoid bone and tongue.

If the mandible be fixed, both bellies of the digastric muscle, acting together, elevate the hyoid bone in a straight line, raising the larynx and mouth floor, e. g., preparatory to swallowing. Acting together, if the hyoid be fixed, the digrastric muscles depress the mandible and assist in opening the mouth.

Stylohyoid [5] (stylohyoideus)

Origin: Styloid process of temporal bone.
Insertion: Body of hyoid bone.
Innervation: Facial (VII).
Action: Draws hyoid and tongue upward and backward.

Mylohyoid (mylohyoideus)

Origin: Mylohyoid ridge of mandible, i. e., from the symphysis in front to the last molar tooth in back.
Insertion: Hyoid bone and median raphe. A few of the more posterior fibers of the mylohyoid pass medialward and somewhat downward to be inserted on the hyoid bone. The medial and anterior fibers insert in a median raphe which runs from the symphysis of the mandible to the hyoid bone.
Innervation: Mylohyoid branch of inferior alveolar of trigeminal (V).
Action: Raises and advances hyoid bone, and hence the tongue; aids weakly in depressing jaw; forms floor of mouth. Because it forms the floor of the mouth it is sometimes called the *diaphragm of the mouth* or the upper diaphragm. Contraction of the mylohyoid muscles produces changes of relationship within the oral and pharyngeal cavities—e. g., by raising the mouth floor and with it the hyoid bone and tongue, by pushing the tongue and hyoid bone forward.

Geniohyoid (geniohyoideus)

Origin: Mental spine of mandible.
Insertion: Body of hyoid bone.
Innervation: C 1, 2.
Action: Lifts and advances hyoid; aids in depressing jaw and opening the mouth when the hyoid bone is fixed and the mouth is closed.

[5] The stylohyoid ligament may be found in connection with the stylohyoid muscles. Its superior attachment is the styloid process of the temporal bone; its inferior attachment is the lesser cornu of the hyoid.

The suprahyoid muscles acting together raise the hyoid bone and the base of the tongue. If the hyoid bone is fixed by hyoid and laryngeal depressors,

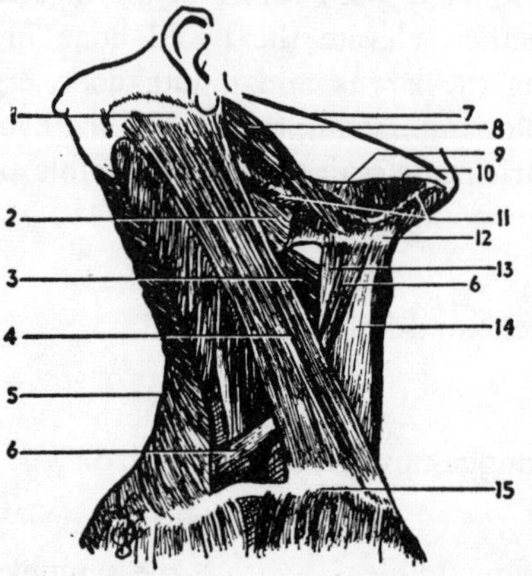

1. Mastoid process; 2. middle pharyngeal constrictor; 3. inferior pharyngeal constrictor; 4. sternocleidomastoid; 5. trapezius; 6. omohyoid; 7. mandible; 8. stylohyoid; 9. hyoglossus; 10. mylohyoid; 11. digastric; 12. hyoid bone; 13. thyrohyoid; 14. sternohyoid; 15. clavicle.

FIG. 27. Neck Muscles. Lateral View.

contraction of the suprahyoid group depresses the mandible. The hyoid bone and tongue are moved forward and upward by the action of the mylohyoid, geniohyoid, and digastric muscles (anterior bellies).

SUMMARY OF FUNCTION AND INNERVATION OF SUPRAHYOID MUSCLES

Muscle	*Function*	*Innervation*
Digastric		
Anterior belly	Elevates the hyoid if the mandible be fixed. Depresses the mandible if the hyoid be fixed.	V cranial nerve
Posterior belly	Elevates the hyoid bone and draws it in a posterior direction. If the anterior belly acts, also, the hyoid is only elevated.	VII cranial nerve
Stylohyoid	Elevates hyoid bone and draws it in a posterior direction.	VII cranial nerve
Mylohyoid	Elevates hyoid bone and tongue and moves them anteriorly. De-	V cranial nerve

presses the mandible if the hyoid be fixed.

Geniohyoid — Same as mylohyoid. C 1, 2

THE MUSCLES OF THE PHARYNX

Superior pharyngeal constrictor
Middle pharyngeal constrictor
Inferior pharyngeal constrictor
Stylopharyngeus
Salpingopharyngeus

In general, the constrictor fibers of the muscular coat of the pharynx are flat and inserted into the median raphe on the posterior aspect of the pharynx. The raphe is formed by the interlacing of the tendinous fibers of the muscles of the opposite side; it extends downward from the pharyngeal tubercle on the basilar process of the occipital bone. The inferior constrictor overlaps the middle constrictor and the middle, the superior.

Superior pharyngeal constrictor (constrictor pharyngis superior; cephalopharyngeus; gnathopharyngeus)

Origin: Palate bone, internal pterygoid plate, pterygomandibular ligament or raphe, alveolar process of jaw, and side of tongue.
Insertion: Posterior median raphe.
Innervation: Pharyngeal plexus.[6]
Action: Contracts pharynx, as in swallowing.

Buccopharyngeus. Part of superior pharyngeal constrictor arising from the pterygomandibular ligament. Really the posterior edge of buccinator muscle.

Mylopharyngeus. A part of the superior pharyngeal constrictor arising from the mylohyoid ridge of the mandible.

Pterygopharyngeus. A portion of the superior pharyngeal constrictor arising from the internal pterygoid plate.

Glossopharyngeus. A part of the superior pharyngeal constrictor arising from the floor of the mouth.

Middle pharyngeal constrictor (constrictor pharyngis medius; hyopharyngeus)

Origin: Cornua of hyoid, and stylohyoid ligament.
Insertion: Posterior median raphe.

[6] The pharyngeal plexus is formed by branches from the Glossopharyngeal (IX), Pharyngeal branch of Vagus (X), and from the superior Cervical ganglion of the sympathetic.

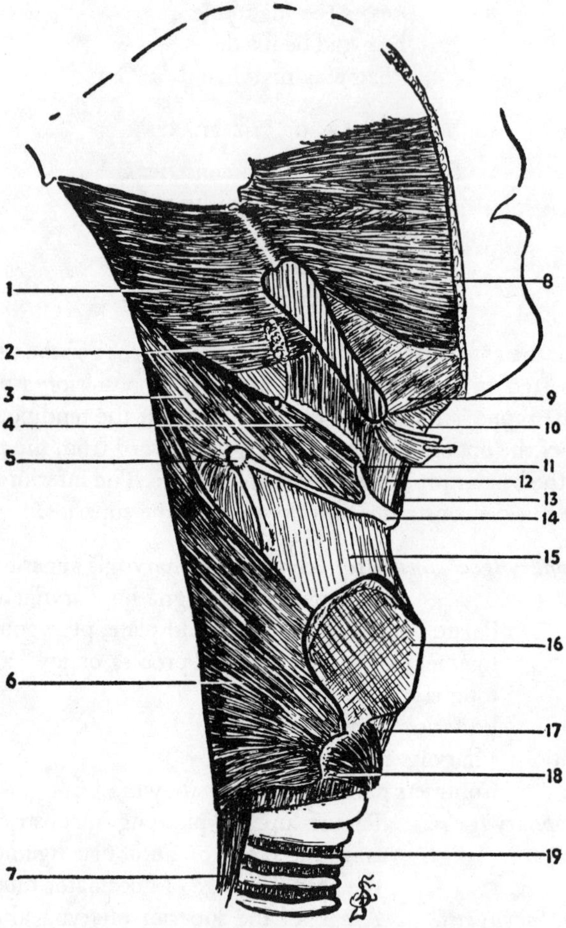

FIG. 28. Pharyngeal Musculature.

1. Superior pharyngeal constrictor; 2. styloglossus; 3. middle pharyngeal constrictor; 4. stylohyoid ligament; 5. greater cornu of the hyoid; 6. inferior pharyngeal constrictor; 7. esophagus; 8. buccinator; 9. mandible; 10. mylohyoid; 11. lesser cornu of the hyoid; 12 hyoglossus; 13. geniohyoid; 14. body of hyoid; 15. hyothyroid membrane; 16. thyroid cartilage; 17. middle cricothyroid ligament; 18. cricothyroid; 19. trachea.

Innervation: Pharyngeal plexus.
Action: Contracts diameter of pharynx, as in swallowing.

Ceratopharyngeus. (Keratopharyngeus) A portion of the middle pharyngeal constrictor arising from the greater cornu of the hyoid bone.

Chondropharyngeus. A portion of the middle pharyngeal constrictor arising from the lesser cornu of the hyoid bone.

Inferior pharyngeal constrictor (constrictor pharyngis inferior; laryngopharyngeus)

Origin: Cricoid and thyroid cartilages.
Insertion: Posterior median raphe. The lower fibers of the muscles are almost horizontal and are continuous with the muscular coat of the esophagus. The upper fibers ascend obliquely.
Innervation: Pharyngeal plexus, and external and recurrent laryngeal (X).
Action: Contracts diameter of pharynx, as in swallowing.

Cricopharyngeus. A part of the inferior constrictor which arises from the cricoid cartilage.

Thyropharyngeus. A slip of the inferior constrictor which arises from the oblique line on the lateral surface of the thyroid cartilage.

Stylopharyngeus

Origin: Styloid process of temporal bone.
Insertion: Side of pharynx between the middle and superior constrictors. Some fibers join the palatopharyngeus and are inserted into the posterior border of the thyroid cartilage.
Innervation: Glossopharyngeal (IX).
Action: Raises and dilates pharynx. Raises larynx.

Stylolaryngeus. A portion of the stylopharyngeus which is inserted into the thyroid cartilage.

Salpingopharyngeus

Origin: Cartilaginous end of Eustachian tube near orifice.
Insertion: Posterior part of pharyngopalatinus.
Innervation: Pharyngeal plexus.
Action: Narrows fauces.

SUMMARY OF FUNCTION AND INNERVATION OF MUSCLES ASSOCIATED WITH THE PHARYNX

Muscle	*Function*	*Innervation*[7]
Superior pharyngeal constrictor	Constricts superior portion of the pharynx at the same time depressing it somewhat.	Pharyngeal plexus
Middle pharyngeal constrictor	Constricts middle portion of pharynx.	Pharyngeal plexus

[7] The innervation of the laryngeal and pharyngeal musculature is still not known definitely. Probably the upper pharyngeal plexus is partly IX, the majority of it X, and the laryngeal branches XI. Some neurologists claim that practically all of it is XI.

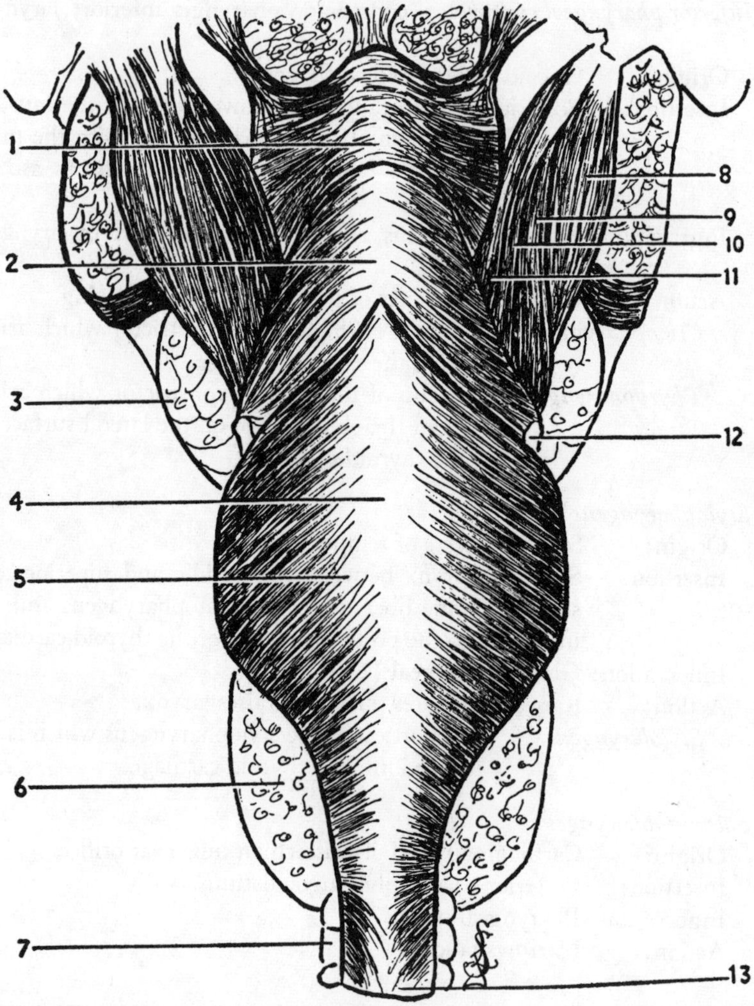

Fig. 29. Pharyngeal Constrictors.

1. Superior pharyngeal constrictor; 2. middle pharyngeal constrictor; 3. submaxillary gland; 4. pharyngeal raphe; 5. inferior pharyngeal constrictor; 6. thyroid gland; 7. trachea; 8. diagastric; 9. stylohyoid; 10. styloglossus; 11. stylopharyngeus; 12. greater cornu of the hyoid; 13. esophagus.

Inferior pharyngeal constrictor	Constricts inferior portion of pharynx.	Pharyngeal plexus
Stylopharyngeus	Elevates pharynx and increases its transverse diameter. Ele-	IX cranial nerve

	vates larynx (thyroid cartilage).	
Salpingopharyngeus	Elevates superior portion of pharynx.	Pharyngeal plexus

The Pharyngeal Cavity as a Resonator

The pharyngeal resonator has these layers: mucous membrane, a fibrous aponeurosis, and the muscular coat of the overlapping pharyngeal constrictors. As a whole, the resonator is subject to alterations in size and shape due to a number of direct or indirect muscle movements. The tongue root may move in to reduce the size. The action of the superior, middle, and inferior constrictors together with thyrohyoid, stylopharyngeal, and pharyngopalatal muscles brings about a diminution of size in all dimensions and at the same time almost obliterates the orifice connecting the pharynx with the oral cavity. It is possible that the nasal quality which is sometimes associated with the naso-oral passages is due in reality to the formation of a small, high-pitched resonance cavity in the pharynx by the constriction of some portion of the tube.

The laryngopharynx is extremely flexible. Its bore and length may be readjusted rapidly. Its surfaces may vary from degrees of laxness to degrees of tenseness. The oropharynx is as flexible as the laryngopharynx. In addition to its own great structural advantages, the adjacent tongue and faucial musculature may by its alterations give further variety to the size and shape of the oropharynx. The nasopharynx is almost constant in shape and volume above, but its lower pharyngeal wall and soft palatal floor are constantly changing their relationships and degree of tenseness. Because of its size, its flexibility, and its possible adjustments described above, the pharyngeal cavity is one of the primary resonators of the voice and speech mechanism.

4. ORAL CAVITY [8]

The mouth may be considered as a single resonator if the tongue lies relaxed on the floor of the cavity as in the production of the sound [ʌ]. Or it may be considered a multiple resonator when the tongue divides the cavity into two cavities connected by a small aperture, as in the production of the sound [i]. In the latter case, the size and length of the aperture connecting the cavities is as variable as the possible combinations of shapes which the tongue may take. Other possible subdivisions within the mouth cavity include that between tongue and palate, that between tongue and teeth or lips, and that between teeth and lips. The importance of these alterations will be appreciated in the discussion of vowels which follows in another section of this chapter.

[8] The anatomy of this region will be considered in detail in Chapter IV.

The resonating properties of the oral cavity are easily demonstrated in whistling. In whistling, the orifice of the lips, partially closed by the action of the orbicularis oris musculature, is nonvibrating. The same condition prevails in whistling "through the teeth." The pitch of the whistle is determined by the resonator—that is, upon its volume and the area of its orifice. The sudden expansion of the air released under pressure through a small orifice, or friction noises caused by the rush of air particles over the sharp edges of the teeth, set the air in the resonator into sympathetic vibration. By varying the positions of the cheeks and tongue, to alter the volume of the resonator, and/or by moving the lips or jaw, to change the size of the orifice, the pitch of the whistle may be varied from approximately 512 ~ to 2048 ~.

Early investigators had easy access to the mouth cavity in the living subject, but the pharynx and larynx remained practically unstudied. Because of this fact, in most early vowel theories the mouth was considered the resonator and the tongue the mobile structure which could divide the cavity into two resonators. It was noted that the farther back in the mouth the point of constriction was located, the lower was the pitch of the anterior cavity and the higher the pitch of the posterior cavity. X-ray photographs tend to indicate that sounds, recognized by the ear to be the same, can be formed by the tongue in so many different positions that no longer is one justified in assigning to the tongue an invariable position in the formation of any given sound.

5. NOSE

The Anatomy of the Nose and Nasal Sinuses

The internal nose consists of a large general cavity extending from the floor of the cranium to the roof of the oral cavity. A median wall (*septum*) divides the cavity into two *nasal fossae*. In from 50 to 90 per cent of adults, the septum is deviated from the median plane, thus decreasing one nasal fossa and increasing the other. In front the fossae open into the vestibules and, thence, to the exterior through the nares (anterior nares); dorsally, they communicate with the nasal part of the pharynx through the choanae (posterior nares).[9] On their lateral walls may be seen the nasal conchae or turbinates (superior, middle, and inferior) which incompletely divide the fossae into nasal meatuses. Above the superior concha is the orifice of the sphenoidal sinus. Between the superior and middle conchae is a nasal passage, the *superior meatus,* into which opens the posterior ethmoidal sinus. Between the middle and inferior conchae is a nasal passage, the *middle meatus,* into which open the middle ethmoidal sinus, the anterior ethmoidal sinus, the frontal sinus, and the maxillary sinus. Below the in-

[9] Each nares and each choana presents an opening having an average area of 3.5 sq. cm. Both nares: 7 sq. cm.; both choanae: 7 sq. cm.

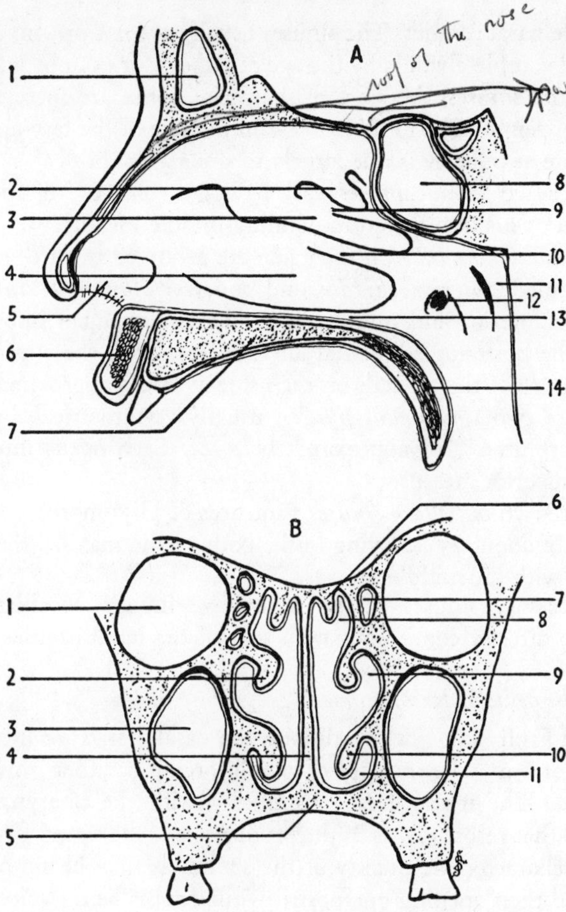

FIG. 30. The Nasal Cavities.

A. Lateral wall of nasal cavity. 1. Frontal sinus; 2. superior concha; 3. middle concha; 4. inferior concha; 5. vestibule of nose; 6. lip; 7. hard palate; 8. sphenoidal sinus; 9. superior meatus; 10. middle meatus; 11. pharyngeal recess; 12. aperture of Eustachian tube; 13. inferior meatus; 14. soft palate.

B. Coronal section through nasal cavities. 1. Contents of orbit; 2. middle concha; 3. maxillary sinus; 4. septum of nose; 5. hard palate; 6. superior concha; 7. ethmoidal air cell; 8. superior meatus; 9. middle meatus; 10. inferior concha; 11. inferior meatus.

ferior concha is the *inferior meatus,* into which opens the nasolacrimal duct.

The *roof* of the nasal cavity is made up of parts of these bones, from anterior to posterior: nasal, frontal, ethmoid, sphenoid. The anterior three-fourths of the *floor* is made up of the palatine process of the maxilla; the posterior one-fourth by the horizontal plate of the palatine bone.

The *nasal sinuses* (sinus paranasales; air sinuses; paranasal sinuses; pneumatic cavities) are a result of the budding outward (evagination) of the walls of the nasal cavities. The sinuses usually are not present at birth and are formed completely only by the age of puberty or even by adulthood. By means of the sinuses, the sizes of the facial bones are increased without increase in weight. The rapid increase in the size of the face and especially of the palate at puberty is due largely to sinus growth.

There are two *frontal sinuses,* each having a volume [10] of approximately 20 cc. Each opens into the corresponding middle meatus.

The *ethmoidal air cells* on each side are arranged in three aggregations and are named, *anterior, middle,* and *posterior ethmoidal sinuses,* respectively. The anterior and middle ethmoidal sinuses open into the middle meatus. The posterior ethmoidal air cells open into the superior meatus. The volume [10] of the air cells on each side averages approximately 7.5 cc.

There are two *sphenoidal sinuses,* usually asymmetrical, but having a combined volume [10] of approximately 20 cc. Each opens into the corresponding superior meatus.

There are two *maxillary sinuses* (antrums of Highmore), each having a volume [10] of about 25 cc. Lying in the body of the maxilla, the sinus communicates with the middle meatus.

The accessory sinuses of the nose have linings of ciliated mucous membrane directly continuous with that of the nasal cavities.

The Nasal Fossae as Resonators

Except for physiological conditions, the nasal fossae are little subject to alteration and may be thought of as reinforcing a rather limited band of frequencies. The fossae are in continuity with the pharynx and when coupled to that resonator, as in the production of the sound [m], definitely affect the characteristic quality of the sound, as may be simply tested by closing and then opening one nostril while [m] is being voiced.[11]

The air of the nasal fossae may be set in motion by vibrations of their floor (the hard palate) if that structure has been set into vibration by sound waves in the oral cavity or by bone conduction.

The Nasal Sinuses as Resonators

That the total volume of all of the nasal sinuses is considerable may be shown by making casts of the cavities. However, the small volume of the individual sinuses—made smaller in the living body by epithelial tissue and secretions—as well as their small apertures, leads us to conclude that the nasal sinuses play no important role in normal speech volume or quality.

[10] Volumes vary so greatly that even though our figures are based on the careful studies of Schaeffer they must be considered only as loose approximations.

[11] By the term *nasality* we mean that the nasal cavity is being used as a resonator coupled directly to the pharyngeal resonator. This is rhinolalia aperta.

A word of summary: The resonators of the human body which have just been described have one of two effects, if any, on sounds generated in the air tract: (*a*) they may serve to reinforce or accentuate certain frequencies or (*b*) they may tend to damp out, absorb, or destroy certain frequencies. If we force a complex sound through a cavity lined with hard surfaces it will not, after its passage through the cavity, be the same as if we had forced it through a cavity lined with soft surfaces. Hard surfaces are friendly to high-frequency partials; soft surfaces are less friendly to high frequencies. When a number of resonators are involved, it is difficult to determine just how many possible combinations of effects may result—the more so, when we consider that certain of the resonators are undergoing momentary, fluctuating changes in their various aperture and cubic dimensions, in their surface characteristics, and in their multiple coupling relations one to another. Add to this, also, the fact that the resonators may respond with sympathetic as well as forced vibrations and it is apparent that the possibility of variations and modifications of speech sounds must be infinite.

VOWELS THE BASIS OF SPEECH

Speech sounds have individual characteristics by which they may be differentiated one from another. Primarily, the sounds utilized in speaking are dependent for their characteristics upon the resonating cavities of the speaker. They are wholly dependent upon the concomitant coupling relations of generator and resonators. Because vowels form the basis of spoken language, we shall consider them first in our study of resonance. Vowels are easily distinguishable because of differences in quality. From one point of view, we might even say that vowels are only various voice qualities to which we have arbitrarily given names and which we make use of in speech.

A. Some Theories of Vowel Production

The manner in which vowels are formed has long been a subject of controversy, mainly because earlier experimenters did not have at their disposal our highly refined modern recording equipment and, also, because often when investigators look at the same thing from different points of view, there arise "schools of thought" on the subject!

1. THE HARMONIC OR RELATIVE-PITCH THEORY OF VOWEL PRODUCTION [12]

At the laryngeal generator, complex sound waves are produced which are composed of fundamentals and a rich supply of harmonics.[13] Certain

[12] These investigators are thought of as contributing to this theory: Wheatstone, 1837; Helmholtz, 1885; Miller, 1916.

[13] Harmonic tones are exact multiples of the fundamental tone.

of the frequencies of these sound waves correspond closely to the natural resonant characteristics of certain of the human resonators. Such frequencies will be reinforced by these resonators; other frequencies will not be reinforced. The amount of amplification will depend upon the damping constant of the cavity. The particular frequency regions reinforced determine the quality of the individual vowel. Because the resonators differ somewhat for each sound produced, it follows that for each sound there will be distinguishable differences of the frequency regions accentuated. Thus, although the resonators themselves add no new tones, they so reinforce and emphasize definite portions of the total sound complex that the listener may sort out vowels into distinguishable families. Such families of speech sounds are called phonemes.

2. THE CAVITY-TONE OR FIXED-PITCH THEORY OF VOWEL PRODUCTION [14]

At the laryngeal generator, complex sound waves are produced which are composed of fundamentals and a rich supply of harmonics. These frequencies, however, do not necessarily correspond to the natural frequencies of the resonators. The puffs of air from the glottic mechanism [15] set into vibration the air of the resonating cavities, just as happens if you blow a blast of air over the edge of a small empty vial. As a result, each cavity produces its own natural tone, a tone which is fixed for a cavity having those particular characteristics.[16] Each new puff which is released excites the resonators; the effect of any one puff is probably extremely transient. The cavity tones thus produced may or may not be in harmonic relation to the glottal tones. In other words, according to this theory, the vowel is composed of two tones, (*a*) that produced by the cavities and which need not have been related or dependent on the glottal tone, and (*b*) that produced at the glottis.[17] Each vowel has its own distinguishing characteristics; they are primarily dependent upon the cavity tones, rather than upon the glottal tones. In part, at least, this theory may be tested by forming the air tract mold for a given vowel, e. g., [ɑ], and then blowing compressed air through a small tube into the oral cavity.

Regardless of theory, we reiterate that vowels may be distinguished one from another because each has its own peculiar frequencies.

[14] These early investigators are usually associated with the theory: Dodart, 1700; Willis, 1829; Scripture, 1902.

[15] Early investigators believed that the puffs were not necessarily produced with any degree of periodicity, hence the theory was known, also, as the *inharmonic theory.* Our more complete knowledge of the larynx indicates that if puffs are produced by the glottic lips the puffs will be produced rhythmically.

[16] More than a hundred years ago, Wheatstone demonstrated that the air in a resonator may vibrate in parts (partials) as well as as a whole (fundamental). Thus more than a single pitch may be reinforced at the same time by the same resonator.

[17] Some of the glottal overtones may be reinforced by cavities tuned to their frequencies as in the relative-pitch theory. In that case three factors would go to make up the vowel sound: glottal tone, resonated overtones, and cavity tones.

3. A COMPARISON OF THE THEORIES OF VOWEL PRODUCTION

That there is not much difference in these theories of vowel production is made apparent by a study of the following comparative chart.

Relative-Pitch Theory	*Cavity-Tone Theory*
1. Puffs of air are released regularly at the glottis, producing a complex sound wave. This original tone consists of fundamental and harmonic frequencies.	1(*a*). Same as for relative-pitch theory. 1(*b*). These frequencies may or may not correspond to the natural frequencies of the resonating cavities.
2. Certain of the original frequencies that correspond closely with what happen to be, also, the natural frequency characteristics of the mouth cavity, pharynx cavity, etc., are resonated by these cavities.	2. The puffs set into vibration the air of the pharynx cavity, mouth cavity, etc., and these resonator cavities respond with tones depending entirely upon the characteristics of the particular resonator or its coupling relations to other resonators.
3. For each vowel, the cavities are characteristic, and hence the particular frequencies that will be resonated will be different. The remaining original frequencies are not reinforced, but still constitute a definite part of the total vowel sound complex.	3. For each vowel, the cavities are characteristic, and hence the particular resonator tones are themselves characteristic.
4. Hence, each vowel is characterized by a definite quality due, in part, to unreinforced glottal tone and, in part, to reinforced glottal tone.	4. The complex sum total of the cavity tones plus the sounds produced by the vibrating vocal folds provide the characteristic vowel quality of each vowel.

B. Vowels—General Considerations

It is an aid to the understanding of vowel production, if we produce a whispered [ʌ]. Inasmuch as there is no laryngeal tone or voice, it would seem to follow that the quality of that vowel must be due to the resonant characteristics of the air tract cavities. Also, if we whisper other vowels they differ because of the differences of the cavities. If, for example, one whispers the vowel series [u], [ɑ], [i], it must be observed that for each vowel there is, because of the cavity tone, characteristically, a progressively higher frequency. Likewise, it is easy to demonstrate the part played by resonance in the production of voiced vowel sounds. Make the voiced sound [u]. Notice the shape assumed by the lips; the position of the tongue in the oral cavity; the degree of tension of the pharyngeal region. Attempt to keep the same mold as if to make [u], but instead make the voiced sound [ɑ]. The lips assume another shape; the tongue moves to occupy a different position on the floor of the mouth; there are different pharyngeal tensions. Try to keep the same mold as if to make [ɑ], but instead make the sonant [i]. Again, there are different adjustments of the resonators. Now produce the sound [u] and move through the [ɑ] position to the [i] position. Repeat, noticing that the [w] sound is heard, combining to form [wi]. Progressing backward from [i] to [u], the [j] is heard, combining to form [ju].

Only the ability of the ear to distinguish the separate sounds places limitations on the otherwise infinite number of vowels which can be made by varying the resonators.

C. The Production of Vowel Sounds

Vowels are produced when the sound waves generated by the laryngeal vibrator are forced through the resonators of the air tract and escape through a relatively large oral orifice with few or no accompanying friction noises.

If it be true, as we believe it to be, that for every vowel sound the degree of elasticity of the vocal folds and the width of the glottis is directly correlated with the fundamental resonance frequency of the sound, then it is probably true, also, that every vowel sound is produced by a set of integrated muscle movements co-ordinating the activity of all parts of the coupled generator-resonator system. In other words, resonance does not just happen; it is not purely passive. The movements of adjustment of the resonators are as active as, and are correlated with, the movements of the laryngeal vibrator. In the production of vowel sounds—as well as other speech sounds—we are dealing with a dynamic totalitarian mechanism.

All vowels require a minimum of three modifications of the physiological airway and foodway systems for their production:

(1) The oral orifice is open in some degree, i. e., the mandible is depressed.

(2) The oropharynx-nasal aperture is closed completely or in some degree.

(3) The vocal folds are approximated to the degree of phonation.

In addition to these, other modifications are required progressively as we proceed from [ʌ] in the production of the so-called front vowels, back vowels, and central vowels. The additional modifications are (*a*) changes in the position of the tongue, which alter the emission of the stream of air, and which alter the oral resonator or resonators, and (*b*) allied changes in the coupling combinations of the resonators of the pharynx and larynx with one another and with the other resonating cavities.

In the production of the vowel [ʌ] only the minimum modifications are required. The tongue lies fairly dormant in the floor of the mouth. The mandible is depressed approximately 1.0 cm.

1. THE FRONT VOWELS

In the so-called front vowel series the mandible is raised progressively toward the maxilla, and there is a resulting or, at least, accompanying narrowing of the oral orifice between the lips. The tongue, likewise, moves progressively upward and forward so that the oral cavity is divided by the tongue mass into two cavities—the anterior cavity growing progressively smaller while, relatively, the posterior cavity is progressively enlarged. In addition to the alterations in the size of the cavities, the orifice formed between the tongue and the hard palate and teeth and connecting the two cavities undergoes variations in size. These coupled cavities act as resonators. The degree of tenseness of the walls of the resonators—e.g., the cheeks—varies with each sound.

THE FRONT VOWEL SERIES

Vowel	*Key words*	*Opening of oral orifice between lips*	*Relation of mandible to maxilla*	*Position of tongue compared to position of rest*
[a]	ask [ask]	widest in the series	depressed 1.5 cm.	forward and upward
[æ] [ɛ] [e] [ɪ]	cat [kæt] get [gɛt] debris [debri] in [ɪn]	PROGRESSIVELY NARROWED AND RETRACTED	PROGRESSIVELY DECREASING DEPRESSION	PROGRESSIVELY MOVED FORWARD AND UPWARD
[i]	green [grin]	narrowest in the series	depressed 0.2 cm.	greatest extent of forward and upward movement

2. THE BACK VOWELS

In the so-called back vowel series the mandible is raised progressively, if somewhat irregularly, toward the maxilla, and the back of the tongue is drawn back and up toward the soft palate. The front of the tongue is depressed and drawn back with each related movement of the back of the tongue. The anterior cavity of the mouth increases in size with each sound in the series while, relatively, the back cavity decreases in size. The aperture between the two resonating cavities is decreased in size and is smallest for the vowel [u].

THE BACK VOWEL SERIES

Vowel	*Key words*	*Opening of oral orifice between lips*	*Relation of mandible to maxilla*	*Position of tongue compared to position of rest*
[ɔ]	cloth	LIPS	A	THE BACK
	[klɔθ]	PROGRESSIVELY		OF THE TONGUE
		MORE PROTRUDED	PROGRESSIVELY	DRAWN
[o]	notion	AND		PROGRESSIVELY
	[noʃan]	ROUNDED	DECREASING	BACKWARD AND
		WITH		UPWARD WHILE
[ʊ]	foot	DECREASED SIZE	DEPRESSION	THE FRONT
	[fʊt]	OF		OF THE TONGUE
		ORIFICE	OF THE	IS DEPRESSED AND
[u]	boot			RETRACTED
	[but]		MANDIBLE	

In a sense [u] and [i] represent the limits of the vowel sounds, for in producing them the air tract is highly constricted. Further constriction would lead us into the realm of the consonants. It is this constriction, at the lips for [u] and between the tongue and palate for [i] that produces these results: (1) because of the blockage in producing [u] and [i] they cannot be heard for as great distances as [ɑ], for example, and (2) bone conduction for [u] and [i] is better than for other vowels. This may be tested by closing the ears while sounding the various vowels. The difference between [i] and [ɑ] is striking.[18]

3. THE CENTRAL VOWELS

In the so-called central vowel series there is to be found a progressively smaller oral orifice, a decrease in the depression of the mandible, and a related elevation of the central portion of the tongue.

CENTRAL VOWEL SERIES

Vowel	*Key words*	*Opening of oral orifice between lips*	*Relation of mandible to maxilla*	*Position of tongue compared to position of rest*
[ɑ]	father	Largest aperture	Depressed	Slight elevation of
	[fɑðɚ]	in the series	2.0 cm.	central portion of
			Depressed	tongue
[ʌ]	up [ʌp]	ORIFICE	1.0 cm.	
		BETWEEN LIPS	DEPRESSION OF	CENTRAL PORTION
[ɜ]	bird [bɜd] [19]	BECOMES	MANDIBLE	OF TONGUE PRO-
		PROGRESSIVELY	DECREASES	GRESSIVELY ELE-
[ɝ]	early [ɝlɪ]	SMALLER	PROGRESSIVELY	VATED

[18] Incidentally, the vowels [i], [u], and [ɑ] which produce the maximum sound differences in the ear may be considered as basic vowels from which others are derived. They are the only vowels represented in hieroglyphs and in Indian and Arabic writing, according to C. Hellwag (1781).

[19] Southern and Eastern pronunciation. See Chapter V.

The tendency in English is for the individual to make a vowel sound in the easiest way, with the least expenditure of muscular movement. The vowel [ʌ] represents the sound requiring a minimum expenditure of energy. All vowels tend, therefore, toward becoming somewhat like [ʌ]. Or, to put it another way, there is a tendency for the mandible, lips, and tongue to approach the position for [ʌ] even while making another vowel.[20]

The vowelized *r* [ɝ] [21] is closely related to the sound [r] phoneme. Somewhat similar, also, is the [l] phoneme. In the latter sound, the air is emitted laterally. Normally, no other English speech sound is so formed. In practice there are at least two *l* sounds, the dark *l* and the clear *l*. The dark *l* [ɫ] is formed with the tip of the tongue farther back in the oral cavity in about the position for [k]. The *l* in *clock* [k ɫ ɑ k] is dark. The clear *l* [l] is formed with the tip of the tongue in about the position for [t]. The *l* in *cattle* [k æ t l] is clear.

Diphthongs, double vowels in a stereotyped combination (e.g., [ɔɪ]), are produced when the resonators are first put in position for one vowel, and then, while continuing the sound, change their position to that necessary in the formation of another vowel (e.g., [ɔ] to [ɪ] as in *oil* [ɔɪl]).

D. The Duration of Vowels

In Chapter II, the *A, B, C, D* positions of the glottis were described and it was shown that various sounds are produced as movements are made from one glottal position to another. The most common position of the glottis before beginning to produce a speech sound is the *D* position. If we produce a vowel sound, a little thought will tell us that it will take some time to produce the sound. This period of time may be divided into three parts: (*a*) the *period of starting,* during which the vocal folds move into the phonative position and produce the initial puff of air, (*b*) the *middle period,* during which the sound is being formed, and (*c*) the *period of finishing,* during which the folds move from the position of the last puff back to the *D* position. On the basis of work by Crandall and Fletcher, we may say that the duration of the average isolated vowel is approximately 0.3 second; of which 0.05 second is occupied in starting, 0.175 second in the middle, and 0.075 second in finishing. Although these figures are but approximations, they do give some idea of the time-movement in space relations of speech sounds.

If the time taken to begin or approach a vowel sound is extremely slow,

[20] To be more accurate, the tendency is toward [ə]—the schwa vowel or unstressed form.

[21] As Kantner and West have done in their book on *Phonetics,* so we have also modified Kenyon in using [ɝ] for the vowelized *r*. An older symbol [ɚ] is also still widely used. The symbols are synonymous.

laryngeal friction noises occur. The resulting sound is called [h]. Any vowel may be approached in this way.

E. Resonators and Frequency Areas

The resonance characteristics of vowels, and, in fact of all voiced sounds, are astonishingly stable, within limited ranges, and easily explainable. Those voiced sounds which issue from the mouth without any complete stoppage of the sound flow or of the air flow are *continuants*. Those which suffer some stoppage of their stream or of the sound pattern before emission are known as *stops*. All of these sounds pass through two major resonating cavities, namely, the pharynx and the mouth, and oscillograph records of the sounds, upon analysis, show that each is characterized by two major frequencies. The argument is that each resonator is responsible for one of the frequency areas.

Characteristic Reinforced Frequency Areas of Certain English Sounds

(A composite table based on the findings of Crandall, Paget, Miller, and Fletcher. These frequencies should be related to those shown on page 157.)

Sound	*Low Frequency Area*	*High Frequency Area*	
[i] peat	320–384	2304–2560	
[ɪ] pit	320–480	2048–2304	
[ɛ] pet	480–576	1706–2048	
[æ] pat	576–853	1706–2048	
[ɑ] palm	682–853	1152–1365	
[ɔ] fall	512–640	853–960	
[ʊ] foot	320–480	853–1152	
[u] food	384–426	576–853	
	Pharyngeal Cavity Resonance Area	*Oral Cavity Resonance Area*	*Nasal Cavity Resonance Area*
[m]	240–341	853–1706	576
[n]	192–256	1365–2048	576
[ŋ]	192–256	2304–2560	576

Two resonators may be coupled by an aperture so large that, in effect, the two resonators become a single resonator. Sounds passing through the two cavities will show the resonance effects of having been reinforced by a single cavity. Beginning with Helmholtz and receiving verification by Miller, the vowels on one side of the so-called vowel triangle, i. e., [u], [ʊ], [o], [ɔ], [ɑ], [ɒ], are said to be singly-resonant. Those on the other side of the triangle, namely, [a], [æ], [ɛ], [e], [ɪ], [i] are said to be doubly-resonant. Produce one of the singly-resonant vowels and notice that the tongue does not divide the oral cavity into two cavities; notice, also, that the oral cavity is quite continuous with the pharynx. Now, produce one of the doubly-resonant vowels. The tongue divides the anterior oral cavity by a narrowed aperture from the posterior oral cavity and pharynx.

The terminology singly-resonant and doubly-resonant is misleading, because it conveys the impression that only one frequency area (or two) has been reinforced in a given vowel. Actually, we mean that this is the dominant or outstanding characteristic of the particular vowel picture. In a singly-resonant vowel there may be one or more other frequency areas reinforced, but the percentage of the whole (100 per cent) of the intensity of the sound to be found in the one area is so high (perhaps 95 per cent) that the remainder of the energy is divided among all of the other frequencies and hence seems unimportant. (See Fig. 32.) Actually, the small percentage of energy in some other frequency area may, by its relation to the easily recognized dominant area, be responsible for the particular quality of the vowel. The same argument holds for doubly-resonant vowels. A third or fourth area may be insignificant in percentage value, but significant in determining the quality characteristics of the sound.

Our present belief is that if an analysis of a sound reveals two or three regions of maximal amplitude this means that in the formation of that sound two or three resonators, respectively, were involved. Two maxima ordinarily indicate that the mouth and pharynx cavities have acted as resonators. Three maxima ordinarily indicate that the mouth, pharynx, and nasal cavities have acted as resonators. Obviously, only the limits of the delicacy of the recording and analyzing equipment, and the investigator's scientific imagination, dictate the number of frequencies, plotted as minima, that may be attributed to such potential resonance cavities as the ventricle, nasal sinuses, etc.

EXPERIMENTAL EVIDENCE SUPPORTING RESONANCE THEORIES

So far in our approach to the study of the human resonators we have relied for evidence upon the ear and upon mechanical recording devices in arriving at decisions concerning the effect of the resonators upon speech sounds. We may now consult the evidence resulting from two types of experimentation: that on the animal organism and that of a synthetic nature.

A. Experiments on the Animal Organism

Because of the difficulties of experimenting with the normal human larynx it is impossible to know just how weak would be the voice produced by the vocal folds if it were not for the resonance cavities below and above the glottis. Observations on wounded persons with various types of openings in the neck region, however, and experiments with excised larynges, point toward an agreement that without resonators the laryngeal generator produces only weak sounds. If a larynx be removed from the animal body and be mounted so that a column of air may be directed against the under sides of the vocal folds with a certain pressure, the tension of the folds being held constant, sounds of a definite pitch will be made. Even though the pitch may be identical with that of the animal in life, it is, nevertheless, a weak tone, lacking in quality when compared with the normal.

B. The Production of Synthetic Speech Sounds

The differences of sounds, apparent to the ear, may also be made apparent to the eye by the use of *acoustic spectra*. Just as a prism will break up the white light complex into the colors of the light spectrum, so with analyzing apparatus, the graphic representation of a sound complex may be broken

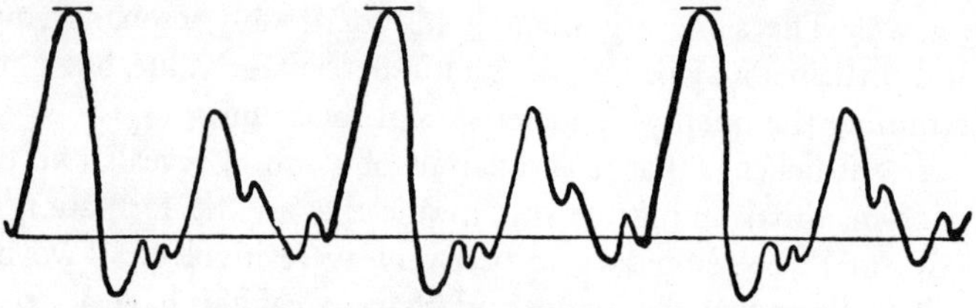

Fig. 31. Oscillograph Record of a Prolonged Vowel Sound.

up into an acoustic spectrum.[22] A complex sound wave, such as that of a vowel, is made up of a fundamental and many partials.

In the analysis of sound we may begin by making an oscillograph record of the sound wave. (See Fig. 31.)

The wave form of the oscillograph record is analyzed by means of an electrical *harmonic analyzer*. The analysis reveals what frequencies went to make up the original sound, and the relative intensity of each pitch. This information, when plotted, gives what is known as the acoustic spectrum of the sound. For example, assuming the total intensity of the complex sound to be 100, we may find that one or two of the partials account for 90 per cent of the total. Such an acoustic spectrum for a vowel might look like Fig. 32. It is not unusual for a vowel to have most of its energy not in the fundamental but rather in two or more upper partials.

If one may take a complex sound wave—for example, of the vowel [i] of *team*—and analyze it into its various simple harmonic components, it seems logical that one may hope, by combining a similar group of components, to produce a sound resembling the original sound. Indeed, such procedures have occupied the time of many scientists. We may illustrate the process

[22] Based on a mathematical principle, Fourier's Theorem (J. B. J. Fourier, 1822).

of the synthetic production of speech sounds. Let us start with Fig. 32 and attempt to produce a synthetic [i]. We may use reed pipes or a pure tone generator to produce each of the frequencies found in the analysis. We need only approximate the pitch, in any case, because the ear will permit a wide divergence and still be capable of identifying the [i] sound. Each reed is set to vibrating by means of a stream of compressed air. Be-

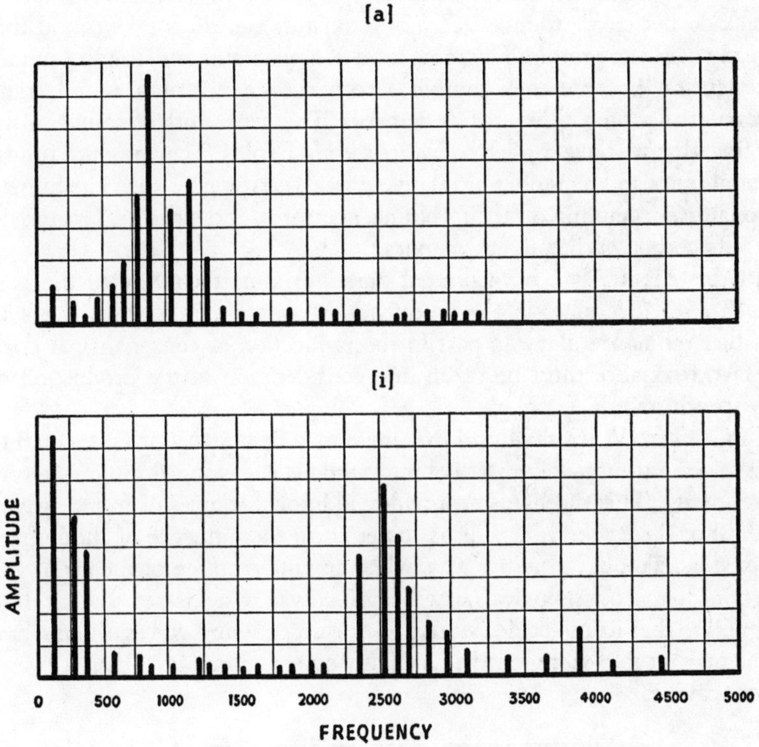

Fig. 32. Acoustic Spectra.

Because no other vowel will give the same spectral picture and because all of the vowels of a given family or phoneme give the same general picture, this method of plotting enables us to differentiate between and among the various vowels.

cause we shall need amplification in the region of approximately 300–400 cycles and in the region of approximately 2500 cycles, we may increase the relative intensity of the tones of these frequencies. Now, if the generators of all the frequencies are set into vibration at the same time, the listener should be able to hear a sound which he will identify as being the vowel [i].

In producing a variety of synthetic sounds, a much more complicated procedure is followed. Most people now know of the speaking robot. In this device, electrical impulses of various frequencies, all amplified many times, are the synthetic speech stuff. After long experimentation, operators of the robot can produce not only all of the vowel sounds but they can initiate, connect, and terminate these sounds in such a way as to produce an easily intelligible speech.

SUMMARY STATEMENT

Our study of the nature of resonance brought out the fact that resonators, alone, do not create sounds. All that resonators can do is take sound that already has been produced by some kind of a generator and amplify certain frequencies. Because they rapidly absorb the energy of a sound train, resonators act on a generator as dampers. The generators of sound in the air tract that we have studied so far are the vocal folds. They produce fundamental tones and overtones of relatively weak carrying power. The human resonators, depending on their volume, apertures, and structural materials, amplify certain of the phonative tones.

In this chapter, we have limited ourselves almost entirely to the part which resonance plays in the production of vowel sounds. This is not to say that resonance plays no part in the production of consonants. It does. In fact, resonance must be taken into consideration in the production of any speech sound.

In Chapter IV, we shall find that there may be obstructions presented to the voiced and non-voiced air column while it is passing through the oronasal cavity. This mechanism provides additional sources of sound waves, and all of these, likewise, will be subjected to the influence of the human resonators. To put it another way, when any interruption of the air in any portion of the physiological airway or foodway systems sets the air into turmoil so that its molecules vibrate to propagate sound waves, those vibrations may set into vibration the air in any one or more of the coupled resonance cavities.

EXERCISES AND QUESTIONS

1. Hold a glass tumbler (preferably one of thin glass) in one hand and tap the bottom of the glass with the other hand. The musical note heard is that due to the resonance of the air in the tumbler, since the glass is prevented from vibrating freely by being held in your hand. Now turn the tumbler so that its mouth faces the palm of the hand which holds it, and tap it as before. The resonant note is now slightly lower than it was. If the mouth of the tumbler is brought progressively nearer and nearer to the palm of the hand—by bending the fingers—the resonant pitch (when the tumbler is struck) becomes progressively lower. Is this a result of changing the volume of the cavity? the size of the orifice? or both?

2. Hold a vibrating tuning fork over a glass tumbler. Gradually pass a paper across the mouth of the glass until at one point the sound of the fork swells out. The air cavity of the glass is now tuned to the fork. Why?

3. Gradually add water to a glass or to a bottle while a vibrating fork of 256 d.v./sec. is held over the aperture. Tune the bottle to the 256 d.v./sec. fork and then sound a 512 d.v./sec. fork over it; tune the bottle to the 512-cycle fork and then place the 256-cycle fork over it. Do you now know whether the tuning forks give simple or complex tones?

4. If recording equipment is available, make a record of the vowel [ɑ] at a low pitch. Play it back at regular speed. Now play it back, but gradually increase the speed of the tape. The vowel is apparently heard as [a] and then as [æ] and its quality is changed. What explanation can you give for these changes? Experiment with other vowels, using various pitches, and sometimes making your recording at lower speeds and sometimes at higher speeds. When the vowel [æ] is made at normal speed and then run at reduced speed, does the vowel [ɑ] result? Explain. Does [bɑ] made at normal speed, become [bɔ], [boʊ], and, finally, [bu], when reproduced at slower and slower speeds? Explain.

5. Make a schema showing all of the possible working resonators of the speech and voice mechanism. What parts, if any, are comparable to: (1) Helmholtz type resonators, (2) closed-end tubes, and (3) tubes open at both ends? Classify these resonators as to whether they (1) respond with forced vibrations or (2) respond with sympathetic vibrations.

6. If it be admitted that the resonant cavities of an individual who, under certain conditions, is in good health and who, under adverse conditions, is in ill health are still the same in size, upon what basis would you explain the differences of voice during health and sickness?

7. Nearly one hundred years ago, Sir Charles Bell wrote, "If on inspecting a musical instrument we should find a spongy body of the consistence of firm flesh in contact with a cord or tube, and an apparatus by which this body might be pressed against the vibrating part, we should not hesitate to conclude that it damped or limited the vibration. The thyroid gland is a vascular, but firm substance, which, like a cushion, lies across the upper part of the trachea." Numerous muscles capable of bracing it to the trachea pass over the gland. "If," he continues, "it be admitted that the vibration of the trachea would only produce a continued drone, rising over the inflections of the voice, and adding nothing to its distinctness, we may perceive in the adjustment of the thyroid gland to the trachea the most suitable means of suffocating or stopping the vibrations from descending along the sides of the tube." Then, appealing to comparative anatomy, Bell observes that in birds, where the sound must ascend the trachea, there is a firm tube of complete circles of cartilage and no thyroid gland to act as a damper! Present a critique of the above.

8. An eminent phonetician has made the claim that all the vowels and all of the consonants except [m], [n], and [ŋ], may be made as whispered sounds by blowing air with a bellows into or across the open mouth while the breath is held. Using a bellows or a source of compressed air, experiment with all of the vowels and consonants in an attempt to verify or disprove the statement. Try tubes of different diameters. Hold the orifice of the tube at different angles in relation to the mouth. What angle and what size tube give the best results?

9. If the claim in question 8, above, be verified in every respect, would we be

justified in concluding that the larynx is not an essential organ of speech? Explain.

10. According to Bell (1910), if one closes the glottis, assumes the vowel position, and strikes gently a piece of wood—e. g., an ordinary lead pencil—held in front of the mouth or against the cheek, there is heard the resonance tone of the mouth cavity. It is a double tone, but that tone due to the anterior cavity is much more prominent than the other. Assume successively the positions for certain vowels, and observe the series of tones produced, first by the anterior cavity and then by the posterior cavity. The difference will be found to be very striking. Attempt to verify Bell's findings. Explain the results of the experiment.

11. What experimental means and what apparatus would you need to prove the truth of the following statement by Paget?

"In whispering the various vowel-sounds, the size of the opening made by the glottis varies directly with the frequency of the lower vowel resonance—the opening being larger for the vowels of high resonance. It is as if the glottal aperture took part in the tuning of the back resonator in order to save the tongue the trouble of making a tighter closure of the central orifice to produce the lower resonances, and vice versa."

Present a critique on the above statement.

12. Elementary Rhinoscopy

Two students. The observer should insert the rhinoscopic mirror into the nasopharynx of the subject.

Make a drawing of the mirror image and identify the structures seen.

13. After determining what resonators of the speech mechanism could be classed as either closed-end tubes, or tubes open at both ends, calculate—from the frequencies—the wave-lengths of the sounds used in your own voice, and compare these wave-lengths with the actual or estimated length of the tube resonators.

14. Plug the ears tightly and whisper the vowels [u], [ʊ], [ɔ], [ɑ], [æ], [ɛ], [ɪ], and [i]. On the basis of what you hear, classify the vowels into groups. Can you determine the location of the chief resonator or resonators involved in the production of each vowel? Explain the results of your experiment.

15. Free all of the strings on a piano from their dampers. Sing [ɑ] at the pitch of middle C. Direct the voice loudly against the sounding board. Many of the strings will respond as the piano "sings back" the [ɑ]. Replace the dampers on all strings except middle C and repeat. What is the difference in the "echo"? Now repeat the experiment several times, each time putting the damper on various strings. What do you discover about the harmonics of the tone of your [ɑ]? Would it be correct to say that a piano can analyze a vowel into its harmonic vibrations? Explain.

16. First, read the following paragraph:

Physical and electrical analogues (analogs) of the physiological vocal tract have been constructed by a number of researchers in attempts to determine whether such equipment will produce recognizable vowels or other speech sounds. Theories are almost as numerous as experimenters. The over-all dimensions of the physical devices, the cross-sectional areas of the coupled resonance systems, the relations of constrictions and the size of apertures—all these and other analogous relations incorporated in the devices are important. Electrical analogues of the physical analogues of the physiological vocal tract utilize current and circuit variations toward the same ends. As far as we know, no one has claimed that his equipment resembles the vocal tract exactly. In some cases, based on the most careful measurements that can be made on the human body, and in other cases, based on best-guessing, the experimenters believe that the dimensions and cross-sectional areas closely approximate those of the human tract. Some researchers take the position that if the synthetic speech sounds produced by a device are so much like humanly-produced sounds as to be indistinguishable to the ears of trained listeners then the device is truly an acceptable analogue. Obviously, there may be fallacies in such reasoning, but careful experimenters attempt to avoid them with proper controls. Without question experimentation along these lines helps advance our knowledge of such devices and of the human mechanisms they represent.

Second, peruse at least two journal articles dealing with vocal tract analogues.

Third, answer the following questions:

(*a*) What is a vocal tract analogue? Explain in your own words, using examples from other fields of human activity.

(*b*) As far as making contributions to the field of speech and voice science is concerned, what differentiates physical analogues and electrical analogues?

(*c*) In your opinion, should a researcher elect to do his experimentation with analogues rather than with the actual vocal tract? Explain your answer, in depth.

(*d*) If you were to give a different answer to the question (*c*) above how could you justify it?

(*e*) What, if anything, limits the research value of using analogues? Develop a rather detailed brief in answering the question.

Chapter IV

ARTICULATION

I. The Anatomy of the Region of the Oral Cavity
  A. The Divisions of the Mouth Cavity
  B. The Tongue
    1. The Extrinsic Muscles of the Tongue
    2. The Intrinsic Muscles of the Tongue
  C. The Muscles of the Palate
  D. The Muscles of Mastication
  E. The Muscles of the Mouth Region
II. The Vowel Links
  A. Consonants
    1. Continuant Fricatives
    2. Stops
  B. Nasals
  C. Vowel Glides
III. Additional Factors in Articulation
  A. The Position of Sounds
  B. Limitation of the Number of Sounds
  C. The Acoustic Perception of Implosions and Explosions
  D. Pressure Pattern Factors
  E. Control of the Tongue
  F. Time Order of Muscle Contractions
IV. Articulatory Evolution
V. Palatography
Exercises and Questions

Speech sounds, other than the vowels which have been described in Chapter III, may be thought of as initiators, connectors, or terminators of vowel sounds—or, as we prefer to say, these speech sounds are vowel links. Such names as stops, glides, continuants, fricatives, and nasals are commonly used to classify the sounds. All of the vowel links rely, as do the vowels, upon a forcibly exhaled breath stream (see Chapter I). Some of the vowel links, as do the vowels, rely upon a *phonated* air stream (see Chapter II). Such vowel links are known as *voiced sounds*. Others do not require that the breath stream be phonated. They are called *voiceless sounds*. All vowel links owe, as do the vowels, some of their individual peculiar acoustic characteristics to resonance (studied in Chapter III). In addition, all vowel links require modifications, other than those already described in the three previous chapters, before each has acquired the entire set of individual characteristics peculiar to itself. These additional modifications we call articulation. *Articulation,* then, is the breaking up or interruption of the phonated or non-phonated breath stream, and, with the important aid of resonance, the finished products are the vowel links.

Articulation takes place within, or because of, structures in or closely connected with the oral cavity. Therefore, for a more complete understanding of articulation, we now describe the anatomy of the region of the oral cavity.

THE ANATOMY OF THE REGION OF THE ORAL CAVITY

A. The Divisions of the Mouth Cavity

The *oral* (buccal) *cavity* is made up of two cavities: an inner and an outer.

The inner mouth cavity has these boundaries:

front and sides:	teeth and gums;
behind:	it opens into the pharynx at the isthmus of the fauces;
top or roof:	hard and soft palate; and
bottom or floor:	mucous membrane, large portion of tongue, mylohyoid muscles, geniohyoid muscles.

The outer cavity, the *vestibule* of the mouth, is bounded by the lips and cheeks externally, and the teeth and gums, internally. It opens upon the surface of the face at the buccal orifice. This rima is between the lips, and its lateral extent is between the angles of the mouth.

The *maxillae,* each consisting of a body and four processes, unite to form the upper jaw. There is a large cavity, the maxillary sinus, in the body of each. Their processes are: alveolar, frontal, palatine, and zygomatic. The palatine process forms much of the roof of the mouth and the floor of the nose. To the maxillae are attached the following muscles: depressor alae nasi, nasalis, caninus, quadratus labii superioris, dilator nares posticus, internal pterygoid, buccinator.

The *mandible,* the bone of the lower jaw, consists of a body with perpendicular rami. The mandible articulates with the two temporal bones by means of its condyles. The projected tip of the mandible is known as the *mental protuberance.* Immediately above it, in the mid-line, is the junction (symphysis) of the two parts of the bone. The horseshoe-shape body gives attachment to these muscles: platysma, mentalis, quadratus labii inferior, triangularis, digastric (anterior belly), mylohyoid, superior pharyngeal constrictor, buccinator, genioglossus, geniohyoid. The rami provide attachment for these muscles: masseter, internal pterygoid, external pterygoid, temporalis.

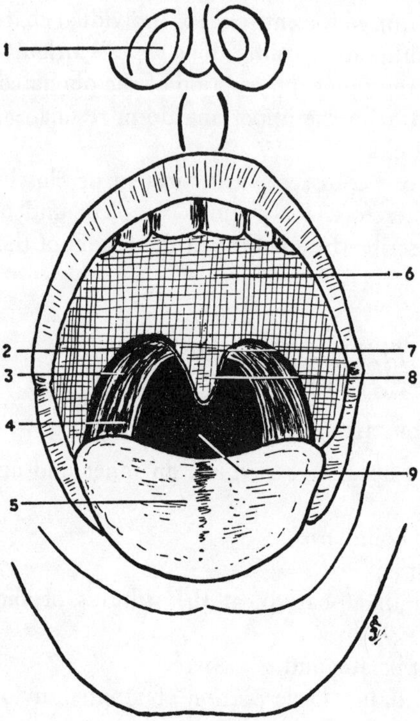

Fig. 33. Structures of the Mouth Cavity.

1. Anterior naris; 2. anterior pillar of fauces; 3. recess of fauces; 4. posterior pillar of fauces; 5. tongue showing median raphe; 6. hard palate; 7. soft palate; 8. uvula; 9. posterior wall of pharynx.

The *gums* (gingivae) are made up of fibrous tissue covering the alveolar processes of the jaws and surrounding the necks of the teeth.

The *permanent teeth* (dentes) of the adult are as follows: 4 incisors, 2 canines, 4 premolars, and 6 molars in each jaw—32 teeth, altogether.

Three large pairs of salivary glands communicate with the mouth, and pour their secretion into its cavity; they are the *parotid, submaxillary,* and *sublingual.*

The roof (palatum) of the mouth is made up of two parts:

The bony *hard palate* is covered by fibrous tissue and mucous membrane. It is limited in front and laterally by the gums; behind, it is continuous with

The *soft palate* (palatum molle), a mobile fold of muscular and aponeurotic tissue invested with mucous membrane and hanging by its upper border from the posterior margin of the hard palate. Laterally, the soft palate is continuous with the pharynx. The lower, free border hanging like a proscenium curtain between the oral cavity and pharynx is known as the *velum* (palatine velum). The uvula is suspended at the middle of the velum. From each side of the uvula, and extending laterally to the pharynx, are the *posterior pillars of the fauces* (faucial arches).

The soft palate, according to most authors, provides a seal between the nasal and oral cavities during the production of all English speech sounds except [m], [n], and [ŋ]. Inasmuch as in normal breathing, the passage between the nasal and bucco-pharyngeal cavities is open, it follows that the movements of the soft palate must have an extremely fine temporal relation to the movements of the other muscles involved in speech. For example, in the production of the plosive [p], the soft palate must move a fraction of a second sooner than the lip muscles so that the exhaled air stream can build up sufficient pressure to produce the "break" of the sound.

Nusbaum tested the velar-pharyngeal seal during the phonation of certain vowels, and found that some or all of the vowels may be made without "nasality" although there be at the time an escape of air through the nose. In fact, some "good" voices probably owe their richness to the use of the additional resonator support afforded by an aperture into the nasal cavity. The experimental procedure was as follows:

Nasal olives, connected to a water manometer and to a source of air under varying degrees of pressure, were fitted into the nostrils. While phonating [i], e.g., air pressure in the nasal cavity was raised until the velar-pharyngeal occlusion broke down, releasing the air into the mouth cavity. The rise in pressure, and the point at which it "broke" were read on the water manometer in millimeters of pressure (H_2O). The breaking point of the pressure, and the condition of "nasality" were checked, simultaneously, with a stethoscope. Unfortunately, the experiment does not indicate what part of the closure is due to velar action, and what part to pharyngeal constrictor contraction.

The *isthmus faucium* is the aperture by which the oral cavity and oropharynx are in communication. Its boundaries, which may be seen by looking in a mirror with the mouth open, are: above, the soft palate; laterally, the glossopalatine arch; and below, the dorsum of the tongue.

There are *pillars* or *arches of the fauces.* On either side, below, they are seen to be separated by a palatine tonsil. The *anterior pillar of the fauces* (glossopalatine arch) is due to the bulge of the glossopalatine muscle with its investing mucous membrane. The *posterior pillar of the fauces* (pharyngopalatine arch) is due to the bulge of the pharyngopalatine muscle with its investing mucous membrane.

The *lips* (labia oris) are the muscular folds bounding the external rima or anterior aperture of the mouth. Their composition is as follows: skin, superficial fascia, orbicularis oris muscle and other muscles inserted around it, areolar tissue, and mucous membrane. A frenulum, the upper being the larger, connects each lip in the median line to its respective gum.

The *cheeks* (buccae) which go to make up the sides of the face have this composition from their outer surface to the inner: skin, superficial fascia, bucco-pharyngeal fascia, buccinator muscle, submucous areolar tissue, mucous membrane.

The attachment of the buccinator muscle to the superior constrictor of the pharynx at the pterygomandibular raphe provides for the continuity of the lateral walls of the oral cavity with the lateral walls of the pharynx.

B. The Tongue

The *tongue* (lingua) is situated in the floor of the mouth. Its *root* (base; radix linguae) is directed backward and has four attachments; namely,

to the soft palate by the glossopalatine arches,
to the pharynx by the superior constrictors,
to the hyoid bone by the hyoglossal muscles, and
to the epiglottis by the glossoepiglottic folds.

Its tip (*apex*) is directed forward against the lingual surfaces of the lower incisors. The upper surface (*dorsum*) of the tongue is convex. It is marked into halves longitudinally by the *median sulcus*. The posterior one-third of the dorsum dips downward in front of the pharynx almost to the level of the hyoid bone and overhangs the epiglottis. The under (inferior) surface of the tongue is connected by the genioglossi to the mandible. The *frenulum linguae* is formed by a fold of mucous membrane which lines the under surface of the tongue and the floor of the mouth. When the mouth is closed, the tongue lies in contact with the palate and almost fills the oral cavity.

Many attempts have been made to give a static picture of the tongue and other related articulatory organs at a given instant during the production of a speech sound. These concepts, usually diagrammed, have been gathered in many ways. During the last fifty years, literature dealing with such studies has shown observers sitting patiently with mirrors in hand, inserting fingers and rulers into their mouths; it has shown them utilizing strips of soft rubber which takes the shape of the tongue. There have been many attempts to utilize fine bent wires, and small rubber balloons have been so placed in the mouth that pressure of the tongue in various places might be graphically recorded. An ingenious application of this form of experimentation utilizes the *tongue tambour*. This is an artificial palate covered with a membranous diaphragm; the air between diaphragm and palate is in direct continuity with a recording tambour. Other attempts to explore tongue movements have been made from outside the mouth. These measures are based on the principle that movements of the floor of the mouth, under the chin, because of its intimate connection with the tongue muscles, are representative of the movements of the tongue.

Before the beginning of the century and continuing up to the present day, the X-ray has been used in the study of the movements of the tongue. Much of the careful, painstaking work of the early experimenters has received confirmation by our more modern methods. The application of high-speed X-ray motion pictures is proving useful, helping us to answer perplexing questions concerning the production of speech sounds.

A median fibrous septum extending the entire length of the tongue divides it into lateral halves. In either half there are extrinsic and intrinsic muscles; the former have their origins outside the tongue, the latter are contained entirely within it. The muscles of the extrinsic group effect changes of position of the mass of the tongue plus changes of form, while the intrinsic muscles influence only the form of the body of the tongue.

1. THE EXTRINSIC MUSCLES OF THE TONGUE

Genioglossus
Hyoglossus
Styloglossus
Palatoglossus (described as the glossopalatinus on page 142)

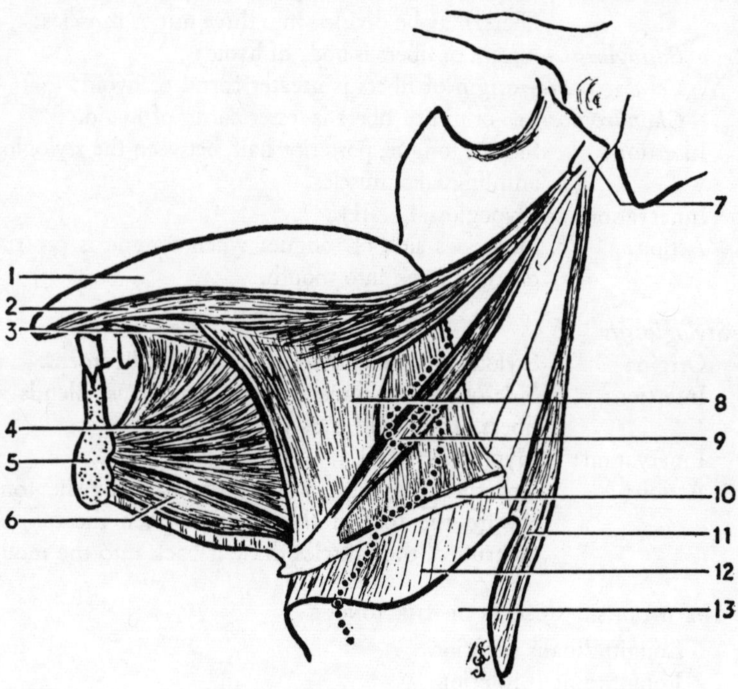

FIG. 34. Extrinsic Muscles of the Tongue.

1. Dorsum of tongue; 2. styloglossus; 3. inferior longitudinal; 4. genioglossus; 5. mandible; 6. geniohyoid; 7. styloid process; 8. hyoglossus; 9. stylohyoid; 10. greater cornu of hyoid; 11. stylopharyngeus; 12. hyothyroid membrane; 13. thyroid cartilage.

Genioglossus (geniohyoglossus)

Origin: Mental spine of mandible.

Insertion: Superior fibers, tongue from root to tip; middle fibers, side of pharynx; inferior fibers, body of hyoid. The fibrous *septum linguae* extends through the middle of the tongue and separates the right genioglossus from its fellow.

Innervation: Hypoglossal (XII).
Action: Superior fibers inserted at root protrude the tongue; superior fibers inserted at tip retract it after protrusion. Inferior fibers aid geniohyoid and anterior belly of digastric in pulling hyoid upward and forward. If hyoid be fixed, they depress the chin. All fibers together depress tongue and groove dorsum.

Hyoglossus
Origin: Body and greater and lesser cornua of hyoid bone. The hyoglossus muscle, depending upon the origin of its fibers, may be divided into three minor muscles:
Basioglossus—origin of fibers is body of hyoid;
Ceratoglossus—origin of fibers is greater cornu of hyoid;
Chondroglossus—origin of fibers is lesser cornu of hyoid.
Insertion: Side of tongue, posterior half, between the styloglossus and lingualis muscles.
Innervation: Hypoglossal (XII).
Action: Depresses side of tongue; when tongue is protruded draws it back into mouth.

Styloglossus
Origin: Styloid process and stylomandibular ligament.
Insertion: Side of tongue, superficial to hyoglossus; blends with fibers of lingualis muscles.
Innervation: Hypoglossal (XII).
Action: Together the muscles raise the back of the tongue toward the roof of the mouth. When the tongue is protruded, the muscles draw it back into the mouth.

2. THE INTRINSIC MUSCLES OF THE TONGUE

Longitudinalis superior
Longitudinalis inferior
Transversus linguae
Verticalis linguae

Longitudinalis superior (longitudinalis linguae superior; superior lingualis; superficial lingual)
Origin: Submucosa and septum of tongue which separates each from its fellow.
Insertion: Edges of tongue.
Innervation: Hypoglossal (XII).
Action: Shortens tongue and makes it wider and thicker; raises its edges and tip; makes dorsum concave.

Longitudinalis inferior (longitudinalis linguae inferior; inferior lingualis; inferior lingual)

Origin:	Hyoid bone and under surface of tongue at base.
Insertion:	Tip of tongue.
Innervation:	Hypoglossal (XII).
Action:	Shortens tongue and makes it wider; pulls apex downward; makes dorsum convex.

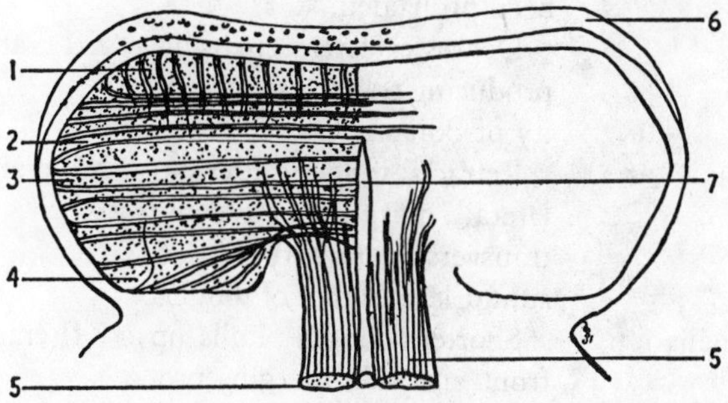

FIG. 35. Intrinsic Muscles of Tongue. Coronal Section of Tongue.

1. Verticalis; 2. transversus; 3. superior longitudinal; 4. inferior longitudinal; 5. genioglossus; 6. mucous membrane of tongue; 7. septum of tongue.

Transversus linguae (transverse lingualis)

Origin:	Median septum of tongue.
Insertion:	Edges of tongue.
Innervation:	Hypoglossal (XII).
Action:	Elongates, narrows, and thickens tongue; lifts its edges.

Verticalis linguae (vertical lingualis)

Origin:	Upper surface of tongue near sides of tip.
Insertion:	Under surface of tongue.
Innervation:	Hypoglossal (XII).
Action:	Widens and flattens tip of tongue.

Direct observation, added to what has been said about the movements caused by the various muscles, will explain the basis of the extraordinary mobility of the tongue. The variety of movement made possible by the simple action of each separate muscle is increased infinitely when several of the muscles act simultaneously or when there is, as in speaking, a rapid succession of simple or compound movements.

SUMMARY OF FUNCTION AND INNERVATION OF THE MUSCLES ASSOCIATED WITH THE TONGUE

Muscle	*Function*	*Innervation*
Genioglossus		
Posterior fibers	Pull root in anterior direction and produce protrusion of apex of tongue.	XII cranial nerve
Anterior fibers	Retracts tongue after it has been protruded.	XII cranial nerve
Hyoglossus	Depresses lateral margins producing transverse convexity of dorsum.	XII cranial nerve
Styloglossus	Retracts tongue. Elevates lateral margins producing transverse concavity of dorsum. Elevates root of tongue.	XII cranial nerve
Longitudinalis superior	Shortens tongue. Pulls up front and side margins producing concavity of dorsum.	XII cranial nerve
Longitudinalis inferior	Shortens tongue. Pulls down front and side margins producing convexity of dorsum.	XII cranial nerve
Transversus linguae	Elongates and narrows tongue.	XII cranial nerve
Verticalis linguae	Broadens anterior half of tongue.	XII cranial nerve

A. *Gross movements of the tongue as a whole.*

Elevated	Elevation of hyoid Mylohyoid
Depressed	Depression of hyoid
Narrowing and elongating	Transversus
Shortening and thickening	Longitudinalis superior Longitudinalis inferior
Elevation of sides of tongue to make dorsum concave	Styloglossi [1]
Depression of sides of tongue to make dorsum convex	Hyoglossi Chrondoglossi

[1] Long fibers.

A. *Gross movements of the tongue as a whole (continued).*

Depression of mid-line region of tongue to make dorsum concave	Genioglossi

B. *Movements of the root of the tongue.*

Elevated	Glossopalatini
Depressed	Genioglossus [1]
Elevated and posteriorly	Styloglossus [2]

C. *Movements of the tip and anterior portion of the tongue.*

Elevated	Longitudinalis superior
Depressed	Longitudinalis inferior Genioglossi [3]
Laterally	Styloglossus [6] Longitudinalis superior [7] Longitudinalis inferior [7] Genioglossi [8]
Flattening or broadening	Verticalis

D. *Movements of root and apex of the tongue.*

Anteriorly, within oral cavity	Genioglossi [4]
Anteriorly, so that apex protrudes in mid-line	Genioglossi [4]
Anteriorly, so that apex protrudes to one side	Genioglossus [5]
Posteriorly, within oral cavity	Genioglossi [3] Styloglossi
Posteriorly, following protrusion	Genioglossi [3] Styloglossi

[1] Posterior fibers acting against anterior fibers.
[2] Short and transverse fibers.
[3] Anterior fibers.
[4] Posterior fibers.
[5] Posterior fibers of the same side; anterior fibers of the opposite side.
[6] Long fibers on side in direction of motion.
[7] Fibers of side in direction of motion.
[8] Anterior fibers of side in direction of motion and posterior fibers of opposite side.

The movements of the tongue above described are autonomous movements, i. e., movements of muscles which either enter into or are contained within the tongue. In addition, there are also numerous passive movements which alter the position of the tongue in relation to other structures. Such movements are imparted to the tongue because it happens to be a part of the floor of the oral cavity. These passive movements of the tongue are important in the articulation of sounds, the more so because they are correlated with movements of the pharynx which alter the resonance characteristics of that tube. The diaphragmatic floor of the oral cavity of the mouth is composed of the mylohyoid muscle. Of secondary interest is the digastric. The mylohyoid muscle crosses from the internal oblique line on one side of the mandible to the similar line on the other side, thus forming the bottom of the oral cavity. It is invested above by the mucous membrane which lines the oral cavity.

The weight of the tongue depresses the diaphragma oris. The attachments of the mylohyoid indicate that contraction of this muscle will produce an elevation of the floor of the oral cavity and, as a result, of the mass of the tongue. The digastric muscle, together with its intermediate tendon, forms a curve, the lowest point of the arc of which is the hyoid bone, from the base of the skull to the mandible. Upon contracting, it raises the hyoid bone, which, in turn, elevates the floor of the oral cavity, thus reinforcing the action of the mylohyoid muscle.

While the digastric and mylohyoid muscles act as elevators of the floor of the oral cavity and larynx, and hence of the tongue, the omohyoid and sternohyoid muscles are antagonists which act to depress the floor of the mouth, the tongue, and the larynx.

C. The Muscles of the Palate

Tensor veli palatini
Levator veli palatini
Glossopalatinus
Pharyngopalatinus
Musculus uvulae

A thin but strong palatine aponeurosis supports the muscles of and gives support to the soft palate. The palatine aponeurosis is attached to the hard palate; it is continuous on either side with the pharyngeal aponeurosis.

Tensor veli palatini (circumflexus palati; tensor palati; palatosalpingeus; sphenosalpingostaphylinus; staphylinus externus)

Origin: Scaphoid fossa, spine of sphenoid, vaginal process of temporal.

Insertion: About hamular process into palatine aponeurosis and palate bone.

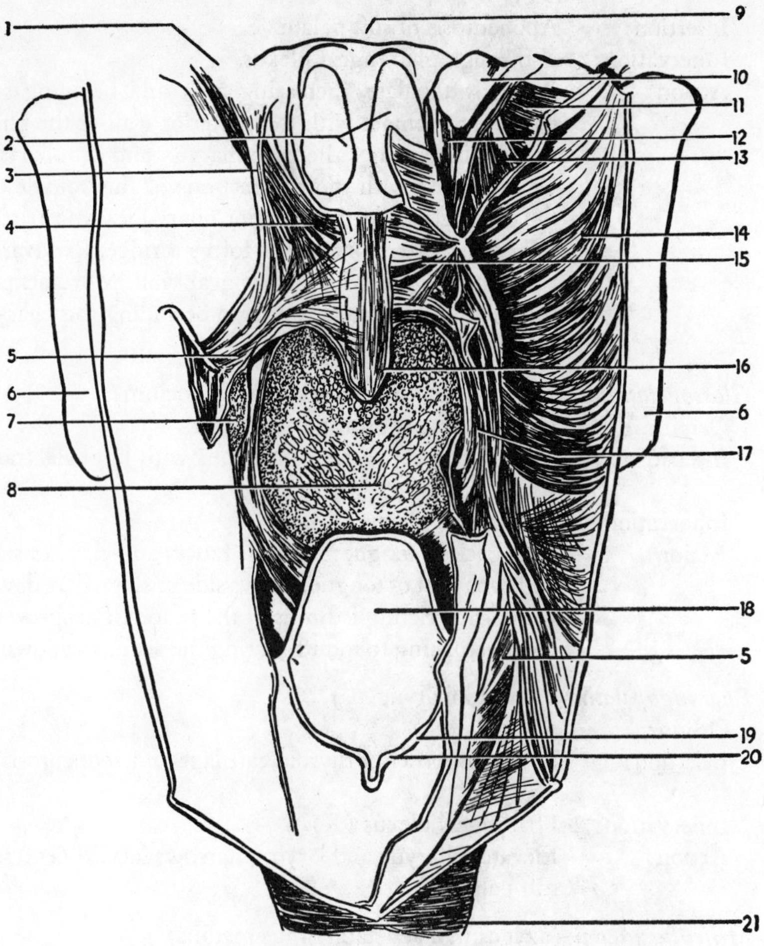

FIG. 36. Muscles of the Palate Region Viewed from Behind.

1. Region of mastoid portion of temporal bone; 2. choanae; 3. salpingopharyngeus; 4. levator palati; 5. pharyngopalatinus; 6. mandible; 7. tonsil; 8. tongue; 9. region of sphenoid bone; 10. cartilage of Eustachian tube; 11. external pterygoid; 12 tensor palatini; 13. internal pterygoid; 14. superior pharyngeal constrictor; 15. aponeurosis of soft palate; 16. musculus uvulae; 17. palatoglossus; 18. epiglottis; 19. cuneiform swelling; 20. corniculate swelling; 21. esophagus.

Innervation: V.

Action: Depresses and flattens arch of soft palate and renders tense the soft palate; opens Eustachian tube during swallowing.

Levator veli palatini (levator palati; staphylinus internus; petrostaphylinus; petrosalpingostaphylinus)

Origin: Apex of petrous portion of temporal bone and cartilaginous Eustachian tube.

Insertion:	Aponeurosis of soft palate.
Innervation:	X through pharyngeal plexus.
Action:	Raises soft palate, increasing arch and bringing soft palate into contact with the posterior wall of the pharynx. This separates the nasopharynx and oropharynx. Co-ordinated with the contractions of this muscle are the contractions of the superior pharyngeal constrictor. When the latter contracts it forms a ridge, Passavant's ridge, in the posterior pharyngeal wall. Movement of the palate to the ridge results in occluding the pharyngeal isthmus.

Glossopalatinus (palatoglossus; constrictor isthmi faucium)

Origin:	Under surface of soft palate.
Insertion:	Side of tongue; partly continuous with lingualis transversus fibers.
Innervation:	Pharyngeal plexus (X).
Action:	Lifts back of tongue; narrows fauces and elevates sides and back part of tongue; draws side of soft palate downward, constricting isthmus of the fauces. This prevents bolus returning to mouth during the act of swallowing.

Pharyngopalatinus (palatopharyngeus).

Origin:	Soft palate.
Insertion:	Posterior border of thyroid cartilage and aponeurosis of pharynx.
Innervation:	Pharyngeal plexus (X).
Action:	Elevates pharynx and larynx; narrows fauces; depresses soft palate.

Musculus uvulae (azygos uvulae; staphylinus medius)

Origin:	Posterior nasal spine.
Insertion:	Mucous membrane of uvula. This muscle forms greater part of uvula.
Innervation:	X through pharyngeal plexus.
Action:	Raises uvula; shortens uvula.

SUMMARY OF FUNCTION AND INNERVATION OF MUSCLES ASSOCIATED WITH THE PALATE

Muscle	*Function*	*Innervation*
Tensor veli palatini	Tenses soft palate.	V cranial nerve
Levator veli palatini	Elevates soft palate to bring it into contact with posterior wall of the pharynx. Hence, narrows pharyngeal opening.	X through pharyngeal plexus

Muscle	*Function*	*Innervation*
Glossopalatinus	Elevates root of tongue and constricts faucial isthmus. Depresses soft palate.	X through pharyngeal plexus
Pharyngopalatinus	Elevates larynx (thyroid cartilage) and pharynx, and constricts posterior fauces. Depresses soft palate.	X through pharyngeal plexus
Musculus uvulae	Elevates uvula.	X through pharyngeal plexus

D. The Muscles of Mastication

Masseter
Temporalis
External pterygoid
Internal pterygoid

As we have said, speech is often referred to as an overlaid or superimposed function. The truth of this statement is well illustrated in the muscles of mastication. The vegetative use of the muscles is indicated in their title. Their chewing movements usually end by bringing the teeth of the two jaws together on some food morsel. In speech, however, the movements of the jaws are usually not so crude; there are a multitude of part-way movements and retreating movements, most of which are practically in mid-air, i. e., there is no solid contact. This seems to mean that speech movements require a greater fineness than do the masticatory movements. It should be added, however, that in both speech and chewing movements the tongue makes many adjustments which directly aid the jaw movements and bring about refinements which would otherwise be impossible.

(All muscles of this group are innervated by the mandibular branch of the Trigeminal [V] nerve.)

Masseter

Superficial portion

Origin: Zygomatic process of maxilla and zygomatic arch.
Insertion: Angle of ramus of mandible.
Action: Raises mandible.

Deep portion

Origin: Zygomatic arch.
Insertion: Ramus and coronoid process of mandible.
Action: Raises mandible against maxillae.

Temporalis (temporal)

Origin:	Temporal fossa and fascia on side of head.
Insertion:	Coronoid process and ramus of mandible.
Action:	Raises mandible against maxillae; posterior fibers retract mandible.

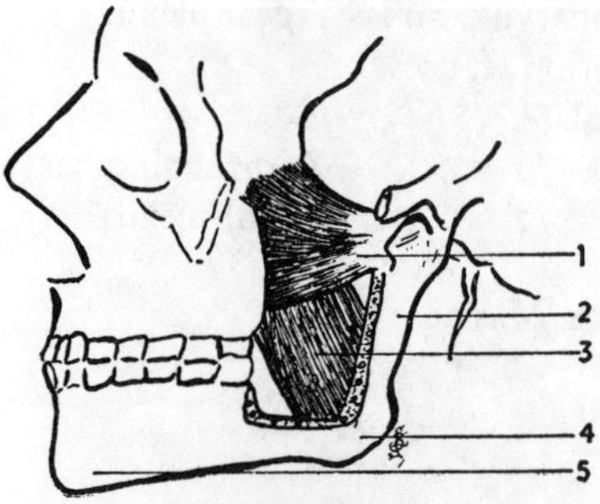

1. External pterygoid; 2. ramus of mandible; 3. internal pterygoid; 4. angle of mandible; 5. mandible.

FIG. 37. Muscles of Mastication.

External pterygoid (pterygoideus externus)

Origin:	Lateral pterygoid plate; great wing of sphenoid, etc.
Insertion:	Condyle of mandible, and joint capsule and interarticular disc.
Action:	Draws lower jaw forward and downward [1] (protraction and depression).

Internal pterygoid (pterygoideus internus)

Origin:	Pterygoid fossa of sphenoid bone, tuberosity of maxilla.
Insertion:	Inner surface of ramus and angle of mandible.
Action:	Raises and draws forward lower jaw (elevation and protraction).

SUMMARY OF FUNCTION AND INNERVATION OF MUSCLES ASSOCIATED WITH MASTICATION

Muscle	*Function*	*Innervation*
Masseter	Elevates mandible against maxilla.	V cranial nerve
Temporalis	Same as masseter. Posterior portion acting independently draws mandible in posterior direction (retraction).	V cranial nerve
External pterygoid	Protrudes jaw and depresses it. Either side acting alone produces lateral movements.	V cranial nerve

[1] The platysma is a weak depressor of the mandible. Other depressors, if the hyoid be fixed, are the digastric (anterior belly), geniohyoid, and mylohyoid muscles.

Muscle	*Function*	*Innervation*
Internal pterygoid	Same as masseter. Acts with pterygoideus externus to protrude jaw, and to produce lateral movements.	V cranial nerve

E. The Muscles of the Mouth Region [2]

Quadratus labii superioris
Caninus
Zygomaticus
Buccinator
Risorius
Orbicularis oris
Triangularis
Quadratus labii inferioris
Mentalis
Platysma

(All muscles of this group are innervated by the facial [VII] nerve.)

Quadratus labii superioris. Composed of three parts:

Caput angulare (levator labii superioris alaeque nasi).
Origin: Frontal process of maxilla.
Insertion: Cartilage of ala nase, and upper lip where its fibers mingle with those of the orbicularis oris.
Action: Raises upper lip.

Caput infraorbitale (levator labii superioris)
Origin: Inferior margin of orbit.
Insertion: Upper lip near caninus.
Action: Lifts and protrudes upper lip.

Caput zygomaticum (zygomaticus minor)
Origin: Malar surface zygomatic bone behind zygomatico-maxillary suture.
Insertion: Upper lip.
Action: Draws upper lip backward, upward, and outward.

Caninus (levator anguli oris; triangularis labii superioris)
Origin: Canine fossa of maxilla.
Insertion: Orbicularis oris and skin at angle of mouth.
Action: Raises angle of mouth.

[2] The muscles of this region arise from the branchiomeric mass (splanchnic mesoderm of visceral arch) of the second arch. The muscles are associated with the skeletal elements of the same arch and are innervated by special visceral motor nerves, thus differing from most skeletal muscles.

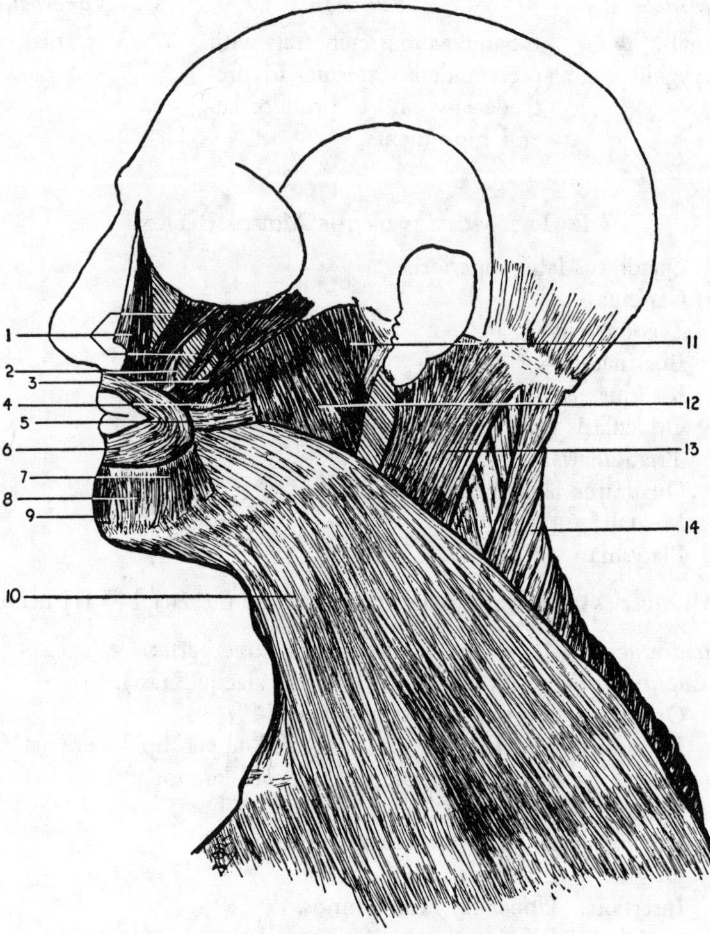

FIG. 38. Muscles of the Mouth Region.

1. Quadratus labii superior; 2. caninus; 3. zygomaticus; 4. buccinator; 5. risorius; 6. orbicularis oris; 7. triangularis; 8. quadratus labii inferior; 9. mentalis; 10. platysma; 11. masseter—deep portion; 12. masseter—superficial portion; 13. sternocleidomastoid; 14. trapezius.

Zygomaticus (zygomaticus major)

Origin: Zygomatic bone before zygomaticotemporal suture.

Insertion: Angle of mouth.

Action: Draws angle of mouth upward and backward as in laughing.

Buccinator

Origin: Outer surface alveolar (molar teeth) processes of maxilla and mandible; pterygomandibular raphe.

Insertion: Orbicularis oris.

Action: Compresses the cheeks and retracts the angles of the mouth.

Risorius
Origin: Fascia over masseter.
Insertion: Angle of mouth.
Action: Draws angle of mouth out; compresses cheek.

Orbicularis oris (sphincter oris)
Origin: Nasal septum, canine fossa of mandible.
Insertion: Angle of mouth.
Action: The sphincter of the buccal orifice. Closes lips; protrudes lips; draws upper lip down; draws lower lip up; draws together corners of mouth; draws lips back against teeth.

There is some question as to whether the orbicularis oris is a distinct entity, partly a separate muscle and partly fibers from other muscles, or merely the continuation of the fibers of other muscles. Probably six muscles enter into the formation of the sphincter of the oral orifice: zygomaticus, caninus, caput longum of triangularis, caput latum of triangularis, orbicularis oris (including quadratus labii superior and quadratus labii inferior), and buccinator. They are arranged in antagonistic pairs as shown in Fig. 39.

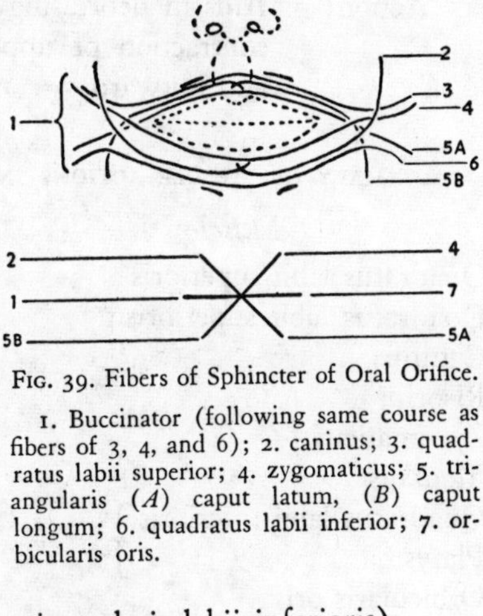

FIG. 39. Fibers of Sphincter of Oral Orifice.

1. Buccinator (following same course as fibers of 3, 4, and 6); 2. caninus; 3. quadratus labii superior; 4. zygomaticus; 5. triangularis (*A*) caput latum, (*B*) caput longum; 6. quadratus labii inferior; 7. orbicularis oris.

Triangularis (depressor anguli oris; triangularis labii inferioris)
Origin: Lower border (oblique line) of mandible.
Insertion: Lower lip near angle of mouth.
Action: Pulls down corners of mouth. (Some fibers cross from muscle of opposite side—Transversus menti).

Quadratus labii inferioris (quadratus menti; depressor labii inferioris)
Origin: Anterior portion of lower border (oblique line) of mandible.
Insertion: Orbicularis oris and skin of lower lip.
Action: Draws lower lip down and lateralward.

Mentalis (levator menti; levator labii inferioris)
Origin: Incisive fossa of mandible.
Insertion: Skin (integument) of chin.
Action: Protrudes lower lip and wrinkles skin of chin.

Platysma (platysma myoides; latissimus colli; tetragonus, subcutaneous colli)

Origin: Fascia over pectoralis major, deltoid and trapezius muscles. Ascends obliquely at side of neck.

Insertion: Anterior fibers: cross to fellows from opposite side to insert in integument of chin.

Middle fibers: lower border of lower jaw.

Posterior fibers: ascend over masseter muscle to be inserted in superficial fascia of cheek and the muscles at the angle of the mouth.

The risorius muscle is in part made up of a continuation of those fibers of the platysma which ascend transversely to the angle of the mouth.

Action: Aids in depressing mandible; depresses angle of mouth; contraction of upper fibers draws lower lip downward and outward.

SUMMARY OF MUSCLE ACTIONS INVOLVED IN MOVEMENTS OF THE LIPS

Muscle	*Action*
Quadratus labii superioris	Elevate and protrude upper lip
Quadratus labii superioris; Caninus	Elevate angle of mouth
Risorius; Zygomaticus	Retract angle of mouth
Mentalis	Protrude lower lip
Quadratus labii inferioris; Platysma	Depress lower lip and move it laterally
Orbicularis oris	Draw lips against teeth
Orbicularis oris	Close and protrude lips

THE VOWEL LINKS

The mouth cavity, listed in Chapter III as an important resonator, now assumes significance as housing the articulatory mechanism so essential in the production of speech sounds. The mechanism which breaks up or interrupts the phonated or non-phonated air stream consists of those structures of the oral cavity which are, relatively, the most movable. Usually, the *articulators* considered of greatest importance are the tongue, lips, teeth, and soft palate. Closely co-ordinated with the above, because of continuity through bony, muscular, or other tissue attachments, and warranting inclusion in a broader classification, are the cheek walls; the faucial boundaries; the mandibular foundation with its hyoid associations; and the maxillary boundaries, including the hard palate. Movements of the tongue, lips, teeth, and soft palate are invariably accompanied by movements of some or all of these related structures.

Although we have included the soft palate as one of the four major articulators, it should be understood that it does not act in the same degree as the others do. It could well be called a deflector rather than an articulator, for by the action of the velum and its attachments (the velar-pharyngeal musculature) the phonated or non-phonated breath stream can be directed either through the mouth, through the nose, or through both these cavities.

In the following description of each vowel link, the relation of the articulators to one another and to adjacent structures is discussed in detail. The tongue, which we found was so important in altering the oral cavity for resonance, is of primary importance in articulation.

The vowel links may be classified as consonants, nasals, and vowel glides.

A. Consonants [3]

The major group of vowel links produced by articulation are consonants.[4] Consonants are either continuant fricatives or stops. As its name indicates, a continuant fricative is a special kind of continuant. (All speech sounds, as stated in Chapter III, are either continuants or stops.)

Continuants are sounds resulting when the air stream, voiced (sonant) or unvoiced (surd), is forced through the resonators of the air tract and escapes into the outer air with or without having encountered some obstruction which produces friction sounds. Vowels, of course, are voiced continuants.[5] The resonators and articulators are held in a relatively fixed position during the production of any continuant. And as long as one holds the position and forces the air stream through the mold pattern, the sound will continue to be produced. *Continuant fricatives* are those continuants which *do* encounter some obstruction, thus producing friction sounds. If the air stream has been previously set into vibration (phonated and resonated), the friction sound waves are added to the already existing sound complex to make it all the more complex. If the air stream has not previously been set into vibration the friction sound waves (when resonated) will constitute the total sound complex. Thus in the production of continuant fricatives, through the same mold, two distinct sounds

[3] From the neurological point of view consonants are more highly developed sounds than are vowels.

[4] It would be foolish to debate at any length whether consonants or vowels are more important in speech, as we have come to know it. When one takes the stand that consonants are more important, that we could get along with a single vowel if it could only be indefinite enough, the basis of the argument has been shifted, for speech with a single vowel would not be speech as we recognize it.

[5] Voiceless analogues of voiced continuants (other than continuant fricatives) are merely the sounds as used in whispering.

may be made; one voiced, the other its unvoiced analogue.[6] For example, the surd [f] is the analogue of the sonant [v].

Stops are produced when an articulatory structure blocks the air stream, holds it blocked for a period of time while the pressure is increased, and then suddenly releases it. In such a sound as [p], for example, the lips are the major articulators involved. The foregoing explanation indicates that there are three phases in the production of a stop. During the implosion phase, the blockage is instituted; during the plosion state, the blockage remains in effect while the air pressure is built up; in the final or explosion stage, the blockage is opened suddenly and releases the pressure blast. Stops have this in common with continuant fricatives, that through the same mold two distinct sounds may be made; one voiced, the other its unvoiced analogue.[6] For example, the surd [t] is the analogue of the sonant [d].

1. CONTINUANT FRICATIVES

The continuant fricative consonants now to be described are the voiceless [f], [s], [ʃ], [θ] and their voiced analogues [v], [z], [ʒ], [ð]. We describe them in pairs, the voiceless sound first, a device which enables us to study the articulatory mechanism unhindered by phonation. The addition of phonation produces the voiced analogue. Whether the sound is voiceless or voiced, resonance is still an important factor in determination of the final speech sound.

The sounds [f], [s], [ʃ], [θ] are produced when the air stream, previously uninterrupted, is articulated by the narrowing of a portion of the mouth cavity to such a degree that the air is set into turbulent vibration, thus producing high-pitched friction sounds.[7] The velar-pharyngeal closure is complete.

In brief, these steps occur in the production of the sonant continuant fricatives [v], [z], [ʒ], [ð]: (*A*) The phonative mechanism sets the air column into vibration; (*B*) articulation takes place; (1) there is a firm closure of the port into the nasopharynx,[8] (2) the lips, teeth, and tongue so alter their relations to one another and to the palate that some constriction is offered to the emerging column of air and to the sound waves produced at the larynx. The constriction forces the air stream in its escape to set up friction noises. These are added to the already complex sound wave to make it more complex. These high-frequency components are the distinguishing characteristics of these continuant fricatives.

[6] Not an absolute analogue. For example, whisper *very* [vɛrɪ] and *ferry* [fɛrɪ]; *tell* [tɛl] and *dell* [dɛl].

[7] These sounds, because of the mode of their formation, are related to the so-called [h] sound, a friction sound produced at the larynx.

[8] Which is true for all sounds but [m], [n], and [ŋ], except as Nusbaum (1935) shows.

[f], a surd, labio-dental continuant fricative, is produced as follows: The velar-pharyngeal closure is complete. Light contact is made between the lower lip and the upper incisor teeth. The air coming from the lungs under pressure forces its way between these obstructions producing a friction sound as it expands and escapes into the outer atmosphere.

[v], a sonant, labio-dental continuant fricative, is produced like its voiceless analogue [f] except that it is voiced.

[s], a surd, lingua-alveolar continuant fricative, is produced as follows: The velar-pharyngeal closure is complete. The air coming from the lungs under pressure is forced by the tongue to pass through a relatively constricted aperture to be released over the cutting edge of one or more of the teeth.[9] This produces a high-frequency friction sound.

[z], a sonant, lingua-alveolar continuant fricative, is produced like its voiceless analogue [s] except that it is voiced.

[ʃ], a surd, lingua-palatal continuant fricative, is produced as follows: The velar-pharyngeal closure is complete. The air coming from the lungs under pressure is forced to pass through a relatively wide aperture between the tongue and hard palate before it is directed against the cutting edges of the teeth. Characteristic high-frequency sounds are produced.

[ʒ], a sonant, lingua-palatal continuant fricative, is produced like its voiceless analogue [ʃ] except that it is voiced.

[θ], a surd, lingua-dental continuant fricative, is produced as follows: The velar pharyngeal closure is complete. The air coming from the lungs under pressure is released between the flattened dorsum of the apex of the tongue in light contact along a wide extent of the sharp edges of the upper teeth. Characteristic high-frequency sounds are produced.

[ð], a sonant, lingua-dental continuant fricative is the voiced analogue of [θ].

2. STOPS

The sounds [p], [t], and [k] are produced when a column of air, uninterrupted at the larynx, is articulated when some structures within the mouth completely close and then suddenly open that cavity. The sounds [b], [d], and [g] which are the voiced analogues of [p], [t], and [k], respectively, are formed in the same manner except that before articulation occurs the air stream has already been set into vibration by the phonative mechanism.

[9] Usually the air follows a narrow groove along the mid-line of the dorsum of the tongue and is directed against the sharp edge of the lower incisors. However, the sound may be made in numerous similar positions between the tongue and the hard palate.

[p], a surd, bilabial plosive, is produced in three phases as follows:

Implosion or Make. There is a firm velar-pharyngeal closure. The mouth is in a fairly relaxed position with the lips closed. The air coming from the lungs under pressure cannot escape.

Plosion or Stop. The pressure builds up. The lips and cheeks may be tensed to dam up the air.

Explosion or Break. The pressure is quickly released by the sudden opening of the lips, making a popping sound.

[b], a sonant, bilabial plosive, is formed in the same manner as [p] except that for [b] there is a vibrating air column rather than a non-vibrating column.

[t], a surd, lingua-alveolar plosive, is produced in three steps as follows:

Implosion. There is a firm velar-pharyngeal closure. The apex and sides of the tongue make contact with the hard palate.[10] The air coming from the lungs under pressure cannot escape.

Plosion. The pressure builds up. The tongue muscles become more tense.

Explosion. The pressure is suddenly released as the tongue is quickly depressed.

[d], a sonant, lingua-alveolar plosive, is formed in the same manner as [t] except that for [d] there is a vibrating air column rather than a non-vibrating column.

[k], a surd, lingua-velar plosive, is produced in three stages, as follows:

Implosion. There is a firm velar-pharyngeal closure. The back of the tongue makes contact with the posterior hard palate and soft palate. The air coming from the lungs under pressure cannot escape.

Plosion. The pressure builds up. The tongue muscles become more tense.

Explosion. The pressure is suddenly released as the tongue is rapidly depressed.

[g], a sonant, lingua-velar plosive, is formed in the same manner as [k] except that for [g] a voiced rather than an unvoiced air stream is utilized.

Affricates are combinations of both types of consonants. Examples include [st] as in *fast* [fæst], [dz] as in *dads* [dædz], [dʒ] as in *fudge* [fʌdʒ].

[10] Usually near the alveolar ridge, but as you can prove to yourself, isolated [t] sounds could be made with the tongue making its contact at numerous places on the palate.

B. Nasals

Vowels may be linked and modified by the *nasals*. These are voiced continuants. Their peculiar acoustic property is the nasal resonance which they have because, unlike all other sounds,[11] they are directed through the port of the nasopharynx into the nasal cavities and escape to the outer air through the nasal orifices. To route the air column and sound waves through the nasal cavities there must be a blockage by the lips or the tongue of the oral exit. If the blockage is at the lips, as in [m], the oral cavity is a large resonator which definitely affects the acoustic perception of the produced sound. In the case of [ŋ], where the tongue forms the dam with the posterior part of the palate there is only a small oral cavity which acts as a resonator. Its effect upon the final sound [ŋ] is different from what it would be if the resonator were larger, as in [m]. The size of the resonator for [n] is somewhere between that for [m] and [ŋ] and, again, the final product [n] is distinguished by a different area of strong resonated frequencies. Probably these alterations in the size of the oral resonator are the distinguishing characteristics of the nasal sounds. Because there are no movable structures within the nasal cavities, their size cannot be altered, and, hence, they must, combined, resonate only one definite area of frequencies. This means that although the whole nasal cavity may give a distinguishing characteristic (the same) to all nasal sounds, it can do nothing to aid the ear in distinguishing one nasal sound from another. This occurs as the result of alterations in the size of the oral cavity resonator.

Although the sounds [m], [n], and [ŋ] are not actually subjected to articulation, they are included here. These sounds are usually classified as standing somewhere between the vowels and consonants. Like the vowels, they are voiced and have laryngeal and resonance characteristics. [m], [n], and [ŋ] differ from the vowels, however, in that they are emitted through the nasal cavity, while in general, vowels are emitted through the oral cavity.

[m] is related to [p] and [b], so far as all of these sounds require a closure of the lips.[12]

[n] is related to [t] and [d], so far as all of these sounds require a closure of the oral cavity between the tongue tip and the hard palate.[12]

[ŋ] is related to [k] and [g], so far as all of these sounds require a

[11] See Nusbaum, Foley, Wells (1935). The oro-nasal port is closed in the formation of most sounds. The muscles involved in this velar-pharyngeal closure are the tensor veli palatini, the levator palati, and the superior constrictor of the pharynx.

[12] In a sense [m], [n], and [ŋ] may be thought of as [b], [d], and [g], respectively, emitted nasally.

closure of the oral cavity between the back of the tongue and the soft palate.[12]

[m], [n], and[ŋ] are not plosives because, unlike the plosives, they need no velar-pharyngeal closure, and consequently the blockage of the mouth cavity by the lips or tongue only serves to route the voiced sound waves through the nasal cavities. [m], [n], and [ŋ] because of the passage of the sound waves through the nasal fossae are characterized by the added resonance of these cavities.

C. Vowel Glides

Vowel glides offer another way of initiating, connecting, or terminating vowel sounds.[13] *Glides* are transitory sounds produced incidentally during the direct movement of the articulatory structure from one position in which a certain vowel sound is being, or can be, formed to another position in which a vowel sound is being or can be formed. The acoustic effect is a result of altering the resonators involved.

Usually one thinks of [w], [j], [r], and [l] as distinct sounds. This is because in our written language we have special letters to represent them just as we do for [m] or [k]. Actually, however, these are not distinct sounds. They are glides, a term used by various writers, including Vietor, Ward, Kenyon, Kantner, and West.

[w] is the product of the movement or glide from [u] to another vowel. For example, assume the position for producing [u] and then say *watch* [wɑtʃ]. As the gliding movement from [u] to [ɑ] is accomplished, the approaching vowel glide [w] results.

Likewise, [j] results from an approaching glide from [i] to some other vowel. For example, *yes* [jɛs].

In a similar manner the movement from [ɝ] to some other vowel produces the approach glide [r]. For example, *rest* [rɛst].

Finally, an approach glide from the vowelized [l] to any other vowel produces the [l] glide. For example, *late* [leɪt].

The alert student will have noticed that sounds may be grouped together on the basis of the chief articulator involved or on the basis of the peculiarity of functioning of a given articulator.

The same alert individual will recall from his own exeriences that, when through error or purpose, sound substitutions occur they usually are within a given group, for example, [p] for [b] or [f] for [v].

[12] See note p. 153.

[13] The articulatory movements in the production of continuants, glides, and plosives may be likened to traffic movements directed by green, amber, and red traffic signals, respectively.

Articulatory Agent		Speech Sounds: Surd	Speech Sounds: Sonant	
Lips		p f	b v m	
Tongue	Tip against teeth or anterior hard palate	t s ʃ θ	d z ʒ ð n	
	Back against posterior palate	k	g ŋ	
	Arched slightly but mouth is single resonator directly coupled to the pharynx		FRONT VOWELS a æ ɛ e ɪ i	Vowels
	Arched in back of mouth so that anterior part of oral cavity forms a resonator coupled to posterior portion of the oral cavity		BACK VOWELS ɔ o ʊ u	Centrally
	Arched in area between that occupied for front and back vowels		CENTRAL VOWELS ɑ ʌ ɜ ɝ	Emitted
	Raised in front to emit air laterally		Laterally emitted vowel [l]	

ADDITIONAL FACTORS IN ARTICULATION

A. The Position of Sounds

In discussing a speech sound, we frequently refer to it as occupying an initial, middle, or final position in a series of sounds. The sounds [t], [p], and [ʃ], for example, occupy an *initial position* in the words *top, pill,* and *show,* respectively. The sounds [f], [b], and [g] occupy a *middle position* in the words *safari, labor,* and *sugar,* respectively. The sounds [s], [k], and [d] appear in a *final position* in the words *less, take,* and *glad,* respectively. In the word *success,* an [s] sound is in the initial, middle, and final positions, i. e., [sʌ ksɛs].

B. Limitation of the Number of Speech Sounds

The limitation of the number of possible speech-useful sounds is not set by the movements of the neuromuscular air-food system. These possible movements are infinite in number. Any limitation to the number of possible speech-useful sounds is set by the number of separate sounds which the ear may recognize. The number is quite limited in any one language. For example, in English we recognize approximately forty phonemes, almost equally divided between vowels and consonants. Not that there is a too sharp demarcation between vowels and consonants; there is not. Whatever the distinction between them, it is an auditory one. Note, for example, the vowel quality of [m]. Note, further, that authorities in the field of phonetics do not agree as to whether [l] and [r], for example, are semi-vowels, vowels, or consonants.

In general, one distinguishing feature of consonants is the relatively restricted oral orifice through which the air stream must pass. The restriction produces friction noises. The smallest aperture is noted for [s], with relatively increasing orifices for [θ] and [ʃ], for example. Vowels are produced through orifices of greater size—that for [ɑ] being greatest—and hence without friction noises. Somewhere between the most restricted and the least restricted orifices are those apertures through which are produced sounds having some vowel and some consonant qualities. These borderline speech sounds are difficult to classify except by arbitrary edict.

C. The Acoustic Perception of Implosions and Explosions

If each of the sounds [p], [t], [k], [b], [d], and [g] is produced in isolation, no acoustic perception results from the implosive and stop stages alone. Continue to build up the pressure as long as you are able, but until you enter the explosive stage no speech sound is produced. In ordinary connected speech, in order for the ear to hear one of these sounds it is not necessary always that there be an explosive stage for *that* sound. For example, in the sentence, "Give me my cap," you need not explode the [p] in [kæp] in order that the listener will understand your request. Or, another sound may be substituted for the explosion stage without the ordinary listener detecting the omission, as, for example, in the word *captain* [kæptə n]. Even [kætən] may not be detected in ordinary conversation. In the word *cupbearer* [kʌpbɛarɝ], the listener hears only the implosion phase of [p], the explosion phase being diverted to the production of [b]. Equally true is it that one may omit the implosive phase of one of these sounds and yet depend upon the stop and explosive phases to produce the required auditory effect. For example, using [p] again, the absence of the implosive phase in the word *path* [pæθ] is not noticeable. But in a word such as *apple* [æ pl] both phases are represented for [p].

D. Pressure Pattern Factors

Whenever plosive sounds are made or whenever the approach to a sound is somewhat explosive, a pressure pattern becomes a part of the sound complex which the ear must analyze. All speech sounds may be classified into three groups according to the prominence of their pressure characteristics. Group I is made up of the most explosive sounds, i. e., [p], [b], [t], [d], [k], and [g]. Group II contains those sounds of medium

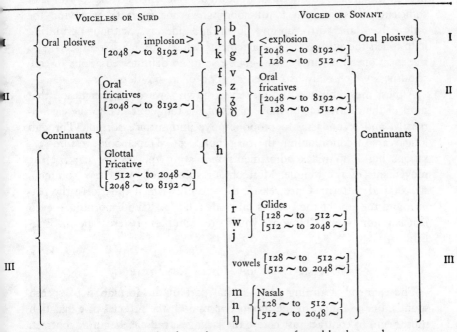

	Voiceless or Surd				Voiced or Sonant	
I	Oral plosives	implosion> [2048 ~ to 8192 ~]	p t k	b d g	<explosion [2048 ~ to 8192 ~] [128 ~ to 512 ~]	Oral plosives	I
II	Continuants	Oral fricatives [2048 ~ to 8192 ~]	f s ʃ θ	v z ʒ ð	Oral fricatives [2048 ~ to 8192 ~] [128 ~ to 512 ~]	Continuants	II
III	Continuants	Glottal Fricative [512 ~ to 2048 ~] [2048 ~ to 8192 ~]	h			Continuants	III
III				l r w j	Glides [128 ~ to 512 ~] [512 ~ to 2048 ~]	Continuants	III
III				vowels	[128 ~ to 512 ~] [512 ~ to 2048 ~]	Continuants	III
III				m n ŋ	Nasals [128 ~ to 512 ~] [512 ~ to 2048 ~]	Continuants	III

Note: The Roman numerals refer to the pressure patterns formed by the sounds:
I indicates a high degree of pressure.
II indicates a lesser degree of pressure.
III indicates a minimum of pressure.

explosive identity, i.e., [f], [v], [s], [z], [ʃ], [ʒ], [θ], and [ð]. Group III contains all other sounds.

The preceding table contains the information on pressure and summarizes the resonance frequency characteristics of various sounds.

E. Control of the Tongue

Because the tongue is such an important articulatory organ, we may well ask ourselves how it is controlled neurologically. If the surface of the tongue be touched at almost any point, and especially if any pressure be placed on it, the sensation is received in consciousness. There is only a fair degree of localization of sensations, however. In the formation of the sounds like [k] and [θ], it is easy to see how the tongue might be guided in making the sounds by sensations of touch or contact. But in the production of such sounds as [u], [ɑ], [ŋ], [z], it is difficult to believe that surface sensations play any great part in the control of the tongue movements.

Much of the control of the movements of the tongue is mediated through kinesthetic sensations arising from proprioceptive nerve endings in the muscle substance of the tongue. But whether this control is of sufficient nicety is open to question when one finds that moving the tongue back and forth, up and down, and sideways, without permitting it to touch the lips or teeth—movements which are gross compared with the exact ones used in speech—gives rise to no definite sensations in consciousness which allow easy identification of its position.

Almost inevitably we find ourselves drawn toward the conclusion that most of the control of the movements of the tongue is due to the ear primarily, and secondarily to proprioceptive and surface stimuli. Through long years of conditioning, the ear-proprioceptive-touch-and-pressure sensations build up reflex adjustments regulating the greater part of the movements of the tongue. Most of our speech follows a few common, stereotyped patterns. Once release the stimulus which calls forth the pattern and the rest of the process proceeds reflexly. "Good morning"—even if it is raining—and "How are you?" are examples of stereotypes in English.

F. Time Order of Muscle Contractions

The element of timing plays a vital part in the formation of speech sounds. For example, in the production of [ɑ], the muscles of exhalation must begin to contract just before the laryngeal muscles begin to contract. And the laryngeal muscles must contract just before or as the muscles of the various resonators contract. And, finally, the muscles producing the velar-pharyngeal closure contract. In the production of [p], the muscles of exhalation contract; the muscles controlling the velar-pharyngeal and oral openings contract; the muscles of the oral opening relax. As these operations usually take place without conscious effort, we are placed in the position of having to find a neurological center or centers which can set off impulses in such split-second series as to operate the marvelously integrated mechanisms of speech. This is almost unexplored territory in the field of Voice Science.

In the chapter on neurology we point out that each of the different levels of the nervous system has its own rate of discharge. Speech, partly involuntary and partly voluntary, is the composite result of impulses coming from various neurological levels. Speech, therefore, is carried on in rhythm with the individual's cerebral discharges, altered if at all by the discharge rate of lower levels. Accent, or stress, indicates a surge or fluctuation in the discharge volley. This accounts for the fact that all persons reading aloud a prose or poetry selection tend to read it with some similarity of pattern.

The neurological patterns of speech are most similar in persons having similar vital capacities. Thus it is that the person who has a small vital capacity feels, unexplainably to himself, irritation when listening to the speech of a person who has a large vital capacity. Even more, we have demonstrated, that speech is so pervasive that a listener is forced, willy-nilly, to give up his own pattern of breathing during a speech and take on the pattern of breathing of the speaker. That is, speech not only alters the behavior of the vegetative system of the speaker; it also alters that of the listener.

ARTICULATORY EVOLUTION

In the evolution of language, most of the changes in sounds may be laid to the attempts of the organism to produce all sounds with a minimum of muscular effort.[14] As we have pointed out, the most nearly relaxed position is that assumed during normal breathing. The closer the articulatory system comes to this breathing position in producing speech sounds, the less the expenditure of energy in producing them. There is a tendency for all sounds made with complex muscle movements and a greater expenditure of energy to become more and more like the sounds made with a minimum expenditure of energy. For example, sounds produced with the *C* or *D* position of the glottis will tend to replace sounds

[14] In the production of speech sounds there will always be a tug-of-war between those which are distinct or pedantic and those which are energy-saving physiologically—those permitting an economy of muscle movement. The latter have won out in the past, as may be demonstrated by the resulting changes in the language. The future should demonstrate similar trends as long as Thanksgiving Day brings with it pumpkin [pʌŋkən] pie!

produced with the *B* position of the glottis,[15] and sounds produced with articulatory movements in the back of the oral cavity, because they involve movements by the great mass of the tongue, will tend to be replaced by sounds produced with articulatory movements in the front of the oral cavity; it is more economical to move the tip of the tongue than to move the entire tongue. Even more economical are the labials. Furthermore, in accord with the laws of inertia, once a movement of the speech mechanism is started it may be less exertion to continue it than to terminate it and then begin it again. Thus with a voiced consonant between two vowels there is a tendency toward perseveration of the *B* position of the glottis uninterrupted by the consonant, e. g., [ubu].

The operation of these tendencies have made our speech what it is today; we see evidences of their continued operation all about us, prophecy of the language of the future.

We wish to reiterate what we have said elsewhere about the possibility of making most speech sounds in an almost infinite number of ways. This fact should make it clear that *speech is not,* and has not been in the past, *static;* it is dynamic, metamorphic. The speech we use today is a chameleonic product; today's speech is but the flux of tomorrow's transmutation.

PALATOGRAPHY

In the production of speech sounds, the tongue takes different positions in the mouth. In many cases it makes contact with the palate. A *palatogram* is a diagram of such a tongue-palate contact.

Palatograms may be made directly or indirectly. In the direct method, some easily identifiable substance is placed on the tongue and the sound is made. With the aid of a laryngeal mirror, the observer can make a sketch of the outline of the deposited material and its location on the palate.

The indirect method makes use of the so-called *artificial palate.* For extremely careful palatographic studies the palate should be made by a dentist. For general laboratory work, however, the following procedure may be followed: One to two cakes of dental gum are softened in lukewarm water by the operator. This modeling compound is then placed in a dental mouth tray and quickly inserted in the open mouth of the subject. It is pressed up firmly against the palate until it begins to harden; it is then released by a gentle oscillating movement and quickly plunged in cold water until hard. After surrounding it with black dental wax or molding clay so that the wax or clay forms a wall, the whole resembling a shallow cup, it should immediately be filled with plaster of paris, freshly mixed to a plastic consistency. Shaking or jarring the cup will permit the

[15] Particularly true of voiced consonants in the final position. They tend to become voiceless or whispered.

escape of any air bubbles which may have accumulated at the bottom or on the walls of the cast. After the plaster of paris has hardened, the clay or wax wall may be removed and the original gum model removed by a brief insertion in warm water.

Using a blunt stick, a thin sheet of dental metal is worked into the plaster mold so carefully that every contour of the mold is faithfully represented in the metal film. It will be found necessary as you work the metal in between the mold teeth to remove it occasionally and to cut out small V-shaped snips. *Do not cut out too much metal at a time.* Care must be taken in forming the vault of the palate; the stretching of the metal in this region makes it thinner than elsewhere and too great pressure or the use of a sharp instrument will rupture it. From time to time, as the work nears completion, the palate may be experimentally fitted into the mouth.

After making a palate which will remain securely in the roof of the mouth during the formation of speech sounds, it should be removed, powdered, and reinserted in the mouth. A single sound is spoken and the palate is at once removed. Wherever the tongue has touched the palate, powder will have been removed and these portions will appear darker. The contacts which occur at either side of the artificial palate or back of the hard palate will not be recorded.

For purposes of comparison the palatogram should be sketched on a previously prepared outline of the palate. By collecting the trial words carefully, it is possible to secure palatograms of initial, middle, and final speech sounds.

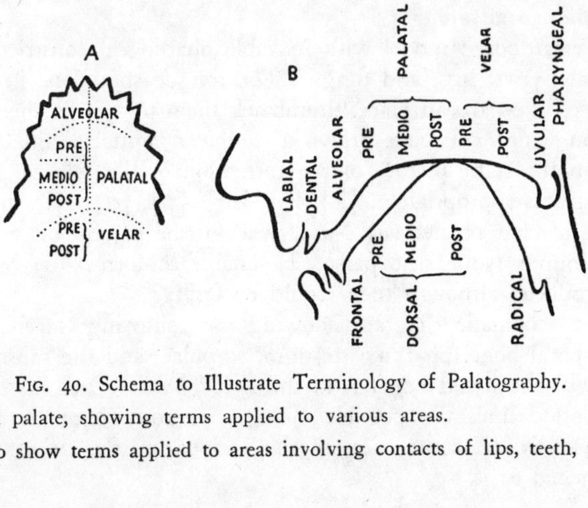

FIG. 40. Schema to Illustrate Terminology of Palatography.

A. Artificial palate, showing terms applied to various areas.

B. Sketch to show terms applied to areas involving contacts of lips, teeth, palate, uvula, and tongue.

Accurate palatograms are almost as individual as fingerprints. Furthermore, a few experiments will satisfy you that great compensatory movements may be made by the tongue—thus producing different palatograms—in the production of sounds which may be perceived by the ear as identical. If no other reason has heretofore presented itself, you are now in a position to explain why some sounds are called "front" sounds, and why some sounds are called "back" sounds. For describing palatograms a specific language consisting of compound terms has been drawn up. Reference to Fig. 40 will explain why [t] may be described as a frontal-alveolar contact.

EXERCISES AND QUESTIONS

1. Each student should take a different speech sound and attempt to determine what muscles associated with movements of the tongue are responsible for its production.

2. In correct time order, list the other muscles which were involved in the production of the speech sound chosen in the above exercise. (That is, laryngeal, pharyngeal, etc., muscles.)

3. Make a list in chronological order of the muscle movements required in the formation of these sounds: [ʌ], [i], [s], [v], [p], [k], [m].

4. Enunciating clearly, how many of each of the following syllables can you produce in sixty seconds? [ɑp], [ɑb]; [ɑt], [ɑd]; [ɑk], [ɑg]; [pɑ], [bɑ]; [tɑ], [dɑ]; [kɑ], [gɑ]. What conclusions may be drawn regarding the effect of certain sound combinations on the tempo of speaking? Compile additional lists of syllables, using other sounds, and make similar tests.

5. If you were undertaking a study to show that all languages in the world were related, or were from a common origin, or that over broad territories language was even now undergoing evolution, how could you use palatographic studies to advantage?

6. Make a cardboard model with movable pharyngeal constrictors, epiglottis, soft palate, jaws, lips, and tongue. The tongue should be in several sections. To keep the parts in place, thumbtack them to a large sheet of heavier cardboard on which you have drawn a *complete* sagittal section of the head region. Form the static picture of the formation of the following sounds by moving the pieces appropriately: [k], [t], [m], [p], [ɑ], [i], [u], [g] [ŋ].

7. In case of cleft palate: (*a*) Nasality would be present on what sounds? (*b*) What sounds would the person be unable to form? (*c*) What sounds could be produced although they would be faulty?

8. Draw a schematic diagram showing the following: larynx, mandible, tongue, temporal bone, pharynx, sternum, scapulae, and the muscles connecting these with the hyoid bone. Add the hyoid bone to the sketch. Now indicate by dotted lines the possible changes of position of the hyoid bone brought about by the contraction of the various muscles or combination of muscles attached to it.

Chapter V

PHONETICS

(*By Claude E. Kantner, Ph.D.*)

A. Phonetics Defined
B. Some Applications of Phonetic Science
C. Fields Allied to Phonetics
D. Phonetics as a Study of Systems of Symbolization
E. Phonetic Alphabets
F. Some Basic Considerations in the Study of Phonetics
  1. Speech sounds are produced by portions of the vegetative system
  2. Speech sounds are received by the auditory mechanism
  3. Speech sounds are symbol units
  4. Speech sounds are learned
  5. Speech sounds are influenced by forces that work to produce variation
  6. Speech sounds are influenced by forces that work to prevent variation
G. The Phoneme Theory Applied to Speech Sounds
H. Approaches to the Classification of Speech Sounds
  1. The acoustic approach
  2. The placement or position approach
  3. The movement or kinesiologic approach
I. A General Classification of Speech Sounds
J. The Vowel Tone as the Acoustic Basis of Speech
K. The Neutral Vowel [ʌ]
L. Other English Vowels
M. A View of Speech as a Series of Devices for Initiating, Connecting, or Terminating Vowel Tones
N. Vowel Glides
O. Laryngeal Modifications of Vowel Tones
P. Velar Modifications of Vowel Tones
Q. Oral Modifications of Vowel Tones
R. Ways and Means of Initiating, Connecting, or Terminating Glides, Nasals, and Consonants
S. Summary of the Analysis of Speech Sounds
T. Bibliography for Further Study

TABLE OF PHONETIC SYMBOLS *

The Neutral Vowel

[ʌ]	up	[ʌp]	

The Front Vowels

[i]	eat	[it]	
[ɪ]	it	[ɪt]	
[e] †	debris	[debri]	
[ɛ]	pet	[pɛt]	
[æ]	pat	[pæt]	
[a]	ask	[ask]	as often pronounced in America between [æ] and [ɑ]

The Central Vowels

[ɝ] ‡	early	[ɝlɪ]	General American pronunciation
[ɜ]	early	[ɜlɪ]	Southern and Eastern pronunciation
[ʌ]	(See Neutral Vowel, above)		
[ɑ] §	palm	[pɑm]	

The Back Vowels

[u]	food	[fud]	
[ʊ]	foot	[fʊt]	
[o] †	notation	[noteɪʃən]	
[ɔ]	all	[ɔl]	
[ɒ]	sorry	[sɒrɪ]	as pronounced in England and often in America. Between [ɑ] and [ɔ]

The Schwa Vowel

[ə]	above, below, constitute	[əbʌv], [bəloʊ], [konstətɪut]

* The symbols are those of the International Phonetic Association. This is a simplified list of the symbols used to represent the sounds of English speech. It is adequate for broad transcription and adapted to the needs of beginning students. The vowels within the respective groups are arranged in order from those with high tongue positions to those with low tongue positions.

† In English, this sound is a relatively pure vowel only in unaccented syllables. In accented syllables, it is a vowel glide.

‡ This symbol is adopted from Kenyon's *American Pronunciation*. We have, however, placed the hook at the top instead of at the bottom of the symbol. An older symbol [ɚ] is still in wide use.

§ [ɑ] may be thought of as being at the foot of each of the vowel series: front, central, and back.

The Vowel Glides (Semi-vowels and Diphthongs)

[w]	witch	[wɪtʃ]
[hw]	which	[hwɪtʃ]
[j]	you	[ju]
[hj]	hue	[hju]
[l]	law	[lɔ]
[r]	raw	[rɔ]
[ɑʊ]	now	[nɑʊ]
[oʊ]	no	[noʊ]
[eɪ]	day	[deɪ]
[ɔɪ]	boy	[bɔɪ]
[aɪ]	eye	[aɪ]

Laryngeal Modifications of the Vowels

[h]	hop, hue, which, how	[hɑp], [hju], [hwɪtʃ], [hɑʊ]
[ʔ]	up not down	[ʔʌp nɑt dɑʊn] as sometimes spoken

Oral Modifications of the Vowels (The Consonants)

The Stop Plosives

[p]	pat	[pæt]
[b]	bat	[bæt]
[t]	two	[tu]
[d]	do	[du]
[k]	class	[klæs]
[g]	glass	[glæs]

The Continuant Fricatives

[f]	fife	[faɪf]
[v]	five	[faɪv]
[θ]	bath	[bæθ]
[ð]	bathe	[beɪð]
[s]	sue	[su]
[z]	zoo	[zu]
[ʃ]	mission	[mɪʃən]
[ʒ]	vision	[vɪʒən]

The Affricates **

[ts], [st]	cats, cast	[kæts], [kæst]
[dz], [zd]	fads, raised	[fædz], [reɪzd]
[tʃ], [ʃt]	church, rushed	[tʃɝtʃ], [rʌʃt]
[dʒ], [ʒd]	judge, rouged	[dʒʌdʒ], [ruʒd]

Nasal Modifications of the Vowels

[m]	mow	[moʊ]
[n]	no	[noʊ]
[ŋ]	sing	[sɪŋ]

** There are other affricate combinations. These are typical examples.

A. Phonetics Defined [1]

Broadly speaking, phonetics is the study of speech sounds. Such a study includes the determination of the speech sounds used in any given language, the consideration of the symbolic nature of these sounds, a study of the way in which they are produced by the speech mechanism, a study of the physical and psychological problems connected with the perception of these sounds by the auditory mechanism, and lastly, a study of the varying usage and variant pronunciations of these sounds in different sections of a given country or in different countries. Usually the study involves the devising and use of a set of symbols, called phonograms, to represent the sounds.

Care must be taken to distinguish between phonetics proper and applied phonetics. As indicated above, phonetics proper is the scientific study of speech sounds from the standpoints of their production, reception, and symbolic use. A set of symbols is usually employed as a tool in the conduct of the study. Phonetics as a study has broad applications, but it is not accurate to call these applications phonetics. Thus, the use of phonetic principles in the correction of defective speech or in the teaching of a standard speech is not to be considered as belonging in the field of phonetics proper, but, rather as applied phonetics.

B. Some Applications of Phonetic Science

We may list, without comment, some other applications of phonetic science:

- to studies made in other branches of the field of general linguistics, i.e., morphology, etymology, dialect studies, etc.
- to the teaching of pronunciation in foreign languages
- to studies and clinical practice in the field of speech correction
- to studies in speech science, speech psychology, and other informational speech courses
- to skill courses in speech such as voice training, interpretation, general speech, etc.
- to dramatics, in the teaching of stage speech or of a given dialect to be used in a play
- to the teaching of pronunciation through grammars, dictionaries, etc.

[1] It is our aim in this section to introduce the science of phonetics to the reader. In addition to defining the field of phonetics and its spheres of usefulness, we hope to lay down some considerations to be kept in mind in the study of this subject, to enumerate with brief comments various approaches to the study, and to discuss with some detail one such approach. We are, obviously, not concerned with the writing of a detailed treatise on phonetics, but, rather, with the giving of a bird's-eye view of the subject. This material should serve to illustrate the connections between phonetics and other branches of speech study, particularly the scientific aspects of speech, and to prepare the student for a further study of the subject.

to speech training as it is carried on in some elementary schools
to the teaching of reading by phonics

C. Fields Allied to Phonetics

It is apparent that the study of phonetics draws heavily upon related fields. A study of the production of speech sounds draws from the fields of anatomy, neurology, and physiology for information as to the functioning of the speech mechanism. These same fields supply material on the functioning of the auditory mechanism when speech sounds are considered from the acoustic standpoint. Likewise, the field of physics contributes to an understanding of the physical nature of sound in general and speech sounds in particular, while psychology helps us to understand the symbolic nature of these sounds. Needless to say, phonetics draws also from other subjects within the speech field. The technical equipment used in the study of speech sounds is varied and extensive and calls for considerable technical knowledge in allied fields. The recording of speech sounds, the taking of X-ray pictures of the mechanism in action, and the making of palatograms are technical activities that illustrate the above statement.

D. Phonetics as a Study of Systems of Symbolization

In a sense, phonetics may justly be called the study of symbols. Our spoken language is, in reality, a series of auditory symbols. These symbols are composed of patterns of physical vibrations known as sound waves. The producing mechanism is that part of the body known as the speech mechanism, including, roughly, the respiratory system and the upper part of the alimentary system. The receiving mechanism is the auditory mechanism (using the term in a broad sense to include also the higher auditory centers of the brain). The speech mechanism is capable of producing, and the auditory mechanism of receiving, a great variety of sounds. A relatively small number of these sound patterns become stereotyped by usage and serve, by common consent of those speaking the language, as units in the formation of acoustic symbols that stand for certain objects, acts, qualities, ideas, or relationships. These we may properly call speech sounds. To illustrate: the sounds represented by the symbols [k], [æ], and [t] qualify as speech sounds because they are produced by the speech mechanism, received by the auditory mechanism, stereotyped in their production so that they are usually recognized as the respective sounds, and used as units in the formation of the auditory symbol [kæt]. We may further qualify our definition of a speech sound by saying that it ought to be a single sound, that is, a sound that, in terms of the fundamental movements and basic sound patterns involved in its production, is incapable of further division.

So far as we know, spoken language has always preceded writing, and the written alphabet as it develops is usually an attempt to symbolize speech sounds that have already been in the language for a long time. This is certainly true of our Roman alphabet. In the sixth century, the native dialects of what is now England had no alphabets and were not written except in a very cumbersome runic form. It was during this period that the Christian missionaries from Rome began to use the Latin alphabet to write the native dialects, and they made the Roman symbols represent, as far as possible, the sounds present in the language. Thus, in our alphabet, as it was originally put into use, each character stood more or less accurately for a given sound. The written alphabet is then, in reality, a series of symbols that stand for other symbols, that is, a series of visual symbols that stand for corresponding auditory symbols or speech sounds. It is, incidentally, a matter of some dispute as to whether these visual symbols—i. e., letters of the alphabet—as they are combined into words, sentences, etc., can ever stand directly for ideas, or whether they must first be translated into auditory symbols—i. e., speech sounds—and thence to ideas. Be that as it may, the fact remains that in the development of language in the race and in the learning of speech by the child, the auditory symbols are learned first and the visual symbols later. It is interesting to note, in passing, that in earlier times, in elementary schools, reading was taught by teaching first the sound value of each letter, then combining these sounds or letters into a word, and then by means of a picture or some other method attaching meaning to the word. Modern methods of teaching rapid silent reading attempt to go directly from the visual symbols—i. e., letters—to the ideas represented, without the intervening step of translation into sounds.

E. Phonetic Alphabets

We have mentioned previously that when the Roman alphabet was first used to represent the ancestors of our English speech sounds, each character in the alphabet stood, generally speaking, for a separate sound; and, supposedly, at least, each sound in the language at that time had a character to represent it. Such an alphabet is called a phonetic alphabet. This representation of sounds by the Roman alphabet was probably very inaccurate even at the beginning, and it has grown increasingly more so with the passage of time, until, at present, any student of speech knows that the letters in a page of writing fall far short of representing the sounds that are present when the material is read aloud.

This means, obviously, that the auditory symbols or speech sounds in English have changed at a vastly more rapid pace than the visual symbols or letters of the alphabet. The reason for this is twofold. The speech mechanism that produces the auditory symbols is much more subject to variation than the mechanism that produces the visual symbols. Thus, the speech sounds as they are produced, from individual to individual, year to year, and generation to generation, vary much more in their production than do the corresponding letters of the alphabet. The reason for this is partly a physiological one, having its basis in the less stable voluntary control of the speech mechanism, and partly a matter of the relative permanence of the media in which the two types of symbols are produced. It is evident that the auditory symbol units have no permanency; they are gone the instant they are produced and, until the invention of recording apparatus, could be retained only in memory. The visual symbols, on the other hand, are as permanent as the material with which and on which they are recorded. This explains why the spoken language of the sixth century has changed so radically that we would be unable to understand it if we heard it today, whereas the alphabet used to record that language is still essentially the same.

The above discussion enables us to understand why the student of phonetics begins his studies either by constructing a phonetic alphabet or learning one previously constructed by others. A phonetic alphabet has been previously defined as one in which each symbol represents only one sound and each sound in the language is represented by one symbol. In addition to this, a good phonetic alphabet should be neither too long and cumbersome for use nor so short and sketchy as to be valueless. Phonetic alphabets are, in general, of two types, the "narrow" and the "broad." Narrow systems use many more symbols for the purpose of distinguishing finer shades of differences in sounds. Broad systems use fewer symbols and disregard the finer details of differences between sounds.

The process of constructing a phonetic alphabet is, then, essentially a matter of revising our present English alphabet so as to bring it up to date, that is, make each character stand once more for only one sound and provide a character for each sound. A number of phonetic systems have been devised from time to time, some of which have been discarded for various reasons. At present, the two most widely used alphabets are those advocated by the American Dialect Society and the International Phonetic Association. They are much alike, with only minor differences in some of the symbols used. A simplified list of the symbols of the International Phonetic Alphabet is given at the beginning of this chapter.

F. Some Basic Considerations in the Study of Phonetics

With this general introduction, we may proceed now to lay down several general principles that are basic considerations in the study of phonetics. This is not an attempt to summarize the whole field of phonetics, but, rather, it is an effort to formulate some broad general principles that will serve as foundation stones or, perhaps, better still, as points of departure for students undertaking the study of phonetics. Six such principles are enumerated. Lack of space forbids a lengthy discussion of each one, but we attempt to indicate the broad applications of the statements. It will be noted that some of the statements are broad enough to apply also to other phases of speech study, while others ramify into the fields of applied phonetics.

1. SPEECH SOUNDS ARE PRODUCED BY PORTIONS OF THE VEGETATIVE SYSTEM

Speech sounds are patterns of physical vibrations within the auditory range produced by activities of a mechanism, comprised, as we have seen, essentially of the respiratory system and the upper part of the digestive system.

This statement indicates that the study of phonetics will be concerned in one of its aspects with contracting and conducting tissues—muscles, and nerves. It will involve a neurological and anatomical study of the various structures that make up the mechanism and of the action of these structures in the production of speech sounds. It means, also, that the nature of the sounds produced will be restricted and governed by the laws and limitations governing muscle movement and the conduction of nerve impulses. It involves, in addition, the implications of the fact that the structures that produce these sounds have other vital functions that take precedence over speech.

2. SPEECH SOUNDS ARE RECEIVED BY THE AUDITORY MECHANISM

These speech sounds so produced are received and interpreted by the auditory mechanism together with its associated higher centers in the brain.

This fact implies the consideration of speech sounds as acoustic phenomena and involves: the physics of sound in general; the anatomy and functioning of the auditory mechanism, its limitations and possibilities; problems of auditory range, carrying power, pitch, volume, resonance, pressure patterns, and the ability to distinguish between sounds; and, lastly, the whole problem of the effect of hearing upon speech as it concerns sound changes in the language, the learning of speech by the child, and the development of speech defects.

3. SPEECH SOUNDS ARE SYMBOL UNITS

These sounds become stereotyped and serve as units in the formation of symbols that, by usage and common consent of those using the symbols, become associated with certain objects, qualities, acts, ideas, or relationships. This statement has been discussed elsewhere and needs no further elaboration here.

4. SPEECH SOUNDS ARE LEARNED

Speech is acquired and not inherited, and each child learns the auditory symbols used by those about him. Moreover, the ability to develop and use any very complicated set of such symbols seems to be limited to the human race.

This statement, once a subject of dispute but now considered a truism, has its main bearing on applied phonetics. It means that the normal child will learn to speak the speech of those with whom he associates in his learning period. This introduces the whole subject of dialectal speech. The statement also covers cases of imitative speech defects and has, in addition, implications for the teacher of foreign languages. In fact, it applies to any phase of speech that has to do with the re-education of speech habits that were formed by imitation, or the teaching of new habits on the basis of imitation.

5. SPEECH SOUNDS ARE INFLUENCED BY FORCES THAT WORK TO PRODUCE VARIATION

There are forces in operation that work to produce a great deal of variation in the way in which speech is produced and, to a lesser extent, in its acoustic effect.

This variation occurs in the speech of any one individual when he makes a certain sound at different times. It occurs also in different individuals subject, apparently, to the same speech environment. It occurs in different sections of a country or in different countries where the same language is spoken with varying dialects. The forces that act to produce this variation may be enumerated as: the inability of the neuromuscular mechanism to repeat a movement after an absolutely exact pattern; the influence of the position of the various structures of the speech mechanism on the production of the sound; the variation in structure from one individual to another; the influence of neighboring sounds; and, lastly, and very important, the tendency of an individual to produce a sound as he hears it. This last means that the production of speech sounds will, in the absence of training, vary according to the variation in hearing and, also, that this variation will grow more pronounced in districts lacking widespread communication. Obviously all this has an important bearing on the study of the way in which speech sounds are produced, on the origins of dialects, and on studies of such dialects.

6. SPEECH SOUNDS ARE INFLUENCED BY FORCES THAT WORK TO PREVENT VARIATION

There are also in operation forces that work to prevent change and to keep speech in general and speech sounds in particular, static. If it were not for these forces working to check change, it is possible that only those living in close proximity would be able to communicate with each other and that speech in isolated districts would become unrecognizable to non-residents at a much faster rate than it does at present.

One of these stabilizing forces is the physiological tendency of the organism to follow the line of least resistance—in other words, to form habits whereby movements or acts are repeated time after time in a similar fashion. This is essentially a matter of laying down neural patterns, or neurograms, in the nervous system for the production of each sound. These patterns become more stereotyped with each repetition, and as they become more stereotyped they become more difficult to change. The similarity of movement is not absolute but there are limits to the probable variations.

Furthermore, though speech mechanisms and auditory mechanisms differ in different individuals, they are alike in their broader aspects. Thus, given mechanisms with no obvious pathologies, the variations brought about in the production of a sound by differences in structure are usually minor, and they do not affect greatly the fundamental nature of the sound.

A third force operating to check change has its basis in the perceptual side of the problem. Since these sound units combine to form symbols that serve to stir up meaning, it follows that they lose their value if they are no longer recognized by the listener as the sound that the speaker intended to use. In other words, the amount of variation in the production of a given speech sound, if it is to remain serviceable, is limited by the ability of those who hear the sound to recognize it as the sound that the speaker thinks he is using.

G. The Phoneme Theory Applied to Speech Sounds

The two forces mentioned above, one working to produce change and the other to prevent it, give rise to what is known as the "phoneme" theory in phonetics.

Perhaps the term "sound family" is the best simple interpretation of the word *phoneme*. Let us take the sound of the letter *t*, symbol [t], as an illustration. We have stated that it is an impossibility for anyone to make two *t* sounds *exactly* alike. Furthermore, it is well known that a *t* can be produced with the tongue tip anywhere from behind the lower front teeth to the edges of the upper front teeth or as far back on the hard palate as the tongue tip can reach by curling upward and backward. In actual practice, these variations are limited, first, by the physiological tendency of the organism to stereotype the movements, and second, by the fact that the resulting sound must still be heard as a *t* or lose its value. Within these limitations, however, there is still considerable variation.

The symbol [t], then, obviously does not stand for a single, distinct sound which is an entity in itself. It is, rather, a general symbol that represents a series of *t* sounds. Such a family of sounds is called a phoneme. The phoneme theory is simply an attempt to take account of the variation that exists in the production of any given speech sound and to place limits on that variation. The limits of variation are, as noted previously, governed by the recognizability of the sound as a *t*. If those who hear the sound perceive it as a *t*, then, for them, it belongs to the *t* phoneme; if not, it belongs to some other phoneme or to no phoneme at all. This conception of sound families, or phonemes, applied to every sound symbolized in our phonetic alphabet. It follows, then, that we must revise our previously stated conception of the interpretation of these symbols. Each symbol stands not for a separate sound but, rather, for *a series of slightly varying sounds that includes all of the variations which are perceived acoustically as the sound under consideration*. A phonetic alphabet, such as that given at the beginning of this chapter, presents one symbol per phoneme and takes no account of variations within the phoneme.

The above discussion indicates that a given variation of a sound may be in one phoneme in one section of the country and in another phoneme in another section. Or, what appear to be the same sounds may belong to different phonemes in different languages. This is not only theoretically but also practically true, especially of the vowels. A single illustration will suffice. Several foreign languages have a vowel sound that is somewhere between our English [ɪ] and [i]. An American hearing this foreign vowel may place it in either the [ɪ] or the [i] phoneme, depending upon how he happens to hear it. A foreigner hearing our American [ɪ] or [i] will probably hear them as belonging to his own phoneme which is between the two and proceed to pronounce them accordingly.

The importance of the phoneme conception of speech sounds to the study of phonetics and especially to the application of phonetics to other phases of speech study is at once evident.

H. Approaches to the Classification of Speech Sounds

The student who takes up the study of phonetics is soon faced with the task of classifying speech sounds. We feel that this task is frequently made more confusing and burdensome than necessary by classifications involving three approaches welded together, with a resultant bewildering mixture of terminology. In order to orient the student and to prepare the ground for a later discussion, the classification used here is prefaced by two others. All three approaches are listed with brief comments, and the terminology applicable to each is noted.

1. The Acoustic Approach

The study of speech sounds can be approached from the standpoint of the effect produced by these sounds upon the auditory mechanism. This is an acoustic approach. It is chiefly concerned with such problems as those of pitch, volume, resonance, pressure patterns, duration, etc. In accordance with such an approach, speech sounds are classified on the basis of their acoustic effect and in terms that apply to auditory sensation. The terminology for such a classification is not complete, but many of the terms present in the usual textbook classification belong to the acoustic approach.

For example, the separation of sounds into vowels, semi-vowels, consonants, and diphthongs is an acoustic division. The terms have auditory connotations. For the vowels and diphthongs, there is no clear-cut acoustic classification, although such terms as stressed, unstressed, long, short, weak, strong, high-pitched, low-pitched, more or less sonant, more or less resonant, etc., are auditory terms used to describe sound. Similarly, the terms *tense* and *lax,* although they really should be used to indicate the degree of muscle tension, have been used so often to describe sound quality that they are almost auditory terms.

For the consonants, there is a fairly complete set of auditory terms to describe the various subdivisions under this heading. The terms *sonant* and *surd,* or *voiced* and *voiceless,* or *voiced* and *silent* belong in this approach, as do also such categories as sibilants, fricatives, affricates, plosives, nasals, liquids, etc. Other auditory terms applying to consonants are rolled, trilled, semi-trilled, scrapes, clicks, aspirate, whispered, etc.

The above discussion should serve to demonstrate that the acoustic approach to the classification of speech sounds has its own field of study and, at least, a partial terminology.

2. THE PLACEMENT OR POSITION APPROACH

The task of classifying speech sounds can also be approached from the standpoint of the position of the articulatory mechanism during the production of the various sounds. Specifically, the investigator wishes to know the position of the tongue, soft palate, mandible, and lips for the production of each speech sound. X-ray and palatographic studies are examples of this type of approach. The placement approach necessitates the study of anatomy in order to determine the nature of the structures making up the speech mechanism and the positions that they are capable of taking. It involves also a study of speech sounds by all methods available, both objective and subjective, in order to determine the position taken by the mechanism during the production of a given sound.

There is, in the literature, a large number of terms dealing with speech sounds that designate placement or position. Vowels, for example, are subdivided into front, central, and back vowels. The front vowels are further subdivided into high front, mid front, and low front vowels; a similar classification may be applied to the central and back vowels. In addition, the terms close, half close, half open, open, narrow, broad, rounded, spread, protruded, etc., are applicable to vowels and are descriptive of position. For the consonants, this placement terminology is even more abundant. The terms labial, dental, rugal, alveolar, palatal, velar, pharyngeal, lingual, nasal, laryngeal, glottal, and all the various combinations such as labio-dental, lingua-velar, etc., are used to designate the position of the mechanism in the production of the various speech sounds. It is plain that the emphasis in this approach is upon the anatomy of the mechanism and the position taken by it when a given speech sound is being produced.

3. THE MOVEMENT OR KINESIOLOGIC APPROACH

Still a third approach to the study of speech sounds is one involving a study of the *movements* of the mechanism requisite to the production of each speech sound. It is closely related to the placement approach and is a continuation of the same type of study. The investigator wishes to know not only the position of the mechanism when the sound was made but also what movements of the structures were necessary to produce that position. Carried to its conclusion, it involves the determination of the muscles in contraction to produce these movements and the nerve centers and pathways by which the activating impulses reached the muscles. There are relatively few terms that describe types of movement; the three in most common use are continuant, stop, and glide.

As suggested before, it is seldom, in the study of phonetics, that any one approach is used exclusively or that the terminology is limited to a single set of terms. It is evident that each approach has its own contribution to make to the study, and the viewpoint of each is necessary to a well-rounded picture. If the terminology seems confusing at times, an understanding of the approaches represented may help to clarify the difficulty. For example, the sound [s] may correctly be referred to as voiceless, lingua-dental, continuant fricative. Of these terms, *voiceless* and *fricative* describe its acoustic qualities, *lingua-dental* refers to the position of the mechanism during its production, and *continuant* to the type of movement involved. In a similar fashion, [b] is described as a bilabial, stop plosive.

I. A General Classification of Speech Sounds

In the succeeding pages our purpose is to set forth a general classification of speech sounds. It must be remembered that a complete classification and description of speech sounds would form the greater part of a phonetics text. The following is, therefore, necessarily abbreviated and in skeleton form. No attempt has been made to discuss each sound in detail or to comment on controversial points. The aim is, rather, to fit these speech sounds into an orderly scheme and to indicate the relationships between and among them, in order that the student may approach a further study of the subject in a systematic and intelligent manner.

In this discussion, speech sounds are first classified according to the kinesiologic approach, and then further subdivisions are made on an acoustic basis. From the standpoint of the movements involved in their production, we may classify sounds into three main groups, i. e., continuants, stops, and glides. We may define each one of these categories as follows:

(1) A continuant is a speech sound in the production of which the mechanism first takes the position typical of the sound and is then, for all practical purposes, held fixed in that position during the period of the utterance of the sound.

Examples: [s], [ɑ], [m]

(2) A stop sound is one in which the articulatory mechanism moves to or from a certain position that momentarily completely blocks the air stream at some point in its exit through the oral cavity. Either the movement to the closed position, the movement from it, or both is sufficient to call forth recognition of the sound.

Examples: [p], [d]

(3) A glide sound is the acoustic effect of the continuous movement of the mechanism from the position of one sound to that of another with unbroken utterance. There may be vowel glides in which the movement is from one open, that is, a vowel or vowel-like position, to another; or consonantal glides in which the movement is from one partially closed, that is, continuant consonant position, to another; or there may be nasal glides in which the movement is from one nasal sound to another.

Examples: [ɑʊ], [wɑ], [fθ], [mn]

From an acoustic standpoint these general types are further divided as follows: Continuants are divided into vowels, consonants, and nasals. A vowel is a continuant emitted through the mouth and made through a relatively open position of the articulatory mechanism so that the voiced air stream escapes without the production of definite friction noises. A continuant consonant is a sound made through a relative closed position of the articulatory mechanism so that definite friction noises are produced by the escaping air stream. The continuant consonants are further subdivided into voiced and voiceless sounds. Nasal sounds are continuants in which the air stream exits through the nasal cavity.[2] The stop sounds are all consonants. They are also called plosives and may be either voiced or voiceless. As mentioned previously, glides may be either inter-vowel, inter-consonantal, or inter-nasal.

This classification is given in outline form below. It should be kept constantly in mind in the study of the following pages.

Classification of speech sounds according to the type of movement involved in their production	*Classification of speech sounds subdivided on an acoustic basis*
continuants	vowels nasals consonants { voiced / unvoiced }
stops	plosive consonants { voiced / unvoiced }
glides	inter-vowel inter-consonantal inter-nasal

J. The Vowel Tone as the Acoustic Basis of Speech

It has been mentioned elsewhere in this book (see page 62) that speech has its basis in the whisper, since it is in whispered speech that the physiological mechanism is using the least energy and following the line of least resistance. It is equally true, however, from an acoustic standpoint that the basis of speech is in the vowel tone, that is, a voiced sound made through an open mechanism. The reason for this is the greater carrying power of the voiced tone. Physiologically, it may be slightly easier to produce a whisper, but a speech that is entirely voiceless has comparatively little value for communicative purposes. Thus, we will not be far amiss if we look upon speech as having its acoustic basis, at least, in the vowel tone.

K. The Neutral Vowel [ʌ]

If we start from the resting position [3] of the speech mechanism—that is, its position in normal, quiet respiration—we find that the easiest vowel

[2] Note the distinction between a nasal sound and a nasalized sound. In the latter a sound that is normally emitted through the oral cavity is nasalized, that is, partially emitted through the nasal cavity.

[3] Strictly speaking, of course, no living mechanism is ever in a completely resting position and at least the respiratory portion of the speech mechanism is always functioning. This term

to make, physiologically, is produced by dropping the mandible slightly, elevating the soft palate so as to direct the air stream through the oral cavity, and vocalizing. This produces a vowel that is approximately [ʌ] as it is usually symbolized in its stressed form. This, physiologically, is the neutral vowel—the vowel that comes nearest to being made in the resting position of the mechanism. It forms a convenient point of departure for a consideration of the remaining vowels.

L. Other English Vowels

We note that by further and more extensive modifications of the resting position, involving essentially changes in the position of the lips, jaw, and tongue, a limited number of other vowels can be formed. The number is limited by the auditory mechanism and not by the neuro-muscular mechanism. The speech mechanism is capable of producing an almost unlimited number of slightly varying vowel tones, but *the number of these sounds* (i. e., phonemes) *that can be used in speech is limited by the ability of the auditory mechanism to recognize them as separate sounds when they are employed in the communicative process.* Probably no language ever uses every distinguishable vowel sound, yet each language that develops beyond the primitive uses almost all such sounds. We may assume that a fully developed language, making exceedingly fine distinctions in meaning and thus needing more symbol units, would use nearly all distinguishable vowel sounds.

The number of vowel phonemes listed for a given language depends on the fineness of the distinctions that are made. In English, we ordinarily assign symbols to sixteen vowel phonemes. They are: [i], [ɪ], [e], [ɛ], [æ], [a], [ɒ], [ɔ], [o], [ʊ], [u], [ɑ], [ʌ], [ɜ], [ɝ], and [l̩]. From the standpoint of tongue position, they are divided into four groups as follows:

(1) *The front vowels.* A group in which the orifice for the emission of the air stream is formed toward the front of the oral cavity. Arranged in order from the highest and most front to the lowest and most back, the sounds of this group are: [i], [ɪ], [e], [ɛ], [æ], and [a].

(2) *The back vowels.* A group in which the orifice is formed toward the back of the oral cavity. Arranged in order from the highest and farthest back to the lowest and farthest front, the vowels in this group are: [u], [ʊ], [o], [ɔ], and [ɒ].

(3) *The central vowels.* A group in which the orifice is more centrally located. Arranged from highest to lowest, the vowels in this group are: [ɝ], [ɜ], [ʌ], and [ɑ]. [ʌ] has already been mentioned as the neutral

---

is used throughout this discussion to mean *resting position as far as speech activities are concerned.*

vowel. [ɝ] is symbolized by [r̩] when it occurs in an unstressed form, and [ə] may be regarded as a variety of an unstressed [ʌ].

(4) *The lateral vowels.* A group of *l* sounds ranging in position from front to back and delivered laterally along the sides of the tongue instead of centrally over its top. *l* usually occurs as a vowel glide, but it is frequently syllabic and a true vowel. The broad transcription symbol for the vowel *l* phoneme is [l̩].

With the exception of [l̩], the vowels mentioned above are shown schematically in the following diagram. This diagram is to be interpreted as only a very rough approximation of the tongue position for the various vowels.

One of the characteristics of English speech that is almost unique is the constant unstressing of vowels when they occur in unaccented positions. Thus any of the vowels above may, if unaccented, be pronounced in such a way as to lose their ordinary vowel value. This unstressing takes the form of a lessened force of utterance and a tendency of the vowel to resemble in acoustic value and in tongue position, the neutral vowel [ʌ]. Unstressing is a matter of relativity, and the degree to which it occurs varies in different sections of the country, with different individuals, and according to the context. Consider, for example, the first vowel in *approach.* If stressed, the vowel would be [æ]. Since the syllable is unstressed, however, it is seldom that the sound is pronounced with full [æ] value. It is likely to be a weak form of [æ] or, more likely still, an unstressed neutral vowel which we symbolize by [ə]. This sound is often called the schwa. It is always unstressed. Note the [ə] vowels in the following words: *above* [əbʌv], *ability* [əbɪlətɪ], *constitution* [kɑnstətɪuʃən], *telephone* [tɛləfoʊn], *patted* [pætəd] or [pætɪd].

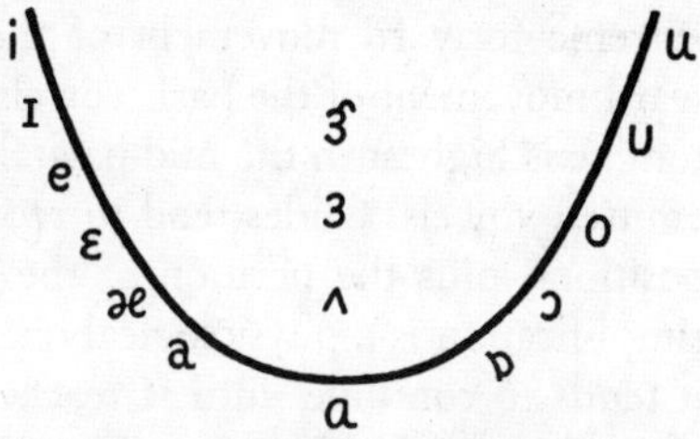

FIG. 41. Schematic Vowel Diagram.

M. A View of Speech as a Series of Devices for Initiating, Connecting, or Terminating Vowel Tones

Obviously, a language restricted to the use of vowel tones would be inefficient in conveying arbitrary meanings. It would be serviceable in carrying direct emotional meaning but sadly deficient if it had to assume the burden of all the multitude of meanings expressed by the English language. There is need, then, for a further modification of these vowel sounds in order, first, to produce a greater number of acoustically distinguishable sounds that can be used as symbol units in communication, and second, to devise ways of articulating or joining these vowel sounds so that the end product can be uttered more rapidly and fluently. We turn now to a consideration of the speech process as a series of devices for initiating, connecting, and terminating vowel tones.

N. Vowel Glides

One of the most common methods of connecting vowel sounds is to glide from the position of one vowel to that of another with continuous voicing. This produces a vowel glide. Theoretically, there are as many glides as there are combinations of vowels in the language. Practically, however, in the development of the language these glides tend to approach or recede from five general positions of the articulatory mechanism. We have already listed the four main groups of vowels. [i] represents the extreme forward movement of the front vowels, [u] the farthest backward movement of the back vowels, [ɝ] is the central vowel in which the tongue is highest in the mid-palatal region, and [l̩] represents the laterally emitted vowels. Glides tend to recede from or approach these four vowel positions, plus the position of the schwa vowel [ə]. The reason for this simplification is a physiological one. Once a gliding movement has started, it tends to continue until it reaches a position somewhere near the limit of movement in that direction. Similarly, the origin of the glide tends to establish itself near the limit of movement in the direction from which the movement starts. These five vowels represent respective limits in the five general directions of vowel movements, i. e., toward the high front position of [i], toward the high back position of [u], toward a high central position with the sound emitted medially as for [ɝ] or laterally emitted as for [l̩], and toward the resting position of the mechanism the nearest to which is the neutral vowel [ʌ], or, as unstressed, [ə]. Glides may be regarded as having either their origin or termination *approximately* in one of these five positions. The other end of the glide may be any vowel or vowel-like sound in the language. Glides that approach the [i] position from the position of some other vowel are represented by using [i] or [ɪ] as the termination. [aɪ], [eɪ], and [ɔɪ] are common examples. Glides of this type have been called diphthongs. Glides receding from the [i] position are represented by [j] thus: [ji] and [jɑ]. Glides that approach the [u] position use either [u] or [ʊ] as the terminating symbol. Common examples are: [aʊ], [oʊ], and [ɑʊ]. Glides that recede from the [u] position are represented by [w], thus: [wi] and [wu]. In connection with the position for the vowels [ɝ] and [l̩], we use the symbols [r] and [l] to designate either approaching or receding glides, thus: [lɔ], [ɔl], [rɑ], and [ɑr]. Schwa glides occur commonly as off-glides and represent what happens when the mechanism goes from the position of a vowel toward the resting position with continuous voicing. Examples: [oʊᵊ], [ɪᵊ], and [ɛᵊ] as often pronounced in the South and East.

It will be noted that in the approaching glides, the stress is on the origin of the movement and there is a descending sonority as the glide approaches its termination, thus: [ɑʊ]. This condition is reversed with the receding glides. Here the stress is on the termination of the glide, and there is an increasing sonority from the origin to the termination: [wɑ].

There are more glides in the language than we are commonly aware of, but they group themselves readily around these five vowel positions. We may safely lay down the rule that if there is to be a glide from one vowel position to another, these positions must not be too close together, either physiologically or acoustically. To illustrate, the vowels [e] and [a] are too close together to form a good glide. If these two sounds come into juxtaposition in the language it is probable that either they will be pronounced separately with a definite break between them, or, if they are glided, the origin of the movement will gradually move farther forward until the combination becomes [ja]. If the sounds come together in reverse order, [ae], the same principles will work to produce [aɪ].

O. Laryngeal Modifications of Vowel Tones

We come now to a consideration of methods of initiating, connecting, or terminating vowel tones based on movements taking place at the glottal opening. We may think of the vocal folds as taking four general types of positions:

(1) Open widely, as in ordinary breathing, so that the air stream passes in and out with little audible friction.

(2) Partially closed, so that the outflowing air stream produces definite friction noises. This is the whisper position.

(3) Closed to the point of phonation, so that the outflowing air stream produces voice, as in all the vowels.

(4) Completely closed, so that no air can escape.

These positions form the basis for three methods of initiating vowel tones:

(*One*) If the vocal folds pass relatively slowly from the open position to the point of vibration, the voicing is preceded by laryngeal friction noises that we symbolize in phonetics by [h]. This is the glottal-fricative approach. Any vowel may be approached by this method. This means that there is a brief period when the articulatory mechanism is in the position of the vowel at the same time that the vocal folds are moving slowly through or pausing momentarily in the whisper position on their way to the position of vibration. The [h] approach is very common in English.

(*Two*) If the vocal folds pass *rapidly* from the open position to the point of vibration, we have the usual vowel attack as we hear it in such words as *on* [ɑn] and *open* [oʊpn]. This we may call the glottal-vibratory approach. It differs from the glottal-fricative approach in the speed of the closure of the vocal folds; the closure is so rapid that the friction noises are greatly reduced and not perceived. This approach is the most common of the three and has no special symbol to represent it. When a vowel symbol is written without any preceding sign, it is to be assumed that the glottal-vibratory approach is indicated.

(*Three*) If the vocal folds close the glottis completely for a brief period —thus causing a rise of subglottal pressure—and then open suddenly, the result is a glottal-explosive approach symbolized by [ˀ]. Any vowel may be preceded by this approach. It is not a standardized sound, although it occurs frequently in German and less frequently in English in unstandardized positions. It is sometimes used to give emphasis, as in the sentence, "I said *up,* not down" [ˀʌp].

Without going into detail, we can state that by applying these same principles to the termination of vowels, we have a glottal-fricative termination, a glottal-vibratory termination, and a glottal-*im*plosive termination. The first and the last can also be used as methods of connecting vowels.

P. Velar Modifications of Vowel Tones

These vowels may likewise be initiated, connected, or terminated by the nasal sounds, sounds that depend in their production upon the action of the soft palate. There are three standard nasal sounds in English, [m], [n], and [ŋ]. In the production of each of these sounds, the air stream is blocked at some point in the oral cavity, the soft palate is allowed to hang relaxed, and the air stream is forced out through the nasal cavity. For all other English sounds, the velum and pharyngeal walls act to close the opening into the naso-pharynx so that the air stream is directed out through the mouth cavity. This closure apparently need not be complete but it must at least redirect the air stream so that the major portion of it passes through the oral cavity. Other speech sounds can be nasalized but such nasalization is not standard in good English speech. The three nasal sounds are continuants, and may be either consonants or vowels, according to their use. [m] is consonantal in *may* [meɪ] and *come* [kʌm]. It is a vowel in *chasm* [kæsm̩]. Likewise [n] is a consonant in *none* [nʌn] and a vowel in *button* [bʌtn̩].

Q. Oral Modifications of Vowel Tones

Vowels may also be initiated, connected, or terminated by sounds, other than vowels, produced by modifications within the oral cavity. These are the consonants. There are both continuant and stop consonants, in voiced and voiceless forms. The continuant consonants, voiced and voiceless, are: [v] [f], [z] [s], [ð] [θ], and [ʒ] [ʃ]. The stop consonants or plosives, voiced and voiceless, are: [b] [p], [d] [t], and [g] [k]. It is obvious that, looked at from the standpoint of this discussion, consonants are used more frequently than any other device to start, stop, or connect vowels. The number of consonants is limited by the same forces as those restricting the number of vowels, namely, those governing acoustic distinguishability. They are also limited in number by the fact that to be of value they must be comparatively easy to make in a rapid fashion and they must combine readily with other sounds. If it seems far-fetched to regard consonants as means of initiating, connecting, or terminating vowel tones, we may say that, essentially, in terms of movement, in going from a stop consonant such as [t] to a vowel such as [i] to form the word *tea,* we are simply moving from a closed position of the oral cavity to a rather open one. Similarly, when we go from [s] to [i] as in *see,* the movement is from a less open to a more open position. The same statements apply to consonants as they occur between vowels and follow vowels.

R. Ways and Means of Initiating, Connecting, or Terminating Glides, Nasals, and Consonants

To complete our classification of speech sounds, we must recognize that there are also various ways of starting, stopping, or connecting glides, nasals, and consonants. Lack of space forbids our going into detail at this point, but the essential principles are listed below with appropriate illustrations.

(1) Glide sounds, like vowels, may have a glottal-fricative approach, *how* [hɑʊ]; or a glottal-fricative termination, *playhouse* [pleɪhɑʊs]. They may have, also, a glottal-vibratory approach or termination, or a glottal-explosive approach or glottal-implosive termination. Glides are sometimes connected by glides as in *bow wow* [bɑʊwɑʊ], and *our way* [ɑʊrweɪ]. Glides can likewise be initiated, connected, or terminated by consonant and nasal sounds.

(2) The nasal sounds are subject to the same laryngeal modifications as the vowels. There are also glides between nasal sounds as in *come now* [kʌmnɑʊ] and *home news* [hoʊmnɪuz]. Like the vowels and glides, they can be started, stopped, or connected by consonants.

(3) Continuant consonants, both voiced and unvoiced can be connected by interconsonantal glides as in *thrives* [θraɪvz] and *tenths* [tɛnθs].

(4) Continuant consonants, both voiced and unvoiced, may have what can be called the oral plosive approach or termination. This produces the so-called affricate sounds. An affricate, by definition, is a sound combina-

tion of a stop plosive and a fricative continuant produced in the same organic position and closely linked in their articulation. If the movement is from the position of one of the stop sounds to that of a homorganic continuant consonant, we have an oral explosive approach as in *chum* [tʃʌm]. The oral implosive termination occurs when the movement is from a continuant consonant to a homorganic stop sound, as in *rushed* [rʌʃt]. There are a number of possible affricate combinations, but the most common ones are [tʃ], [ʃt], [dʒ], [ʒd], [ts], [st], [dz], [zd], [tθ], [θt], [dð], and [ðd]. Examples: *church* [tʃɝtʃ], *judge* [dʒʌdʒ], *best* [bɛst], *cots* [kɑts], *eighth* [eɪtθ], *bathed* [beɪðd], etc. In such a word as *casts* [kæsts], the plosive sound [t] serves as an oral plosive termination of the first [s] and an oral plosive approach to the last [s].

(5) What we may call an incidental *h,* which differs slightly from the *h* described under "Laryngeal Modifications," occurs in such words as *tea* [t^{h}i], *pay* [p^{h}eɪ], *kite* [k^{h}aɪt], *say* [s^{h}eɪ], *ship* [ʃ^{h}ɪp], etc. Whereas the *h* that precedes vowels is produced by a laryngeal modification that takes place while the articulatory mechanism is held relatively stable, the incidental *h* is produced while the articulatory mechanism is in movement from one sound to another. In this respect, it resembles the *h* approach to the various vowel glides. This *h* occurs when there is a movement of the articulatory mechanism from the position of a voiceless plosive or continuant consonant to that of a vowel *if* the voicing does not begin until the mechanism has reached the position for the vowel. It occurs also if the conditions are reversed and the movement is from a vowel to a voiceless plosive or continuant consonant, *if* the voicing ceases the instant the mechanism leaves the vowel position. We commonly speak of voiceless plosives in English as "aspirated" and "fortis" because of this *h* puff of unvoiced air which follows them, particularly when they occur in initial positions.

S. Summary of the Analysis of Speech Sounds

In undertaking this classification, we first divided speech sounds into continuants, stops, and glides on the basis of the type of movement involved. We then proceeded to make further subdivisions of these three main categories on an acoustic basis. At this point, we turned to view the speech mechanism in its resting state and discussed the neutral vowel [ʌ] as resulting from minor changes in this position. The remaining English vowels were looked upon as further modifications of this basic vowel position. We turned next to a consideration of the various ways and means by which these vowel tones can be initiated, connected, or terminated. This was done under the headings of glides, laryngeal modifications, velar modifications, and oral modifications. Lastly, we have indicated very briefly the ways in which these glides, nasals, and consonants may themselves be initiated, connected, or terminated.

Perhaps the best way to summarize the material contained in this analysis of speech sounds is to describe a short sample to English speech according to the kinesiologic approach and the terminology used herein. It should be understood that such a description, in order to represent completely an approach from the standpoint of speech and voice science, should include also an analysis of the movements of the mechanism involved in the production of each of the sounds as well as enumerating the muscles and nerves that act to produce these movements. For obvious reasons of space, this part of the analysis has been omitted from this introductory study of phonetics and is likewise omitted from the following description.

The phrase chosen for illustrative purposes is *will you come here,* or, as written in phonetic symbols, [wɪl ju kʰʌm hɪr]. The speech mechanism passes from its resting position to approximately that of the continuant vowel [u]. At the same time, the vocal folds close to the point of vibration, and, without producing a continuant, the articulatory mechanism glides to the position for the vowel [ɪ]. This is a glottal-vibratory approach to a glide receding from the [u] position and passing to the [ɪ] position, producing [wɪ]. From this point, the mechanism continues its glide, without pausing, to the position for the continuant vowel [l̩]. This is an approaching glide from the [ɪ] to the [l̩] position, producing [wɪl]. In rapid speech, the articulatory mechanism, again without pausing, continues the glide on to approximately the [i] position and goes thence to the [u] position to produce the receding glide [ju]. The vowel [u] is terminated as the vocal folds open and the articulatory mechanism passes to the position for the voiceless stop consonant [k]. As the explosive phase of the [k] is completed, the mechanism passes to the position for the vowel [ʌ] and an incidental *h* is produced. The vocal folds again close to phonation and the continuant vowel [ʌ] is produced. This vowel is terminated by the lowering of the velum, thus opening the port into the nasopharynx, and the assuming of the mechanism of the position for the continuant nasal [m]. This sound is produced, and terminated in turn, as the velum raises to close off the nasal passages and the articulatory mechanism passes to the position for the vowel [ɪ]. Simultaneously, however, the vocal folds open to the whisper position and close again relatively slowly to the point of vibration thus producing a glottal-fricative approach to the vowel [ɪ]. The sound [ɪ], however, is not produced as a continuant, but instead the mechanism glides to the position for the vowel [ɝ]. The vocal folds then return to a wide-open position and the rest of the speech mechanism returns to the resting position without any noticeable acoustic effects.

T. Bibliography For Further Study

The following books are recommended for those students who may wish to pursue further studies in phonetics and who may lack an opportunity to take a formal course in the subject. It should be remembered, however, that, although it may be possible to learn phonetic theory and principles by reading, a keen discrimination of sounds and the ability to use phonetic symbols accurately can be acquired only by practice under the tutelage of an expert in the field.

Barrows, Sarah T., and Cordts, Anna D., *The Teacher's Book of Phonetics.* Ginn and Co., New York, 1926.

Jones, Daniel, *An Outline of English Phonetics.* G. E. Stechert and Co., New York, 1922.

Kantner, C. E., and West, R. W., *Phonetics.* Harper and Bros., New York, 1941.

Kenyon, John S., *American Pronunciation.* 6th ed., revised. George Wahr, Publisher, Ann Arbor, Michigan, 1935.

Ward, Ida C., *The Phonetics of English.* D. Appleton and Co., New York, 1929.

Guide to Pronunciation. From Webster's *New International Dictionary.* 2nd edition, unabridged. G. and C. Merriam Co., Springfield, Mass., 1934.

[*Ed. note.* Additional references will be found in the revised Bibliography and Chronicle. Exercises and questions for this chapter are found in the Appendix.]

Chapter VI

EMBRYOLOGY

I. Introduction
- A. The Characteristics of Protoplasm
- B. Specialization of Functions
- C. Germ Cells

II. The Origin and Early Development of the Embryo
- A. Fertilization
- B. Segmentation
- C. Differentiation

III. The Development of the Nervous System
- A. General Development
- B. Spinal Cord and Nervous Tissue
- C. Brain

IV. The Development of the Pharyngeal Region

V. The Development of the Respiratory System

VI. The Development of the Facial Region
- A. The Frontonasal Process and the Nose and Air Sinuses
- B. The Mandibular Processes and the Lower Jaw
- C. The Maxillary Processes and the Upper Jaw
- D. The Palatal Processes and the Palate
- E. The Lateral Nasal Processes and the Cheeks
- F. The Oral Cavity

VII. Summary: Chronology Table

Exercises and Questions

INTRODUCTION

Embryology, like history, aids in interpreting existing conditions by clarifying preceding progressive developments. In the adult human body, most of the structures and systems appear to be extremely complex. Through the study of embryology, enough information about the rudiments of these systems may be gained to make it less difficult to account for them and for their complexity.

The usual approach to the study of man is by way of a preliminary study of lower animals. Such a study reveals many basic principles which are directly applicable to human development. Before turning to a simple one-celled animal, however, such as the amoeba, certain fundamental conceptions regarding the morphological unit, the cell, need to be reviewed.

A. The Characteristics of Protoplasm

A typical cell is a protoplasmic mass containing a *nucleus*. It must be kept in mind that the cell is a tri-dimensional object. Cells may take any conceivable shape. Cells live in a fluid medium. The *cell membrane,* which may or may not be demonstrable, permits an interchange of substances through it between the protoplasm and its surrounding medium.

Protoplasm (Greek *protos,* first; *plasma,* thing formed) is the living substance of animal and vegetable tissues. It is a colloidal fluid. Chemically, it is a complex of proteins, carbohydrates, lipoids, and inorganic salts, together with a high percentage of water. The following twelve chemical elements are always found in protoplasm: Calcium (Ca), carbon (C), chlorine (Cl), hydrogen (H), iron (Fe), magnesium (Mg), nitrogen (N), oxygen (O), phosphorus (P), potassium (K), sodium (Na), and sulphur (S). Life is inherent in protoplasm. Protoplasm, therefore, demonstrates those manifestations which we have come to associate with life and the living.

The *amoeba* will serve to illustrate the characteristics of protoplasm. The amoeba is capable of surviving alone; it is able to perform all of the vital functions. Touch the cell and it moves, thus demonstrating receptivity of stimuli, transmission of impulse, and response. The amoeba, also, carries on such processes as digestion, respiration, heat-production, growth, and reproduction. These inherent characteristics of protoplasm may be listed:

Motility	Digestion	Growth
Irritability	Assimilation	Repair
Conductivity	Heat production	Reproduction
Respiration	Excretion	

B. Specialization of Functions

The reader has already realized that a microscopic mass of protoplasm, as represented by the protozoon, appears to be able to do everything basic that can be done by a multicellular animal (metazoon) such as man. As one studies, in ascending order, the forms of animal life between the amoeba and man, he will notice that cells increasingly assume specialized functions. In *hydra,* for example, some cells have to do primarily with locomotion; others with food-getting. At the top of the scale, in man, we find the highest type of specialization. Some cells are receptors of stimuli; others are transmitters of impulses; others have functions of digestion, motility, respiration, or reproduction. But now, in metazoa, no cell is able to survive alone. Every specialized cell is dependent for existence on the co-ordinating action of all the aggregates of specialized cells.

C. Germ Cells

Between the independent type of cell (e.g., the amoeba) and the dependent specialized cell (e.g., the nerve cell), may be classed the *germ cell.* Germ cells are ordinarily incapable of independent development, but constitute such intermatching systems that the union of a female germ cell with a male germ cell gives rise to a new individual. The uniting human germ cells carry every quality essential to the creation of a human being.

There are two kinds of germ cells. The female germ cell (*ovum*) is nonmotile and has a diameter of about 0.2 mm. The male germ cell (*spermatozoon*) is motile and has an overall length—i.e., head and neck plus tail—of 0.05 mm.; the head alone is about 0.005 mm. long. The relative volume of spermatozoon to ovum is as 1 to 85,000.[1]

THE ORIGIN AND EARLY DEVELOPMENT OF THE EMBRYO

A. Fertilization

Complex man is developed from the union of two single germ cells. Impregnation of the ovum, i.e., *fertilization,* is said to take place when a spermatozoon unites with an ovum. The united cells may be called the *zygote.* Imagine a common pin (*spermatozoon*) approaching, and finally piercing, head first, an apple (*ovum*). After the pin has entered the apple the area of its entrance is repaired and immediately profound changes begin to take place within the apple.

B. Segmentation

Imagine, further, that as a result of these changes the apple divides to form two apples. Now each of the two apples divides. Thus, from one original apple, there have been produced four apples. Further division produces eight, sixteen, thirty-two, sixty-four, and so on. At some part of its surface each complete apple is in contact with at least two other apples. This means that as more and more apples are produced there will be a tendency for them to be pushed farther and farther out toward the periphery of the mass of apples.

Although nothing actually is known about human development from fertilization until the establishment of the embryonic disc, we may conjecture as to what takes place during that period of time. If now, we re-

[1] It has been said that the number of ova which would fill a three-inch cubical container, and the spermatozoa which would fill a spherical vessel having the diameter of a pinhead, would be sufficient to produce the next generation in all of North America.

place our original apple with the fertilized ovum and follow the process of *segmentation* [2] or *cell division,* we surmise that the egg is split up or fractionated into small cells called *blastomeres,* in a 2, 4, 8, 16, 32, 64, etc., sequence. (See Fig. 42.) So rapid is this cell division that the *daughter cells* do not have an opportunity to assume the size of the mother cell. They are, in fact, progressively halved in size until a certain minimum is reached. Thus, although segmentation is not development, per se, it is preparation for development. The mass of cells at about the 32-cell stage may be likened, in external appearance, to a mulberry, and hence receives the name *morula* (Latin dim. of *morus,* mulberry). This is the morula stage in the production of an embryo.

One of the reasons that the rapid increase in the number of cells forces them to form a hollow sphere is the fact that the life of every cell is dependent on its surrounding aqueous environment for sustenance. The more surface the cell can expose to the medium in which it lives, the more readily can it carry on an exchange with its environment through its cell membrane. Inasmuch as the cell is tridimensional, its growth (volume) increases as the cube, while its surface (area) increases only as the square. Because two cells are formed from one, cell division tends to double the surface while halving the volume. Each new cell assumes a position that will offer as great an exposure on its surface as possible. The spherical envelope form provides, short of the separate and individual independence of each cell, the maximum exposure.

Our information in this field comes from studies made on monkeys and other mammals. What little is known about the human process is highly theoretical. But probably in the human embryo the first cleavage is complete within an hour or two from the time of penetration of the egg by the sperm. Following this there is about one cleavage per day for the first four to seven days, i. e., during the passage through the uterine tube. Approximately, the 64-cell stage has been attained at the time the blastocyst reaches the uterus about one week after fertilization. (The trophoblast begins to implant within a few hours after entering the uterus.) The multiplication of cells continues; the 128 forming 256, etc. The doubling is probably only theoretical, however. Some cells divide more rapidly than others, so that, in actual cases, a few more or less than 256, for example, would be found. Quite likely, the progression may be 2, 3, 4, 6, 8, 10, 12, etc.

C. Differentiation

Up to and including the 32-cell stage, the morula is a solid sphere of cells; at about the 64-cell stage a central cavity appears and the *blastocyst*

[2] Instead of segmentation, such synonyms as mitosis and cleavage may be found in the literature.

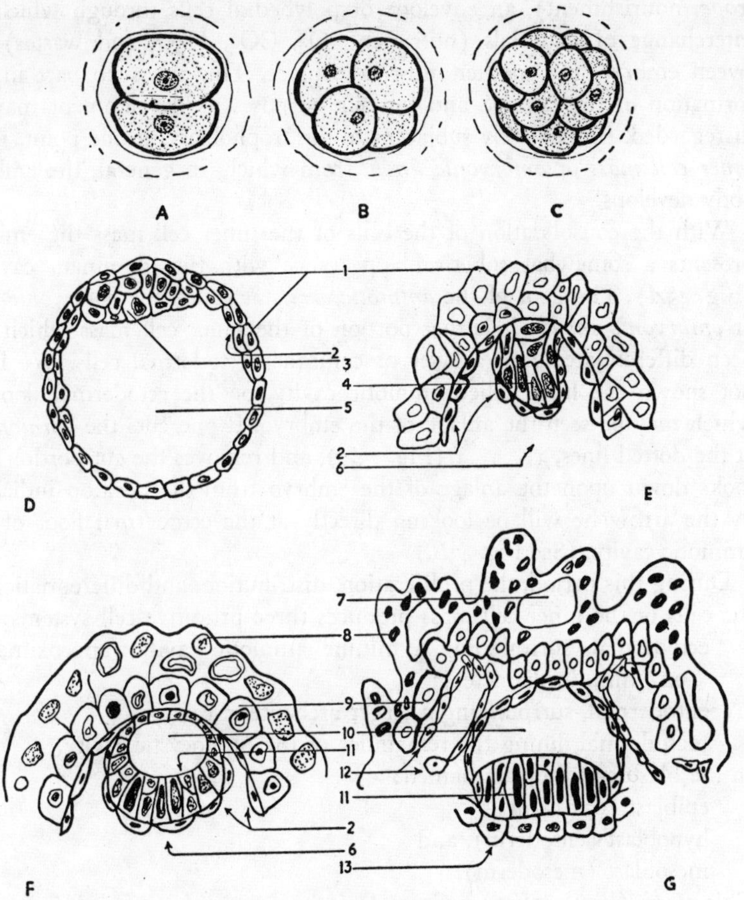

FIG. 42. Development from the Two-cell Stage to the Stage of the Amniotic Cavity.

A. Two-cell stage.
B. Four-cell stage.
C. Morula stage.
D, E, F, G: Stages of development from blastocoel to amniotic cavity.

1. Trophoblast; 2. entoderm (migrating out from inner cell mass); 3. inner cell mass; 4. ectoderm; 5. blastocoel; 6. primitive yolk-sac; 7. blood lacuna; 8. plasmoditrophoblast; 9. cytotrophoblast; 10. amniotic cavity; 11. embryonic ectoderm; 12. extra-embryonic ectoderm; 13. embryonic entoderm.

stage is reached. This is largely a monovesicular structure, perhaps 0.250 mm. in diameter. The inner cavity, which is filled with liquid medium, is called the segmentation cavity or blastocele (Greek *blastos,* germ; *koilos,* hollow). The blastula is made up of a single layer of blastomeres; this primitive cell layer is known as the blastoderm. The mammalian blastula is called a blastocyst (Greek *kytis,* bladder) or blastodermic vesicle. The covering layer of cells about the cavity gives rise to the *trophoblast* (Greek *trope,* nourishment), an envelope of polyhedral cells through which all interchange of materials (nutriment, O_2, CO_2, H_2O, and wastes) between embryo and mother must take place. This takes no part in the formation of the embryo and for our purposes its development may be disregarded. Immediately subjacent to the trophoblast, at one point, is an *inner cell mass* or *embryonic knob,* from which, in general, the embryo body develops.

With the consolidation of the cells of the inner cell mass the embryo presents a somewhat spherical appearance with two dominant cavities (Fig. 43*A*). The floor of the *amniotic cavity* is called the *embryonic disc* or *embryonic shield.* It is that portion of the inner cell mass which has been differentiated into a layer of columnar ectodermal cells. We have not shown the liquid-filled amniotic cavity, on the ectodermal floor of which may be seen the anlage of the embryo. If one cuts the *amnion,* as at the dotted lines, *x*......*x* (Fig. 43*A*), and removes the cut portion and looks down upon the anlage of the embryo from the position indicated by the arrow he will be looking directly at the ectodermal floor of the amniotic cavity. (See Fig. 43*B*.)

During this period, the proliferation, distribution, and differentiation of the cells of the inner cell mass produces three primitive cell systems:

ectodermal, surrounding a minute amniotic cavity (approximately 0.15 mm. in diameter);
entodermal, surrounding a larger archenteric cavity;
mesodermal, lining the remainder of the blastocystic cavity.

In the blastocyst they are named:

epiblast (ectoderm),
hypoblast (entoderm), and
mesoblast (mesoderm).

This stage (Figs. 42*F* and *G;* 43*A*) is known as that of the bivesicular blastocyst or chorionic vesicle.

At about three weeks, the ectodermal floor of the amniotic cavity and entodermal roof of the *yolk-sac,* lying in apposition, constitute an oval plate approximately 1.25 mm. in length. Cell growth has resulted in giving this area, the embryonic disc, first an oval shape, and finally, a somewhat pear-like shape. (Fig. 43*B*.) The wide end of the disc represents the head and the narrow stem end the tail. From this disc is developed the entire embryonic body.

At about the center of the disc there now appears a small knob of cells, the *primitive knot* or *Hensen's node;* in fresh specimens under the microscope it looks like a dark spot. What appears to be an opaque line or shadow extends caudally from the node. This is the *primitive streak,* the result of the axial thickening of the ectoderm. Extending rostrally from the node is the notochordal primordium (head process).

In order to understand the formation of the primitive streak one must know that nature demonstrates in protoplasm the setting up of definite areas, divisions, and poles of growth, development, and differentiation. For example, although no single physical, electrical, or chemical explanation seems to supply a definite *raison d'être,* embryos normally demonstrate polarity—i. e., one end or area becomes the dominant one at which the most rapid growth or development occurs. Also, usually, from one pole toward another which may be subordinate, may extend an actual or imaginary axis upon either side of which takes place a similarity of growth.

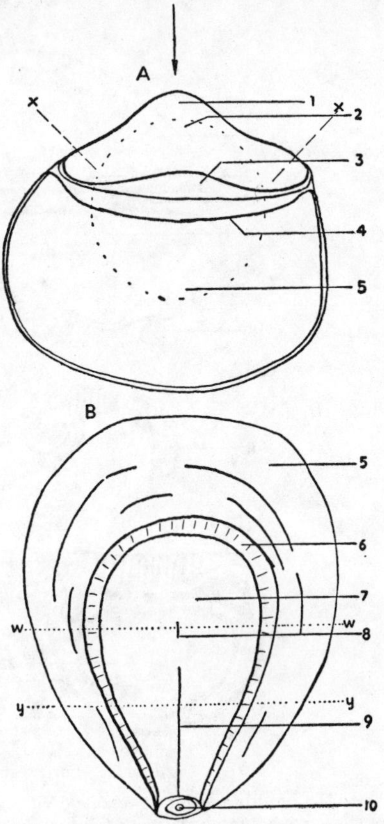

FIG. 43 (*A* and *B*). The Floor of the Amniotic Cavity.

All of the parts not included in the dotted circle in *A* are, for our purposes, relatively unimportant. Most texts adopt the practice of showing in figures of advanced growth only the area or a portion of the area included within the dotted circle.

1. Trophoblast; 2. amniotic cavity; 3. embryonic ectoderm; 4. entoderm; 5. yolk-sac; 6. cut edge of amnion; 7. floor of amniotic cavity; 8. head process; 9. primitive groove; 10. body stalk.

The primitive streak is merely an elongation of an area of rapid proliferation from which migrates the mesoderm. Somewhat later, at the rostral end of the streak there originates the notochordal primordium or head process. The notochord appears later than does the mesoderm and it does not spread out over such an extensive area, confining its advance rostrally as a cord-shaped mass of cells.

A cross section through the primitive streak shows that from each side of this line of thickening of the ectoderm the body mesoderm grows out laterally.

With the pushing out cephalad of the notocordal rudiment from the node, the node appears to be driven back or caudad.

A very narrow cavity in the notocordal process establishes communication between the amniotic and archenteric cavities. It is called the neurenteric canal. (Fig. 44*A*.)

As seen in the cross section (Fig. 44*F*), the thickened ectoderm in the median longitudinal line forms a sort of keel. The slight groove on the dorsal surface of the ectoderm is the *primitive groove.* From each side of the primitive streak, laterally, there migrates and pushes out a third germ layer, the *mesoderm*. The mesoderm tends to keep the *ectoderm* and *entoderm* from coming into contact. The spreading out of the mesoderm goes

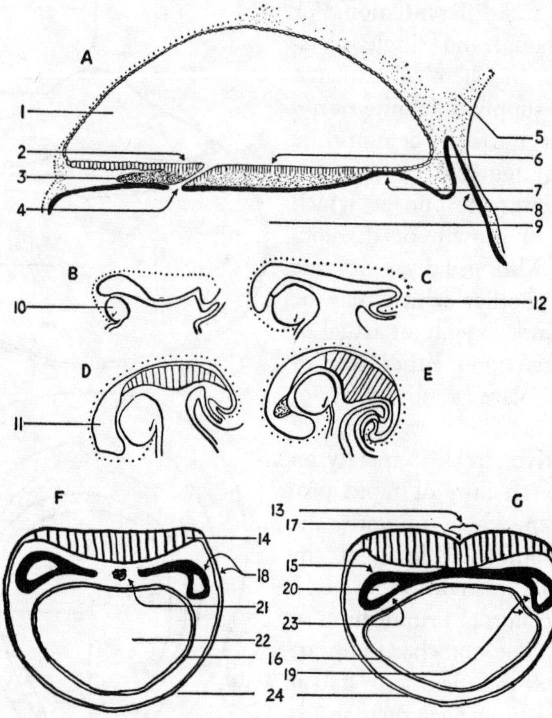

FIG. 44. Early Embryonic Development.

A. The head process: 1. Amniotic cavity; 2. primitive node; 3. head process; 4. neurenteric canal; 5. connecting body stalk; 6. primitive streak; 7. cloacal membrane; 8. allantois; 9. yolk-sac cavity.

B, C, D, E: Rostral growth of head region. 10. Heart; 11. head region; 12. cut edge of amnion.

F, G: Differentiation of the mesoderm. 13. Primitive streak; 14. ectoderm; 15. somatic mesoderm; 16. entoderm; 17. primitive groove; 18. somatopleure (somatic mesoderm plus trophectoderm); 19. splanchnopleure (splanchnic mesoderm plus entoderm); 20. coelom; 21. notochord; 22. primitive gut; 23. splanchnic mesoderm; 24. trophectoderm.

on in every part of the embryonic area except in the mid-line where ectoderm and entoderm are in contact. One of the special areas devoid of mesoderm is just rostral to the anterior end of the notochord. Here the mesoderm extends forward on either side as a crescent, meeting at the mid-line rostral to the notochord and enclosing an area known as the *buccopharyngeal area* (Fig. 45*A*). A cross section through that area (Fig. 44*F*) shows that the ectoderm and entoderm are in close contact forming a thin membrane, the *oral plate* or *buccopharyngeal membrane,* which constitutes a thin dam between the primitive mouth cavity and the primitive pharynx (Fig. 45*B*).

Rostral to this primitive mouth-pharynx region will be formed the pericardium, and hence the area is termed the pericardial area.

In approximately the third week the mesodermal cells are separated into two layers. The outer layer lines the inner aspect of the trophoblast and continues as a thin layer covering the ectodermal wall of the amniotic cavity. This mesodermal layer plus the ectodermal layer is called somatopleure

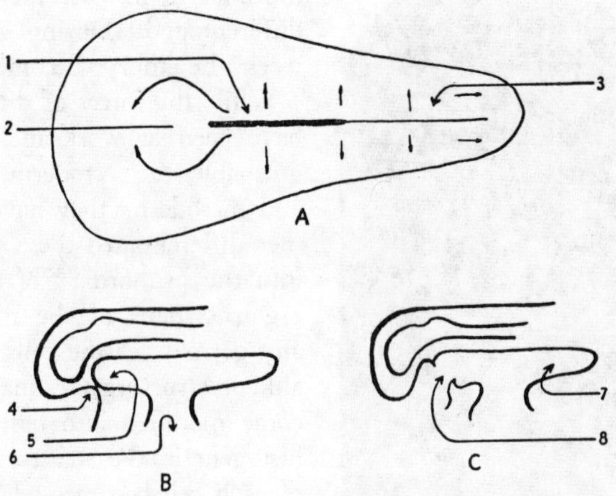

FIG. 45. Development of the Buccopharyngeal Region.

A. 1. Head process; 2. buccopharyngeal area; 3. primitive streak. Arrows indicate direction of growth of mesoderm.

B, C. 4. Buccopharyngeal membrane; 5. foregut; 6. yolk-sac; 7. hindgut; 8. opening for stomodeum into foregut.

(Greek *soma,* body; *pleura,* side); from its continuation into the embryo body proper will come the walls of the future thoracic and abdominal cavities. The inner layer of mesoderm surrounds the entodermal wall of the archenteric cavity (Archenteron—Greek *arche,* beginning; *enteron,* intestine). This double layer of mesoderm and entoderm is called splanchnopleure (Greek *splanchnon,* viscus; *pleura,* side). It will form the walls of the future digestive and associated systems.

The margin of the plate, embryonic rim, is comparatively slow in growth—so much so that intraembryonic formation may almost be said to take place within a rigid circumference. The growing structures, therefore, cannot maintain themselves in a platelike plane; they must by their growth throw the plate into curves and project over the rim. The *cephalic* (head) and *caudal* (tail) ends of the embryo soon project above (dorsally) and beyond the longitudinal limits of the embryonic disc. (Fig. 46.) The rostral growth of the head region overrides the area occupied by the buccopharyngeal membrane and the caudal portion of the pericardial area so that they are folded under the embryonic head. The buccopharyngeal and the pericardial areas are now ventral to the neural structure. The originally rostral wall of the pericardium now becomes its caudal wall; the buccopharyngeal area is now cephalic to the pericardium, whereas, before, it was caudal to it. (See Fig. 44*B, C, D, E.*) The rostral *diverticulum* created in the ventrally located yolk-sac and enclosed by this folding is called the *fore-gut.*

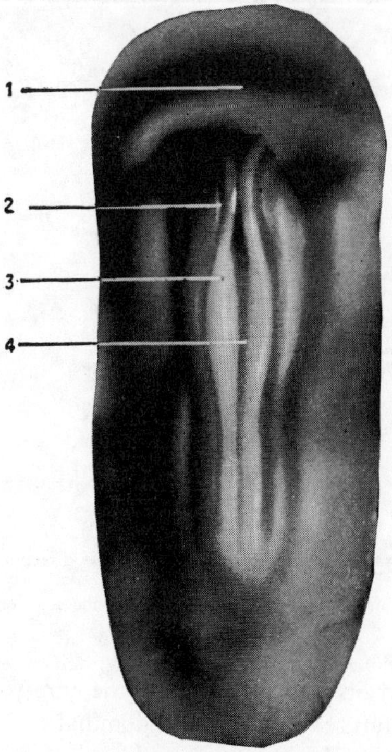

FIG. 46. Development of Embryo on Floor of Amniotic Cavity.

1. Floor of amniotic cavity; 2. cephalic end of embryo lifted up from plane of embryonic disc; 3. neural folds; 4. neural groove.

At about five weeks (5 mm. stage) the embryo has become quite fully differentiated. During the eighth week, the embryo becomes a *fetus.*

While the forces of differentiation have been at work making distinguishable the ectoderm, entoderm, and mesoderm, they have, also, further differentiated these germ layers into the primordia[3] of the various organ systems of the mammal. In any germ layer the cells are at first alike in structure. Gradually, they become modified into tissues. During histogenesis, the structure and form of each cell becomes adapted to the performance of distinct functions. This fact gives rise to the so-called law of genetic restriction. Succinctly stated, it is that any differentiation progressively restricts further differentiation. The static condition or the changes, at any given time, are determined by the nature and by the progress of previous differentiation. For example, ectoderm gives rise to the nervous tissue and to epidermis; thereafter, the nervous tissue cannot form epidermis.

From its position it is apparent that the ectoderm will come into relation with the external world and, hence, its two great duties are to produce the protective covering of the body and the system for receiving and utilizing sensations. The entoderm, as would be guessed from its position inside, forms the epithelium of the outer terminations of the digestive canal. The mesoderm, lying as it does between the other two layers, is shut off from direct relation with the external environment or with food sources. This

[3] Primordium is a term applied to the earliest discernible cell aggregation destined to form any organ or part of the embryo. The German word *anlage* and the French term *ébauche* have comparable meanings.

makes it apparent that its derivatives will be restricted to a series of internal functions. Three of these important functions have to do with movement, supporting the body structures, and circulation. The following outline shows the body tissues eventually formed by further growth and differentiation of the three germ layers. Of the derivatives listed, only those classifications starred (*), and not all of the tissues within any starred group, need attract the special interest of the reader.

Ectoderm (Greek *ektos,* outside; *derma,* skin)
- *Nervous system
- Epithelium of skin (dermis); hair; nails; sebaceous, sudoriferous, and mammary gland lining cells
- *Epithelium of nose and adjacent air sinuses; of cheeks and roof of mouth; of anterior surface cornea; of conjunctiva, of external auditory meatus, and of lacrimal glands
- *Neuroepithelium of sense organs
- Anterior lobe of hypophysis cerebri
- Enamel of teeth

Entoderm (Greek *entos,* inside)
- *Epithelial lining of digestive tube, except part of mouth and the terminal part of the rectum (ectoderm)
- Lining cells of all glands opening into digestive tube
- *Epithelium of auditory tube, tympanic cavity, and mastoid air cells, trachea, bronchi, and lung air cells; of urinary bladder and part of urethra; of follicles of thyroid gland, thymus, and parathyroids.

Mesoderm (Greek *mesos,* middle)
- *The remaining body tissues (muscles, bones, cartilages, connective tissues, heart, blood vessels and blood cells)

During the approximately 270-day period between fertilization and birth, the various cells form tissues which in turn form organs and systems. Thus, running parallel in development, there are laid down such systems as the digestive, nervous, and respiratory. Even though, for the sake of clarity, we now consider each given system alone, it must be kept in mind that while it is developing, other great and far-reaching changes are taking place in the embryo at the same time. Further, the development of any one system is intimately bound up with the development of each and every other. Only as the developmental processes in all progress, does the embryo grow in a normal manner. This means, then, that as we now begin our study of the development of the nervous system we must remember that the pharyngeal region, the respiratory system and the facial region—all of which we consider later in this chapter—are developing more or less concurrently.

THE DEVELOPMENT OF THE NERVOUS SYSTEM

A. General Development

About the fourteenth day of embryonic development the ectodermal cells begin to show a gradual modification of form. The cells, hitherto poly-

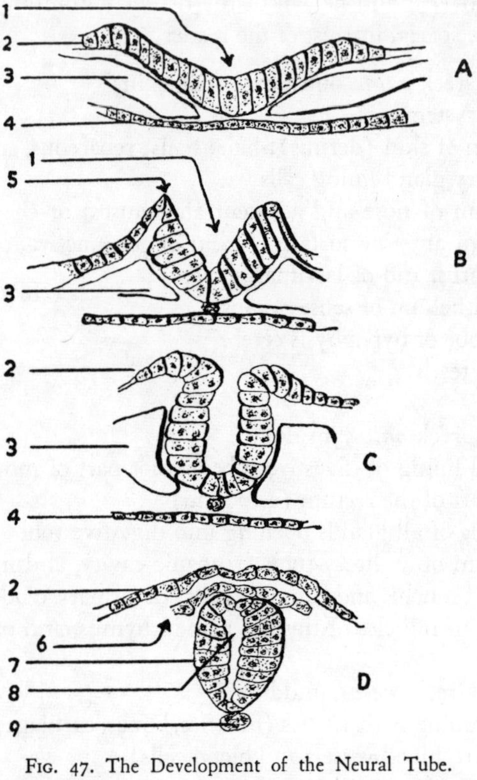

Fig. 47. The Development of the Neural Tube.

1. Neural groove; 2. ectoderm; 3. mesoderm; 4. entoderm; 5. neural fold; 6. neural crest; 7. neural tube; 8. neural canal; 9. notochord.

hedral, become columnar. Compare Fig. 42*A* and Fig. 47. This differentiation presages the appearance of the nervous elements. The cells most affected are in, and on either side of, the mid-dorsal line of the embryonic area, rostral to the primitive streak. The change in the shape of the cells as well as *proliferation* makes this longitudinal median zone thicker than the surrounding area. It is called the *medullary plate* or *neural plate*. At the time of the formation of this plate there is a heaping up of the ectodermal cells on either side of the median line to form the *medullary folds*. (Fig. 47.)

The plate soon displays a concavity on the dorsal surface, forming a longitudinal groove, the *medullary groove* or *neural groove* (2.2 mm. stage). With the further heaping up of the cells the *neural folds* become more elevated and at the same time the neural groove becomes, relatively, more depressed. As it deepens, the forces of cell growth tend to bring closer and closer together the tops of the ridges of the neural folds. In time they come

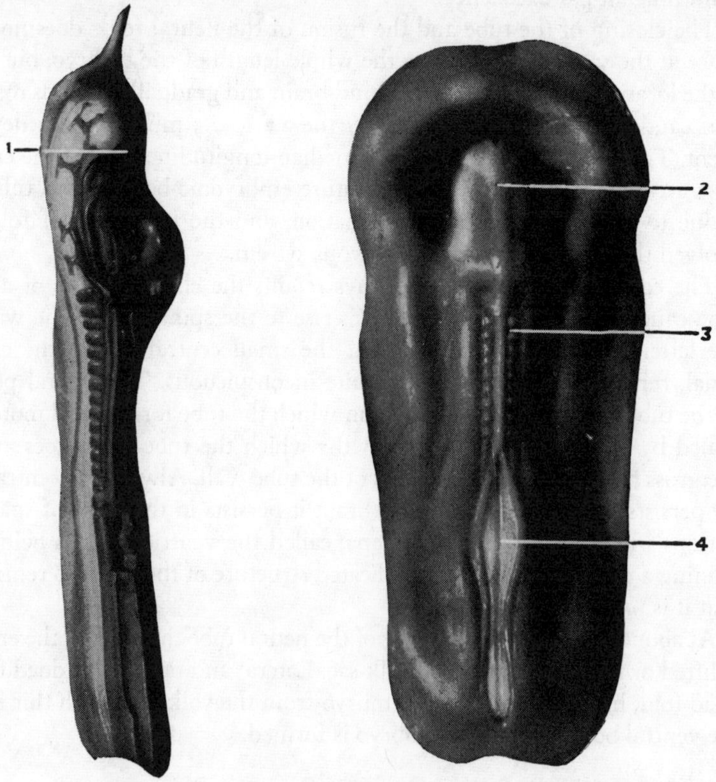

FIG. 48. Closure of the Neural Groove.

1. Rostral end of embryo curved over heart region; 2. neural groove closed at rostral end of embryo; 3. somites; 4. neural groove open at caudal end of embryo.

into contact in the region of the future hind-brain and the cells fuse in the median line above the groove so that a hollow tube or canal now replaces the groove. This is called the *neural tube*. The hollow tube of ectoderm lying beneath the surface of the embryo is later more widely separated from this surface by an ingrowth of mesoderm between it and the more superficial ectoderm. Figure 47*B* shows the beginning of the upward growth of the mesoderm around the neural tube. Soon this grows over the tube, entirely separating the ectodermal elements of the tube from the over-covering ectoderm. This is quite in accord with the idea that the ectoderm is that tissue peculiarly adapted to be in contact with the external environment. The overlying ectoderm is still in contact with the outer environment and will remain so as the dermal covering of the body. The ectoderm which seems to have retreated toward the embryonic interior, and therefore apparently contradicts the environment-relationship idea, is to give rise to the nervous system which, through modifications, becomes the environment contact-agent par excellence.

The closing of the tube and the fusion of the neural folds does not take place at the same time or along the whole length of the embryo, but starts at the location of what is to be the hind-brain and gradually extends rostrally and caudally. This is approximately the 2.2 to 2.5 mm. stage of development. The neural tube occupies the median longitudinal axis of the embryonic area and consequently of the future embryonic body. From this tube—due to unequal growth, differentiation, and the formation of folds—is evolved the entire adult central nervous system.

The central nervous system always retains the characteristics of a tube. The caudal portion of the tube gives rise to the spinal cord. The walls of the latter become so thickened that the small central cavity, the central canal, remaining in adult life is quite inconspicuous. The rostral portion of the tube develops into the brain, in which the tube form is still more concealed by the foldings and outgrowths which the tube undergoes and by the gross but irregular thickenings of the tube wall. Always the central cavity persists, however. In the adult brain it persists in the form of spaces of various irregular but constant shape, called the ventricles. It is helpful in gaining a conception of the complicated structure of the brain to remember that it is primarily a tube.

At about the time of the closing of the neural tube the head of the embryo is lifted or folded off from the yolk-sac. Lateral and tail-folds, added to this head-fold, lift and constrict the embryo from the yolk-sac. With this lifting the ventral body wall of the embryo is formed.

B. Spinal Cord and Nervous Tissue

The neural tube is not of uniform thickness. The side walls of the tube are thicker than the top (dorsal) and bottom (ventral) walls. The external outline of the tube is almost circular, but the lumen of the tube is a narrow dorsoventral fissure or slit. The boundaries of the fissure are the thickened lateral walls connected by a thin *dorsal roof-plate* and a thin *ventral floor-plate*.

The neural tube, as such, does not at first constitute functional nervous tissue. Its cells are not nerve cells. It is made up of unspecialized ectoderm. Nerve cells and nerve tissue becomes differentiated in the following manner:

Certain cells in the tube wall bordering the lumen become active, divide, and produce daughter cells. These move toward the periphery but stop midway. They change their form and send out branches which unite with branches from other similar cells to create a network of fibers, a framework, a scaffolding. These are not nerve cells, or nerve tissue. It is *neuroglia* (*glea,* glue), the special type of connective tissue found in the central nervous system.

Nerve cells originate in a similar manner. Large round or oval germinal cells first appear; at about thirty days they have increased in number to such an extent that they present a fairly continuous layer on each side of the lumen or central canal. Upon division the germinal cells give rise to *neuroblasts.* These migrate peripherally, away from the area bordering the lumen, into the mantle layer and, at the same time, as though to aid their migration, become streamlined or pear-shaped. They stop at the middle of the wall—i. e., in the mantle zone—perhaps because there they encounter the dense layer of neuroglia fibers. The transition from neuroblast to *nerve cell* is effected by the accumulation of the cell's protoplasm on one side of the nucleus and its elongation into a process. This process is a neurit or *axon;* it becomes the axis-cylinder of a nerve fiber. The *dendrites* appear considerably later. Continued growth extends the axon into the marginal layer; here it may course up or down the cord in a *segmental* or *intersegmental fiber tract* or it may emerge from the cord as the *efferent root* of a spinal nerve. In the brain wall the evolution of the efferent nerve fibers is similar to that in the cord.

The roof-plate and floor-plate contain no germinal cells, and hence do not become thickened as do the side walls. They either retain their initial epithelial character or else their cells become spongioblasts which give rise to supporting elements for various nerve fiber tracts.

To recapitulate, briefly: rapid cell growth and migration cause the neural tube to become multi-layered, while differentiation produces two kinds of nervous system elements—

(1) a supporting tissue system of neuroglia cells, and
(2) neuroblasts, which form nerve cells demonstrating a high degree of irritability and conductivity.

After the appearance of the neuroblasts the wall of the neural tube may be divided into three layers, or zones. (Fig. 49*C*.) From the inside of the tube laterally, there may be named:

the *ependymal layer* of epithelial lining cells,
the *mantle layer* (the area to be occupied by the future gray columns), and
the *marginal layer,* or reticular zone (occupying the position of the future tracts of fibers constituting the white substance of the cord).

Figure 49*B* shows a stage of development somewhat more advanced than that seen in Fig. 49*A*. The change in the shape of the lumen of the tube, which is widened laterally in the dorsal portion, is due to the addition of the two laterally projecting angles resulting from the rapid proliferation of the cells in the lateral walls. This has the effect of dividing each lateral wall into a dorsal and a ventral region. These regions are related respectively to the *afferent* or *sensory* (dorsal) *roots* and the *efferent* or *motor* (ventral) *roots* of the spinal nerves. Later, the wide dorsal part of the canal is narrowed and finally obliterated, while the ventral part widens out in comparison. Ultimately, however, the ventral part becomes almost insignifi-

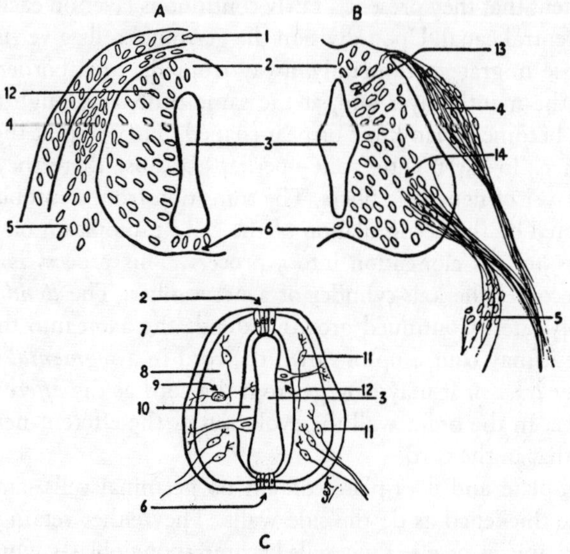

FIG. 49. Differentiation of Cells in the Neural Tube.

1. Ectoderm; 2. roof plate; 3. neural canal; 4. spinal ganglion; 5. sympathetic ganglion; 6. floor plate; 7. marginal layer; 8. mantle layer; 9. germinal cell; 10. ependymal layer; 11. neuroblast; 12. spongioblast; 13. alar lamina; 14. basal lamina.

cant, persisting in the adult as the minute *central canal* of the medulla spinalis. (Figure 64, page 236.)

The efferent nerve cells located in the ventral portion of the mantle layer are numerous and lie close together. Their axons emerge from the ventrolateral side of the tube and make up bundles of fibers which pass through the marginal zone and out to the developing muscle tissue (motor roots). With the growth of the fetus, the muscle becomes removed from its proximity to the neural tube, and, hence, the nerve axons must increase in length.

Not all of the axons of efferent nerve cells emerge from the tube. Some, central axons, when they reach the marginal zone, turn upward or downward within it, serving to connect the segments of the cord as *intersegmental fibers.* Others, *commissural fibers,* pass through the marginal zone, horizontally, and cross its ventral portion, at the ventral commissure, to the opposite side of the tube. These commissural fibers serve to connect the right and left sides of the tube.

Part of the ectoderm which formed the caps of the neural folds or lips of the neural groove, and which was left between the neural tube and the ectoderm when the tube closed, is called the *neural crest.* It lies close and somewhat dorsolateral to the tube, a longitudinal strip or band along either side.[4] At certain intervals, active proliferation forms bulges in the bands of the neural crest cells. These enlargements are the *spinal ganglia.* In these ganglia are to be found, as in the cord, neuroblasts. The neuroblasts develop into nerve cells [5] whose axons enter the cord as part of the dorsal afferent roots and pass up and down in the marginal layer. Ramifying processes of these fibers make contact, in the mantle layer, with the dendrites of efferent neurons. The dorsal root joins the ventral root from the same segment, the two forming a spinal nerve. These are in pairs for each segment, one on the left and one on the right side of the tube.[6]

The neural crest gives rise to other cells which do not remain near the dorsal aspect of the neural tube and which do not send axons into the tube. These cells migrate to a position ventral to the tube and form nerve cells. Each cell develops an axon which may pass to some organ within the body, e. g., heart, pancreas. Upon reaching the organ, the axon becomes intimately associated with the glandular or muscular tissue there. The cell bodies of these nerve fibers are aggregated in the sympathetic nervous system ganglia. Some of the ganglia lie in two rows or chains along the ventral aspect of the vertebral column; others migrate greater distances and are found scattered among the internal organs. While the cell bodies and axons of these ganglia are entirely outside the neural tube and do not send processes to it, they are connected with it by axons of central cells which grow out to the sympathetic system ganglia by way of the ventral roots.

At about two weeks, an embryo displays transverse segmentation of the mesoderm along its longitudinal axis. The symmetrically arranged cubical masses are easily seen on either side of the neural tube and notochord. To each segment there is distributed a spinal nerve. Each segmental division of mesoderm grows medially, dorsally, and ventrally, around the neural tube and notochord, toward its fellow and fusing with it encloses notochord and tube. Likewise, the segments are joined together in a chain longitudinally. This covers the neural tube with a complete envelope of mesoderm, the membranous vertebral column. At about four weeks chondrification (*chondros,* cartilage) begins and there results the cartilaginous vertebral column, which in turn gives rise, in great part, to an osseous (*os,* bone) vertebral column.

[4] From it are derived, directly, the cranial nerve ganglia, the spinal nerve ganglia and, indirectly and probably in part only, the sympathetic nervous system ganglia.

[5] The differentiation and development of the nerve cell in the ganglion is quite like that of the nerve cell in the tube, except that this cell develops two rather long processes. One, the axonic-dendrite, grows toward the periphery of the body and connects with some sensory end organ; the other, the axon, grows centrally, toward and enters the neural tube.

[6] Each root, dorsal or ventral, is simply a bundle of nerve fibers either entering the neural tube or leaving it.

There is no actual transverse segmentation visible on the surface of the medulla spinalis; nevertheless, for convenience the cord is conceived to be made up of a series of segments, called spinal segments, arranged serially. Each segment is as long as the extent of the attachment of its particular pair of spinal nerves.

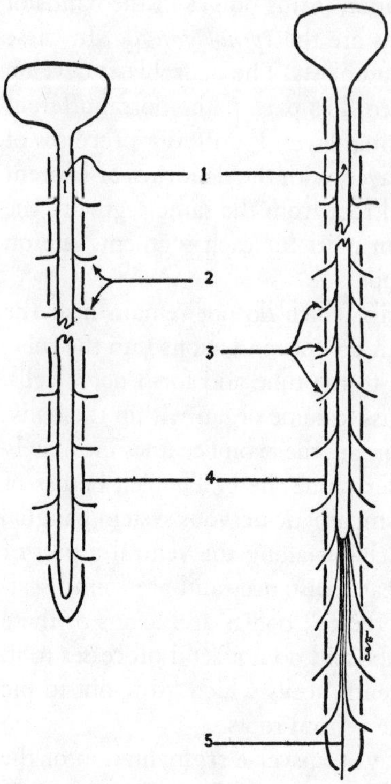

FIG. 50. Unequal Growth of Medulla Spinalis and Vertebral Column.

1. Medulla spinalis; 2. spinal nerves; 3. intervertebral foramina; 4. vertebral column; 5. filum terminale.

The first nerve fibers of the *medulla spinalis* to develop (about four weeks) are the short intersegmental fibers—passing between adjacent spinal segments—originating from the mantle zone nerve cells, and the fibers of the dorsal root ganglia which migrate (*biotaxis*) into the cord. The long intersegmental fibers—passing between a given spinal segment and other segments at some distance away—next appear (third month), followed by the *cerebrospinal fibers* (fifth month)—passing between brain and cord. None of the fibers are at first invested with *medullary sheaths*. Not all groups of fibers get their sheath coatings at the same time. The dorsal and ventral root fibers are invested at about five months. The cerebrospinal fibers are sheathed after birth.

At first, the pair of spinal nerves in any segment leaves the cord and passes through the respective opposite intervertebral foramina at approximately right angles. The cord and vertebral column have unequal rates of growth, the column growing more rapidly than the cord. Therefore, the nerve roots become more oblique in the direction they take when leaving the cord and before finding exit from the vertebral column. (Fig. 50.) The following comparative figures indicate the difference in growth of column and cord: 90 days, same length; 180 days, the cord reaches only to the upper end of the sacrum; 270 days, the cord reaches only to the level of the third lumbar vertebra; adulthood, the cord reaches only to the level of the lower border of the first lumbar vertebra. However, the filum terminale extends from the caudal end of the medulla spinalis to the coccyx.

C. Brain

The growth of the cells of the neural groove is not entirely directed toward the production of a simple tube of approximately uniform diameter along the longitudinal axis of the future embryo. Under certain natural forces some cells, in specific and regularly identical areas from embryo to embryo, produce a widening of the groove. Between the 2 mm. and 3 mm. stage the neural groove in its cephalic portion shows three areas of enlargement; growth areas, demarcated by two constricted areas, limited growth areas. All of this is the future brain region. With the formation of the neural tube three expanded brain parts [7]—anatomically distinct and demarcated by portions of the tube which have not expanded—are clearly laid down and are called, beginning with the most caudal:

rhombencephalon (*rhomb,* rhomboid in appearance; *encephalon,* brain. Hind-brain)
mesencephalon (*mes,* middle. Mid-brain)
prosencephalon (*pros,* before. Fore-brain)

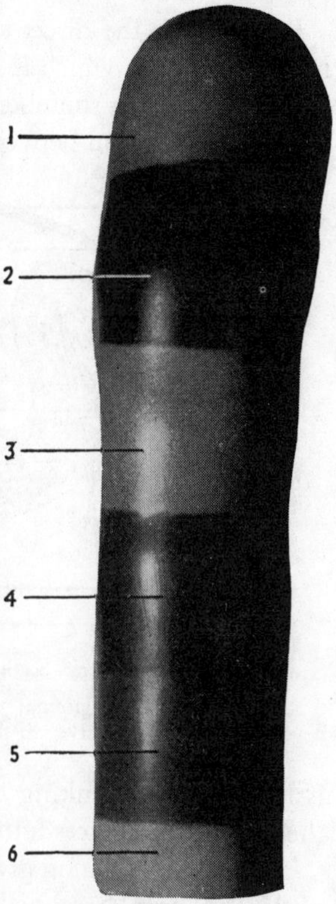

Fig. 51. Five Early Brain Areas.

1. Telencephalon; 2. diencephalon; 3. mesencephalon; 4. metencephalon; 5. myelencephalon; 6. medulla spinalis (rostral portion).

At about the 7 mm. stage the rhombencephalon is demarcated into two parts called, beginning with the more caudal, the *myelencephalon* and the *metencephalon.*

The mesencephalon retains its fundamental original character.

At about the 3 mm. stage the prosencephalon is demarcated into two fairly distinct portions called, beginning with the more caudal, the *diencephalon* and the *telencephalon.* (Fig. 51.)

Now, beginning with the most caudal, the five brain areas are:

Myelencephalon }
Metencephalon } Rhombencephalon

[7] Not only are there areas of expansion bounded by areas of relative constriction or failure to expand, but due to unequal growth of parts of the brain-portion of the neural tube there are produced three bendings or flexures: the ventral cephalic flexure (third week); the cervical flexure (lasts from about the third to the fifth week), and the pontine flexure. The pontine flexure is the only one which presents its convexity forward.

Mesencephalon } Mesencephalon

Diencephalon
Telencephalon } Prosencephalon

Because it is the direct continuation or cephalic end of that part of the neural tube from which is formed the medulla spinalis, it is logical that we consider, first, the rhombencephalon or hind-brain. Structurally, the hind-brain is a transition between the cord and the rostral part of the brain; it

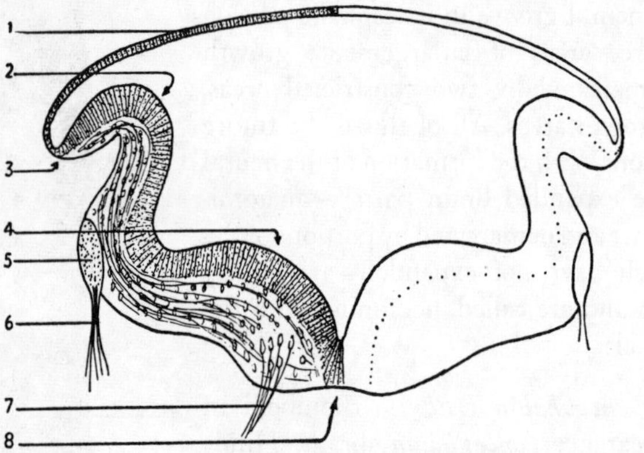

FIG. 52. Transverse Section through Medulla Oblongata of Human Embryo.

1. Roof plate; 2. alar lamina; 3. rhombic lip; 4. basal lamina; 5. tractus solitarius; 6. vagus nerve; 7. hypoglossal nerve; 8. floor plate.

is the functional linking path which welds the higher brain centers and the lower cord centers into a whole system.

The myelencephalon gives rise to the *medulla oblongata* by a thickening of the floor and lateral walls of the tube. Because of its intimate connection with the medulla spinalis we might expect that the development of the medulla oblongata would resemble that which takes place in the cord. To a great extent this is true, but there are differences. As in the case of the cord, the brain stem may be divided arbitrarily into *dorsal* (alar) and *ventral* (basal) *laminae* or plates. (Fig. 52.) Notice that in the medulla oblongata the lumen of the tube [8] is relatively more prominent than it is in the cord.

The metencephalon gives rise to the *cerebellum* and the *pons*. Each lateral half of the cerebellum arises as a fold from its respective dorsal lamina.[9] The lateral plates fuse on the roof-plate forming a bridge, the *vermis*. That is, at first the cerebellum is just a thick transverse band in the anterior part of the roof of the fourth ventricle. This plate (three months) becomes de-

[8] The lumen is given the name of ventricle in the brain.

[9] It should be remembered that the alar laminae are associated with sensory nerves.

marcated by two transverse fissures into three lobes. Other fissures and sulci develop later (four to seven months). The cerebellum is associated with the ear for equilibration, or balancing; it is also instrumental in the maintenance of body muscular tone (*tonus*). Nerve fibers enter or leave the cerebellum by way of the cerebellar peduncles, of which there are three on each side.

In an early embryo, the developing *pharyngeal* or *visceral arch* region lies directly ventral to the rhombencephalon. It is logical, therefore, that the centers of the nerves to the pharyngeal and related regions—nerves involved in mastication, swallowing, speaking, and breathing—should be located in the rhombencephalon even though, through subsequent growth, the pharyngeal (and visceral) region comes to be removed from its original proximity to the hind-brain. Incidentally, this means that the nerve fibers involved must grow longer as the embryo gets older. The hind-brain is sometimes called the visceral brain because it is in such intimate and reflex connection with structures of visceral (splanchnopleure) origin.

The mesencephalon is a relatively unmodified portion of the neural tube continued rostrally from the rhombencephalon and in turn demarcated at its cephalic extremity by the continuation of that part of the tube called the prosencephalon. In the adult brain its lumen or cavity is the *cerebral aqueduct*. The basal laminae of the mesencephalon form the cerebral peduncles. As early as the sixteenth week, four dorsal eminences are displayed as a result of the thickening of the alar laminae and a subsequent subdivision. These are the *corpora quadrigemina;* the rostral pair, called the *superior colliculi,* are associated with vision, and the caudal pair called the *inferior colliculi* are associated with hearing. The two pairs are closely integrated.

The prosencephalon or fore-brain consists of two parts: the diencephalon is its most caudal division, which is continuous, caudally, with the mesencephalon; the telencephalon is its cephalic part. In the diencephalon the alar lamina gives rise to the *thalamus, metathalamus,* and *epithalamus*. The thickening of the anterior two-thirds of each dorsal lamina produces its respective thalamus which may be seen on the brain surface at an early stage as a slight bulge. (See Fig. 54.) By growth toward the mid-line, the thalami may be united along their medial aspects, although this is a variable condition. In the diencephalon the basal lamina gives rise to the pars mamillaris, hypothalami, tuber cinereum, infundibulum, and the posterior lobe of the hypophysis.

The dorsal laminae of the telencephalon, by lateral evaginations, form the *cerebral hemispheres*. The cerebral cortex of the telencephalon is the most highly specialized and newest development of the brain. It mediates conscious and learned responses as opposed to the unconscious and reflex responses of the lower brain and cord levels. Each cerebral hemisphere may

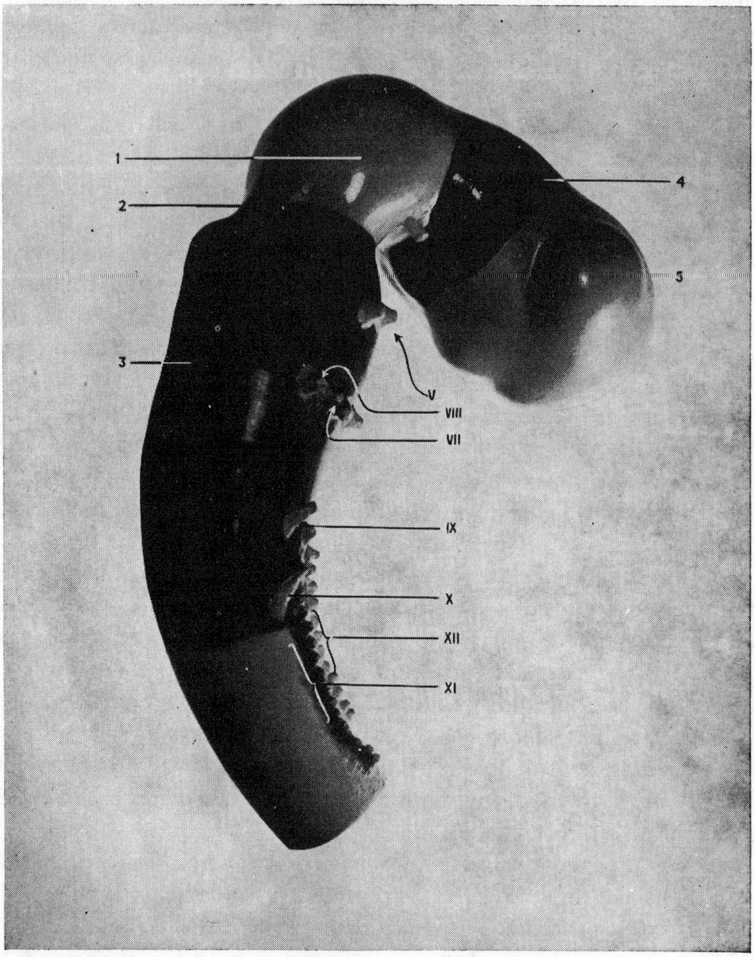

FIG. 53. Exterior of Brain of Human Embryo (About 4 Weeks).

1. Corpora quadrigemina region; 2. isthmus; 3. cerebellum area; 4. thalamus area; 5. cerebral hemisphere.

V. Trigeminal nerve.
VIII. Auditory nerve.
VII. Facial nerve.
IX. Glossopharyngeal nerve.
X. Vagus nerve.
XII. Hypoglossal nerve.
XI. Accessory nerve.

be said to consist of rhinencephalon and archipallium, corpus striatum, and neopallium. The neopallium makes up the greater part of the cerebral hemispheres. At about two months the telencephalon consists of a cavity (ventricle) enclosed by a thin wall. The evagination of the lateral walls of the telencephalon forms the primitive cerebral hemispheres. Growth is directed

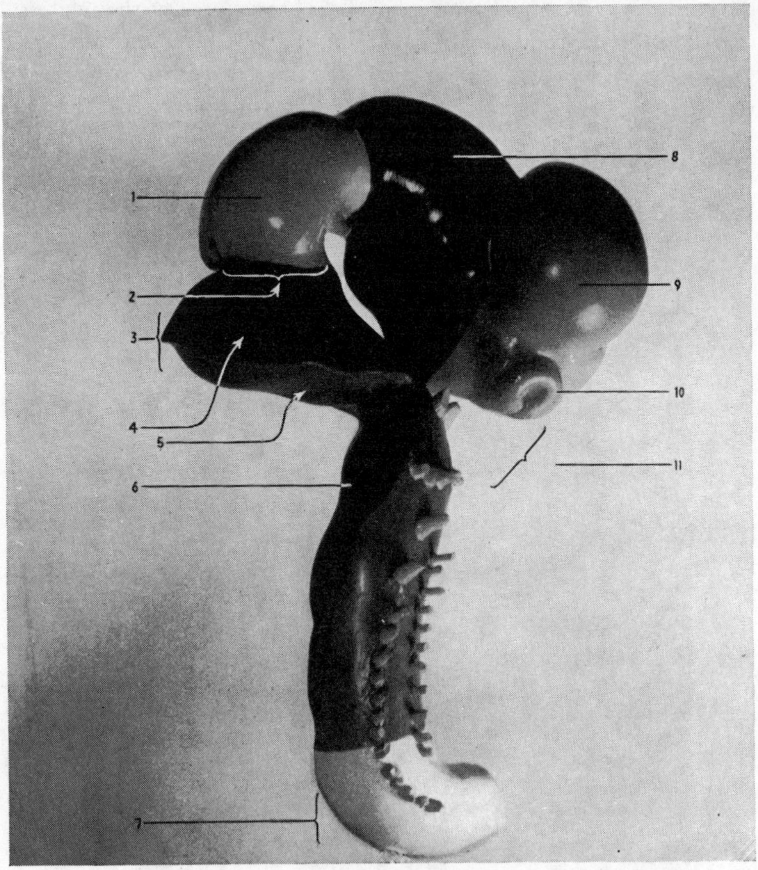

FIG. 54. Exterior of Brain of Human Embryo (About 5 Weeks).

1. Corpora quadrigemina region; 2. isthmus; 3. cephalic flexure; 4. cerebellum; 5. rhombic lip; 6. floor of rhomboid fossa; 7. cervical flexure; 8. thalamus region; 9. cerebral hemisphere; 10. optic stalk; 11. pontine flexure.

dorsally and posteriorly, as well as laterally, around the thalamus, covering progressively, the diencephalon (three months), mesencephalon (six months), and rhombencephalon (eight months). Because the median lamina which unites the two hemispheres does not undergo great growth, it has the effect of separating the hemispheres by a cleft, the *longitudinal fissure*.

Like other parts of the neural tube, the pallium, at first, presents ependymal, mantle, and marginal layers. At three months, however, the neuroblasts migrate to the marginal layer and the nerve cells produced there give rise to a superficial layer of gray substance, the *cerebral cortex*. The deep layer of white substance on which the cortex rests is made up of nerve fibers and is called the white medullary substance. In growth, the volume of the cortex expands much more than does the volume of the white substance. This difference in rate of expansion produces *gyri* separated by *fissures* or *sulci*. At about four or five months the hemispheres are relatively

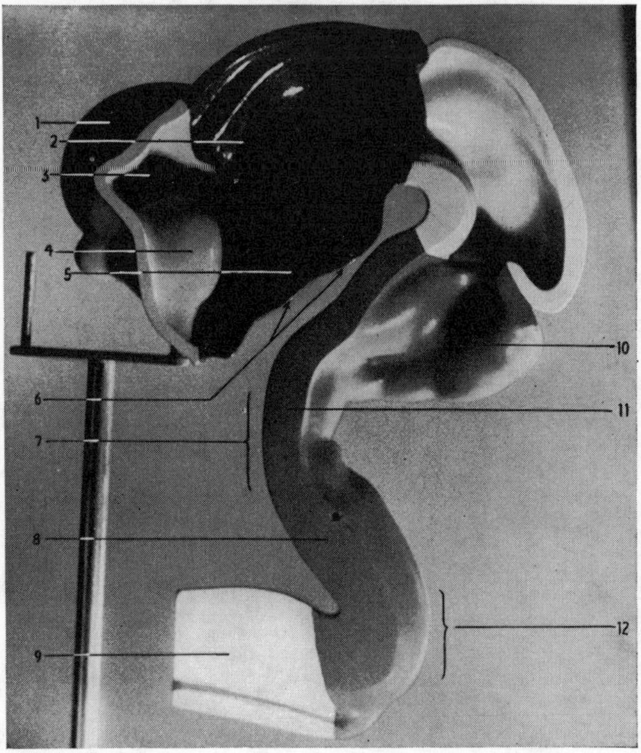

FIG. 55. Sagittal Section of Brain of Human Embryo (About 5 Weeks).

1. Cerebral hemisphere; 2. thalamus; 3. foramen of Munro; 4. corpus striatum; 5. hypothalamus; 6. mammillary bodies; 7. pontine flexure; 8. medulla oblongata; 9. medulla spinalis; 10. cerebellum; 11. pons; 12. cervical flexure.

smooth, but with each added month of development more and more gyri are formed.

THE DEVELOPMENT OF THE PHARYNGEAL REGION

On page 196 the formation of the fore-gut was described. At the cephalic end of this diverticulum is located the buccopharyngeal membrane. If one were to increase the scale of size of an embryo and insert his hand through a ventral opening into the yolk-sac and then stick the forefinger into the fore-gut, the tip of the finger would be in the *primitive pharynx* and would press against the entodermal layer of the buccopharyngeal membrane. The curvature of the finger in the region of the phalanges of the first and second row would form an arc over the heart of the embryo. The fore-gut would fit the forefinger like the finger of a glove.

If it were possible for one to put on two rubber gloves, wrinkle the rubber on the sides of the forefinger, and then without disturbing the wrinkles remove the gloves and make a longitudinal section of the forefinger of the glove, it might, conceivably look like Fig. 57*A*.

This is something like what may be imagined as happening to the lateral

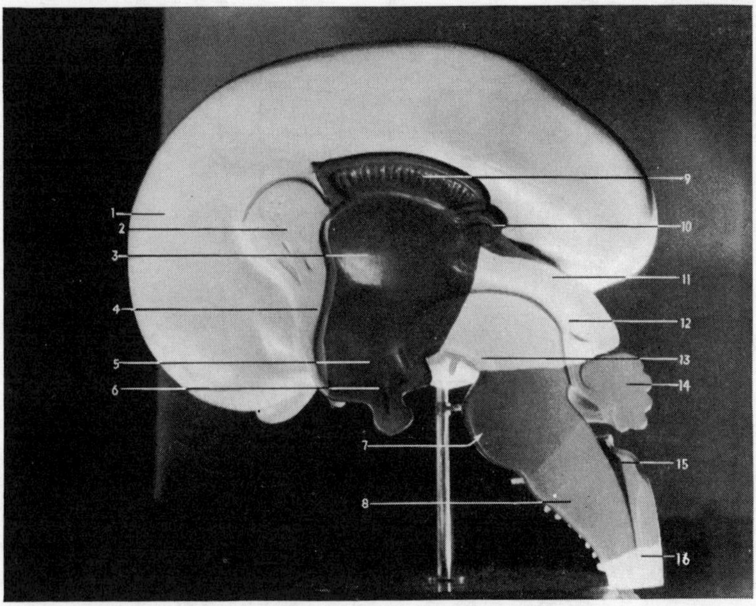

FIG. 56. Median Sagittal Section of Brain of Human Fetus (About 4 Months).

1. Cerebral hemisphere; 2. corpus callosum; 3. thalamus; 4. anterior commissure; 5. hypothalamus; 6. third ventricle; 7. pons; 8. medulla oblongata; 9. choridal fissure; 10. posterior commissure; 11. corpora quadrigemina; 12. cerebral aqueduct; 13. cerebral peduncle; 14. cerebellum; 15. fourth ventricle; 16. spinal canal.

walls of the cephalic portion of the fore-gut. Five pouches, themselves small diverticula or evaginations, called *pharyngeal pouches* or *visceral pouches*, are formed on each side and, in turn, from each of the four most rostral pouches is pushed out a small dorsal and a small ventral diverticulum. The pouches are in the entodermal layer, and are designated by number; the pouch nearest to the primitive mouth is the first, the next the second, and so on. Over each pouch there is a corresponding indentation or invagination of the ectodermal layer which produces the *branchial groove* or *gill slit* (*outer pharyngeal groove; visceral groove*).

The anterior portion of the fore-gut has undergone an important evolution. While other derivatives of visceral origin have smooth muscles and appropriate involuntary innervation, its muscles have become striated and are under voluntary control. It is this neurological phenomenon which has made possible the voice mechanism we know today.

Some students find that the following is helpful in picturing developments in the pharyngeal region:

Bring hands together to form a sphere with the tips of the fingers and thumbs touching. The tips of the fingers should point downward.

Keep the tips of the forefingers in contact but separate or draw apart the

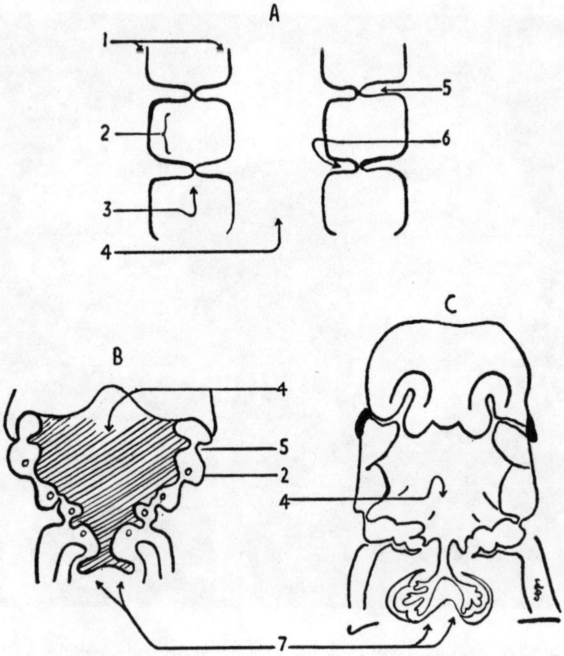

FIG. 57. Development of the Pharyngeal Region.

1. Ectoderm; 2. visceral arch of concentrated mesoderm; 3. closing membrane; 4. primitive pharynx; 5. branchial groove; 6. pharyngeal pouch; 7. lung buds.

tips of the other fingers. The forefingers now represent the mandibular processes fused in the ventral mid-line to form the lower jaw.

By separating and bringing together the sides of the remaining fingers of each hand one may pretend to make appear or disappear the visceral clefts.

Each finger represents a visceral arch.

Separate the tips of the thumbs enough so that the nose will just close the gap. The thumbs represent the maxillary processes, the nose represents the fronto-nasal process, which fusing together form the upper jaw.

By moving the thumbs horizontally, the coming together of the lateral palatine processes may be imagined.

Figure 57*A* makes it clear that where the opposing indentations occur the intervening mesoderm is entirely or almost entirely forced from between the entoderm and ectoderm so that for a time they come into contact and form what are known as thin *closing membranes* or *gill slit membranes* between the fore-gut and exterior.[10] In man the ectoderm and entoderm do not normally remain in contact; some mesoderm, although not as much as in the arches, migrates between the other two cell layers.

The grooves and pouches separate the consecutive *pharyngeal arches* or *visceral arches*. In each of these arches there is a concentration of mesoderm which produces muscle, cartilage, and/or bone, together with an arterial loop (a so-called *aortic arch*). The dorsal ends of the visceral arches become attached to the sides of the embryo head; the ventral ends of the arches meet in the mid-line of the neck. Of the six visceral arches formed, four are visible externally.

The visceral arches, pouches, and grooves are examples of embryonic structures which have disappeared in the adult. The appearance of such structures in the embryo may be explained by saying that, in the ancestors of the animal in which they are now found to be present only in the embryo, they must have performed some real function in the adult. They may be considered the homologues of the branchial arches and clefts of fishes. The fact that they continue to be found in human embryos, although in the adult they are not needed as organs of respiration, may be interpreted to indicate that the ancestors of modern man originally had an aquatic existence.

From the visceral arches arise the following structures of importance to speech students:

- 1st visceral arch (This is called the mandibular arch.[11])
  - Mandibular process
    - Mandible[12]
    - Lower lip
  - Maxillary process
    - Maxilla
    - Upper lip
    - Palate
    - Cheeks
  - Mouth boundaries
  - Muscles of mastication
  - Digastric (anterior belly)

[10] In gill-bearing animals the closing membranes break through and the grooves become clefts, called gill-clefts. The gills, of course, have a respiratory function.

[11] The mandibular arch and its derivatives subserve masticatory processes, primarily. Only in mammals are lips separated off from the alveolar processes.

[12] The lower jaw and the clavicle are the first bones in the body to ossify.

- Mylohyoid
- Tensor veli palatini
- Tensor tympani
- Teeth
- Incus
- Malleus
- Sphenomandibular ligament
- Primordium anterior two-thirds of tongue (into which the musculature migrates from occipital segments or somites)

2nd visceral arch (This is called the hyoid arch.)

- Lesser cornua of hyoid
- Side and front of neck
- Styloid process of temporal bone
- Stylohyoid ligament
- Stapes
- Muscles of expression
- Stapedius
- Posterior belly of digastric
- Stylohyoid

2nd and 3rd visceral arches combined

- Body of hyoid
- Posterior ⅓ of tongue (into which the musculature migrates from the occipital segments or somites)

3rd visceral arch[13]

- Greater cornua of hyoid
- Epiglottis (furcula)
- Stylopharyngeus muscle

4th and 5th visceral arches[13]

- Thyroid cartilage[14]
- Intrinsic muscles of the larynx
- Pharyngeal muscles[15] except stylopharyngeus
- Trapezius and sternocleidomastoideus
- Although they are in the proper region there is some question about the following:
  - Cricoid cartilage
  - Arytenoid cartilage
  - Corniculate cartilages

[13] The products of the last three arches subserve respiratory functions.

[14] In lower animals the thyroid cartilage may be seen to have two segments demonstrating the dual nature of its origin. Sometimes in the human, a vascular foramen in the cartilage reveals the union of the fused processes.

[15] With the evolution in mammals of the use of the pharynx for mastication and swallowing purposes its structure, originally suited to respiratory needs, was modified.

Cuneiform cartilages
Aryepiglottic folds

The following is a summary of the muscles formed in this region:

Origin	*Muscles*	*Innervation*
1st arch	Mastication	V
2nd arch	Expression	VII
3rd arch	Pharyngeal	IX, X (and XI?)
1st, 2nd, and 3rd arches	Tongue primordium	V, VII, IX, X sensory
Occipital somites	Tongue muscles	XII
4th and 5th arches	Intrinsic of larynx	XI (X?)
	Sternocleidomastoideus and trapezius	XI

The 2nd and 4th outer branchial grooves or gill slits do not persist.

- 1st outer branchial groove
  - Auricula or pinna (by elevation of tissue around it)
  - Meatus acusticus externus
- 3rd outer branchial groove or cervical sinus
  - Cortex of embryonic thymus and Hassal's corpuscles

The internal pharyngeal pouches give rise to the following structures:

- 1st pharyngeal pouch
  - Auditory tube or Eustachian tube
  - Tympanic cavity and mastoid air cells
- Closure membrane of 1st pouches (1st pharyngeal membrane)
  - Tympanic membrane
- 2nd pharyngeal pouch
  - Region of palatine tonsils but probably not the tonsils directly
- 3rd pharyngeal pouch
  - Thymus (medulla only)
- 3rd and 4th pharyngeal pouch
  - Parathyroids
- 5th pharyngeal pouch (Ultimobranchial bodies)
  - Thyroid gland (lateral portion)

THE DEVELOPMENT OF THE RESPIRATORY SYSTEM[16]

The *pulmonary primordium* (about two to three weeks) appears as a short longitudinal groove, the *laryngo-tracheal groove* or *pulmonary groove* in the mid-line of the ventral wall of that part of the fore-gut which later becomes the esophagus. Figure 58 shows how gradually the mesoderm

[16] As early as 12 weeks, rhythmic chest movements simulating respiratory movements may appear; after the fifth month expect respiratory movements.

in the region of the groove pushes in to pinch off the groove from the fore-gut and to form from the groove a ventral tube, the cephalic opening of which is in the ventral floor of the caudal portion of the pharynx.[17] Thus the esophagus (digestive system) and the laryngo-tracheal tube (respiratory system) have common openings into the pharynx and hence into the mouth. The future *glottis* will appear at the junction of the laryngo-tracheal tube with the pharynx. The separation of the laryngo-tracheal tube begins with the caudal end. With the establishment of two tubes, the dorsal tube becomes the esophagus, while the ventral derivative gives rise to the larynx, trachea, and lungs. As the separation progresses, the caudal termination of the ventral tube sprouts two hollow buds, forerunners of the *primary bronchi.* According to some observers, a phylogenetic interpretation of the ontogeny of the lungs indicates that the organ was originally an unpaired structure; that later it became paired; that the trachea was a relatively recent acquisition. It is also claimed that paired lung placodes occur on the pharynx, caudal to the pharyngeal pouches, before the tracheal tube separates. If this is true, it suggests the homology of the lungs with the pouches.

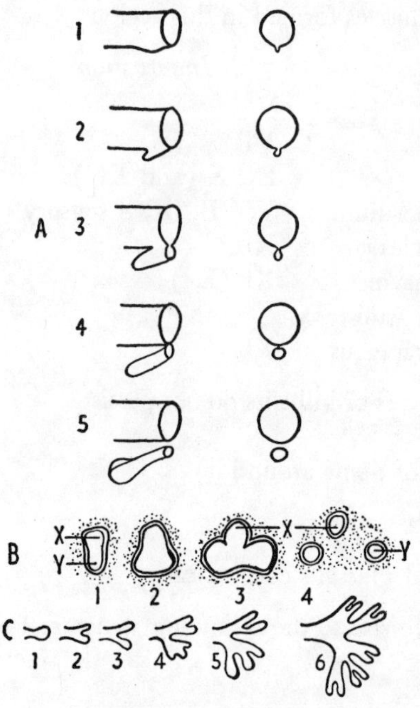

FIG. 58. The Development of the Lungs

A. Five steps showing the formation of the trachea. 1. Appearance of pulmonary groove. 2, 3, 4. The laryngo-tracheal tube is pinched off from the fore-gut. 5. The lung buds appear.

B. Four steps showing the mesoderm (stippled) pushing in as the pulmonary diverticula (y) are pinched off from the foregut (x).

C. Six steps in the branching of the lung buds.

The *lung buds* develop rapidly. They become lobulated (five weeks), but are not symmetrical. The right bud gains three *lobes;* the left bud, two. Thus, early in life, are the lobes of the adult lungs indicated. Following this fundamental division, further branching occurs.[18] Each terminal vesicle divides and the one or two resulting stalks in turn divide. Each lobule undergoes rapid subdivisions and extensive ramification until finally the minute expanded extremities of the respiratory system, the *alveoli,* are formed.

[17] Before the evolution of a mammalian type of mastication and swallowing, the pharynx was structurally designed for respiration. The muscles which originally moved the branchial arches become muscles of deglutition.

[18] Perhaps eighteen divisional branchings of the lungs occur before birth; then about six more occur by middle childhood.

The divisions of the respiratory system beginning at the larynx are as follows:

- larynx
- trachea
- primary bronchi
- secondary bronchi
- tertiary bronchi
- bronchiole
- respiratory bronchiole
- alveolar duct
- infundibula or atria
- alveolar sacs
- alveoli or air sacs

During the time the lungs are pushing their way back caudally, occupying what are to be the pleural cavities of the coelom, they become covered with a thin envelope of mesoderm, the *pulmonary pleura.* At birth the bifurcation of the trachea is on a level with the 4th thoracic vertebra.

The original evaginations of entoderm gives rise only to the epithelial lining cells of the lungs. All other constituents—i. e., the connective, muscular, vascular, and cartilaginous tissue elements—are products of the mesoderm into which the diverticuli force their way and grow. All the tubes are at first solid epithelial cylinders; the lumina are acquired later. At first, also, the lining epithelial cells are cylindrical, but at about the fourth month the cells alter their shape and acquire cilia.

The air sacs or pulmonary alveoli are evaginations from the alveolar passages and the infundibula. Their walls are extremely thin or, in fact, the epithelial wall may disappear entirely. If this be the case, as many believe, the endothelium of the capillaries lining the alveoli comes into direct contact with the air.

The trachea may be considered the elongated stalk of the pulmonary diverticulum. A condensation of mesenchyme begins to differentiate the muscles and cartilages of the trachea by the eighth week. Its incomplete cartilaginous rings appear at about the ninth week.

The development of the *larynx* begins with the appearance (fifth week) of a prominence, the *arytenoid swelling,* on each side of the cephalic end of the laryngo-tracheal groove. These rudiments are continuous in front of the groove—i. e., rostrally—and meet with a transverse swelling located between the ventral ends of the third and fourth arches. While these elements are in a union a Λ-shaped ridge, the *furcula* (little fork), is formed. From the anterior portion of this union is formed the *epiglottis.*

Subsequent to the separation of the laryngo-tracheal tube from the esophagus, the arytenoid swellings come into contact medially, and with the caudal part of the furcula to form a T-shaped cleft which is the entrance to the larynx. For a short period the opening is occluded.

From the arytenoid swellings are differentiated the *arytenoid cartilages, corniculate cartilages,* and the posterior part of the *cricoid cartilage.* The laryngeal cartilages are joined to the epiglottis by the *aryepiglottic folds* in which, as derivatives from the epiglottis, are formed the *cuneiform cartilages*. The cricoid cartilage arises from two centers of cartilaginous growth which unite ventrally. Later the cartilage fuses with the tracheal tube on its dorsal aspect. The *thyroid cartilage* with its laminae, likewise, has two originating centers of chrondrification. The plates are joined in the mid-

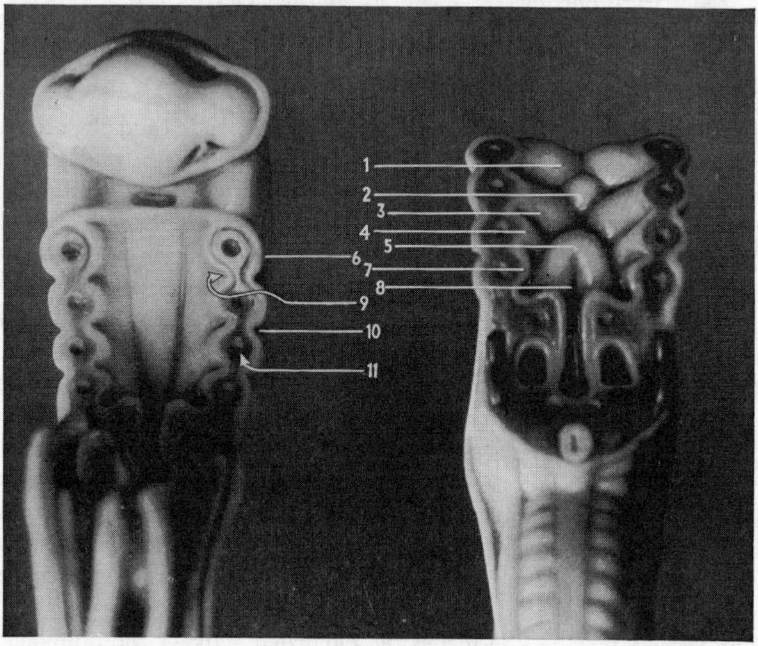

FIG. 59. Development of the Tongue and Epiglottis.

1. Mandibular arch; 2. tuberculum impar; 3. second arch; 4. third arch; 5. copula; 6. visceral arch; 7. fourth arch; 8. furcula; 9. pharyngeal pouch; 10. branchial groove; 11. mesoderm of arch.

line by a membrane in which there is a third active center of cartilage formation.

At about the seventh week the cephalic sections of the arytenoid swellings push out laterally in such a manner as to be at right angles to their posterior portions.

At eight weeks the *ventricles of the larynx* appear as the result of an evagination of the lateral wall; the apex of the diverticulum is the *laryngeal saccule*. The posterior margins of the ventricles (tenth week) indicate the future position of the true *vocal folds*. The false vocal fold or upper *ventricular band* is the upper lip of the ventricle in which there is some condensation of mesenchyme.

Condensation of mesenchyme in the laying down of a skeletal frame-

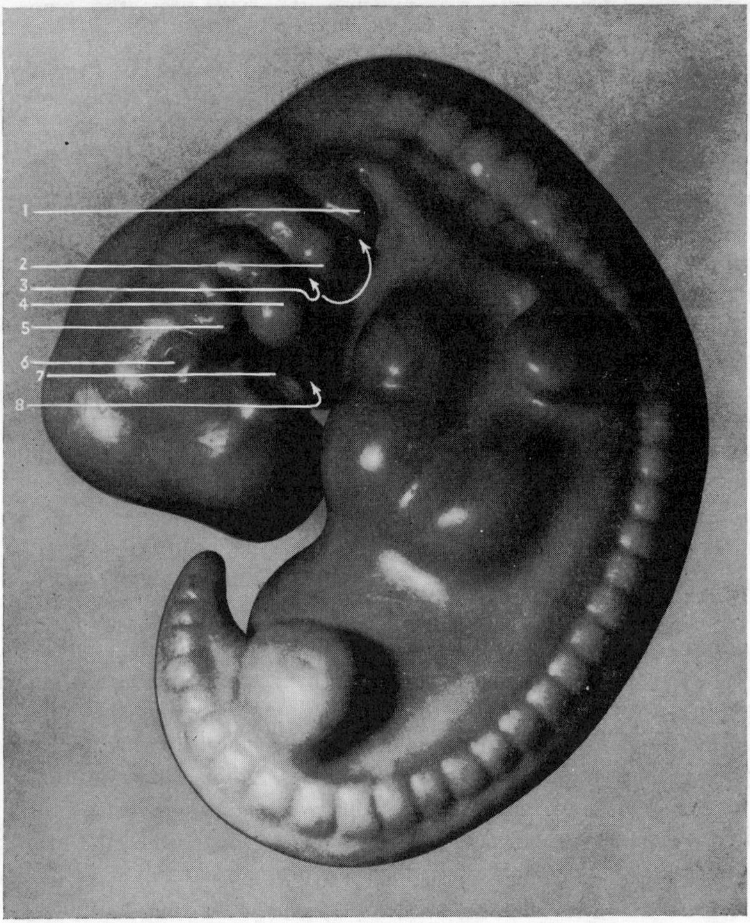

FIG. 60. External View of Visceral Arches of Human Embryo (About 4 Weeks).
1. Third arch; 2. hyoid arch; 3. branchial grooves; 4. mandibular arch; 5. maxillary process; 6. eye; 7. olfactory pit; 8. stomodeum.

work is apparent as early as the seventh week. The cartilage of the epiglottis does not appear until about the sixth month.

The laryngeal muscles are products of the fourth and fifth visceral arches.

THE DEVELOPMENT OF THE FACIAL REGION

The development of the face with its cavities and openings is a provision of nature operating to bring the central nervous system—e. g., the sensory and organs of sight, taste, and smell—and the alimentary and respiratory tracts into direct relationship with the external environment. The normal development of this region is an extremely complicated progressive series of ordered phenomena; growth and fusion must take place according to a precise developmental plan which neither halts prematurely nor continues excessively.[19]

As an aid to orientation, before taking up the steps in the formation of the face, it will be helpful to study Fig. 61*A,* which shows the head [20] of an embryo of about thirty-five days. Prominent is the *oral fossa* or *stomodeum,* a wide, roughly quadrilateral depression on the ventral surface. If one were to stick a pencil far enough into the primitive mouth opening, the pencil point would be in the primitive pharynx, because by now the buccopharyngeal membrane has disappeared. Directly caudal to the pencil point would be found the paired, medially approximated *mandibular processes.* These have grown in ventrally from each side from their respective *mandibular arches* and their ventral ends have united and fused. On each side of the pencil—i. e., forming the lateral boundaries of the fossa—would be located the ventrally directed *maxillary processes.* Bounding the fossa, cephalically, would be seen the broad *frontonasal process.*[21]

A. The Frontonasal Process and the Nose and Air Sinuses

Two areas of thickened ectoderm, the olfactory areas or placodes,[22] appear on the cephalic margin of the oral fossa during the third week of development. In the fourth week they are depressed, relatively, due to the more rapid growth of the surrounding tissue. They are then called *nasal,* or *olfactory, pits.* The pits are separated from each other by the median nasal portion of the frontonasal process. In the fifth week the *medial nasal process* thickens along its lateral margins; these thickened borders are the *globular processes.* They make up the inner boundaries of the nasal pits. At the same time, the *lateral nasal processes* grow out from the frontonasal process, one on each side, above the nasal pits. They then grow toward the maxillary processes, forming the outer boundaries of the pits. At this stage the nasal pits are quite well defined on every side except caudally, where they are in direct continuity with the stomodeum. The pits become deeper. The caudal portions of the lateral nasal processes and the rostral portions of the maxillary processes, after uniting with each other, advance toward the median line caudal to the nasal pits where they unite with the median nasal process

[19] Abnormal development produces such abnormalities as the following:
macrostomia (Greek *makros,* large, plus *stoma,* mouth)
microstomia (Greek *mikros,* small)
astomia (no mouth)
aprosopia (absence of all or most of the face)

[20] As in the fish, there is no neck at the first month; the head and body are directly related.

[21] The olfactory pits serve to divide the frontonasal process into three distinct parts: the medial nasal process, and two lateral nasal processes. The lateral angles of the medial nasal process are rounded and are called the globular processes. The globular processes grow backward as plates or laminae, the nasal laminae, approach and finally fuse, forming the nasal septum.

[22] The nerve cells of the olfactory areas become the olfactory nerve cells.

(sixth week). This serves to separate the nasal pits from the oral fossa; it also furnishes the basis of the upper lip. The external orifices of the nasal pits are now called the *anterior nares*. The nasal pits have become short canals which open by their deep orifices, the *posterior nares,* into the primitive mouth cavity about the level of the developing palatal shelves. The nares are separated from each other by the broad median nasal process, but this gradually becomes thinner and produces the *septum* of the nose. The fusion in the mid-line of the medial nasal process provides the nose with a septum and separates the right and left nasal chambers from each other at about the same time as the nasal region as a whole is separated from the oral region by the laying down of the palate.

The pushing in of the *palatal processes* toward the median line, resulting in their union with each other and with the nasal septum, divides the nasal chambers from the oral cavity. The posterior nares now open into the nasopharynx (three months). At first, the nose is extremely broad and flat (three months) but, from this time on, it begins to develop its characteristically adult form.

The *air sinuses* of the nose are produced by evaginations of the nasal mucous membrane into the surrounding cartilage and bone.

B. The Mandibular Processes and the Lower Jaw

The ventral extremities of the mandibular processes unite in the mid-line and fuse to form the *mandible* or lower jaw (about thirty-five days). Almost at once a transverse groove appears along the oral margin of the united processes; on either side of the groove are relatively elevated ridges. The elevated portion in front (ventral) of the groove is the lip ridge from which is developed the lower lip and a part of the cheek and chin. The ridge behind (dorsal) the groove is the gum.

C. The Maxillary Processes and the Upper Jaw

Each maxillary process is a triangular offshoot growing rostrally and laterally from the mandibular arch. In Fig. 61*A,* the wedge-shaped (>) notch between the maxillary process and the mandibular process, on the same side, is easily seen. The angle formed corresponds to the angle of the future mouth.

The maxillary processes do not come all the way to the median plane and fuse as is the case of the mandibular processes. They come almost to the mid-line, where they fuse with the two contributory processes (globular processes) of the medial nasal process. Figure 61*B* makes clear the part played by the frontonasal process [23] in the formation of the maxilla and hard palate. The result of the fusion of these parts is seen in the philtrum

[23] A remaining, cephalic portion of the frontonasal process forms the forehead.

of the adult. Cheiloschisis, or harelip, occurs when there is a failure of the maxillary and globular processes to fuse.

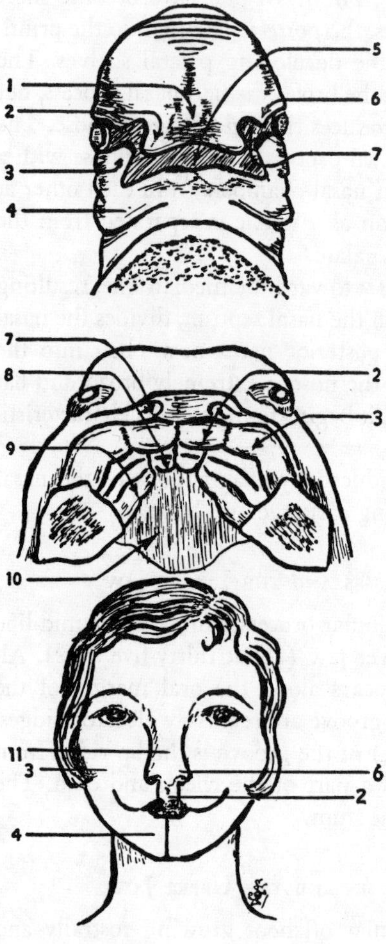

FIG. 61. Development of the Face.

1. Medial nasal process; 2. globular process; 3. maxillary process; 4. mandibular arch; 5. stomodeum; 6. lateral nasal process; 7. olfactory pit; 8. palatine process of globular process; 9. palatine portion of maxillary process; 10. pharynx; 11. frontonasal process.

After its formation, the upper jaw becomes divided into gum and lip in exactly the same manner as described for the lower jaw.

D. THE PALATAL PROCESSES AND THE PALATE (URANISCUS)

There is still no demarcation between the mouth and the nasal cavity. Posterior to the partition resulting from the union of the frontonasal, lateral nasal, and maxillary processes, the nares open into the primitive mouth cavity. It is with the formation of the palate that the nasal and oral cavities become separated and permanently delimited. Thereafter, the mouth cavity has a roof and the nasal cavity a floor. From the inner or oral surface of the maxillae, are formed, on each side, horizontal shelf-like projections. These constitute the rudiments of the palate. They gradually grow toward each other and first begin to unite in the mid-line along their anterior extremities (eighth week). Uraniscochasma or cleft palate occurs upon failure of the union of the palatine processes. The fusion progresses until by the ninth week the framework of the future hard palate has been completed. Originally, the mass of the tongue forces its way up between the uniting *palatal processes,* but as they approach each other the tongue recedes from between them to sink lower in the oral cavity. By the eleventh week the entire primitive palate, *hard palate* and *soft palate,* has been formed. The completed palate leaves openings between the nasal and the oral cavities known as the permanent choanae and establishes the division between the nasopharynx and the oropharynx. The palate is prolonged backward in the palatine arches. These mark off the oral from the pharyngeal cavity. The palatine arches are brought about by an invasion of the palatine folds with mesoderm from the third visceral arches. From these same sources come the muscles of the palate. The soft palate is derived from a fold prolonged dorsally from each palatal process. The *uvula*[24] appears (fourth month) as a small protuberance on the posterior margin of the soft palate. Into the palatal folds migrate derivatives of the superior pharyngeal constrictor to form the palatopharyngeus, palatoglossus, azygos uvulae, and levator palati muscles. The continuation of the palatal folds into the pharynx forms the *posterior pillars of the fauces.*

E. The Lateral Nasal Processes and the Cheeks

Most ventral views of embryos indicate that the mouth opening has considerable lateral extent. This width is progressively decreased by the fusion of the mandibular, maxillary, and derived processes, with the consequent formation of the cheeks. The lateral nasal processes fuse with the maxillary processes on each side.[25]

F. The Oral Cavity

The mouth (Greek *stoma*) is developed from two sources: the stomodeum and the floor of the cephalic region of the fore-gut. As has been explained (page 195), the growth of the head of the embryo plus the cephalic flexure (page 196), results in the pericardial area and the buccopharyngeal membrane being located on the ventral aspect of the embryo. As the brain expands and the heart bulges out the pericardial area, the buccopharyngeal membrane comes to be in an ever-deepening depression between them. This is the *stomodeum* or oral pit. As may be seen in Fig. 45*B,* it is lined with ectoderm and separated from the cephalic end of the fore-gut (entoderm) only by a thin membrane devoid of mesoderm (page 195). The buccopharyngeal membrane disappears at about twenty-five days. The mouth assumes the appearance of a somewhat pentagonal orifice after the growth of the mandibular and maxillary processes which bound it caudally and laterally. The frontonasal process bounds it rostrally. The stomodeum is divided into two parts by the fusion of the palatine processes; an upper, nasal part and a lower, oral or buccal portion. The oral portion is the mouth proper. From the walls of the stomodeum are formed the gums, teeth, and lips. The tongue is developed from the pharyngeal floor.

At about the sixth week of embryonic life thickening of the oral epithelium can be made out on both the upper and lower jaw. This bank of

[24] In some few adults the uvula is bilobed. This is the embryonic condition in almost every individual. It indicates the bilateral origin of the palate.

[25] The air sinuses are produced by the lateral invagination of the cartilage of the lateral nasal processes and into them extends the nasal mucous membrane.

epithelial cells, the labio-dental ledge, pushes into the underlying mesenchyme around the entire arc of each jaw forming a shallow groove, the primary labial groove. From the bottom of the groove, ectodermal cells grow into the subjacent mesoderm. With the degeneration of the central cells of this downgrowth, a secondary labial groove is produced. This deep-

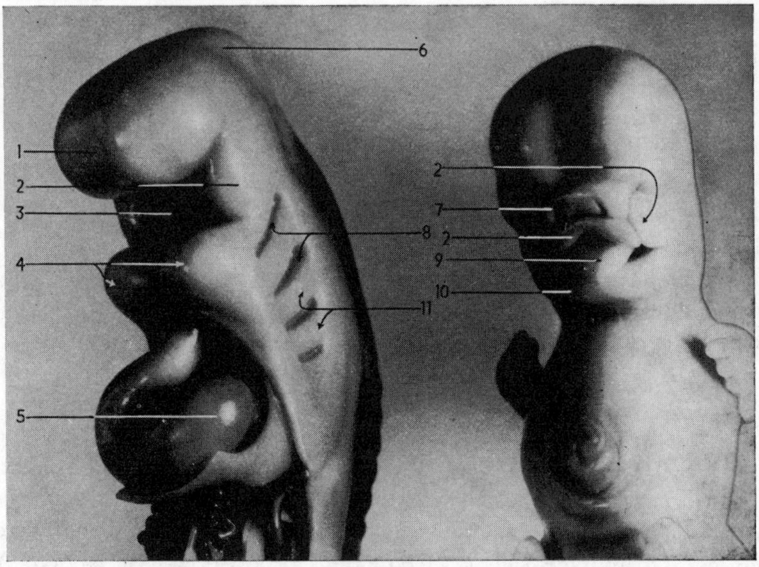

FIG. 62. Development of the Mouth Region.

1. Forebrain; 2. maxillary process; 3. stomodeum; 4. mandibular arches; 5. heart; 6. Midbrain; 7. lateral nasal process; 8. branchial grooves; 9. tongue; 10. mandibular process; 11. visceral arches.

ens, and, as a result, the lips and cheeks become separate from the teeth-bearing gums of maxillae and mandible.

The salivary glands may be seen in the second month. The elements of the submaxillary appear at about the sixth week; of the parotid at about the eighth week. The sublingual may be identified some time later.

The tongue (Greek *glossa*), composed chiefly of muscular substance, is the result of the fusion (seventh week) of five primordia on the floor of the pharynx into one mobile structure. When the *tuberculum impar* becomes discernible on the floor of the pharynx, there may be detected, likewise, two pairs of bilaterally symmetrical tongue primordia. The cephalic pair are called the *anterior lingual primordia,* and are located on the floor of the pharynx at the level of the first visceral arches; the caudal pair are called the *root primordia* and are located on the floor of the pharynx at the level of the second visceral arches. These two pairs and the tuberculum impar are the five primordia which unite to form the tongue. (See Fig.

59.) Diglossia (also termed glossoschisis, or forked tongue) is a developmental abnormality due to the failure of the two anterior primordia to fuse.

The tuberculum impar is a round, mid-line protrusion on the floor of the pharynx at the level of the first branchial grooves. This, plus the anterior primordia, makes up the anterior two-thirds of the tongue. On this fused derivative, only, develop the *tongue papillae* (three months). The posterior segment is the result of the fusion of the root primordia. In the adult tongue the V-shaped row of circumvallate papillae on the dorsum indicates the line of union of the three anterior and the two posterior segments. The foramen caecum of the adult tongue is the vestige that remains of the opening of a now obliterated canal or duct leading from the tongue surface, at the point of junction of the diverse segments, to the middle lobe of the thyroid gland.

At first, and until the palatal processes begin to meet and fuse, the tongue rises because of the growing into it of somatic muscle fibers and occupies both the future oral and nasal cavities. With the formation of the palate the tongue retreats into the confines of the oral cavity.

The body or apical portion of the tongue is designed primarily for masticatory purposes. It arises from tissue rostral to the second pharyngeal arch. Its sensory nerves are the trigeminal and the facial and its motor, the hypoglossal.

The root of the tongue is primarily concerned with swallowing. It arises from the second pharyngeal arches. Its sensory nerves are the glossopharyngeal and the vagus and its motor, the hypoglossal.

The striated musculature of the tongue does not come from the pharyngeal arches, but from the posterior three head segments or occipital somites. It carries with it in its migration into the tongue motor fibers from the XIIth cranial nerve. The sensory fibers of the tongue, however, are derived from the nerves of the visceral arches. The primitive tongue muscles are the genioglossus and hyoglossus. The transversus and verticalis muscles are derived from the genioglossus; the longitudinalis muscles are derived from the hyoglossus.

In the tongue are found derivatives of all the three primary cell layers. The epithelium of the anterior two-thirds of the tongue is of ectodermal origin; that of the posterior third, entodermal; while the muscles arise from the mesoderm.

CHRONOLOGY OF APPEARANCE OF EMBRYOLOGICAL STRUCTURES OF INTEREST TO STUDENTS OF SPEECH

Ovum Stage

Second Week

Oral pit

Nasal areas

Embryo Stage

Third Week

Visceral arches and clefts
Nasofrontal process
Pulmonary anlage seen as longitudinal diverticulum of ventral wall of fore-gut
Cells of neural tube show differentiation
Fourth ventricle
Three brain vesicles clear
Auditory pit

Fourth Week

Visceral arches at peak of their development
Pharynx and esophagus
Buccopharyngeal membrane disappears
Bifurcation of pulmonary anlage
Walls of brain vesicles thicker
Ventral roots of spinal nerves

Fifth Week (Length: 1 cm.)

Lateral nasal and globular processes
Right and left bronchi subdivide
Roof of mid-brain thickens
Union of mandibles

Sixth Week

Maxillary, nasofrontal, and lateral nasal processes unite
Tracheal dilation indicates larynx
Arytenoid cartilages
Brain and cord membranes
Dorsal roots of spinal nerves
Lumen of spinal cord altered
External ear
Ossification of lower jaw begins
Ossification of clavicle begins
Chondrification of ribs begins

Seventh Week

Disproportionate increase in size of vesicles of fore-brain
Muscles recognized

Eighth Week

Chondrification of larynx begins
Sympathetic nerves
Formation of external nose

Fetus Stage

Ninth Week (Length: 25–30 mm.; Weight: 0.7 oz.)

Completion of hard palate
Corpora quadrigemina

Third Month (Length: 60 mm.; Weight: 4 oz.)
Oral cavity divided from nose by palate
Completion of soft palate
Tongue papillae
Epiglottis
Fissure of Sylvius

Fourth Month (Length: 150 mm.; Weight: 8 oz.)
One-quarter of body is made up of head
Ciliation of cells of trachea and bronchi mucous membrane
Parieto-occipital fissure
Eustachian tube, cartilaginous portion
Malleus and incus ossify

Fifth Month (Length: 200 mm.; Weight: 1 lb.)
Fissure of Rolando
Organ of Corti
Stapes ossifies

Sixth Month (Length: 300 mm.; Weight: 2 lbs.)
Air cells of lungs
Cerebral hemispheres cover midbrain

Seventh Month (Length: 350 mm.; Weight: 3 lbs.)
Cerebral convolutions
Direct cerebellar tract fibers myelinated

Eighth Month (Length: 400 mm.; Weight: 5 lbs.)

Ninth Month (Length: 500 mm.; Weight: 6 to 7 lbs.)
Bony lamina spiralis and modiolus of ear ossify
Body and great horns of hyoid bone begin to ossify

EXERCISES AND QUESTIONS

1. In the beginning, a frog's egg is a sphere. The first indication of the direction in which growth will take place is a difference in potential between two opposite poles on the sphere. They establish the axis along which the frog body will develop.

(*a*). Is there anything similar in the earliest stages of development of a human body?

2. What determines the orientation (or direction of growth) of the primitive streak? Explain.

3. Simple undifferentiated protoplasm has a number of different characteristics.

(*a*). For the student of normal speech, which *one* of these characteristics is most important? Explain.

(*b*). For the student of normal hearing, which *one* of these characteristics is most important? Explain.

4. Using one of the answers to the preceding question, explain how, in man, differentiation serves to develop this characteristic to the highest level.

5. Statement: The study of embryology is like the study of history.

(*a*). Do you agree or disagree? Explain.

6. In the development of the lungs, some branchings occur before and some after birth.

(*a*). How many occur before birth?

(*b*). How many occur after birth?

(*c*). On the basis of (*a*) and (*b*), above, how many alveoli are there in the lungs? Explain.

(*d*). The way in which you arrive at your answer to (*c*) should remind you of something else in embryology. What is it?

(*e*). The way in which you arrived at your answer in (*c*), should remind you of something similar in the relative-pitch theory. What is it?

7. In your own words state the so-called *Law of Genetic Restriction.*

(*a*). Give an example, in the field of embryology.

(*b*). Give an example, in the area of phonation and articulation.

(*c*). Give an example, in the area of house building.

8. Statement: A phylogenetic interpretation of the ontogeny of the lungs indicates that the organ was originally an unpaired structure.

(*a*). Rewrite in simpler words being sure to include all the meaning.

9. What is the meaning of *polarity* in embryology? Give an example.

10. (*a*). Give a brief description of the development of the trachea and lungs.

(*b*). Illustrate with drawings. Use colors. Label the drawings.

Chapter VII

NEUROLOGY

INTRODUCTORY STATEMENT

Treatises on man and animals always assign at least two reasons for the superiority of man: speech and neurological development. These two are one. The anatomical equipment which man can utilize for speech, as well as for its primary and vital purposes, per se, has not given him speech. It is the high level of neurological control which he has attained over this vegetative mechanism that permits him to use it for speech. For this reason, we shall now undertake to state in considerable detail the neurological foundations of speech.

In simple forms of life, such as the amoeba, all the vital processes are carried on by the one cell. In more complex forms, there is a *division of labor;* i.e., certain cells are primarily concerned with locomotion, others with food-getting, and others with respiration. One of the most highly specialized of these functions is that of *conduction*. The cells entrusted with this function make up the nervous system. As the telephone network binds together the nation, so the nervous system integrates the activities of the body. This organization, the most complicated and highly integrated system in the human body, performs specialized duties having to do with the reception of stimuli from the environment; the reaction and adjustment of the body to the environment; consciousness and thinking; the reception of stimuli from points within the body; and the correlation and integration of the diverse processes within the organism. Because of it, hearing and speech, for example, are possible.

The process of living may be defined as the adjustment of the internal activities of the body to the significant external environment of the body. The body is able to make such adjustments because stimuli from the environment impinge upon the receptors of the organism. The body may be conceived as surrounded by a covering impervious to environmental stimuli except at certain points where, like windows, sense organs are placed to admit certain specific kinds of physical energies; for example, the eye, light waves; the ear, sound waves. The body may be thought of also as a mechanism for producing responses to stimuli. Responses always have to do with modifications of the activity of glands and/or muscles, i.e., there can be an increase or a decrease in the level of activity. In muscles, contraction is a manifestation of an increase in activity; relaxation, of a decrease in activity. In glands the degree of activity is indicated by the volume of secretion.

The living organism is characterized by its reaction to stimuli. Stimuli may be classified as external or internal. External stimuli are those influences which originate outside the organism—in its environment—and act upon the organism. Internal stimuli are those influencing forces which have their origin within the organism. Any stimuli within the range of our receptors may disturb the equilibrium of the nervous system. Static phenomena do not serve as stimuli; only change, difference, or fluctuation gives rise to stimuli.

The use of the terms *stimulus* and *reaction* implies that the organism has terminal or gradient characteristics; that between the termini lies a non-terminal, non-specific portion. Such non-specificity is a fundamental characteristic of protoplasm. In the simple one-cell organism, a stimulus applied to any part of the cell appears to elicit a response. With differentiations of function, as found in higher animals, the nervous system has been adapted terminally for stimulus-response co-ordination. Stimuli are effective only if they are received by a receptor. A *receptor,* whether it be general or special, is the terminus of a nerve fiber which normally carries impulses only centripetally. Once the impulses are received and distributed in the central nervous system, co-ordinated adjustments are made so that other fibers may carry impulses to an effector. The series of steps between stimulus and reaction may be diagrammed in this manner:

Stimulus . . .	Sensory . . . receptor	Neural integration . . . process	Motor . . . effector	Reaction

BASIC CONCEPTS OF NEUROLOGY

In order that the student may gain a background of knowledge regarding the system which carries these nerve impulses, we shall now consider some of the basic concepts of neurology.

A. The Neuron

The neuron is the structural unit of the nervous system. Neurons are concerned in nerve-impulse conduction.[1] Potentially, millions of them are linked together in almost innumerable combinations to form an almost infinite number of conduction systems.[2] Typically, a *neuron* consists of a nerve cell body and its various processes. The nerve cell body is called a *cyton.* Primarily, the cell body serves a nutritive function for the neuron. Nerve cells vary in size, shape, and structure. By determining the character of a nerve cell, histologically, one may place it, with limitations, according to its function. A nerve cell innervating striated or voluntary muscle differs histologically from a nerve cell innervating smooth or involuntary muscle, and still different is the nerve cell innervating cardiac or heart muscle.

Nerve cells are either *unipolar* (having one process) or *multipolar* (having more than one process). There are three fundamental types of neurons:

Unipolar	Dorsal spinal root cells.
Bipolar	Cells in ganglion of VIIIth cranial nerve.
Multipolar	Golgi type I. (Pyramidal cells of cerebral cortex; ventral horn cells of cord; Purkinje cells of cerebral cortex.)
	Golgi type II. (Intermediary or internuncial neurons.)

[1] The *neuron doctrine* was stated by Waldeyer (1891), who named the neuron.

[2] If neurons be arranged in conduction chains so that impulses pass from neuron to neuron, the first to undergo excitation is designated arbitrarily as a *neuron of the first order;* the second, a *neuron of the second order,* and so on through the series.

The nerve cell processes are either *axons* or *dendrites.*

Some parts of the brain and spinal cord are largely made up of nerve cells and non-medullated fibers; other portions are made up of nerve fibers predominantly. The difference is obvious even to the unaided eye. Where there are mainly cell bodies, the brain or spinal cord looks gray; these areas are known as areas of *gray substance.* Where there are mainly nerve fibers, the brain or spinal cord looks white; these areas are known as areas of *white substance.* Nerve fibers are found in the white substance of the brain and medulla spinalis and in the peripheral nerves. They are either medullated or non-medullated.

Medullated fibers are made up of two parts; axis-cylinder, and *medullary* or *myelin* sheath. The axis-cylinder, the essential part of the nerve fiber, may be considered a prolongation of the cell body. Medullated fibers give to cranial and spinal nerves and to the white part of the brain and spinal cord their whiteness. The explanation for this is that many nerve fibers are surrounded by a fatty sheath of white myelin. The sheath is of greater area than the gray axon it encloses; this accounts for the predominance of white in an area containing myelinated nerves. Medullated nerve fibers are almost indefatigable. Medullated fibers conduct impulses faster than non-medullated fibers; the former, 100–125 *meters* per second; the latter 65–100 *centimeters* per second.

CLASSIFICATION OF NERVE FIBERS

Nerve fibers are classified as *efferent* (motor) *fibers,* which carry impulses in a direction away from the central nervous system to the periphery, and *afferent* (sensory) *fibers,* which carry impulses from the peripheral tissues to or toward the central nervous system.

No fundamental structural difference in the two kinds of fibers has been revealed; in general, nerve impulses do not differ. Probably the impulses carried in the auditory nerve are like those carried in the optic nerve or in a motor nerve. It is not the impulses or the nerve fiber, but the tissue in which the nerve ends, in specific parts of the cerebral cortex or in a muscle, which produces in one case the sensation of sound, in another the sensation of color, and in another the contraction of a muscle. Any nerve fiber may conduct an impulse in both directions, and does so conduct if the fiber is artificially stimulated at any point in its course. Artificial stimuli capable of affecting the nerve fiber may be (*a*) *chemical,* (*b*) *mechanical,* (*c*) *thermal,* and (*d*) *electrical.* Normally, however, an afferent nerve is stimulated only at its peripheral termination (e. g., skin, sense organs), while an efferent nerve is stimulated only from its central cell body.

Hundreds or thousands of nerve fibers are assembled into larger or smaller *nerve trunks,* yet these fibers may be entirely independent in their physiological activity. In the vagus nerve trunk, for instance, we have nerve fibers running side by side, to supply the heart, the larynx, and the stomach and intestines.

B. The Nerve Impulse

The rapidity of transmission of the nerve impulse is directly correlated with the metabolism of the fiber. The power of rapid recovery after a stimulus, a short *latent period,* and rapid transmission are vital in the proper functioning of the nervous system. In the internal organs, where speed and agility or indefatigability are not the prime requisites, the nerves are, for the most part, non-medullated.

The nerve fiber for a short period after functional activity is nonirritable toward a second stimulus. This loss of excitability is designated as the *refractory period.* For from 2 to 3 sigma (a sigma is 1/1000 of a second) after an excitation there is an absolutely refractory condition in which no stimulus, however strong, can excite the nerve. This is followed by a period, the relative refractory period, of about 13 sigma in which the excitability is returning rapidly to normal. If the refractory period of a nerve is known it is possible to calculate the upper limit of the frequency with which nerve impulses can be transmitted along it. Some theories of hearing attempt to make use of such calculations.

The nature of the nerve impulse is not definitely known. Using sensitive galvanometer oscillographs and cathode-ray oscillographs, valuable information has been gained from studies of the electrical phenomena which invariably accompany the passage of a nerve impulse. *Action currents,* negative potential variations detectable when a portion of a nerve (or muscle) is placed in series with delicate electrical equipment, have a velocity identical with that of the propagated impulse. The wave of negative potential probably depends upon an accompanying or preceding chemical activity, progressively propagated. If a nerve cell is excited at all, its excitation is *ipso facto* the greatest which is normally possible for it. It follows the principle of *all or none.*

The source of energy of an impulse in the nervous system is the neuron cell body. This energy arises from physiological changes in the nerve cell. Metabolism and the expenditure of new energy are necessary in restoring a nerve fiber after it has been stimulated. The nerve uses oxygen, carbohydrates, and other foods, and gives off carbon dioxide, heat, and other waste products, much like a muscle, but in minute quantities. Application of anesthetics and narcotics, deprivation of oxygen, and compression of a nerve, all lessen or suspend the conductivity of the nerve.

The nerve impulse is a propagated disturbance which proceeds along the nerve and "sets off" an effector. The impulse is self-contributory; [3] the energy is not propagated by the stimulus but takes place along the fiber.

[3] Burning a gunpowder fuse is an illustration of a self-propagated impulse.

Each nerve (and muscle cell) has a characteristic speed of reaction. This can be measured by determining its *chronaxy,* which is: "The duration of action of a constant electrical current, instantaneously applied, which is required to excite the cell, when the intensity of the current is double (two times the rheobase) that which will just excite if infinite time is allowed." The shorter the chronaxial time, the more rapidly the impulse is conducted, the more rapidly does it develop at the point of excitation, the shorter are the refractory period and the latent period. The chronaxy of a fiber is inversely proportional to its cross-sectional area; the larger the fiber, the more rapidly its processes occur.

C. The Synapse

In vertebrates at least two neurons are required to receive a nerve impulse from a receptor and transmit it to an effector. Connection is made, in the central nervous system, when the *terminal arborization* or branched end-plate of an axon lies in physiological contact with the dendrites of another neuron. This junction is called a *synapse.* In relation to the cell body, an axon carries exodic or centrifugal impulses; dendrites, esodic or centripetal impulses.

In man, the two-neuron *reflex arc* is probably an academic myth. Undoubtedly, three or more neurons are involved in even the simplest stimulus-response reaction. The more complex an activity, and the more involved the higher brain centers, the more neurons may be added between the receptor and effector.

An important and controversial question in neurology is this: How is one neuron related to another so that an impulse may be propagated from the first to the second? Figure 63*B* shows that where one neuron stops, i. e., at the termination of the axon, and another begins, i. e., the dendrites of the second neuron, or, in other words, where they come into functional relation, there is located the synapse. At the synapse, the processes of one neuron are not fused with the processes of another. Each neuron remains a distinct unit. There may be contact of neurons but it is probable that continuity of substance is lacking; there is contiguity, but not continuity.

Presumably, across a synapse a nerve impulse may travel in but one direction—that is, from axon to dendrites. This dynamic polarity is a property of the synapse, not of the nerve fiber.

THE NERVOUS SYSTEM

Now that we have become acquainted with the neuron—the genetic, structural, functional, and trophic unit of the nervous system—we are in a position to study the complex arrangements of neurons in the nervous system. We may consider the nervous system to be made up of two divisions: the *central nervous system* (*CNS*), and the *peripheral nervous system*.

The central nervous system consists of a single continuous nervous organization which, however, for ease of study is arbitrarily divided at the

1. Afferent neuron; 2. spinal ganglion; 3. nerve cell body of afferent neuron; 4. sensory nerve ending or receptor; 5. skin, 6. pin pricking skin; 7. nerve cell body of efferent neuron; 8. axon of efferent neuron; 9. muscle (effector); 10. synapse; 11. intermediate or intercalary neuron making up third neuron of three-neuron reflex arc.

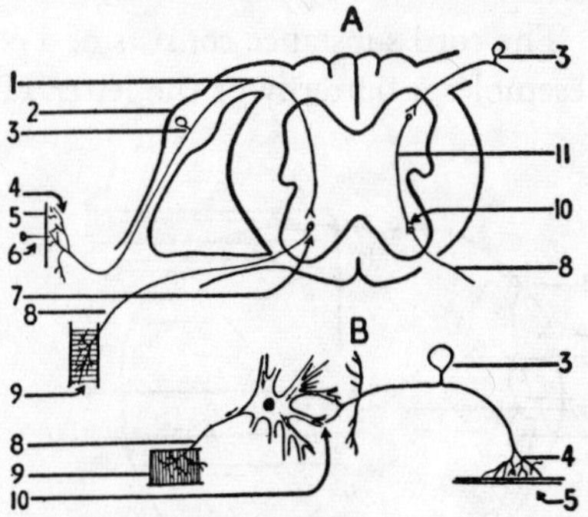

FIG. 63. Schematic Diagram of (*A*) Reflex Arc and (*B*) Synapse.

level of the upper border of the *atlas* or *first cervical vertebra* into two parts. That part of the central nervous system above the atlas is the *encephalon*, lodged within the cranium. The remainder or caudal part is the *medulla spinalis,* protected within the vertebral column.

The peripheral nervous system consists of nerves connecting the central nervous system [4] with the various body tissues. They may be classified as *spinal nerves* and *cranial nerves.* There are 43 *cerebrospinal nerves* on either side of the central nervous system. There are 12 pairs of cranial nerves with brain attachments. Thirty-one pairs of spinal nerves are attached to the medulla spinalis—one pair for each spinal cord segment.

A. The Central Nervous System

It is customary to consider the central nervous system as made up of these divisions: medulla spinalis, myelencephalon, metencephalon, mesencephalon, diencephalon, and telencephalon. We shall look at them in that order.

1. THE SPINAL CORD (MEDULLA SPINALIS)

The spinal cord is a long (45 cm.), somewhat cylindrical mass of nervous tissue, continuous rostrally with the brain (medulla oblongata) at the level of the *foramen magnum* and suspended within protective sheaths in the vertebral column. Caudally, it extends to about the level of the second lumbar vertebra. A transverse section of the cord shows it to be partially

[4] The somatic efferent and sympathetic efferent nuclei and the somatic afferent and sympathetic afferent nuclei are located in the central nervous system.

bisected, anteroposteriorly, by two fissures and a septum: the *fissura mediana anterior,* and the *sulcus medianus posterior,* and *posterior median septum.* Each lateral half is divided into three *funiculi,*[5] *anterior, lateral,* and *posterior,* by two furrows: *sulcus lateralis anterior* and *sulcus lateralis posterior.*

The cord substance consists of a central gray mass which in cross section resembles a butterfly or the letter H—with the cross bar of the H at right

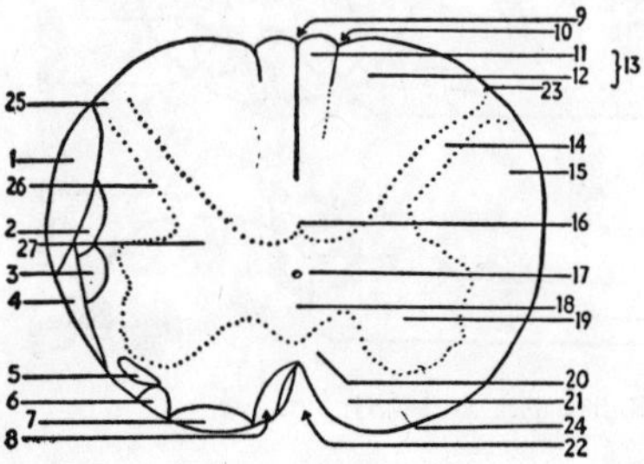

1. Dorsal spinocerebellar tract; 2. lateral corticospinal tract; 3. rubrospinal tract; 4. ventral spinocerebellar tract; 5. ventral spinothalamic tract; 6. spino-olivary tract; 7. vestibulospinal tract; 8. ventral corticospinal tract; 9. posterior median sulcus and septum; 10. posterior intermediate sulcus and septum; 11. fasciculus gracilis; 12. fasciculus cuneatus; 13. posterior funiculus; 14. posterior column; 15. lateral funiculus; 16. posterior commissure; 17. central canal; 18. anterior gray commissure; 19. anterior column; 20. anterior white commissure; 21. anterior funiculus; 22. anterior median fissure; 23. posterolateral sulcus; 24. anterolateral sulcus; 25. apex; 26. caput; 27. cervix.

FIG. 64. Outline Section through Spinal Cord.

angles to the anteroposterior bisectors mentioned above—and a surrounding area of white substance. The gray substance is made up of cytons, dendrons, myelinated and non-myelinated fibers, and neuroglia.[6] The nerve cells are of three types: those whose axons form the anterior nerve roots, those whose processes, ascending and descending, serve to connect all levels of the cord, and association cells of the Golgi Type II.

The more enlarged ventral ends of the H are called the anterior or ventral horns or—considering that they extend the length of the medulla spinalis—*anterior columns* or *ventral columns.* The smaller dorsal ends of the H are called the posterior or dorsal horns or the *posterior columns* or *dorsal columns.* The bar of the H is called the *gray commissure.* The gray columns are not straight; each anterior column projects toward its respective anterolateral sulcus, and each posterior column toward its respective posterolateral sulcus.

The ventral gray column is relatively short and thick. In it are located the cell bodies of the ventral root fibers. These are the *cell bodies of the lower motor neurons* of the cord. Each axon originating here constitutes a *final common pathway* for nerve impulses to the structure it supplies.[7]

[5] Funiculus (Latin diminutive of *funis,* cord), a gross division of the white matter.
In the cervical region, the sulcus intermedius posterior, between the sulcus medianus posterior and the posterior median septum, and the sulcus lateralis posterior serves to demarcate the fasciculus gracilis and fasciculus cuneatus.

[6] Neuroglia serves as the connective tissue of the nervous system but it is of ectodermal origin, whereas true connective tissue is mesodermal in origin.

[7] It has been shown that there are one and a quarter million sensory fibers and only a

The dorsal gray column is relatively long and thin, in transverse section, and is divided into three regions called the cervix, caput, and apex (substantia gelatinosa Rolandi).

The *lateral gray column* contains the cell bodies of *pre-ganglionic* fibers of the thoraco-lumbar part of the general visceral efferent system.

A transverse line through the central canal in the *commissura grisea* serves to divide it into two parts: the *posterior gray commissure* and the *anterior gray commissure.* Just ventral to the latter is the *anterior white commissure,* where numerous medullated fibers cross from one side of the cord to the other.

The white substance, entirely surrounding the gray portion, makes up the remainder of the cord mass. It is composed of medullated and non-medullated nerve fibers and neuroglia. The fibers, whether *intersegmental* (i. e., confined to the cord) or *cerebrospinal* (i. e., connecting cord and brain), have both *ascending* and *descending tracts.* They offer the possibility of placing each area and part of the body in contact with the environment, in integrative relationship with the cortex or lower brain centers. In the white substance of the cord are located numerous bundles or tracts of fibers.

The spinal cord is all of the central nervous system that is needed for the simplest animal functions. Indeed, it presents a relatively complex organization when compared with the nervous systems of many of the lower animals. Reflex activity may be carried on entirely at the level of the cord. It involves at least two neurons [8]—a sensory neuron and a motor neuron. For example, if a pin stimulates a sensory nerve ending in the finger, the stimulus will be carried along the fiber of an afferent neuron whose cell body is located in a dorsal root ganglion. From the ganglion to the cord, the axon of the neuron will convey the impulse. In the cord, the axon will come into synaptic relation with the dendrites of a motor cell located in the ventral horn. This efferent neuron will convey the stimulus to a muscle which will contract to cause the finger to be withdrawn from the pin.

Associated with the spinal cord are the spinal nerves, many of which innervate muscles used in the integrated mechanism of speech production.

Reciprocal Innervation

Reference has been made to diadochokinesis, and the fact that muscle agonists are contracted while antagonists are relaxed. This alternating muscular activity is a result of reciprocal innervation. Presumably when a stimulus is sent to one muscle to contract, an inhibitory stimulus is not sent to an antagonist muscle to relax. Stimuli do not differ thus qualita-

half million motor fibers in sections of dorsal and ventral roots. The final common pathway is like the small end of a funnel. Many different kinds of stimuli may come into the central nervous system to produce the transmission of stimuli to a specific effector.

[8] In man, three. There is at least one association neuron between the two.

tively. Rather, it is an inhibition of the transmission of the stimulus to the antagonist which causes the decrease of tonus or relaxation. In normal articulate speech the inhibition is rapidly, successfully, and efficiently shifted from one muscle group to another.

Before leaving the medulla spinalis, the student will do well to consider the evolutionary development of the nervous system. The spinal cord, older than the brain, subserves *all* the nervous system functions in lower animals; hence, we would not expect to find the more primitive, vegetative processes which have been raised above cord (reflex) level far removed anatomically. As we shall see, the fact that the medulla oblongata is considered to be an extension of the cord, and that it is the controlling center of many biological functions (e. g., breathing) is in agreement with such an observation.

2. THE BRAIN (ENCEPHALON)

a. The Medulla Oblongata (Myelencephalon or Afterbrain)

External appearance

The medulla oblongata [9] is continuous with the medulla spinalis, rostrally, at the level of the foramen magnum. A surface indication of where the spinal cord becomes the medulla oblongata may be taken as just cephalad of the highest rootlet of the first cervical nerve. Its upper extremity is a horizontal groove which demarcates it from the pons. The dorsal surface is covered over by the cerebellum; the ventral surface is seated in the basilar part of the occipital bone.

The following longitudinal fissures and sulci [10] provide convenient landmarks:

Posterior median fissure.

Anterior median fissure. This fissure is interrupted by the decussation of the pyramids.

Anterior lateral sulcus. The root filaments emerging from this sulcus belong to the XIIth cranial nerve.

The olive, an expanded portion on the ventral surface of the medulla oblongata, splits this sulcus into an anterior limb, the preolivary sulcus, and a posterior limb, the postolivary sulcus.

Posterior lateral sulcus. The root filaments emerging ventral to this sulcus belong to the IXth, Xth, and XIth cranial nerves, respectively.

[9] Shaped somewhat like a small pyramid or truncated cone with the larger end directed cephalad, the medulla oblongata is approximately 3 cm. long, 2 cm. wide, and 1¼ cm. thick.

[10] Many of them are continuations of the same landmarks noted in the study of the medulla spinalis.

Internal structure

A cross section through the caudal portion of the medulla oblongata resembles a section through the spinal cord. In the rostral part of the medulla oblongata, however, because of the rearrangement of the fiber tracts, a cross

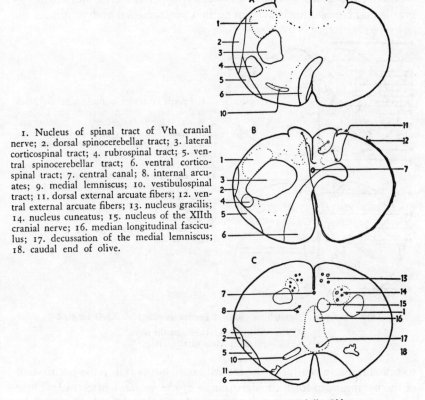

1. Nucleus of spinal tract of Vth cranial nerve; 2. dorsal spinocerebellar tract; 3. lateral corticospinal tract; 4. rubrospinal tract; 5. ventral spinocerebellar tract; 6. ventral corticospinal tract; 7. central canal; 8. internal arcuates; 9. medial lemniscus; 10. vestibulospinal tract; 11. dorsal external arcuate fibers; 12. ventral external arcuate fibers; 13. nucleus gracilis; 14. nucleus cuneatus; 15. nucleus of the XIIth cranial nerve; 16. median longitudinal fasciculus; 17. decussation of the medial lemniscus; 18. caudal end of olive.

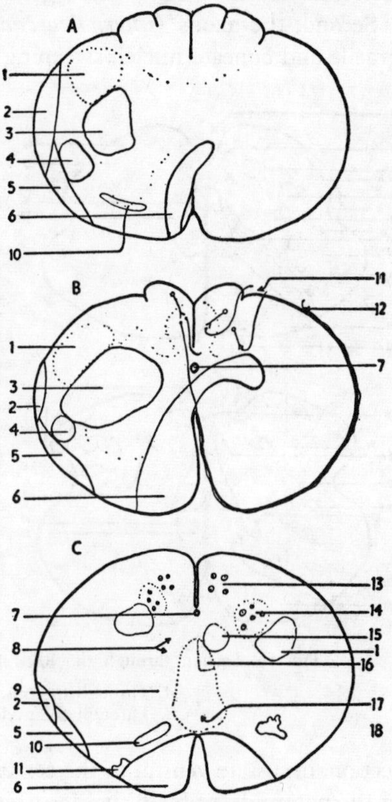

Fig. 65. Sections through the Caudal Portion of the Medulla Oblongata.

A. Region of transition between medulla spinalis and medulla oblongata.
B. Caudal end of pyramidal decussation.
C. Caudal end of olive.

section looks quite different. Compare Figs. 64, 65, and 66. This change of internal structure is dependent on several factors.

First, the fibers of the posterior funiculi—composed of the fibers of the gracile and cuneate fasciculi—terminate and synapse in the gracile and cuneate nuclei, respectively.[11] The numerous cell bodies here act like a

[11] All of this takes place within a few millimeters of the length of the medulla oblongata beginning at about the middle of the olive. The mass of cells produces surface elevations, the clava and cuneate tubercle.

wedge to force the characteristic posterior arms of the H apart ventrolaterally. The posterior columns now occupy lateral positions with respect to the central canal. Here in a lateral position is located the *spinal tract* and the *nucleus of the Vth cranial nerve,* continuous caudally with the dorsolateral fasciculus and substantia gelatinosa of the cord.

Second, the axons (*internal arcuate fibers*) of the cells located in the gracile and cuneate nuclei, sweeping in a ventromedial and yet rostral di-

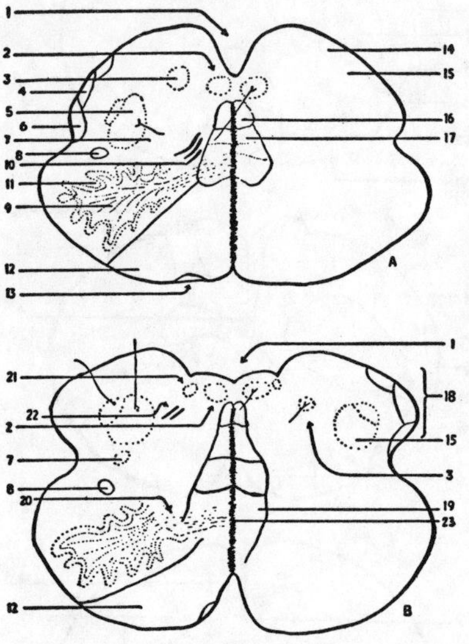

1. Fourth ventricle; 2. nucleus of the XIIth cranial nerve; 3. tractus solitarius and nucleus; 4. dorsal spinocerebellar tract; 5. nucleus and spinal tract of the Vth cranial nerve; 6. ventral spinocerebellar tract; 7. nucleus ambiguus; 8. rubrospinal tract; 9. olivocerebellar fibers; 10. XIIth nerve fibers; 11. inferior olivary nucleus; 12. pyramid; 13. arcuate nucleus; 14. nucleus gracilis; 15. nucleus cuneatus; 16. medial longitudinal fasciculus; 17. tectospinal tract; 18. restiform body; 19. medial lemniscus; 20. hilus of olivary nucleus; 21. dorsal motor nucleus of Xth cranial nerve; 22. vagus nerve fibers; 23. median raphe.

FIG. 66. Section through the Rostral Portion of the Medulla Oblongata.

A. Through the caudal third of the olive.
B. Through the middle of the olive.

rection, decussate ventral to the central canal, but dorsal to the decussation of the pyramids, to form the *decussation of the medial lemniscus.*[12] These fibers, after crossing, continue in a rostral direction on either side of the medial plane as the medial lemnisci.[13] The lemnisci are of such size that, together with the corticospinal tracts, the central canal is forced dorsally so far that now there is no nervous tissue dorsal to it; it has opened out into the *floor of the fourth ventricle.* At this level is the so-called open part of the medulla oblongata.[14] The central gray matter now constitutes the gray

[12] The sensory decussation of the medial lemniscus begins at the rostral border of the motor decussation of the pyramids and extends to the middle of the olive.

[13] The fibers of the medial lemniscus terminate in the thalamus.

[14] The student should recall that the lumen of the original neural tube became dilated rostrally to form three primitive vesicles. From the first are formed two lateral ventricles in the proscencephalon; the second forms the third ventricle of the diencephalon; the most caudal forms the fourth ventricle.

matter of the floor of the fourth ventricle. Much of the altered picture of this level of the medulla oblongata is seen to be due to the many crossing internal arcuate fibers.

Third, the fibers of two tracts from the spinal cord to the cerebellum, namely, spino-olivocerebellar and dorsal spinocerebellar, form a large bundle, the *restiform body* or *inferior cerebellar peduncle.* The dorsal spinocerebellar and vestibulo-cerebellar fibers are located on either side along the lateral periphery of the medulla oblongata. The fibers of the tract skirt the spinal tract and nucleus of the Vth cranial nerve peripherally (i. e., laterally) and pass dorsally to the restiform body. Just ventral to the dorsal spinocerebellar tract and dorsolateral to the olivary nucleus is located the *ventral spinocerebellar tract.*

Fourth, the presence of the olivary nuclei aids in changing the appearance of the structure of the medulla oblongata. The function of the *inferior olivary, medial accessory olivary,* and *dorsal accessory olivary nuclei* prominent in Fig. 67 is not well known.

Fifth, the crossing over [15] and the joining of the *lateral corticospinal tracts* with the ventral corticospinal tracts bulges out the medulla oblongata at this point and produces the landmark called the *pyramid.* The lateral corticospinal tract fibers in the medulla oblongata in crossing over ventral to the central canal cut the ventral legs of the H-shaped gray matter of the cord as shown in Fig. 65.

Sixth, the *spinal tract and nucleus of the Vth cranial nerve* aid in altering the picture. The tract is made up of descending afferent fibers which terminate and synapse or give collaterals to the cells of the nucleus of the spinal tract of the Vth cranial nerve. The gray column of the nucleus is continuous with the substantia gelatinosa Rolandi, caudally. The tract is lateral to the nucleus. Lateral to the tract are the external arcuate fibers and those of the dorsal spinocerebellar tract; lateral and somewhat dorsal is the restiform body. The slight external bulge on the surface of the medulla oblongata which is caused by this aggregation of cells and fibers is called the *tuberculum cinereum.*

Seventh factor is the *nucleus of the XIIth cranial nerve.* This long column is just lateral to the median plane and beneath the trigonum hypoglossi on the floor of the fourth ventricle.

Eighth factor is the *dorsal motor nucleus of the Xth cranial nerve.* It is just lateral to the nucleus of the XIIth cranial nerve and beneath the ala cinerea on the floor of the fourth ventricle.

[15] On each side, approximately 80 to 90 per cent of the corticospinal fibers, and those situated nearest the medial line, cross to form the lateral corticospinal tract. This tract is located in the lateral funiculus of the medulla spinalis. The remaining 10 to 20 per cent of the more laterally placed fibers descend as the ventral corticospinal tract, eventually crossing. This tract is located in the ventral funiculus.

Ninth factor is the *nucleus ambiguus of the IXth, Xth, and XIth cranial nerves*. It is in the reticular formation and lies ventromedial to the nucleus of the spinal tract of the Vth cranial nerve.

Tenth factor is the *nucleus of the tractus solitarius*. Herein terminate and synapse the afferent fibers of the VIIth, IXth, and Xth cranial nerves. The

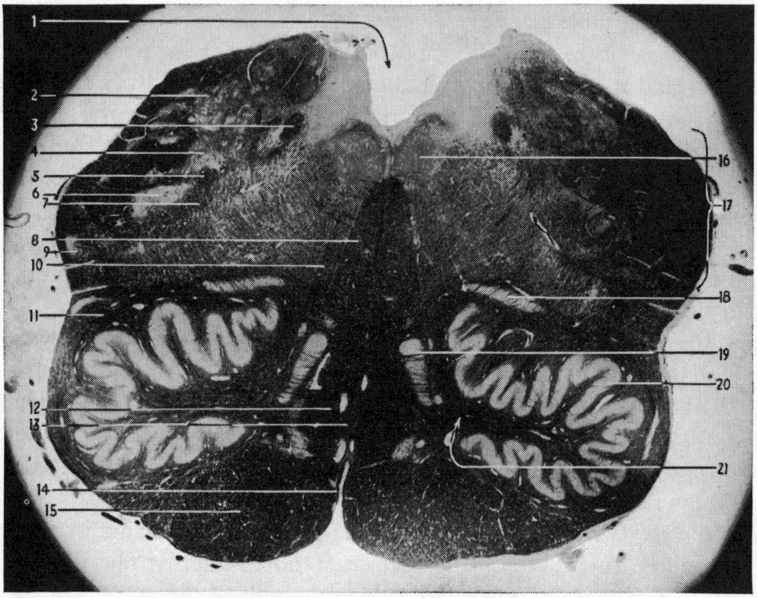

FIG. 67. Photomicrograph of Section through the Medulla Oblongata near the Central Portion of the Olive.

1. Fourth ventricle; 2. nucleus gracilis; 3. tractus solitarius and nucleus; 4. nucleus of spinal tract of Vth cranial nerve; 5. nucleus ambiguus; 6. spinal tract of Vth cranial nerve; 7. internal arcuate fibers; 8. medial longitudinal fasciculus; 9. dorsal spinocerebellar tract; 10. fibers of XIIth cranial nerve; 11. thalamo-olivary tract; 12. medial lemniscus; 13. median raphe; 14. ventral external arcuate fibers; 15. pyramid; 16. nucleus of XIIth cranial nerve; 17. restiform body; 18. dorsal accessory olivary nucleus; 19. medial accessory olivary nucleus; 20. inferior olivary nucleus; 21. hilus of olivary nucleus.

tractus solitarius and its nucleus lie just ventrolateral to the dorsal motor nucleus of the Xth cranial nerve.

In brief tabular form, these nuclei of cranial nerves involved in speech processes are located in the medulla oblongata:

SSA—Cochlear nucleus. Terminal nucleus of the cochlear division of the acoustic (VIII) nerve.

GVE—Inferior salivatory nucleus. (IX cranial nerve) Parotid gland.

GVA—Nucleus tractus solitarius. (IXth, Xth cranial nerves) Posterior one-third of tongue; pharynx; larynx; esophagus; trachea; thoracic viscera.

SVE—Nucleus ambiguus. (IXth, Xth, XIth cranial nerves) Stylopharyngeus muscles; striated muscles of the pharynx and larynx.

GVE—Dorsal motor nucleus of the Xth. Thoracic and abdominal viscera.
SSE—Hypoglossal nucleus. (XIIth cranial nerve) Muscles of the tongue.

The Neurological Mechanism of Breathing

In the caudal portion of the myelencephalon is located the *respiratory center*. It is probably part of the nucleus ambiguus or of the dorsal motor nucleus of the vagus. It is extraordinarily richly supplied with blood and its cells are extremely sensitive to chemical changes in the carbon dioxide content of the blood. The center is bilateral. Rhythmically, as the cells become stimulated by a greater carbon dioxide content in the blood, impulses are initiated which pass from the cells along their nerve fibers in the tractus solitariospinalis. These neurons synapse at various levels in the spinal cord and neurons of the second order convey the impulses to the respiratory muscles. For examples, neurons with cell bodies in the cervical region innervate the diaphragm,[16] (C 3, 4, 5) and neurons with cell bodies lower down in the thoracic region (T 1–12) innervate the intercostal muscles. In brief, the impulses of inhalation and exhalation for the breathing mechanism originate in the medulla oblongata centers, and are distributed to the lower motor centers in the medulla spinalis or to the motor centers of such cranial nerves as the vagus.

Two kinds of afferent fibers, from the lungs to the medulla oblongata, stimulate or inhibit the respiratory center: (*a*) *inspiratory fibers,* which by inhibiting the brain center permit a more rapidly functioning lower level to operate, thus increasing the breathing rate, and (*b*) *expiratory fibers* (inspiratory inhibiting), which bring about a decrease in the rate of breathing.

The sensory endings of these fibers are probably stimulated by the alter nate expansion and collapse of the lungs. During inhalation, a point is reached in the expansion of the lungs when, perhaps due to pressure upon the nerve endings, the inhibitory fibers are stimulated and inhalation is stopped—short of what otherwise would be the case. During exhalation the collapse of the lungs stimulates inspiratory fibers which start inhalation. Thus a definite rhythm and depth of breathing are maintained. Either rhythm or depth, or both, may be varied.

Sensory nerves from the lungs convey impulses via the vagus ganglion, in which are located their cell bodies, to the solitary nucleus or to the dorsal motor nucleus of the Xth cranial nerve where they synapse. Efferent impulses from the dorsal motor nucleus of the Xth cranial nerve pass from

[16] Without a knowledge of embryology it would be difficult to explain the innervation of the diaphragm. In its early development from the cervical myotomes it lies in the cervical region and it would be expected to have cervical innervation. In later growth with the descent of the diaphragm in respect to the cervical region, the nerve fibers must of course follow. Thus the fibers from the 3d, 4th, and 5th cervical nerves lengthen as the phrenic nerve to innervate the diaphragm

the brain via preganglionic fibers to sympathetic ganglia on the lung, and postganglionic fibers from these are distributed to the lung.

It is possible that the respiratory center also provides for rhythmical constriction and dilatation of the bronchi, the lumen of the bronchi being constricted by stimuli from the cranial autonomic system, and dilated by stimuli from the thoraco-lumbar system.

Stimulation of any of the sensory nerves of the body may affect the rhythm or depth of the respiratory movements. Emotional and mental states are accompanied by changes, often easily detectable, in breathing. The medulla center is in connection with the sensory fibers of the cranial and spinal nerves and is influenced by interconnections with fibers of tracts passing between the cerebral cortex and the medulla oblongata. These sensory nerves may affect changes in breathing rate with an increase or decrease in amplitude; the inhalations and exhalations may each be increased, or either phase may be affected more than the other.

Ordinarily the period of inhalation occupies about the same time as that of exhalation. During the production of speech, however, there is a decrease in the time spent in inhalation, and an increase in the expiratory phase. The total time, inhalation plus exhalation, bears a fairly close relation to the total time occupied by the two phases in normal breathing.

b. The Metencephalon (Hindbrain)

I. The Pons

The basis pontis constitutes a bridge between the cerebral cortex and the cerebellum. This suggests that these portions of the brain must work in close harmony, one with the other. The tegmentum, furthermore, is a continuation of the medulla oblongata, and likewise contains the nuclei of several cranial nerves important in speech functions:

GSA—Main sensory nucleus, and nucleus of spinal tract of Vth (terminal nuclei). Skin and mucous membrane of head.

SVE—Motor nucleus of the Vth. Muscles of mastication.

SVE—Motor nucleus of the VIIth. Face and scalp muscles, platysma, stylohoid, posterior belly of the digastric.

GVE—Superior salivatory nucleus (VII). Submaxillary and sublingual salivary glands. Palate.

SSA—Cochlear nucleus (VIII).

External appearance

The ventral view of the brain shows the pons located between the medulla oblongata and the cerebral peduncles. It is ventral to the cerebellum. It is made up of a mass of transverse fibers. This portion of the pons is known as the *basilar portion*. Its fibers form a bridge connecting the cerebral with the opposite cerebellar hemispheres. As they are gathered together in a large strand to enter the cerebellum they are given the name ***brachium pontis*** or *middle cerebellar peduncles*. On the ventrolateral surface of the pons near the peduncle may be seen the two roots of the Vth cranial nerve.

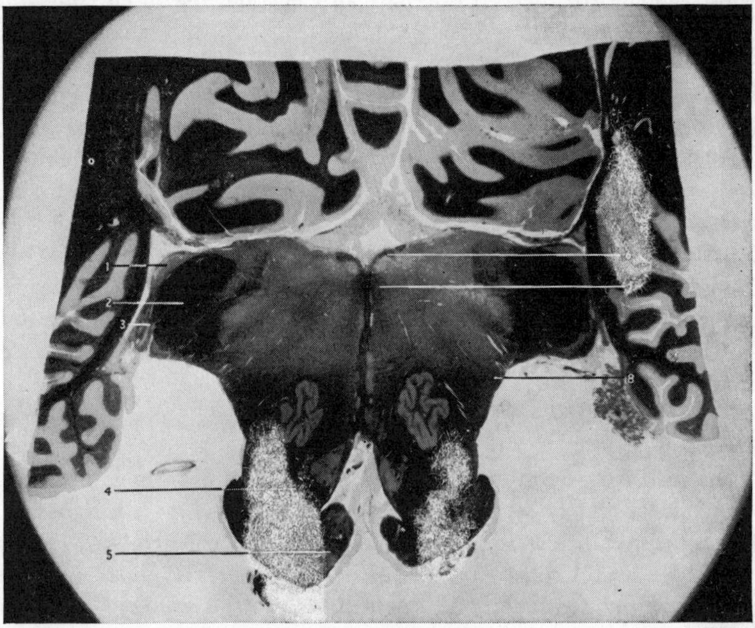

FIG. 68. Section through Rostral End of Medulla Oblongata and Caudal Border of Pons.

1. Dorsal cochlear nucleus; 2. restiform body; 3. ventral cochlear nucleus; 4. corticospinal tract (pyramid); 5. pons; 6. striae medullares acusticae; 7. medial longitudinal fasciculus; 8. ventral spinocerebellar tract.

The large root (portio major) is the sensory root; the smaller (portio minor) is the motor root.

The dorsal surface is the ventral wall of the rostral part of the fourth ventricle. The brachia conjunctiva (superior cerebellar peduncles) form its lateral boundaries.

In a median sagittal section of the brain, the fourth ventricle may be seen bounded dorsally by the cerebellum and ventrally by the medulla oblongata and the pons. Caudally, it is continuous with the central canal of the closed portion of the medulla oblongata; rostrally, with the cerebral aqueduct of the mesencephalon. With the cerebellum removed, along with the thin roof (anterior medullary velum, and tela chorioidea), a dorsal view reveals the floor of the ventricle which is called the rhomboid fossa. From what has been said above it is apparent that the floor of the ventricle constitutes the dorsal surface of the medulla oblongata (open part) and pons. The lateral boundaries include the restiform bodies, clavae, and cuneate tubercles, and brachia conjunctiva. The median sulcus, running longitudinally, divides the fossa into lateral halves. The rhomboid fossa may be divided into a superior part (most rostral), an intermediate part, and an inferior part (most caudal). In the superior part an elevation, the *facial colliculus* is caused by the bundle of subjacent fibers of the VIIth cranial nerve. The *striae medullares acusticae,* arising from the dorsal cochlear nuclei, cross the fossa in the intermediate portion. In the inferior portion—belonging to the medulla oblongata—immediately lateral to the median sulcus is a triangular elevation, the *trigone of the hypoglossal nerve,* formed by the subjacent nucleus of the XIIth cranial nerve. Lateral to the trigonum nervi hypoglossi is a sulcus, and, lateral to the sulcus, is another triangular elevation, the *ala cinerea,* caused by a subjacent nucleus of the Xth cranial nerve. Through the choroid plexuses, the fourth ventricle gives an intimate connection with the circulatory system. In the lateral recesses of the fourth ventricle, are openings which assure the ventricles of the brain access to the circulating cerebrospinal fluid.

Internal structure

The basilar or ventral portion of the pons does not resemble the medulla oblongata, as may be seen in the cross-section view (Fig. 68). Familiar are the corticospinal tracts, however. These give off collaterals in the pons. Near these are the corticopontine tracts, whose fibers originate in the cerebral cortex but terminate and synapse here in the scattered nuclei basis pontis. All of the fibers from the cerebral cortex enter the pons by way of the basis pedunculi.

In addition to these longitudinally coursing fibers, the basilar portion of the pons is particularly distinguished by the great mass of transverse fibers. Most of these axons of the nuceli pontis cross the median plane and, joining with the few uncrossed fibers of the other side, enter the cerebellum in a thick band called the brachium pontis or middle cerebellar peduncle. These fibers are the last link in a cortico-ponto-cerebellar path. The dorsal or tegmental portion of the pons bears more resemblance to the medulla oblongata with which it is continuous.

In the ventrolateral part of the tegmentum is the motor nucleus of the VIIth cranial nerve whose fibers pass dorsally and medially and then laterally and ventrolaterally (genu of facial nerve) around the nucleus of the abducens nerve; thence, laterally to the nucleus of the VIIth cranial nerve to exit on the ventrolateral surface of the pons.

Just ventral to the nucleus of the facial nerve is the superior olivary nucleus. It is not a continuation of the inferior olivary nucleus, but is a part of the auditory system.

Ventral to the superior olivary nucleus is the trapezoid body, a prominent bundle of transverse fibers. These fibers originate in the cochlear nuclei and superior olivary nucleus of the same side, and pass to the median plane to decussate and turn rostrally, laterally and somewhat dorsally, to form the lateral lemniscus, in which fillet they run to the inferior colliculus of the mesencephalon and the medial geniculate body of the metathalamus of the diencephalon.

The cochlear nuclei, dorsal and ventral, are on the restiform body at the

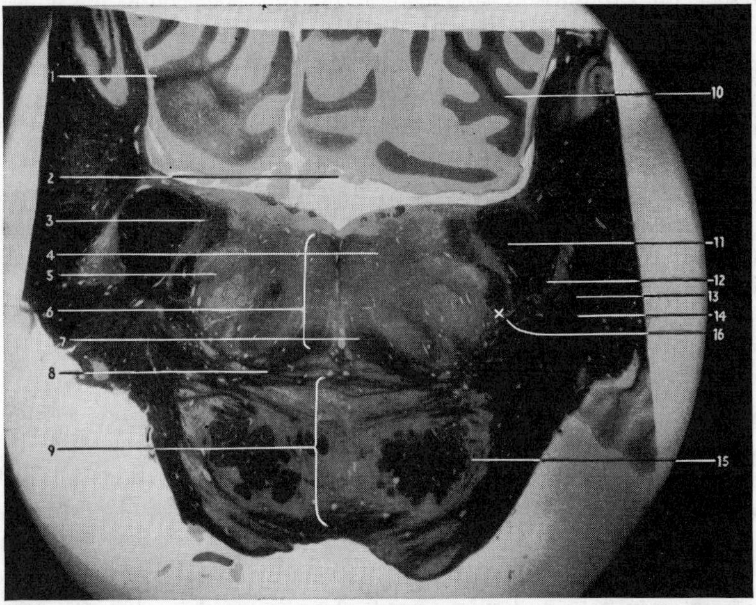

FIG. 69. Section through Caudal One-third of Pons.

1. Dentate nucleus of cerebellum; 2. fourth ventricle; 3. restiform body; 4. medial longitudinal fasciculus; 5. facial nerve; 6. dorsal part of pons; 7. medial lemniscus; 8. trapezoid body; 9. basilar part of pons; 10. cerebellum; 11. lateral vestibular nucleus; 12. spinal tract and nucleus Vth cranial nerve; 13. brachium pontis; 14. facial nerve; 15. corticospinal and corticopontine tracts; 16. nucleus of VIIth nerve.

level where the medulla oblongata gives place to the pons. Here terminate and synapse the central processes of the fibers of the neurons of the first order of the auditory nerve. But the auditory pathway continues to higher levels by means of neurons of the second and third order.

At the level of the middle of the pons is located the motor nucleus of the Vth cranial nerve, and the main sensory nucleus of the Vth cranial nerve. They are somewhat dorsolaterally located with respect to the superior olive. The main sensory nucleus may be considered a rostral continuation of the nucleus of the spinal tract of the trigeminal nerve. Between the motor and sensory nuclei are other fibers of the trigeminal nerve (mesencephalic root of the trigeminal nerve) which originate in the mesencephalic nucleus of the Vth cranial nerve.

II. The Cerebellum

External appearance

The cerebellum makes up the greater part of the hindbrain. It is oval-shaped, displaying on its surface numerous sulci, which give it its characteristic appearance. Viewed either ventrally or dorsally the cerebellum presents numerous fissures and lobules; the whole looks rather like a loosely wound ball of gray yarn that has been stepped on. A ventral view of the cerebellum shows the possibility of dividing it arbitrarily into three parts: two lateral paired portions, the cerebellar hemispheres, connected by a median unpaired vermis. The median portion of the cerebellum contains the co-ordination centers for mid-line musculature functioning in bilateral synergy; e. g., the musculature of the jaws, pharynx, and larynx.

The cerebellum is connected to the mesencephalon by the superior peduncle, to the pons by the middle peduncle, and to the medulla oblongata by the inferior peduncle.

Internal structure

In cross section of the cord and lower brain, the areas of gray substance, in the main, have been deep with respect to the areas of white substance. In the cerebellum the reverse is true; the gray substance is superficial in its relation to the white substance. The thin layer of gray substance is called the cerebellar cortex; the central white substance is the medullary substance. Sagittal sections through the cerebellum have the appearance of foliage with the edges of the leaves gray and the veins white. This type of structure with so many folia and sulci permits the placing in a small space of an extensive area of gray substance. In the medullary substance of each hemisphere are nuclei; the largest, the dentate nucleus, resembles the inferior olivary nucleus in appearance.

The medullary substance is made up of the many fibers entering the cerebellum through its three peduncles: the brachium pontis or middle cerebellar peduncle made up of fibers from the cerebral cortex which cross as the transverse fibers of the pons and pass to the opposite cerebellar hemisphere; the restiform body or inferior cerebellar peduncle made up of ascending vestibulocerebellar, olivocerebellar, dorsal spinocerebellar, dorsal external arcuate, and ventral external arcuate fibers, and descending fibers from the cerebellum to the reticular formation of the medulla oblongata; and the brachium conjunctivum or superior cerebellar peduncle made up of descending fibers from the dentate nucleus to the red nucleus and thalamus of the opposite side, as well as ascending fibers of the ventral spinocerebellar tract. Ascending fibers (i. e., afferent fibers), through intricate branching dendrites, may diffuse their stimuli to large areas of the cortex of the cerebellum. The cytons of descending (i. e., efferent) fibers are the large

Purkinje cells. The efferent fibers terminate in central nuclei located in the medullary substance (white matter) of the cerebellum, whence arise—as, for example, in the case of the dentate nucleus—neurons of the second order which descend in the extrapyramidal system or descending reflex paths.

The cerebellum acts like an energizer or a step-up transformer, augmenting the activity of the neuro-muscular apparatus of the body. It provides

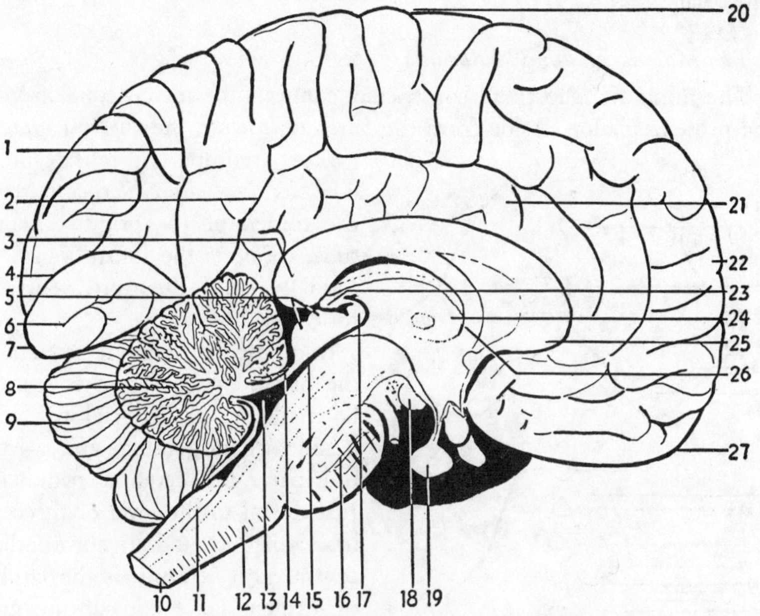

FIG. 70. Median Sagittal Section of the Human Brain.

1. Parieto-occipital fissure; 2. subparietal sulcus; 3. splenium of corpus callosum; 4. calcarine fissure; 5. lamina quadrigemina; 6. occipital lobe; 7. occipital pole; 8. superior and inferior vermis of cerebellum; 9. hemisphere of cerebellum; 10. medulla spinalis; 11. central canal; 12. medulla oblongata; 13. fourth ventricle; 14. anterior medullary velum; 15. cerebral aqueduct; 16. pons; 17. posterior commissure; 18. mammillary body; 19. hypophysis; 20. central sulcus; 21. gyrus cinguli; 22. superior frontal gyrus; 23. pineal body; 24. thalamus; 25. genu of corpus callosum; 26. body of fornix; 27. frontal pole.

continuous, although varying degrees of, reflex tonus for all muscles. Without this co-ordinating center, asynergy in speech and movement results. The cerebellum is the proprioceptive integrating center. From the cerebellum go efferent fibers to regulate the muscle tone and to produce synergy. Co-ordination is a synonym for synergy. In muscle action, which invariably means that several muscles are in action, synergy means that each muscle will contract, in relation to each other muscle, in that correct spatial and temporal relationship which will produce the required complete co-ordinated action. For example, playing a piano and singing at the same time requires a high degree of co-ordination, especially because many delicate muscles are used. Walking, batting a ball, or grasping a pencil are perhaps simpler activities, but each places demands for synergy upon the cerebellum.

Cerebellar influence is *ipsilateral;* the left half of the cerebellum exerts influence on the left side of the body, and the right on the right side of the body. The connection of the cortical motor areas with the cerebellum is *contralateral*—left cerebral cortex to the right half of the cerebellum and vice versa. The cerebellum regulates the degree of tonicity of the neuromuscular systems.

c. The Mesencephalon (*Midbrain*)

The midbrain, short and constricted, connects the metencephalon with the prosencephalon. Aside from the *bases pedunculi,* the *corpora quadrigemina* are important reflex centers. The *cerebral aqueduct,* a part of the lumen of the original neural tube, connects the fourth ventricle, caudally, with the third ventricle, rostrally.

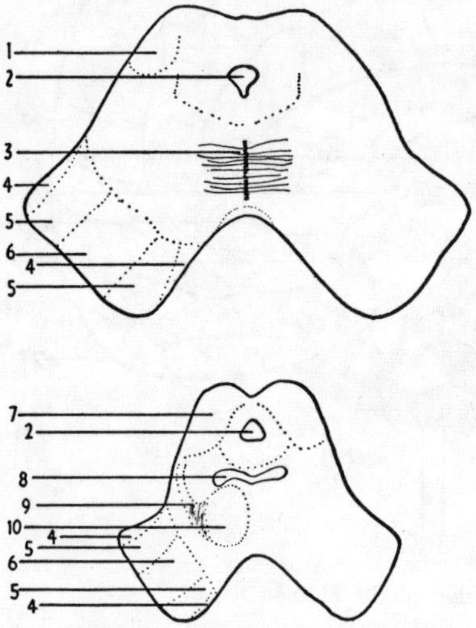

FIG. 71. Sections through the Mesencephalon.
A. At the level of the inferior colliculi.
B. At the level of the superior colliculi.

1. Nucleus of inferior colliculus; 2. cerebral aqueduct; 3. decussation brachium conjunctivum; 4. corticospinal aberrant tract; 5. corticoponto-cerebellar tract; 6. corticobulbar and corticospinal tracts; 7. superior colliculus; 8. medial longitudinal fasciculus; 9. medial lemniscus; 10. red nucleus.

In a median sagittal section of the brain, the midbrain is seen to be made up of a dorsal part, the lamina quadrigemina, and a ventral part, the cerebral peduncles. Just dorsal to the level of the cerebral aqueduct and its surrounding central gray stratum is the lamina quadrigemina, made up of gray and white matter, and displaying four rounded elevations, the quadrigeminal bodies. The larger, superior quadrigeminal bodies, superior colliculi, subserve visual reflex functions; the smaller, inferior quadrigeminal bodies, inferior colliculi, subserve auditory reflex functions. In the nucleus of the inferior colliculus, terminate and synapse most of the fibers of the lateral lemniscus. Fibers from the nerve cells of this nucleus run caudalward, after a partial decussation, in the tectobulbar tract and after complete decussation in the tectospinal tract. Thus, this nucleus is a reflex center for responses to sound. The remaining fibers of the lateral lemniscus continue to the medial geniculate body in a tract known as the inferior quadrigeminal brachium.

Each cerebral peduncle is divided into a ventral portion, the *basis pedunculi;* dorsal to this is a darkly pigmented area of nuclear substance, the substantia nigra, and dorsal to this and continuing to the aqueduct is an area of reticular formation, the *tegmentum*. The tegmentum is the rostral continuation of the tegmentum of the pons. Located medially in this area of the mesencephalon is the continuation of the longitudinal fibers of the brachium conjunctivum which, at the level of the inferior colliculi, decussate in the decussation of the brachia conjunctiva. After the decussation the crossed fibers immediately terminate in the red nucleus, except a few which continue to the thalamus. The red nucleus is reflex motor in function, providing a station for the cerebellar influencing of lower brain and cord centers. Efferent fibers from the red nucleus descend to the cord, after decussation, as the rubrospinal tract. In the tegmentum, the medial lemniscus, from the cuneate and gracilis nuclei of the opposite side, is quite prominent just dorsolateral to the red nucleus. Its fibers and others from the central sensory tract of the Vth cranial nerve, as well as from the spinothalamic tract continue through the mesencephalon to the thalamus. Located in the lateral part of the central gray stratum surrounding the aqueduct is the column of cells of the nucleus of the mesencephalic root of the Vth cranial nerve. In the basis pedunculi are gathered the bundles of longitudinal fibers of the corticospinal, corticobulbar, and corticoponto-cerebellar pathways.

d. The Diencephalon (Interbrain)

A median sagittal section through the brain shows that the diencephalon lies hidden by the cerebral hemispheres. This portion of the prosencephalon, the diencephalon, is made up of these structures: thalamus, metathalamus, epithalamus, hypothalamus, and subthalamus.[17] The diencephalon is the great way station for all sensations that need correlation. All sensory impulses (in which we are interested) to the cortex come through this part of the brain; all the fibers carrying the impulses synapse in this region.

The *thalamus,* made up almost entirely of gray matter, consists of three nuclei—*medial nucleus, anterior nucleus,* and *lateral nucleus*—separated by thin zones of white matter called the internal medullary laminae. The

[17] The paired thalami may be connected across the mid-line by the massa intermedia, but otherwise separated by the third ventricle—i. e., each thalamus forms a lateral wall of the ventricle. The rostral ends approach each other near the median plane; the caudal ends are more widely separated, and in the angle separating them are located the corpora quadrigemina and the pineal body. The convex dorsal surface of the thalamus is the floor of the transverse fissure, which fissure separates the thalamus from the overlying cerebral hemisphere (corpus callosum and fornix). Dorsolaterally, a slight groove separates the thalamus from the caudate nucleus. Laterally and ventrolaterally the thalamus is bounded by the internal capsule which is made up of fibers connecting the telencephalon with lower brain and cord levels. Streaming out of the thalamus, laterally, into the internal capsule are many fibers which flow in the *thalamic radiation* to the cerebral cortex. Ventrally, the thalamus rests on the subthalamus, which in turn rests on the tegmentum of the mesencephalon. Through this intimate connection such tegmental tracts as the medial lemniscus, spinothalamic, and brachium conjunctivum pass into the thalamus.

lateral nucleus is of recent *phyletic* development. Here terminate the fibers of the spinothalamic tracts, the central tract of the trigeminal nerve, and the medial lemniscus. From the nucleus, third-order neurons are distributed to the cerebral cortex. This makes it possible for cutaneous sensations and deep touch-pressure sensations to rise into consciousness. The *metathalamus*

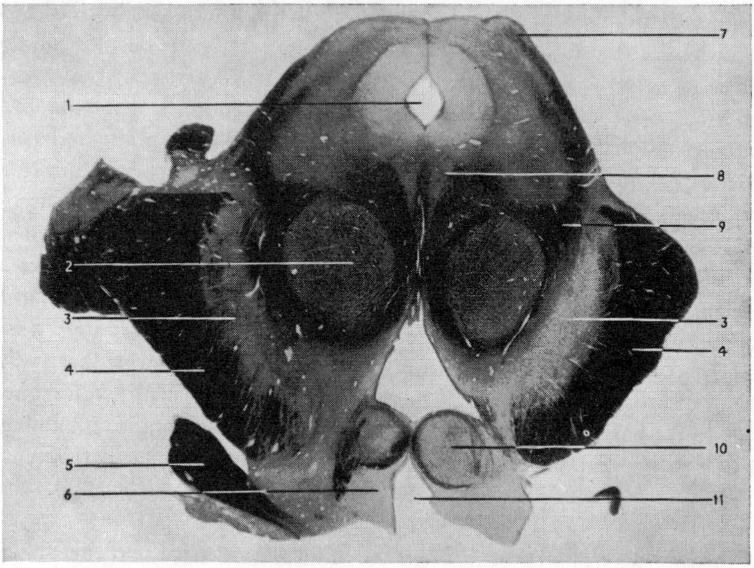

FIG. 72. Section through the Mesencephalon at the Level of the Superior Colliculus.

1. Cerebral aqueduct; 2. red nucleus; 3. substantia nigra; 4. basis pedunculi; 5. optic tract; 6. turber cinereum; 7. superior colliculus; 8. medial longitudinal fasciculus; 9. medial lemniscus; 10. mammillary body; 11. third ventricle.

consists of the geniculate bodies, lateral and medial. The medial geniculate body is associated with the inferior quadrigeminal brachium and lateral lemniscus as part of the auditory pathway. From the medial geniculate body, thalamotemporal fibers ascend (acoustic radiation) to the auditory area of the cerebral cortex. The *epithalamus* consists of the pineal body, habenular trigone, and stria medullaris. The *hypothalamus* is made up of the mammillary bodies, tuber cinereum, infundibulum, and hypophysis. In the *subthalamus* is located the subthalamic nucleus.

It cannot be pointed out too strongly that at innumerable points in the cord, medulla oblongata, pons, mesencephalon, cerebellum, diencephalon, and telencephalon, an ascending or a descending fiber may be provided with an opportunity to give off collaterals or to synapse with one or more of thousands of other neurons which may be ascending or descending. Thus, while for simplicity we usually diagram the path taken by an impulse with the minimum number of neurons, it is conceivable that an impulse once started at any place in the complex nervous system may continue from neuron to neuron *ad infinitum*. In fact, such a continual circuitous arrangement has been advanced to explain memory! Such an integrating system means that every part of the body is in intimate relation with every other part of the body.

e. The Telencephalon (*Endbrain*)

The cerebral hemispheres constitute the bulk of the brain. The separation of the hemispheres by a cleft, the *longitudinal cerebral fissure,* gives

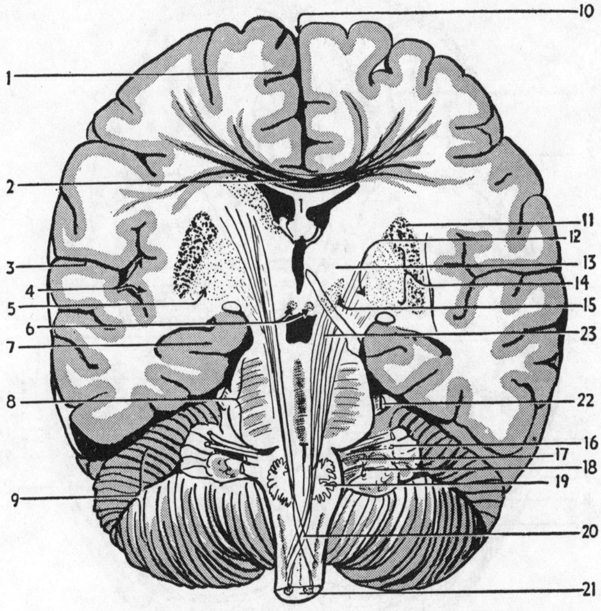

FIG. 73. Section through Human Brain in Axis of Brain Stem.

1. Superior frontal gyri; 2. corpus callosum; 3. lateral cerebral fissure; 4. insulae; 5. globus pallidus; 6. nuclei of mammillary bodies; 7. hippocampus; 8. pons; 9. cerebellar hemisphere; 10. longitudinal fissure; 11. putamen; 12. internal capsule; 13. hypothalamic nucleus; 14. lentiform nucleus; 15. substantia nigra; 16. VIIIth cranial nerve; 17. IXth cranial nerve; 18. Xth cranial nerve; 19. olivary nucleus; 20. pyramidal decussation; 21. medulla spinalis; 22. Vth cranial nerve; 23. fasciculi longitudinalis (pyramidales) pontis.

each of them three surfaces: *lateral, medial,* and *inferior*. The anterior end of the hemisphere is the *frontal pole;* the posterior end, the *occipital pole.* The anterior end of the temporal lobe is the *temporal pole*.

Eminences [18] (*gyri* or *convolutions*), separated by furrows [19] (*fissures* and *sulci*) configure the surfaces, permitting an increase in the area of gray

[18] Gyri are non-invaginated portions of the wall of the hemisphere marked off by the deep invaginations called fissures or sulci.

[19] Fissures are ordinarily considered to be sulci of extreme depth.

matter—which here, different from the cord, is external to the white matter—without necessity of additional bulk.

Acquaintance with these landmarks will aid in the study of the brain:

The *lateral cerebral fissure* or *fissure of Sylvius*.

A short cleft on the inferior and lateral surfaces which divides into three rami: anterior horizontal, anterior ascending, and posterior. This

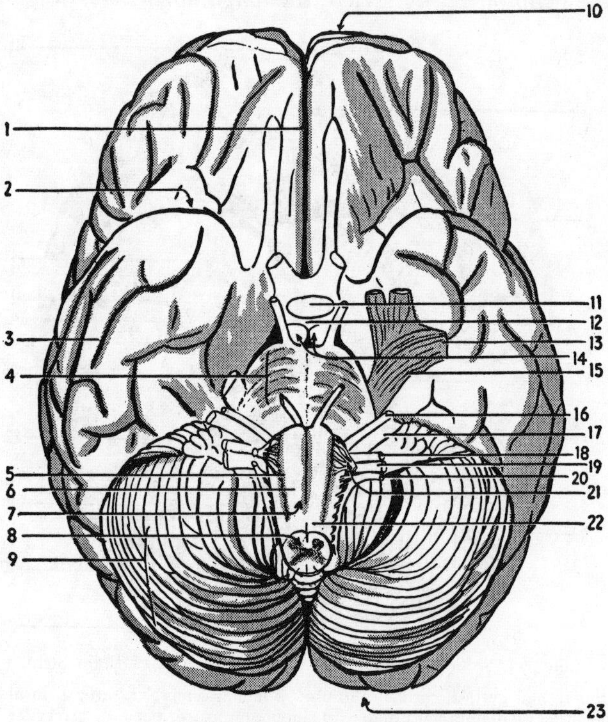

FIG. 74. Basal Aspect of Human Brain.

1. Longitudinal fissure; 2. temporal pole; 3. temporal lobe; 4. pons; 5. olive; 6. pyramid; 7. medulla oblongata; 8. medulla spinalis; 9. cerebellum; 10. frontal pole; 11. hypophysis; 12. tuber cinereum; 13. Vth cranial nerve; 14. mammillary bodies; 15. semilunar ganglion; 16. VIIth cranial nerve; 17. VIIIth cranial nerve; 18. IXth cranial nerve; 19. Xth cranial nerve; 20. XIth cranial nerve; 21 XIIth cranial nerve; 22. pyramidal decussation; 23. occipital pole.

fissure serves to separate the frontal and parietal lobes from the temporal lobe.

The *central sulcus* or *fissure of Rolando*.

Begins in or near the mid-point of the longitudinal cerebral fissure; runs downward and forward in the middle of the lateral surface. The central sulcus separates the frontal and parietal lobes.

The *parieto-occipital fissure.*
Chiefly located on the medial surface.
The *calcarine fissure* and the *cingulate sulcus.*
On the medial surface of the hemisphere.
The *collateral fissure.*
On the tentorial surface of the hemisphere.

These fissures and sulci, assisted by certain arbitrary lines, serve to divide each hemisphere into lobes, which in turn are divided into gyri.

Frontal Lobe
Boundaries: Lateral surface: frontal pole, central sulcus
Sulci: Precentral, superior, inferior
Gyri: Anterior central, superior, middle, inferior

Parietal Lobe
Boundaries: Central sulcus, parieto-occipital fissure and arbitrary line from end of fissure to preoccipital notch, posterior ramus of lateral fissure and arbitrary line from it to preoccipital notch.
Sulci: Postcentral, intraparietal
Gyri: Superior, inferior

Temporal Lobe
Boundaries: Lateral fissure and line extended from its posterior ramus to the parieto-occipital fissure—preoccipital notch line.
Sulci: Superior, middle
Gyri: Superior, middle, inferior

Occipital Lobe
Boundaries: Lateral surface: parieto-occipital fissure and arbitrary line from it to preoccipital notch.
Median surface: calcarine fissure
Sulci: Transverse, lateral
Gyri: Cuneus, lingual

Insula (Island of Reil; central lobe)
A triangular area hidden in lateral fissure under opercula of insula; pars orbitalis, par triangularis, and pars opercularis of inferior frontal gyrus.

The *cerebral cortex,* which contains approximately ten billion neurons, is a layer (1 to 4 mm. thick) of gray (cell bodies) matter investing the surface of the hemispheres. Within this layer are located the motor cells of the cortex. Here are the cell (Betz) bodies of the upper motor neurons. Below the gray cortex is the white medullary substance, composed of nerve fibers. The fibers in the various regions of the hemispheres acquire their myelin sheaths at different times. Fibers of like function tend to become myelinated at the same time. All of the areas dealing directly or indirectly with speech, contain fibers which myelinate comparatively late.

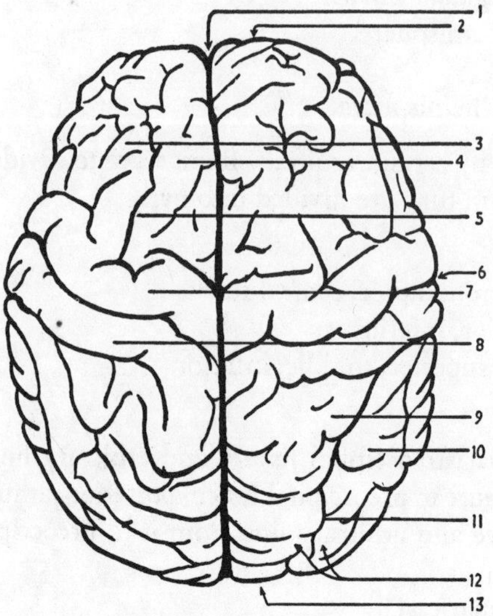

FIG. 75. Convex Surface of Brain Viewed from Above.

1. Longitudinal fissure; 2. frontal pole; 3. middle frontal gyrus; 4. superior frontal gyrus; 5. superior frontal sulcus; 6. central sulcus (Rolando); 7. anterior central gyrus; 8. posterior central gyrus; 9. superior parietal lobule; 10 inferior parietal lobule; 11. parieto-occipital fissure; 12. superior occipital gyri; 13. occipital pole.

Cortical Areas

A considerable amount of work has been done in mapping out brain areas which appear to be associated with definite functions of the organism (cerebral localization).[20] In general, there are three great areas: motor, sensory, and association. Their limits are indicated in Fig. 76.

Motor areas. On the lower portion of the precentral gyrus are located the motor areas associated with the musculature of the larynx, pharynx, mouth, and tongue. If various points in this area be stimulated with an electrode, the stimuli will produce contractions in the respective muscle groups of the larynx, pharynx, mouth, and tongue. *Broca's convolution* (*Broca's area*) on the inferior frontal and precentral gyri of the *left hemisphere* is often called the *motor speech center*. In experimental animals such as the monkey, electrical stimulation of what corresponds to the motor speech area in man, and in either hemisphere, produces adduction of both vocal cords. The effect lasts as long as the stimulation is continued, except that the need of breathing will cause abduction of the cords momentarily while air is taken into the lungs. This action demonstrates the control of the cerebral cortex over lower brain centers.

Sensory areas. The middle third of the area of the superior temporal gyrus constitutes the *auditory area*. On the posterior central gyrus and the superior parietal lobule are found the areas serving the tactile senses and the sense of form, respectively.

Association areas. The areas of the brain not indicated as motor or sensory are the association areas.

[20] The motor center for phonation was noted by *H. Krause* as early as 1884.

Internally, the cerebral hemispheres contain three kinds of fibers: (1) *projection fibers*—those axons which connect cortex with the brain stem; (2) *association fibers*—connecting different areas of the cortex, taking part in the association of functions and acts; (3) *commissural fibers*—which pass between the cortices of the opposite hemispheres. A study of the cerebral

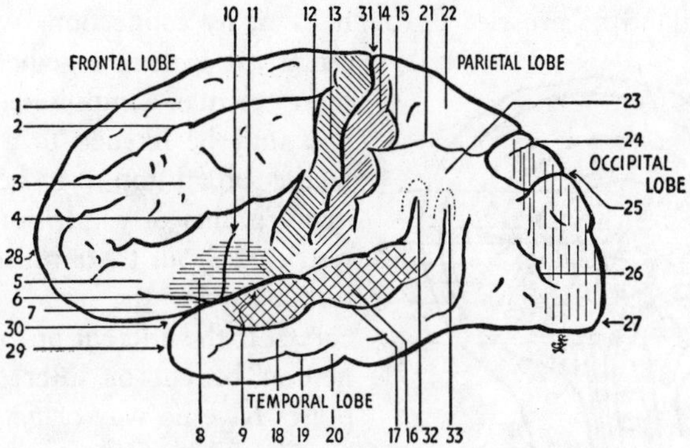

FIG. 76. Convex Surface of Left Cerebral Hemisphere.

1. Superior gyrus of frontal lobe; 2. superior sulcus of frontal lobe; 3. middle gyrus of frontal lobe; 4. inferior sulcus of frontal lobe; 5. inferior gyrus of frontal lobe; 6. anterior horizontal ramus; 7. pars orbitalis; * 8. pars triangularis; * 9. posterior ramus; * 10. anterior ascending ramus; * 11. pars opercularis; * 12. precentral sulcus; 13. precentral gyrus (motor); 14. postcentral gyrus (sensory); 15. postcentral sulcus; 16. superior temporal gyrus (auditory); 17. superior sulcus; 18. middle temporal gyrus; 19. middle sulcus; 20. inferior temporal gyrus; 21. intra-parietal sulcus; 22. superior parietal lobule; 23. inferiol parietal lobule; 24. parieto-occipital fissure; 25. transverse occipital sulcus; 26. lateral occipital sulcus; 27. occipital pole; 28. frontal pole; 29. temporal pole; 30. lateral cerebral fissure (Sylvius); 31. central sulcus (Rolando); 32. supra marginal gyrus; 33. angular gyrus. (* Overlies insula.)

localization of function is enhanced by a consideration of these fibers. For example, if one is asked a question, the auditory receptive center, through association fibers, connects with the motor speech area so that an answer may be made.

In addition to the above mentioned fibers the hemispheres also contain basal nuclei. Two of these (*caudate* and *lenticular* or lentiform), making up the *corpus striatum,* are in intimate relation to the *internal capsule* and the *external capsule,* and are in anatomically close relation to the insula and the thalamus. At present experimental evidence is lacking on the point, but this relationship of lower and older brain centers with newer and higher centers, together with many of the other peculiarities of the superimposed speech mechanism, may in the future provide just the insight needed for a more definite understanding of speech.

3. SUMMARY

The divisions of the nervous system just described are connected one with another, and with all parts of the body, by an intricate network of nerve fibers. These are the processes of the nerve cells. There are efferent neurons, afferent neurons, and connective intercalary or associative neurons. The major part of the student's interest, however, will be directed toward the motor neurons responsible for the carrying of impulses which produce the contractions of the muscles used in speech.

The cell bodies of the *lower motor neurons* are located in the anterior column of the cord. The lower motor neuron is the final common pathway (*fcp*) to a gland or muscle. Through its many connections with higher centers, it gathers together and concentrates many impulses. The situation may be likened to a funnel at whose broad top can be gathered many grains of sand, but at whose restricted spout there must be a conflict between the sand grains for egress. If the efferent or lower motor neuron be cut or injured, the impulses have no way of getting to the muscle. This produces a flaccid paralysis of the muscle.

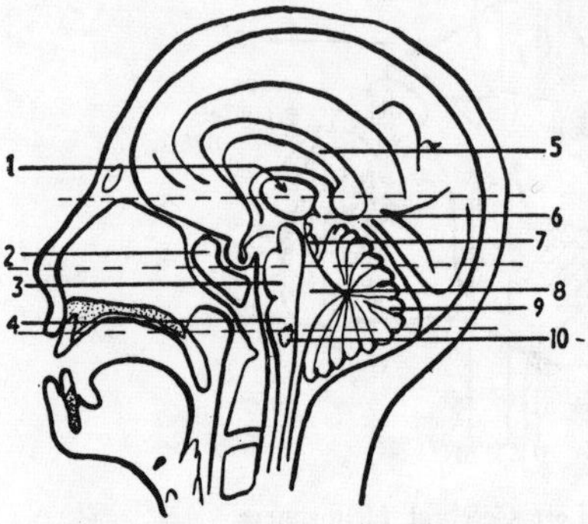

FIG. 77. Showing Relation of Parts of Brain to Various Structures of the Head.

1. Thalamus; 2. sphenoidal sinus; 3. pons; 4. medulla oblongata; 5. corpus callosum; 6. pineal body; 7. corpora quadrigemina; 8. fourth ventricle; 9. cerebellum; 10. olive.

The *upper motor neurons* have as their cell bodies, the giant pyramidal (Betz) cells of the anterior central gyrus. Fibers from the motor area of the cerebral cortex carry impulses having to do with purposeful co-ordinated activities—activities resulting from the contraction of more than a single muscle. By means of numerous collaterals, each upper motor neuron may be in association with many lower motor neurons. Destruction of the upper motor neuron, leaving the lower motor neuron intact, destroys the inhibitory control of the higher center over the lower, so that the latter is unimpeded in functioning at its own rhythm.

Between the highest neurological level of the cerebral cortex and the lowest level of the medula spinalis, are other levels whose influence may be recognized in the functioning of the nervous system. Each level has its own natural rate for discharging impulses; the higher the level, the lower the rate of discharge. The rates of discharge for some of the better-known levels are as follows: cerebral cortex level, 8–10 per second; thalamus (emotional) level, 20 per second; medulla oblongata-cerebellum level, 30 per second; cord level, 60 per second. The rate of discharge is always dominated by the highest level which is functioning. Thus, in the normal person the cortical level dominates. Under conditions of disease, injury, or alcoholism, lower centers may gain dominance. For example, an individual with Wilson's disease when holding a teacup will be unable to keep it from vibrating at a rather rapid rate. Again, an elderly individual in speaking may do so with a tremulous voice. Finally, during emotional upsets, the normal rhythm and rate of speech may be completely altered.

a. The Voluntary Control of the Muscles Involved in Speech

Muscles which can be made to contract voluntarily are under the control of the motor cells of the cortex of the cerebral hemispheres. Voluntary control of the muscles used in the production of speech sounds indicates the involvement of upper motor neurons whose cell bodies are located in the lower two-fifths of the anterior central gyrus of the cerebral cortex.

The upper motor neuron fibers from the pyramidal cells of the cerebral cortex descend as the corticobulbar tract in the genu of the internal capsule —a band of fibers separating the lentiform nucleus, laterally, from the caudate nucleus and thalamus, medially, of the telencephalon; continue in the bases pedunculi of the mesencephalon, and into the medulla oblongata to synapse [21] in the motor nuclei of the Vth, VIIth, IXth, Xth, XIth, and XIIth cranial nerves. A majority of the upper motor neuron fibers cross, although some descend without crossing.[22] Thus, the supply to the motor nuclei, by way of the corticobulbar tract, is bilateral—i. e., homolateral (Greek *homos,* the same; Latin *latus,* side) or ipsilateral (Latin *ipse,* same) and contralateral (Latin *contra,* opposite). The innervation of the muscles of the lower part of the face is contralateral.

The decussation of the upper motor neuron fibers accounts for the fact that stimuli originating in the cortex of the left cerebral hemisphere produce contractions of muscles on the right side of the body, and vice versa. Thus, a lesion affecting the upper motor neuron—e. g., a lesion in the internal capsule on the left side—produces hemiplegia (Greek *hemi,* half; *plege,* stroke) or paralysis of the right side. This contralateral paralysis is spastic and the muscles do not atrophy, except by disuse.

A lesion affecting the lower motor neuron produces a flaccid paralysis and an associated atrophy of the muscles involved.

The lower motor neurons of the trigeminal, facial, glossopharyngeal, vagus, accessory, and hypoglossal nerves have their cell bodies located in the various motor nuclei. From the large multipolar cells of the motor nuclei, arise fibers which leave the brain by means of the cranial nerves and end in so-called voluntary or striated skeletal muscles of the mouth, lips, tongue, and larynx.

In the innervation of the muscles concerned with the control of respiration for speech purposes, we are interested in the corticospinal (pyramidal tract, cerebrospinal fasiculus) pathway. Like the corticobulbar pathway, the

[21] This provides a simple two-neuron relationship; upper and lower motor neurons. In all likelihood, there are one or more intercalated neurons which tend to make the motor pathway more flexible and complex.

[22] The innervation of the muscles of the upper part of the face is homolateral.

upper motor neuron fibers from the cell bodies in the cerebral cortex pass through the internal capsule—rostral half of the posterior limb—and the bases pedunculi. From here on, their course differs. They now traverse the basilar part of the pons, undergo partial decussation in the pyramid of the myelencephalon, and continue to synapse in the spinal cord at various levels with the cell bodies (anterior gray column) of lower motor neurons which innervate the striated muscles used in breathing. The corticospinal fibers which do not cross over in the pyramid ultimately cross over at lower levels.

b. Subcortical Control of the Muscles Involved in Speech Production

The organization of the efferent mechanism of the body is extremely complex. When we attempt, quite sketchily, to describe the efferent mechanism concerned with vocal speech we must remember that in actuality the apparatus is probably more integrated than we even imagine. For example, to simplify matters we assign to the cerebral cortex most of the control over the primary (*fcp*) motor neurons in the cord or brain, for the reason that higher centers usually inhibit lower centers. Because higher centers are later evolutionary additions, they may be thought of as curbs or checks on lower, more primitive centers. Actually, the cerebral cortex is but one of numerous higher levels competing for the right to get its impulses accepted by the primary neurons. True, it is the highest and dominant level, but there are several others also functioning constantly: cerebellum, thalamus, subthalamus, red nucleus, corpus striatum, corpora quadrigemina. These many motor centers function together, each having some influence on one and all of the others, so that the end result of all of this integrated activity finally reaches the primary or lower motor neuron.

As we have seen, it is an accepted fact that the muscles in man utilized in the production of speech serve in much more vital acts, such as sucking, chewing, swallowing, and breathing. When utilized in such acts, the muscles are controlled from reflex centers in the medulla oblongata. And, of course, all muscles are dependent for their normal tonus on the reflex centers of the cerebellum and basal nuclei. Between these primitive activities and completely voluntary voice production, there are, however, a series of steps involving what might be called automatic speech and unconscious speech. We may designate as unconscious speech that which results when the cortical control has been eliminated by ether or alcohol, for example. Thus, a patient under the influence of ether talks without any conscious knowledge of the process. By automatic speech we mean that part of speech which goes on during conscious speaking but is nevertheless carried on without direct conscious effort—so much so, in fact, that one may say something not meant. An even more automatic type of speech which may border on unconscious speech is that performed during sleep. Sometimes the person asleep may carry on logical conversation with someone who is awake.

It seems to us that either there are degrees of cortical control of speech or else there are degrees of neurological control of the muscles of speech between that of the cerebral cortex and that of the visceral brain. Neuroanatomy and the clinical findings of accompanying speech defects in Parkinsonism, multiple sclerosis, etc., leads one to speculate as to the possibility of subcortical centers of control of the speech musculature in such structures as, for example, the island of Reil, but definite evidence that this or any other similar region may be so designated is slow in accumulating.

B. The Peripheral Nervous System

Nerves are named and/or numbered according to one or more of these factors:

(*a*) Origin (e. g., cranial)
(*b*) Anatomical location (e. g., 3rd thoracic)
(*c*) Terminus (e. g., intercostal)
(*d*) Function (e. g., acoustic)
(*e*) A term, usually Latin or Greek, describing an important characteristic (e g., *vagus,* wanderer).

Cerebrospinal nerves. The peripheral nervous system, connecting the central nervous system with the various parts of the organism, is made up of the cerebrospinal nerves and the sympathetic nervous system. The cerebrospinal nerves include the *spinal nerves* and the *cranial nerves.*

1. THE SPINAL NERVES

There are 31 pairs of spinal nerves arising from the medulla spinalis. They are named for their relation to the vertebral column, as follows:

Cervical nerves	8 pairs
Thoracic nerves	12 pairs
Lumbar nerves	5 pairs
Sacral nerves	5 pairs
Coccygeal nerves	1 pair

Each spinal nerve is the result of the union of two roots. The anterior or ventral root contains motor fibers (*fcp*) leaving the central nervous system; the posterior or dorsal root contains sensory fibers coming from the periphery, via the dorsal spinal ganglion, to the central nervous system.[23] The two roots join, subsequent to leaving the spinal column, and emerge through the intervetebral foramen.

All bodily reactions are either somatic or visceral. By *somatic* is meant the

[23] It is estimated that there are 250,000 axons in each ventral root—i. e., approximately 15,000,000 in the thirty-one pairs. There are approximately 600,000 axons entering the thirty-one pairs of dorsal roots.

stimuli and responses relating body and environment; movements involving striated somatic musculature. By *visceral* is meant the stimuli and responses relating internal parts of the body to each other; adjustments involving unstriated visceral musculature and glands, and striated visceral musculature derived from the branchial arches.

On the basis of their developmental origin, muscles may be classified as somatic (general and special) or visceral (general and special).

General somatic muscles (GSM) are striated or voluntary muscles derived from the general body somites and acting upon the bony skeleton.

Special somatic muscles (SSM) are in all respects like the GSM except that they act in relation with highly specialized sense organs. For example, tongue muscles may be classified as SSM.

General visceral muscles (GVM) are unstriated or unstriped or smooth or involuntary muscles derived from the splanchnopleure. Heart muscle may be included.

Special visceral muscles (SVM) are striated voluntary muscles which are, however, of visceral (from the pharyngeal arches) origin.

In general, the sense organs excited by stimuli from without the body may be termed *exteroceptors*. Those sense organs excited by stimuli from within the body may be termed *interoceptors*. A third group of sense organs —nerve endings in muscles, tendons, and joints—are called *proprioceptors*.

Visceral efferent fibers innervate smooth muscles and glandular tissues. The cell body is located in the lateral gray column. Myelinated fibers, called *preganglionic* fibers, run via the white rami to end and synapse in the *sympathetic ganglia* with neurons of the second order. The fibers of these nerve cells, called *postganglionic* fibers, run to smooth muscles or glands.

Visceral afferent or interoceptive fibers convey stimuli from the thoracic and abdominal viscera to the central nervous system. (From the larynx and pharynx, sensory fibers run in the IXth and Xth cranial nerves.) The cell bodies of these neurons are located in the dorsal root ganglia. Their peripheral processes are in contact with the viscera; the axons enter the cord and make synaptic connections at various levels.

Somatic efferent fibers innervating skeletal muscles are of relatively large caliber and are myelinated. The axons originate in cytons located in the anterior gray columns of the cord and terminate in motor end-plates located in the muscle fibers. The myelin sheath ends before reaching the muscle, and the neurilemma becomes continuous with the sheath (sarcolemma) of the muscle. The axis-cylinder forms short, thick, irregular terminal branches in a specialized sarcoplasm layer which gives intimate contact with muscle fibrils just beneath the sarcolemma. A nerve impulse or wave of activation is transmitted through the efferent nerve endings to the muscle, initiating contraction of its fibers.

Somatic afferent fibers may be grouped into two kinds:

(1) *Exteroceptive*—those conveying impulses from any part of the surface of the body which receives stimuli from the environment. The processes convey impulses to the cell body located in the dorsal root ganglia. The axon of this cyton enters the cord and establishes both reflex and cortical connections within the central nervous system. Sensations received are those of touch and pressure, pain, and temperature.

(2) *Proprioceptive*—those conveying impulses from muscles, tendons, and joints within the body. Close your eyes. Raise your arm at your side. Proprioceptive sensations indicate that the arm is raised and how high. Or, lift two pails, one filled with water, the other filled with sawdust. Proprioceptive sensations enable you to judge the difference in weight. If a muscle contracts or relaxes; if a tendon is put under pressure, or pull, or is released from tension; if body parts change their spatial relationships at a joint, impulses flow along the nerve processes to the cell body in the dorsal root ganglia and hence by the axon into the central nervous system to make, for the most part, reflex connections in the cord and brain.

Because the spinal nerves deal with generalized and often stereotyped or reflex functions the above-described *nerve components* are all general. The four components of the spinal nerves may be listed, in summary, as follows:

General visceral efferent (GVE)
General visceral afferent (GVA)
General somatic efferent (GSE)
General somatic afferent (GSA)
  Exteroceptive
  Proprioceptive

Many of the muscles used in the production of speech sounds, especially those involved in respiration, are innervated wholly or in part by spinal nerves.

2. THE CRANIAL NERVES

Only seven of the twelve pairs of cranial nerves are of direct interest to the student of Voice Science. They are the following:

Vth	Cranial nerve or Trigeminal nerve
VIIth	Cranial nerve or Facial nerve
VIIIth	Cranial nerve or Auditory nerve
IXth	Cranial nerve or Glossopharyngeal nerve
Xth	Cranial nerve or Vagus nerve

XIth Cranial nerve or Accessory nerve
XIIth Cranial nerve or Hypoglossal nerve

We are not interested in all of the divisions of the above nerves; neither are we necessarily interested in all of the components of each nerve.

Some cranial nerves, in addition to having certain general somatic fibers, have certain special afferent and efferent fibers which are not present in spinal nerves. These special fibers supply the special somatic sense organs (e. g., ears, eyes, and nose) as well as the special visceral sense organs (i. e., taste buds). Thus, on the afferent side we have special somatic afferent and special visceral afferent fibers. On the efferent side we have special visceral efferent fibers to the musculature derived from the visceral or pharyngeal arches. This, although of visceral origin, as described in Chapter VI, is not smooth muscle like other visceral muscle, but is striated like somatic muscle. In the cranial nerves, therefore, are these nerve components:

Special visceral afferent (SVA)
Special visceral efferent (SVE)
General visceral efferent (GVE)
General visceral afferent (GVA)
Special somatic afferent (SSA)
Special somatic efferent (SSE)
General somatic afferent (GSA)
  Exteroceptive
  Proprioceptive

As explained previously, proprioceptive sensory end organs are found in muscles, tendons, and joints. Many, if not most, of the proprioceptive sensations never get into consciousness. From lower neurological levels, efferent stimuli go back to the muscles, tendons, and joints, and automatic adjustments are made. Although neurologists have little information on the course followed by proprioceptive fibers to muscles supplied by cranial nerves, their presence may be assumed.[24] Thus, in habitual repetitive movements producing such sounds as [dɑ dɑ dɑ] it is presumed that unconscious proprioceptive adjustments are made.

The movements of articulate speech are delicate and accurate, yet a speaker is not conscious of the movements of the vocal folds, of the velum, and hardly of the tongue and lips during speaking. That is, GVA and GSA sensations from these areas seldom rise into consciousness during the production of speech sounds. Probably only the lips and the area of the apex of the tongue show enough sensory discrimination for speech. Certainly the pharynx and larynx are not so well represented in consciousness. For example, produce [t] and [k]. Are you aware of the contact of tongue

[24] Probably proprioceptive fibers accompany the cranial nerve motor fibers to the muscles.

against palate? Of soft palate against the pharyngeal wall? Or, in the production of [d] are you aware of the approximation of the vocal cords? Does this greater conscious recognition of stimuli arising from the anterior areas of the mouth account for the fact that the majority of the sounds in English are formed in this region? Or does it account for the fact that the child learns these front sounds sooner than he learns the back sounds? At any rate, the delicacy of the reflex movements involved in articulate speech indicates that almost complete responsibility for the habitual parts of the act must be placed on afferent proprioceptive sensations.[25]

No one cranial nerve has all of the components which have been listed. The components in the cranial nerves of interest to the reader will be discussed in the following pages.

Accompanying the information about the anatomical location of each cranial nerve is a tabular chart showing the areas supplied by the afferent fibers, and the muscles or glands supplied by the efferent fibers of the nerve. As in spinal nerves, the cell body of a motor neuron of a cranial nerve is located in the central nervous system. Cell bodies within the central nervous system are grouped together in aggregations, each collection called a *nucleus*. A nucleus, because of the great number of cells of which it is composed, occupies a rather extensive area in the brain, as noted in our discussion of the brain. It cannot be emphasized too strongly that each one of the nuclei to be described is in integrated relationship with all other nuclei and with the various fiber tracts involved in cortical or subcortical reactions. Especially in the recticular formation, great numbers of intercalary neurons are in synaptic relation with both ascending and descending afferent and efferent fibers.

A *motor nucleus* or *nucleus of origin* is made up of the cell bodies of motor nerves. Axons from these nuclei leave the brain through the motor roots of the cranial nerves and are distributed to innervate the various muscles. The nuclei of origin or efferent nuclei of the following cranial nerves are of interest to the student: Vth, VIIth, IXth, Xth, XIth, and XIIth.

Nuclei of termination are aggregates of cells of afferent neurons of the second order. Cranial afferent nerves have their cell bodies located in ganglia outside the central nervous system. From these ganglia, central fibers of *neurons of the first order* enter the central nervous system and synapse with sensory neurons in the so-called nuclei of termination. In these nuclei are located the cell bodies of the *neurons of the second order*. For example, if the mucous membrane surface of the posterior one-third of the tongue be stimulated, the sensory receptor endings of the IXth cranial nerve receive

[25] Probably not true during the learning of speech habits. At first reliance is placed on all types of sensations. Soon, however, speech movements become stereotyped; the proprioceptive stimuli initiated by one movement, themselves call forth the efferent stimuli for the chain of succeeding movements.

and convey the stimulus along peripheral fibers to the cell bodies of the neurons located in the ganglion petrosum. From here, the central fibers of the cell bodies running in the tractus solitarius pass on the impulses to neurons of the second order whose cell bodies are located in the nucleus of the tractus solitarius.

The nuclei of termination or afferent nuclei of the following cranial nerves are of interest to the student: Vth, VIIIth, IXth, and Xth.

Associated with the cranial nerves are these ganglia:

Vth cranial nerve, semilunar ganglion
VIIIth cranial nerve, spiral ganglion
IXth cranial nerve, ganglion petrosum
Xth cranial nerve, ganglion nodosum

Semilunar ganglion or *Gasserian ganglion*

In this ganglion are located the cell bodies of the GSA fibers associated with the *trigeminal nerve*. The peripheral branches of the neurons supply the skin and mucous membrane of the head; the central branches terminate in the main sensory nucleus of the Vth cranial nerve and the nucleus of the spinal tract of the Vth cranial nerve.

Spiral ganglion

In this ganglion are located the bipolar cell bodies of the SSA fibers associated with the *auditory nerve*. The peripheral branches of the neurons run from the spiral organ of Corti; the central branches synapse in the caudal portion of the pons in either the *dorsal* or *ventral cochlear nucleus*.

Ganglion petrosum

In this ganglion are located the cell bodies of the GVA fibers associated with the *glossopharyngeal nerve*. The peripheral branches of the neurons supply the pharynx and posterior one-third of the tongue; the central branches run in the tractis solitarius and terminate in the nucleus of the tractus solitarius.

Ganglion nodosum

In this ganglion are located the cell bodies of the GVA fibers associated with the *vagus nerve*. The peripheral branches of the neurons supply the larynx, pharynx, and trachea; the central branches run in the tractus solitarius and terminate and synapse in the nucleus of the tractus solitarius.

The Vth Cranial Nerve

The *trigeminal* (Latin for triplet) or trifacial nerve arises by two roots, a larger (portio major) or *sensory root* and a smaller (portio minor) or motor root. They emerge from the lateral portion of the surface of the pons. The sensory root expands to form the *semilunar ganglion*. From the ganglion there are distributed three branches: the *ophthalmic* and *maxillary* which are sensory exclusively, and the *mandibular,* in which branch run the motor fibers of the nerve. All of the branches give off numerous smaller branches, but not all of them are of interest to the student. The following components warrant attention:

GSA

(*a*) *Exteroceptive*

Cell bodies in ganglion: semilunar ganglion
Peripheral fibers: from skin and mucous membrane of head
Central fibers: sensory root of Vth cranial nerve
Nuclei of termination: main sensory nucleus and nucleus of the spinal tract of the Vth cranial nerve [26]

(*b*) *Proprioceptive*

Peripheral fibers: to the muscles of mastication
Sensory root of the Vth cranial nerve to the mesencephalic nucleus of the Vth cranial nerve.[27]

SVE

Nucleus of origin: motor nucleus of the Vth cranial nerve [28]
Muscles innervated: tensor tympani
tensor veli palatini
masseter
internal pterygoid
external pterygoid
buccinator
digastricus, anterior belly
mylohyoid

[26] *Main sensory nucleus of the Vth cranial nerve and nucleus of the spinal tract of the Vth cranial nerve.* The main sensory nucleus is located at about the level of the middle of the pons in the lateral portion of the reticular formation. Continuous, caudally, is the nucleus of the spinal tract of the Vth cranial nerve, which lies ventral to the restiform body in the medulla oblongata and is continuous with the substantia gelatinosa Rolando in the medulla spinalis.

[27] *Mesencephalic nucleus of the Vth cranial nerve.* This nucleus is made up of a column of cells and is continuous, caudally, with the chief sensory nucleus of the Vth cranial nerve. Its rostral end is in the mesencephalon in the lateral wall of gray substance bounding the cerebral aqueduct; its caudal limits are in the rostral part of the pons in the lateral wall bounding the fourth ventricle.

[28] *Motor nucleus of the Vth cranial nerve.* The cell bodies of this nucleus form a rather compact mass located at the level of the middle of the pons in the lateral portion of the reticular formation.

TRIGEMINAL OR VTH CRANIAL NERVE

(Great sensory nerve of head and face and motor nerve to muscles of mastication.)

Ophthalmic nerve
    (mucous membrane nasal cavity [in part]; skin of nose)
  Nasociliary nerve
    External nasal branches
      (skin of ala and apex of nose)
    Internal nasal branches
      (mucous membrane front part of septum and laterial wall of nasal cavity)

Maxillary nerve
  Zygomatic nerve
    Zygomaticofacial branch
      (skin, prominence of cheek)
    Posterior superior alveolar branches
      (mucous membrane of gum of maxilla, cheek, and maxillary sinus)
    Middle superior alveolar branch, unites with the
    Anterior superior alveolar branch to form the
      Nasal branch
        (mucous membrane anterior part of inferior meatus and floor of nasal cavity)
    External nasal branches
      (skin of side of nose)
    Superior labial branches [29]
      (skin of upper lip; mucous membrane of mouth)
    Sphenopalatine (two) branches [29] to *sphenopalatine ganglion* from which the following are distributed:
      Palatine nerves
        Anterior palatine nerve
          (gums, mucous membrane of hard palate and soft palate)
          Posterior inferior nasal branches
            (inferior nasal concha and middle and inferior meatuses)
        Middle palatine nerve
          (uvula, tonsil, soft palate)
        Posterior palatine nerve
          (uvula, tonsil, soft palate)
      Posterior superior nasal branches
        (septum and lateral wall of the nasal fossa)

[29] Joins with filaments from the VIIth cranial nerve.

Nasopalatine nerve, unites with anterior palatine nerve
Pharyngeal nerve
(mucous membrane of the nasopharynx)
Mandibular nerve
(teeth and gums of mandible; lower lip; lower part of face; muscles of mastication; mucous membrane anterior ⅔ of tongue
Internal pterygoid nerve
(pterygoideus internus; tensor tympani; tensor veli palatini) [29 30]
Masseteric nerve
(masseter)
Anterior deep temporal nerve
(temporalis)
Posterior deep temporal nerve
(temporalis)
Buccinator nerve [29]
(buccinator; skin over buccinator and mucous membrane of its inner surface)
External pterygoid nerve
(pterygoideus externus)
Auriculotemporal nerve [29]
Branches to external acoustic meatus
(tympanic membrane)
Lingual nerve [29 31]
(mucous membrane anterior ⅔ tongue) to *submaxillary ganglion* which supplies branches to mucous membrane of mouth
Inferior alveolar nerve
Mylohyoid nerve
(mylohyoideus; anterior belly of digastricus)
Mental nerve [29]
(skin of chin; skin and mucous membrane of lower lip)

The VIIth Cranial Nerve

The *facial nerve* emerges by two roots from the lateral aspect of the brain between the caudal extremity of the pons and the rostral end of the olive of the medulla oblongata. The following components are of interest:

GVE
Cell bodies in nucleus of origin: nucleus salivatorius superior
Fibers via nervus intermedius, chorda tympani, lingual, and facial to submaxillary ganglion.

[29] Joins with filaments from the VIIth cranial nerve.
[30] Joins with filaments from the IXth cranial nerve.
[31] Joins with filaments from the XIIth cranial nerve.

Glands innervated:	submaxillary salivary
	sublingual salivary

SVE

Cell bodies in nucleus of origin:	motor nucleus of facial nerve[32]
Muscles innervated:	stapedius
	digastricus, posterior belly
	stylohyoideus
	zygomaticus
	quadratus labii superior
	buccinator
	orbicularis oris
	caninus
	risorius
	triangularis
	quadratus labii inferior
	mentalis
	platysma

Facial or VIIth Cranial Nerve

(*Genicular ganglion* connected with *otic ganglion* and *sphenopalatine ganglion;* also, with Vth, IXth, and Xth cranial nerves.)

Greater superficial petrosal nerve
(mucous membrane and glands of soft palate)
Chorda tympani nerve
(fibers through submaxillary ganglion to submaxillary and sublingual glands)
Nerve to the stapedius
(stapedius muscle)
Digastric branch[30]
(posterior belly digastricus)
Stylohyoid branch
(stylohyoideus)
Buccal branches[33]
(superficial muscles of face: caninus
risorius)

[32] *Motor nucleus of the VIIth cranial nerve.* This relatively compact mass of nerve cells is located near the caudal end of the pons in the ventrolateral portion of the reticular formation. Experiments show that the motor nucleus of the facial nerve is in reality two nuclei. The more rostrally located cell bodies send axons to the superior muscles of the face and their upper motor neuron connections are both homolateral and contralateral. The more caudally located cell bodies have a contralateral upper motor neuron supply and send axons to the lower muscles of the face.

[30] Joins with filaments from the IXth cranial nerve.

[33] Joins with filaments of the Vth cranial nerve.

(zygomaticus
(quadratus labii superioris
(buccinator
(orbicularis oris)
Mandibular branch
(muscles of lower lips and chin: triangularis
quadratus labii inferior
mentalis)
Cervical branch
(platysma)

The VIIIth Cranial Nerve

The *acoustic nerve* has its superficial origin in the lateral part of the lower border of the pons. It is made up of the *vestibular* and *cochlear* nerves; the student will be interested in the latter.

SSA

Cell bodies in ganglion:	spiral ganglion of cochlea
Peripheral fibers:	from spiral organ of Corti
Nuclei of termination:	cochlear nuclei of pons and medulla.

The IXth Cranial Nerve

The *glossopharyngeal nerve* has its superficial origin, by five or six rootlets which join to form a single trunk, from the rostral end of the posterior lateral sulcus of the medulla oblongata. GVE fibers of this nerve synapse in the *otic ganglion.*

GVA

Cell bodies in ganglion:	ganglion petrosum
Peripheral fibers:	mucous membrane of pharynx and posterior ⅓ of tongue
Central fibers:	solitary tract
Nucleus of termination:	nucleus of tractus solitarius [34]

SVE

Cell bodies in nucleus of origin:	nucleus ambiguus [35]
Muscles innervated:	stylopharyngeus

[34] *Nucleus of the tractus solitarius.* (NOTE: *This is also a nucleus of termination for certain fibers of the vagus nerve.*) This nucleus extends as a slender column for the length of the medulla oblongata. It is located ventrolateral to the dorsal motor nucleus of the vagus.

[35] *Nucleus ambiguus.* (NOTE: *This is also the efferent nucleus of the vagus and accessory nerves.*) The cell bodies of this nucleus constitute a slender column extending from the caudal border of the pons, caudally, to the pyramid of the medulla oblongata and located in the ventrolateral portion of the reticular formation.

GLOSSOPHARYNGEAL [36] OR IXTH CRANIAL NERVE

(Nerve of sensation to mucous membrane of pharynx, fauces, and posterior portion of the tongue.)

Tympanic nerve
(to help form tympanic plexus [37] which supplies mucous membrane of middle ear, round and oval windows, and Eustachian tube.)
Pharyngeal branches
(to help form pharyngeal plexus [38] which supplies mucous membrane and muscles of muscular coat of pharynx:)
inferior constrictor
middle constrictor
superior constrictor
salpingopharyngeus
Muscular branch
(stylopharyngeus)
Tonsillar branches
(palatine tonsil, soft palate, and fauces)
Lingual branches
(mucous membrane of posterior part of tongue)

The Xth Cranial Nerve

The *vagus* (Latin for wandering) or pneumogastric (Greek *pneuma,* air or breath; *pneumon,* lung; *gaster,* stomach) nerve arises by several roots from the rostral part of the posterior lateral sulcus of the medulla oblongata.

GVA

Cell bodies in ganglion:	ganglion nodosum
Peripheral fibers:	pharynx, larynx, trachea
Central fibers:	tractus solitarius
Nucleus of termination:	nucleus of the tractus solitarius [34]

SVE

Nucleus of origin:	nucleus ambiguus [35]
Muscles innervated:	cricothyroideus
	posterior cricoarytenoideus
	lateral cricoarytenoideus
	arytenoideus

[36] Joins with fibers from the VIIth and Xth cranial nerves, and from the sympathetic nervous system.

[37] Joins with fibers from the Vth and VIIth cranial nerves.

[38] Joins with fibers from the Xth cranial nerve, and from the sympathetic nervous system.

[34] *Nucleus of the tractus solitarius.*

[35] *Nucleus ambiguus.*

thyroarytenoideus
inferior pharyngeal constrictor

GVE

Nucleus of origin: dorsal motor nucleus of the vagus [39]

Distribution: to sympathetic ganglia—
to innervate thoracic and abdominal viscera
trachealis and bronchial musculature

The Protective Cough Mechanism

If the mucous membrane of the larynx be stimulated, say by a cracker crumb, the visceral afferent nerves of the vagus with cell bodies in the vagus ganglion convey the impulses in the tractus solitarius to the nucleus of the tract. There synapses are made and reflex efferent impulses travel down the tractus solitariospinalis to various levels of the spinal cord where neurons of the second order convey them to the muscles of respiration and produce forceful expiratory blasts designed to dislodge the foreign body.

Vagus or Xth Cranial Nerve

(Jugular ganglion,[40] ganglion nodosum [41]

Pharyngeal branch
(aids in forming pharyngeal plexus [42] which supplies muscles and mucous membrane of pharynx and muscles of soft palate except tensor veli palatini)

Superior laryngeal nerve
External branch
(cricothyreoideus, constrictor pharyngeus inferior, pharyngeal plexus)
Internal branch
(mucous membrane of larynx)

Recurrent nerve [43]

[39] *Dorsal motor nucleus of the vagus.* This column of gray cells is located in the medulla oblongata. In the closed part of the medulla oblongata it is just ventrolateral to the central canal; in the open part of the medulla oblongata it lies beneath the ala cinera in the floor of the fourth ventricle. Just medial is the hypoglossal nucleus. The GVE fibers originating in this nucleus are preganglionic fibers being distributed to vagal sympathetic plexuses. Postganglionic fibers innervate, for example, the smooth muscles of the respiratory system and alimentary tract.

[40] Joins with filaments from the VIIth, IXth, and XIth cranial nerves and with fibers from the sympathetic nervous system.

[41] Joins with filaments from the XIIth cranial nerve and with fibers from the sympathetic nervous system.

[42] Joins with filaments from the IXth cranial nerve and with fibers from the sympathetic nervous system.

[43] Sectioning of one recurrent nerve produces adduction of the corresponding vocal cord; sectioning of both recurrent nerves produces adduction and immobility of both vocal cords. This is due to the fact that the cricothyroid muscles which are innervated by the superior

(all muscles of larynx except cricothyreoideus, i.e., cricoarytenoideus posterior, cricoarytenoideus lateralis, arytenoideus, and thyroarytenoideus; mucous membrane and muscular fibers of trachea; constrictor pharyngeus inferior)

Anterior bronchial branches

(anterior surface of root of lung; anterior pulmonary plexus [44])

Posterior bronchial branches

(posterior surface of root of lung; posterior pulmonary plexus [44])

The XIth Cranial Nerve

The *accessory* nerve has its superficial origin from the lateral surface of the caudal part of the medulla oblongata and the cervical part of the spinal cord, cervical segments 1 to 6.

SVE

(*a*) Cell bodies in nucleus of origin:	nucleus ambiguus [35]
(Fibers of the Xth nerve probably involved as well as those of the XIth)	
Muscles innervated:	musculus uvulae levator veli palatini glossopalatinus pharyngopalatinus
(*b*) Cell bodies in nucleus of origin:	anterior gray column [45] of cervical segments 1 to 6 of the spinal cord.
Muscles innervated:	trapezius sternocleidomastoideus

Accessory (Spinal accessory) or XIth Cranial Nerve

Joins with pharyngeal and superior laryngeal branches of Xth cranial nerve. Through the pharyngeal branch of the Xth cranial nerve, supplies musculus uvulae, levator veli palatini, glossopalatinus, and pharyngopalatinus.

laryngeal are now unopposed. If the superior laryngeal nerves be sectioned there is created a balance of forces, due only to the natural elasticity of the tissues, and the glottis is opened to the so-called intermediate position. (See pp. 62-3, positions C and D.)

[44] Joins with filaments from the sympathetic nervous system.

[35] *Nucleus ambiguus.*

[45] Motor cells in lateral part of anterior gray column of cervical segments 1 to 6 of the spinal cord.

Joins with Xth cranial nerve to be distributed with the recurrent nerve.

Supplies trapezius [46] and sternocleidomastoideus [47] by external branches which contain fibers from cell bodies located in the cervical part of the cord.

The XIIth Cranial Nerve

The *hypoglossal* (Greek *hypo,* beneath, *glossa,* tongue) nerve has its superficial origin between the olive and pyramid in the anterior lateral sulcus of the medulla oblongata.

SSE

Nucleus of origin:	hypoglossal nucleus [48]
Muscles innervated:	genioglossus
	hyoglossus
	styloglossus
	geniohyoideus
	inferior longitudinalis
	superior longitudinalis
	transversus
	verticalis

In bilateral hypoglossal paralysis the tongue cannot move; there are gross disturbances in speech. In unilateral paralysis the tongue is higher on the paralyzed side. While the tongue is in the mouth the apex is deflected toward the non-paralyzed side. If the tongue is protruded from the mouth it is deflected toward the paralyzed side. Speech is but slightly disturbed.

HYPOGLOSSAL OR XIITH CRANIAL NERVE

Motor nerve of tongue.

Joins with fibers from Xth and IXth cranial nerves, 1st and 2nd cervical nerves, and sympathetic.

Supplies filaments to pharyngeal plexus.

Muscular branches

(styloglossus, hyoglossus, genioglossus, and probably some fibers of the geniohyoideus; and intrinsic muscles of tongue, i. e., inferior longitudinalis, superior longitudinalis, transversus, verticalis)

[46] Joins with branches from the 2d, 3d, and 4th cervical nerves to form a plexus.

[47] Joins with branches from the 2d cervical nerve.

[48] *Hypoglossal nucleus.* This column of gray cells is located in the medulla oblongata. In the closed part of the medulla oblongata it is just ventrolateral to the central canal; in the open part it lies beneath the trigonum hypoglossi in the floor of the fourth ventricle. Just dorsolateral is the dorsal motor nucleus of the vagus.

3. THE AUTONOMIC NERVOUS SYSTEM

By the *autonomic nervous system* (or general visceral efferent system) is meant that part of the nervous system which supplies the efferent innervation of glands, heart, and smooth musculature. It includes efferent elements whose preganglionic neurons lie in part within the cerebrospinal nervous system. The terminal portions of the preganglionic fibers are in sympathetic ganglia. From these ganglia postganglionic fibers arise and conduct impulses to different organs.

Based on the origin of the preganglionic fibers, the autonomic system is divided for our purposes into:

(1) *cranial autonomic system*
Preganglionic fibers by way of the VIIth, IXth, Xth, and XIth cranial nerves.

(2) *thoraco-lumbar autonomic system*
Preganglionic fibers by way of thoracic and upper lumbar spinal nerves

(3) *sacral autonomic system*
Preganglionic fibers by way of visceral rami of 2d, 3d, and 4th sacral nerves.

Functionally, the cranial and sacral systems work together but in antagonism, in general, to the thoraco-lumbar system. Thus, viscera innervated by both the cranio-sacral and thoraco-lumbar systems may be slowed up in their functions when one system is dominant, and speeded up when the other system is dominant. This antagonism receives recognition in our use of the terms *cranio-sacral* and *thoraco-lumbar*.

The cranial section conveys efferent impulses which bring about secretion of saliva, inhibition of the heart, and an increase in digestive activity. Together with the thoraco-lumbar, it is also involved in adjusting the degree of contraction of the bronchial tubes.

The thoraco-lumbar division of the autonomic system—also called *sympathetic nervous system*—conveys outgoing impulses through the ventral roots of the thoracic and upper lumbar spinal nerves and after synapsing in some ganglion makes connections with a large number of organs and structures—e. g., stomach, intestines, heart, adrenal glands, and blood vessels.

The cranio-sacral division acts to conserve body resources, e. g., by slowing the heart rate, by providing for the flow of salivary and gastric juice. The thoraco-lumbar division acts in emergencies to accelerate the heart rate, to contract the arterioles, and to raise the blood pressure.

EXERCISES AND QUESTIONS

1. In the integrated functioning of the nervous system in the production of the isolated sound [i], what nerves are involved? List them in the chronological order in which they function during the formation of the sound.

2. Differentiate neurologically between the *B* and *D* positions of the glottis.

3. What muscles and nerves are involved in each of the following?

(*a*) The mouth is opened and the tongue protruded.

(*b*) A puff of air is blown out as in [p].

(*c*) The tongue is moved up as though to produce the implosive phase of [t].

4. Explain neurologically and in time order the difference between swallowing a bolus of food and producing the sound [k].

5. Present a critique of the following statement.

If the medulla spinalis of a man be crushed at the region of the 6th cervical vertebra he will inspire with force; he can yawn; he cannot expire by muscular effort but only because of gravity or the elasticity of the parts involved; he cannot sneeze.

6. During fifteen minutes of talking, which, primarily is true:

(*a*) vegetative medulla oblongata and pons activities are interfered with by the cerebral cortex, or

(*b*) cerebral cortex dominance is interrupted by the vegetative functions of pons and medulla oblongata?

7. How do you explain the fact that if your voluntary control of the laryngeal muscles, the thoracic muscles, and the diaphragm interferes in any manner with the need to sneeze, cough, or breathe, such voluntary control will be abrogated by lower centers?

8. In your opinion, what is the neurological explanation of speech carried on while the subject is asleep?

Chapter VIII

SOUND: PHYSICS AND PSYCHOLOGY

I. Sound Defined
II. Musical Sound and Noise
  A. Musical Tones
    1. Is There a Relation Between the Development of Music and the Development of Speech?
  B. Noise
    1. Masking
III. The Molecular Nature of Air
IV. The Source of Sound
  A. The Vibrating Body or Generator of Sound Waves
  B. A Departure From the Classical Concept
  C. Generators of Sound
    1. Vibrating Strings
    2. Vibrating Column of Air
      a. Tube Closed at One End
      b. Tube Open at Both Ends
  D. Types of Vibrations
V. Characteristics of Sound
  A. Frequency
    1. Doppler Effect
  B. Intensity
    1. Relation of Amplitude to Intensity and Loudness
    2. Relation of Intensity to Distance
    3. Relation of Amplitude and Intensity to Frequency
    4. Speech Power
    5. The Unit of Measurement of Intensity
    6. Loudness
  C. Quality
  D. Time
    1. Phase
      a. Beats
    2. The Velocity of Sound
    3. Wavelength of Sounds
  E. The Reflection and/or Absorption of Sound

Sounds produced by the human speech mechanisms are like other sounds in their basic physical attributes. Therefore what we shall have to say about sound in general may be applied to speech sounds in particular. And because, normally, speech is transmitted in a medium of air, we shall confine ourselves to a study of sound waves in air.

SOUND DEFINED

Sound, as defined by the psychologist, is the sensation resulting from the action of certain kinds of stimuli on the ear and auditory nerve. To the physicist, the hearing aspect is beside the point; ear or no ear, sound is produced when a body is vibrating within certain frequency ranges or when the vibrating body, in turn, sets the surrounding air into vibration within the same ranges.

Perhaps, this definition will satisfy both camps: sound is (1) a vibratory disturbance in a material medium (2) which is capable of eliciting an auditory sensation in a normal ear. The disturbance is due to a body being in vibratory motion. The sonorous body may be a gas or mixture of gases, a liquid, or a solid. The disturbance (i.e., vibratory motion) is conveyed to the ear by wave motion, usually, in air.

The sound wave is a longitudinal wave—i.e., the particles of the medium in which it is propagated move to and fro periodically, in the direction in which the sound is being propagated.

Sounds may be classified as being (*a*) *tones,* or notes, or (*b*) *noises.* Only in extreme cases are noises and notes clearly distinguishable. Most tones are accompanied by some noise; most noises have some definite tone. Usually the distinction between the two classes is far from sharp, being frequently only a matter of individual opinion. Or the difference may be one of degree. To the ear a *tone* is either simple or, if complex, composed of easily related simple tones; a *noise* is too complex or of too short duration to be easily analyzed by the ear. In other words, whether a sound be a tone or a noise may be primarily a matter of psychology rather than of physics.

MUSICAL SOUND AND NOISE

A. Musical Tones

We may think of all sounds as being arranged on a continuum between musical tones at one end and noises at the other. At either extreme one may distinguish between them; sounds falling between the extremes may be perceived as either musical tones or noise depending upon the circumstances and the individual hearer.

Complex sounds whose wave forms are repeated, physically, are perceived by the ear as being musical tones. Analysis shows that the complex waves of each such sound are made up of a fundamental frequency and overtones. The overtones are called harmonics if their frequencies are multiples of the fundamental frequency.

1. IS THERE A RELATION BETWEEN THE DEVELOPMENT OF MUSIC AND THE DEVELOPMENT OF SPEECH?

It seems to us that the ear, which impels us by reasons of what appears to be pleasant (as opposed to what seems unpleasant) to develop a certain kind of music, plays at least as important a role in our development of a certain kind of speech.[1] In both cases the key to what is developed is *ratio* [2]—the ratio between pitches or the interval between frequencies.

Ratios are relatively simple mathematical relationships, easily translatable into a code of nerve impulses for transmission by our neuron system. A ratio, *ipso facto,* expresses the interval in time-space between or among a relatively small number of frequencies, but implies other intervals and other frequency groupings. If all ratios were spread out linearly, the number of designated key frequency relationships and their intervals would provide one of the simplest possible systems for minimum coding at maximum efficiency.

B. Noise

Physically, noise usually lacks the repetitive or periodic wave form; its frequencies and intensities display irregularity. It is difficult, if not impossible, to determine a fundamental frequency.

1. MASKING [3]

Masking occurs when noise or any sound interferes with the audibility of any other sound. The sounds of conversation may be masked by the

[1] This holds for any race.

[2] We use a variety of terms in music to designate ratios pleasing to our ears and important in the composition of western music: for example, unison, 1:1; octave, 2:1; perfect interval; fifth, 3:2; fourth, 4:3; major third, 5:4; major sixth, 5:3; major seventh, 15:6; minor third, 6:5; minor sixth, 8:5; minor seventh, 9:5; major triad, 4:5:6 (e.g., C:E:G); and major chord (e.g., C,E,G,2C).

[3] In audiometry noise may be used for purposes of masking tones. *White noise* (employs a wide band of frequencies—often separated by one cycle or less—of relatively equal in-

sound of wind during a storm, by the sound of a jet plane or the hissing of escaping steam; the sounds of applause in a theater may have the effect of masking some of the words of an actor.

THE MOLECULAR NATURE OF AIR

Air has mass and elasticity. This is more apparent when air is compressed, as in an automobile tire. By elasticity is meant the ability of a mass of air to return to its former volume after compression. Air is made up of minute particles called molecules. Relative to their size, the molecules of the air are separated from each other by considerable distances. Although the molecules are free to move in any direction, and do so move, they tend to remain apart by about the same relative distances. In general, the number of molecules is greater per cubic unit in a solid than in a liquid, and greater in a liquid than in a gas. For example, there are many more molecules in a cubic centimeter of iron than in a cubic centimeter of water and more in a cubic centimeter of water than in a cubic centimeter of air. In a perfect vacuum there would be no molecules.

Any body surrounded by air may be conceived as being surrounded by an almost infinite number of layers of molecules. When we talk of single

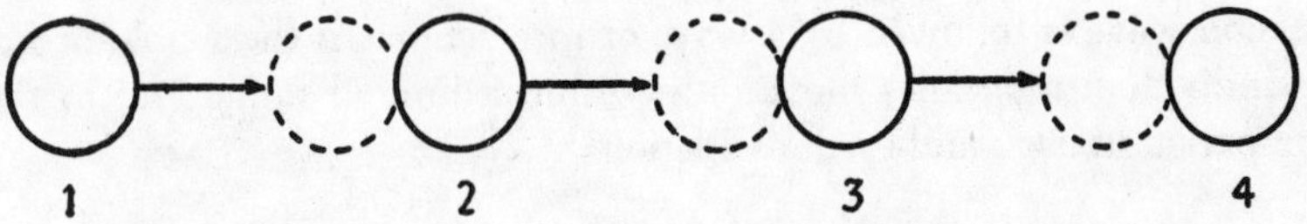

FIG. 78. Schematic Drawing of Molecules Moving in a Wave of Compression.

Let us suppose that in the plane represented, a sounding body displaces air molecule 1 so that it collides with molecule 2. The energy imparted to molecule 1 when it was displaced is in great part transmitted to molecule 2, thus displacing molecule 2. There is a passing on of the energy to the successive molecules 3, 4, etc., as each is displaced in turn.

molecules, we usually mean a layer of molecules. If a molecule of air be moved or displaced from a given position—called, for convenience, its point of rest—in a certain direction so that it comes into contact with, and imparts energy to, another molecule, the second one tends to be moved in the same direction. The second molecule, in turn, transmits its energy to a third; the third to a fourth, and so on. This produces what is known as a *wave of compression,* or a wave of condensation. This type of transfer of energy is demonstrated crudely when one sets on end a number of dominoes close together so that if the first is knocked

tensity) or *saw-tooth noise* (employs a complex composed of a fundamental frequency—say, 100~, and its harmonics to, say, 12,000~, but with the overtones somewhat out of phase or in random phase) may be employed as masking noise in one ear while testing the other.

over it falls against the second, the second falls against the third, and so on.

After being displaced, the initial molecule because of its elasticity tends to rebound, i.e., return to its original position, the rebound carrying it beyond its original point of rest and removing it more than a normal distance from its neighboring molecules. This results in a state of rarefaction. Now, in turn, the second, third, fourth, and other molecules rebound,

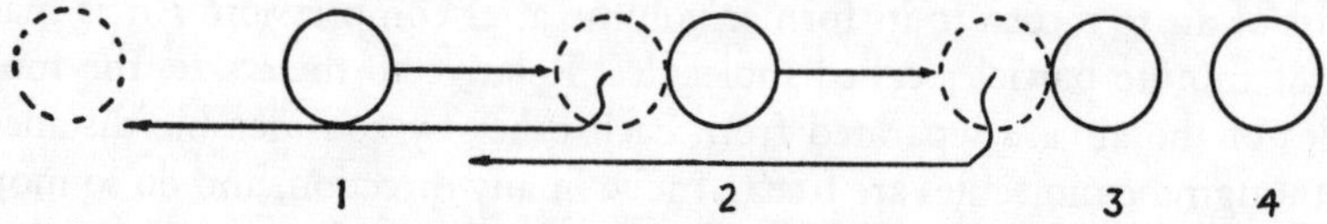

FIG. 79. Schematic Drawing of Molecules Moving in a Wave of Rarefaction.

Molecule 1, having struck and displaced molecule 2, is represented as rebounding approximately as far left of its original position as it first moved to the right of that position. Solid-line circles represent molecules in a state of rest. All of the molecules (dotted-line circles) are represented as rebounding simultaneously. However, this is never the case. There must always be some time difference between the movements of the successive molecules. Molecule 1 rebounds at once toward the left, passing its original position before molecule 2 can return to its original position. Thus, molecule 1 is momentarily farther separated from molecule 2 than originally. This produces a state of rarefaction.

thus producing a *wave of rarefaction,* or a wave of expansion. Each compression wave is followed by a wave of rarefaction. In the whole process, the individual molecules move only within a limited range and in their own period of back-and-forth oscillation.

THE SOURCE OF SOUND

A. THE VIBRATING BODY OR GENERATOR OF SOUND WAVES

Sound has as its source a vibrating body. Any vibrating body, for example, a tuning fork,[4] strikes against the surrounding molecules of the air, that is, sets into vibration the surrounding medium. Thus, the vibrations are transmitted from the vibrating body to the ear of a listener, where the molecules nearest the tympanic membrane impart their energy to the membrane. Hence, as the body in vibration alternately moves toward the ear, compressing the molecules, and then away from the ear, releasing the pressure on the molecules, there is set up a wave train of successive compressions and rarefactions. This *wave train* or train of waves, alternately pressing upon and then releasing the tympanum, gives us the sensation of sound.[5]

[4] The tuning fork, invented by John Shore, trumpeter for Handel and one of Queen Anne's twenty-four musicians, has been the most widely used sound-producing instrument in inquiries into the nature of sound.

[5] For information on the other factors involved see the chapter on *The Ear and Hearing.*

If it were not for the gases—or, rather, the molecules which make up the gases—we could not hear in the air. This may be demonstrated by ringing an electric doorbell in a glass jar, from which the air is slowly exhausted. At first, while there is air in the container, the bell is heard distinctly; at the same time it can be seen that the clapper arm is rapidly striking the gong of the bell. As less and less air remains in the jar, the sound of the bell becomes fainter and fainter, until finally, when all or nearly all of the air has been removed, it is impossible to hear the bell, although it can still be seen to be struck by the clapper arm. Sound is not transmitted in a vacuum.

So far, our explanation may have conveyed the impression that sound is transmitted by transferring energy to a single straight row of molecules between the sounding body and the ear, that it is a one-dimensional phenomenon and that a single movement of the vibrating body will result in audible sound. However, we must visualize the sounding body as vibrating a number of times. All of the molecules about it, in all directions from it in all planes of its movement, will be disturbed by it and pass on the disturbance to other molecules. These molecules occupy all dimensions; if any molecules are disturbed the equilibrium of the pressure of the whole system is upset and a pressure disturbance is propagated in all directions. In other words, we must conceive of a shell of molecules surrounding the sounding body at all points. If, indeed, it were possible for us to make a cast of the layer of molecules lying immediately about the object, the cast would have the same shape as the object. So, in turn, casts of the immediately successive shells about the body would likewise have the same shape.

If, then, the object is set into vibration, the adjacent molecules transmit their energy on to successive molecules, and a compression wave will be flung off by the sounding body in all directions, with a wave-front pattern depending on the shape or mode of vibration of the sounding body.

B. A Departure From the Classical Concept

We too greatly simplify the concept of sound propagation when we think of the particles having only straight-line directions of movement[6] between the generator (i.e., point of excitation) and the ear or receiver. Presumably, it is in the nature of the cosmos that all molecules at normal temperatures, including those of air, i.e., gases,[7] are in constant motion at high velocities and in all directions, whether random or otherwise, in all dimensions.

Although the illustration is a simple one, it may help to think of one molecule (already in motion along some momentary path) as a cue ball

[6] Nevertheless, Lord Kelvin's dictum that sound is a function of one variable—that sound waves move in one dimension, i.e., in a straight line—is the classical concept.

[7] Air is composed of various gases, the molecules of each of which have their own inherent velocities.

being hit by the cue (sound generator) so that a new motion is imparted to it, with the result that it strikes a group of a dozen billiard balls which move off at high velocity in all directions. Of course, we should have to assume that the dozen balls were in motion themselves, rather than stationary until the moment of impact of the cue ball, and that they were in all planes rather than in one plane on the billiard table. Also, we would have to assume that while some may shoot off at right or other angles to the line of propagation of the sound wave, depending upon the resultants of the vectors of force acting upon them, enough travel in the straight-line direction to carry the sound wave energy from generator to receiver. In other words, while we represent the outward flow of energy as concentric circles, such as we apparently see occurring when we toss a stone into clear water, this is a fiction of simplification. The sound shell must, because of the divergent angles at which particles are propelled, be randomly irregular as it moves through space. We are not now talking about a dozen or so billiard balls; we are talking about millions of vibrating particles.

C. Generators of Sound

1. VIBRATING STRINGS

Pythagoras (6th century B.C.), perhaps in connection with his astronomical ideas about the music of the spheres, made a study of stringed instruments, such as the lyre and the monochord (attributed to him). He noted that the pitch he heard when he plucked a string depended upon its length, its tension, its size (diameter), and the material of which it was made. When he stretched a string and struck or plucked it[8] he noticed that its pattern of vibration was altered, depending on where he touched it and where he plucked it. For example, if he fastened it at both ends and plucked it in the middle he could see, in the Samos sunlight, that the whole string vibrated (Alpha). If he and his assistants put their fingers on the same strings they were able to see other patterns of vibration (e.g., Beta or Gamma) and to hear that the sounds varied by an octave or some other interval.

Early in his experiments he noted that a section of a vibrating string half as long as another produced a note an octave higher. He might have used the term *node* (N) to designate a point at which his string was attached or held with his fingers, and the term *antinode* to indicate the midpoint between nodes, i. e., at the point he plucked or struck the string.

His students learned that when the entire string vibrates it produces its *fundamental tone*. If it vibrates in segments, the tones produced by the segments are *partials*. If, in a certain string, for example, the tone of

[8] A string may be bowed, also, to set it into vibration.

Alpha is 100~, the respective tones for Beta and Gamma are 200~ and 400~. These are all simple vibration patterns. A string may produce complex sounds by vibrating simultaneously as a whole (producing its fundamental) and in segments (producing partials).

The arrows represent the degree of amplitude of the vibrations or the distance above, +, and below, −, the midpoint or position of rest, o. The number of double vibrations (d.v.), i.e., excursions or displacements (e.g., o to + to o to − to o; or + to − to +; or − to + to −) establishes the frequency of the tone. Because this represents a complete cycle of events we give the frequency in cycles per second (cps or ~).

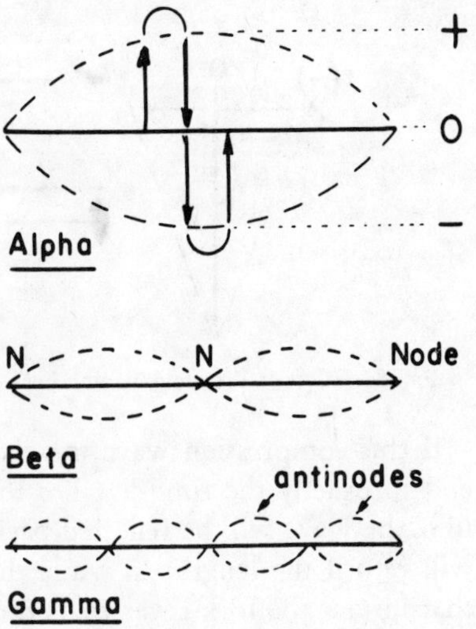

FIG. 80. Patterns of Vibrations of Plucked Strings.

At one time, it was thought that the vocal cords (note the similarity of the terminology) vibrated like cords or strings to generate voice sounds. Although we now subscribe to a different causative factor, a glance at Alpha and Beta, for example, and on the assumption that when you look at the drawings you are looking down on the glottis, may give you some ideas about combining the two theories.

In any case, a vibrating string itself usually does not produce a sound loud enough for our needs; hence, a resonator (the body of a violin, for example, or the sounding board of a piano) is almost always essential.

In the case of strings (and bars, tuning forks, rods, plates, bells, drums, and electric oscillators, for example) the sonorous body is a solid which, in turn, transmits its energy to the surrounding air particles, creating sound waves.

2. VIBRATING COLUMN OF AIR

As we have indicated in a previous chapter, air may be considered as a sonorous body which may be set into vibration as is a solid or a liquid. When confined in a tube or some other container the air follows certain definite laws.

a. Tube Closed at One End

Fig. 81 explains how a tuning fork vibrates. As it moves from one extreme position (—), through its position of rest (0), toward its other extreme position (+), it pushes against and, therefore, displaces the adjacent air particles, producing a wave of compression.

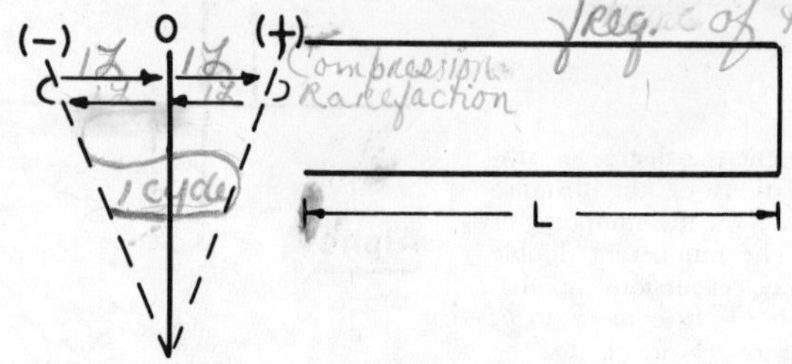

FIG. 81. Effect of Vibrating Tuning Fork on Air Particles in a Tube Closed at One End.

If this compression wave travels the length L of a tube closed at one end in exactly the time it takes for the fork prong to move from (—) to 0, the wave will be reflected back from the closed end of the tube and will return the length, L, while the fork is moving from 0 to (+). At that instant the fork reverses its direction of movement. The air particles in the tube which have been under pressure slightly greater than that of the open air, now escape from the open end of the tube into the open air. This produces a rarefaction which travels the distance L to the closed end of the tube and is reflected back the distance, L, during the time it takes the fork to move from (+) to (—). These periodic cycles of compression-rarefaction continue as long as the fork continues to vibrate.

A tube having the above characteristics must be one which resonates naturally to the frequency of the fork, or one in which $L = \lambda/4$, hence,

$$F \text{ (frequency of the fork or vibrating generator)} = \frac{1100 \text{ ft/sec (velocity of sound in air)}}{4L}$$

If we have tubes of other lengths, so that $L = 3/4\lambda$, or $L = 5/4\lambda$, or $L = 7/4\lambda$, etc., tubes of such lengths will also be in resonance with the fixed frequency of the fork-generator.[9]

As in the case of strings, the air columns display nodes and antinodes in the standing waves created. In any tube closed at one end there must be a node (N) at the closed end (somewhat similar to the attachment of a string) and an antinode (loop) at the mouth of the tube.

A tube closed at one end may respond simultaneously to tones of its fundamental and its partials (odd-numbered: 1,3,5,7,9,etc.).

[9] $\lambda = 4L$ (approx.). Because of the end effect of the tube $\lambda = 4\ (L + .6r)$, where r = radius of the tube.

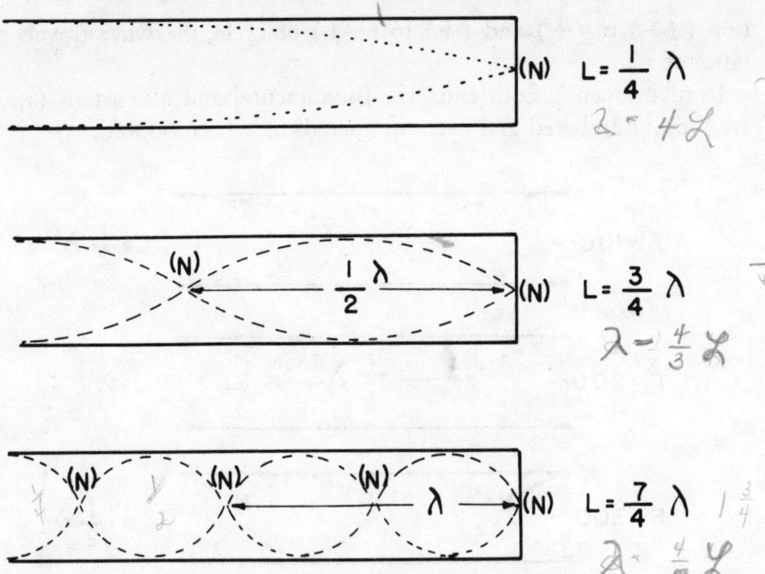

FIG. 82. Patterns of Nodes and Antinodes in Tubes Closed at One End.

b. Tube Open at Both Ends

In tubes open at both ends, an antinode must exist at each end. In such tubes the length of the tube L is equal to one-half the wave length of the sound produced. Thus,

$$F \text{ (frequency of generator)} = \frac{1100}{2L}$$

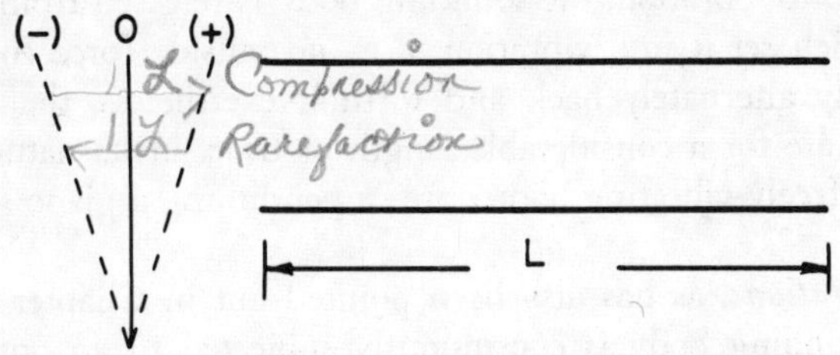

FIG. 83. Effect of Vibrating Tuning Fork on Air Particles in a Tube Open at Both Ends.

In a pipe or tube open at both ends a wave of compression of air particles is generated as the fork prong moves from (−) toward (+). During this time the wave of compression travels the length of the tube L. At the far end, due to the lower pressure outside the tube, the wave is reflected back as a wave of rarefaction, traveling the distance L while the fork prong is displaced from (+) to (−). Thus, during one complete double vibration ((—) to (+) and (+) to (—)) or cycle, the wave travels a distance of $2L$.

In tubes open at both ends, the fundamental and all partials (1,2,3,4,5, etc.), odd-numbered and even-numbered, may be produced.

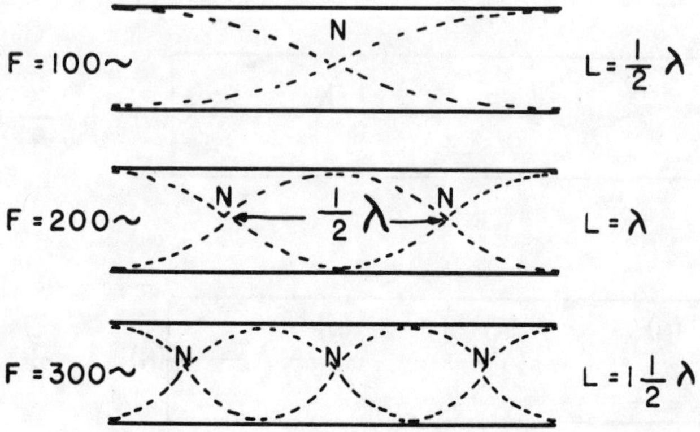

FIG. 84. Patterns of Nodes and Antinodes in Tubes Open at Both Ends.

If each has the same pitch, a tube open at both ends will be twice as long as one open at one end. (Of course, such a generalization disregards other characteristics of the tubes.)

D. Types of Vibrations

Vibrations may be classified as free, forced, or maintained.

Free vibrations, as we have said in Chapter III, result when, once having been set into vibration, the sounding body is released from the original force which set it into vibration, i. e., no outside force continues to urge the body alternately back and forth. Nevertheless, the body continues to vibrate for a considerable length of time, in its natural period. Examples of freely vibrating bodies are: a pendulum, a piano string, and a bell.

Forced vibrations, as has also been pointed out in Chapter III, result when the sounding body is continuously subjected to an outside force which urges it alternately back and forth—the body vibrating with the frequency imposed upon it by the outside force. The body continues to vibrate only briefly—if at all—after the outside force is withdrawn. Examples of bodies which vibrate in this manner are: a card forced to vibrate by a notched rotor wheel, and the drum of the ear.

Maintained vibrations result when an outside force keeps a body vibrating without imposing a frequency of its own; that is, the vibrations are of a frequency close to or exactly that of free vibrations for that body. Examples: a clock pendulum with an escape mechanism, a violin string during bowing.

Even free vibrations do not last indefinitely; they die away. Part of their energy is carried away by sound waves; part is turned into heat by the bending of the vibrating body; part is dissipated in other ways. The loss of mechanical energy shows itself by a decrease in the amplitude of vibration. The decrease is known as *damping*. When the amplitude dies rapidly, we say that the damping is large; when the amplitude dies slowly, we say that the damping is small.

When a critic refers to an uninformed person's speech as "hot air" he has something else in mind, but it is strictly true that the production of speech sounds raises the temperature of the surrounding air. The particles of the wave of compression upon collision with adjacent particles use up part of their energy at the moment of collision by generating heat. The amount is comparatively infinitesimal. This is not a major reason but it contributes to the fact that the energy of a sound wave falls off with distance from the generator.

CHARACTERISTICS OF SOUND

We are able to distinguish among sounds because they differ in these four respects, at least: frequency, intensity, quality, and time.

A. Frequency

One of the most variable factors in sound results from the rate of movement of the body or object producing the sound. Objects, if they move at all freely, do so with their own peculiarities of movement. A rocking chair will rock with its own individual oscillatory rate; a different chair will rock differently. A pendulum or a lawn swing or a tuning fork demonstrates the tendency of objects to oscillate or vibrate back and forth with a definite frequency. In physics, the *frequency* is stated in the *number of complete cycles,* swings or rockings to-and-fro—i. e., the *vibrations*—which occur *in a unit* (second) *of time.* The frequency of a sound is measured by the number of complete vibrations of the sounding body in one second.

If we suspend a heavy weight at the end of a wire we have a simple pendulum. If we move the weight and wire to one side of its position of rest—i. e., the perpendicular—and let it go, gravity acts on it to move it downward and forward with increasing velocity. The momentum is so great that it swings past its point of rest. However, it at once begins to lose momentum; it slows down and finally stops, momentarily, at the farthest point of its swing. Then it starts back again with constantly increased velocity until it reaches the midpoint; its momentum carries it past this toward the point where it originally began. This completes one cycle, or double swing, or *double vibration* (*d.v.*). Another cycle begins and others follow until, due to resistance, the swings die out or are damped out and the pendulum comes to rest at the midpoint position. Unless a body completes a minimum of 16 to 20 double vibrations per second it does not produce an audible tone.

Not only are extremely low frequencies inaudible, but, at the other extreme, some persons are unable to hear the shrill, high-frequency tones of bats or of certain insects. No one is able to hear tones of all frequencies. The normal range of audible frequencies lies between a lower limit of 20 d.v./sec. and an upper limit of 16,000 to 20,000 d.v./sec. If any body vibrates back and forth so as to send out wave trains within this range, we may hear a definite tone. The limits of pitch audibility for any person can be determined easily with an audiometer. Above such limits of human audibility (20,000$\sim$) are ultrasonic sounds, heard, for example, by dogs.

The *number* of vibrations per second gives a sound its pitch. For example, middle C_1 on the piano is established at 256 d.v./sec., in scientific work. Notice the relation of one note to another in the following table. One octave below middle C_1 is C (128 d.v./sec.), while an octave above C_1 is C_2 (512 d.v./sec.). The average pitch of the male voice is 128–144 d.v./sec. The average pitch of the female voice is 288–320 d.v./sec., that is, about an octave above that of the male.

One may write: 500 double vibrations per second (500 d.v./sec.), 500 cycles per second (500 cps.) or, simply, 500$\sim$.[10]

That pitch is related closely to the frequency of vibration may be demonstrated with a Seebeck siren.[11] The apparatus consists of a circular disc mounted so that it spins on an axis through its center and perpendicular to its plane. In a concentric circle, on the disc, is bored a series of equally spaced holes. Compressed air is blown from a nozzle through the holes. As the disc is rotated, the series of puffs of air coming through the holes give rise to a definite tone. The faster the disc is rotated, the more frequently do the air puffs come through and the higher becomes the pitch of the tone.

Fig. 86 demonstrates graphically the difference between sounds which differ in pitch. That is, the higher the pitch of the sounding body, the greater the number of vibrations in each second; the lower the pitch, the fewer the number of vibrations per second. Two or more bodies vibrating at the same frequency are said to have the same pitch.

While frequency is a physical attribute, pitch is psychological. An in-

[10] The equivalent German notation may be written 500 Hz.

[11] Baron Charles Cagniard de la Tour devised the siren in 1819 and called it a siren because it could sing under water. The Seebeck siren is named after Ludwig Friedrich Wilhelm August Seebeck (1805–1849), who was professor of physics at the University of Leipzig.

TABLE OF PITCHES

Pitch standard for musicians	Physical scale d.v./sec.	
	4096	C_5
	3840	
	3413	
	3072	
	2730	
	2560	
	2304	
	2048	C_4
	1920	
	1706	
	1536	
	1365	
	1280	
	1152	
	1024	C_3
	960	
	853	
	768	
	682	
	640	
	576	
	512	C_2
	480	
440A	426	
	384	
	341	
	320	
	288	
(female)	256	C_1
	240	
	213	
	192	
	170	
	160	
	144	
(male)	128	C
	120	
	106	
	96	
	85	
	80	
	72	
	64	C_{-1}
	60	
	53	
	48	
	42	
	40	
	36	
	32	C_{-2}

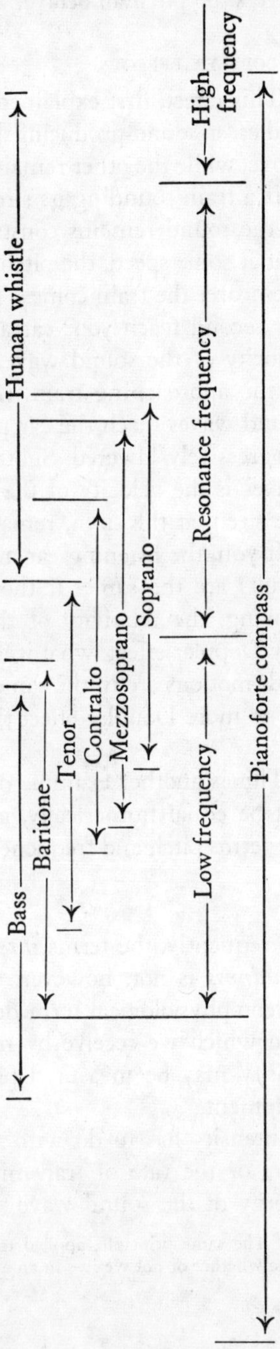

crease in frequency is perceived as an increase in pitch. Frequency and pitch are related logarithmically (log_2). Doubling the frequency (intensity being unchanged) raises pitch an octave; halving the frequency lowers the pitch an octave.

1. DOPPLER EFFECT

This effect, first explained in 1842, is due to the relative motion of two bodies, a sound-producing body and a sound-receiving ear. Either may move, while the other remains fixed, or both may move.

If a train sounding its siren is not moving in relation to you, the pitch of the sound remains constant. If, however, the train is moving toward you at some speed, the pitch of the sound seems to be progressively raised the nearer the train comes. This is due to the fact that more sound waves per second reach your ear as the train approaches. Added to the natural velocity of the sound waves (approximately 1100 ft/sec) is the velocity of the approaching train. If the train is moving away from you, fewer sound waves reach the ear per second and the pitch is perceived as being progressively lowered. Subtracted from the natural velocity of the sound waves is the velocity of the receding train. In all cases the frequency of the siren, at the siren, remains constant.[12]

If you, the listening ear, move relative to a stationary sound source the results are the same. If the listener is moving and the sound source is moving, the relativity of the motions will determine whether there is any Doppler effect, what it is, and the degree of the effect. If, for example, both motions are in the same direction and at the same velocity there will be no more Doppler effect than if listener and sound source were stationary.

This is another example of the way in which frequency and pitch may not be equal numerically, and of why one should take care not to use the terms pitch and frequency interchangeably.

B. Intensity

Frequently, the terms *intensity* and *loudness* are used interchangeably. *Loudness* is not, however, strictly a physical term; it is a comparative psycho-physiological term describing the degree of strength of the sensation which we receive by means of our hearing apparatus. Though intensity may be measured physically, loudness is a matter of individual judgment.

Intensity has to do with the flow of energy in the wave of compression, or the rate of transmission of sound energy in the medium. The energy of the sound wave varies as the square of the amplitude of the

[12] The same principle, applied to light, is used by astrophysicists in attempting to determine whether or not we live in an expanding universe.

wave. It is measured in *ergs* [13] per second per square centimeter, or in *dynes* per square centimeter, or in *microbars*. In terms of time rate of energy flow, i.e., power, it may be expressed in units of watts/cm^2.[14]

The response of the ear to the energy of the sound wave is proportional to the logarithm [15] of the intensity of the wave. Thus,

$$R = k \log I$$

where k is a constant.[16]

1. RELATION OF AMPLITUDE TO INTENSITY AND LOUDNESS

Since a sound wave results from compressions and rarefactions of the air in proximity to the sounding body, it is apparent that if, in equal time intervals, the body moves from o to y^+ (Fig. 85), or from o to x^+, the air

In this diagram, o–o represents a single prong of a tuning fork which is not vibrating. x^- to x^+ represents the range of the prong excursions when the fork is vibrating with a certain amplitude, and y^- to y^+ represents the increased range of excursion when the fork vibrates with greater amplitude. Theoretically, of course, a sounding body may vibrate with any degree of *amplitude,* between zero and the maximum, which its elasticity permits.

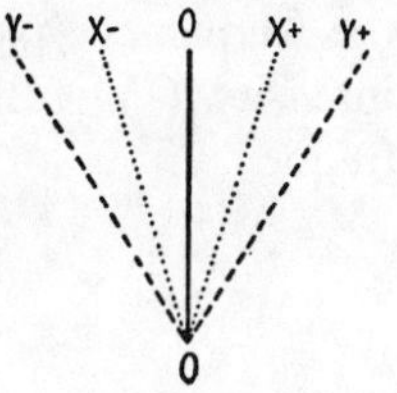

FIG. 85. Diagram of Amplitude Range of a Single Prong of a Tuning Fork.

will be placed under greater compression in the first case (o to y^+). This means that greater pressure will be exerted by the sound wave when it impinges against any object (e.g., a diaphragm), and, further, that greater energy must be expended at the sound source to cause the body to vibrate.[17] The degree of amplitude, or range of vibration, of the sound source will determine the amplitude, or intensity, of the sound waves and hence will determine the loudness with which we hear a sound. It also will determine the amplitude of the excursions of the diaphragm of a loudspeaker, the beam of a cathode ray oscilloscope, or the writing lever of graphic recording equipment, such as the sound spectrograph. We know that the loudness of a sound is related to the work done in producing it,

[13] An *erg* is a unit of energy, e.g., 980 ergs of energy are expended in lifting a weight of 1 gram a distance of 1 cm.

[14] A *watt* is a unit of power, e.g., 1 watt is equivalent to an expenditure of energy at the rate of 10,000,000 ergs/sec.

[15] A *logarithm* is the power (expressed as an exponent) to which a given number is raised to obtain another number, e.g., $10^2 = 100$ and $10^4 = 10{,}000$. Thus, 2 is the logarithm of 100 and 4 of 10,000.

[16] According to the Weber-Fechner Law.

[17] An insignificant fraction of the mechanical energy expended by a source is transformed into sound. For example, the voice with an energy input of 11.6×10^5 erg/sec. has a sound output of only 110.0×10^2 erg/sec. That is, the voice is only about 95/1000 of one percent efficient.

and so we now see why to speak loudly requires more effort than to speak quietly.[18]

2. RELATION OF INTENSITY TO DISTANCE

As we have said, sound energy is transmitted equally in every direction from its source. *Intensity varies inversely as the square of the distance from the source.* A sound of a given intensity at a certain distance has one-fourth that intensity at twice the distance and one-ninth the intensity at three times the distance.

3. RELATION OF AMPLITUDE AND INTENSITY TO FREQUENCY

If the frequency of vibration of a sounding body remains constant, the intensity will vary as the square of the amplitude of the vibration (A^2). If the amplitude remains constant, the intensity will vary as the square of the frequency (pitch) (N^2). If both amplitude and frequency vary, the intensity (I) will vary as the square of the product of amplitude and frequency.[19]

$$I = (NA)^2 \text{ or } I = N^2A^2$$

$$N = \frac{\sqrt{I}}{A} \text{ or } N = \frac{1}{A}\sqrt{I}$$

$$A = \frac{\sqrt{I}}{N} \text{ or } A = \frac{1}{N}\sqrt{I}$$

The intensity of a complex tone is equal to the sum of the intensities of its partials.

4. SPEECH POWER

Much of the present and developing state of our knowledge about speech and hearing we owe to researchers in commercial laboratories (e.g., manufacturers of telephone, radio and television equipment, and of hearing aids) and in governmental laboratories. This is true, for example, of the definitions developed by communications engineers.

Instantaneous speech power is the rate of radiation of speech sound energy at any given instant. It is measured in microwatts.[20] In successive

[18] It has been estimated that the energy which a public speaker expends during a twenty-minute address is equivalent to that expended playing three sets of tennis. In speaking, other factors are involved also. Almost inevitably after delivering a public speech, a speaker feels tired physically, and experiences a correlated let-down feeling psychologically.

[19] This relationship was assumed as the basis of the discussion on intratracheal pressure and vocal-fold tension in Chapter II.

[20] A microwatt (micro = one millionth of) is one millionth of a watt. A watt is 1/746 of a horsepower. When an agent does work at the rate of 550 foot-pounds per second it is said to be working at one horsepower.

instants the figures fluctuate greatly. At one instant it may be high; at another, low.

Phonetic speech power is the average of the rate of radiation of sound energy during the production of a single vowel or consonant. It is measured in microwatts.

Average speech power is the sum total of all of the speech sound energy radiated during a complete speech divided by the elapsed time of the entire speech. It is measured in microwatts.

By taking the averages of the energy radiated by numerous persons in many conversations, it has been estimated that, in this country, the average speech power of the average person is about 15 microwatts. If the same individual talks as loudly as possible, his average speech power may be 1000 microwatts. If he talks as softly as possible, his average speech power is only 0.1 microwatt. And if he whispers softly his average whisper power is a mere 0.001 microwatt.[21]

The average speech power is obtained when we average up all of the variations in energy radiated by a speaker.[22] The energy radiated during the production of some sounds is great and, during others, low. For example, the faintest speech sound—[θ], as in *thin*—has an average phonetic power of only 0.05 microwatt. Considering the population as a whole, it is unlikely that the sound of the weakest average phonetic power which will be encountered will be less than 0.01 microwatt. Also, probably the value of the loudest sound will not exceed 5000 microwatts. That is, the greatest range of intensity which we should expect to find would be one one-hundredth of a microwatt to five thousand microwatts, or 1 to 500,000. This is a range of about 60 decibels.

5. THE UNIT OF MEASUREMENT OF INTENSITY

The intensity of a train of sound waves equals the amount of energy that the waves carry through unit area in unit time. In comparing the intensities of two sounds, the ratio of the flow of energy per second is compared. If the logarithm of the ratio is used, the unit of measurement is the *bel*.[23]

If the power of sound *A* is ten times that of *B*, the logarithm of the power ratio is 1. The intensity level of *A* may be said to be one bel higher than that of *B*. If the power of *A* is one hundred times that of *B*, the logarithm of the power ratio is 2, i. e., the intensity level of *A* is two bels higher than that of *B*.

In practice, it is usual to use the term *decibel* (1/10 of a bel) instead of

[21] Compare with an electric light bulb rated at 100 watts (100,000,000 microwatts).

[22] To convey the energy at this level, the molecules of air at the oral orifice must vibrate with an amplitude of 1/100 to 1/75 of a millimeter.

[23] In honor of Alexander Graham Bell (1847–1922), but spelled with one *l*.

bel to express differences in levels of intensity. The decibel is also a logarithmic unit. The abbreviation *db* stands for decibel. Thus, if sound *A* has ten times the intensity of sound *B,* its intensity level is 10 db higher. If sound *A* has one hundred times the intensity of sound *B,* its intensity level is 20 db higher. The following figures indicate the intensity levels of several well-known sounds.

NOISE LEVEL	NOISE
0 db	Threshold of hearing
20 db	Leaves rustling in light breeze
40 db	One typewriter in small room
50 db	Animated conversation
70 db	Range of symphony orchestra
85 db	Riveter, heard from street
95 db	Niagara Falls
100 db	Subway train or station
120 db	Airplane, close at hand
130 db	Loudness at this level is painful.

The decibel may be directly related to the levels of speech power, as is shown by the following figures (which should not be confused with those above). Here it is assumed, as a basis of comparison, that the average speech power is zero decibels.

Speech power level in microwatts		*Equivalent level in decibels*
Loud speech	= 1000 microwatts	+20 decibels
Average speech power	= 15 microwatts	Zero decibels
Soft speech	= 0.1 microwatts	—20 decibels
Soft whisper	= 0.001 microwatts	—40 decibels

From the above, it is apparent that the range of speech in decibels is about 60 decibels, that is, from +20 to —40 decibels. This is much greater than the range encountered in the conversations of 95 percent of the population; that range is only about 20 decibels.

In accord with the psychological law of Weber-Fechner—that the intensity of the sensation is proportional to the logarithm of the strength of the stimulus—the smallest change of intensity that can be detected by the ear is one decibel or one *sensation unit.*

To determine the *sensation level* of any sound, we first determine the threshold level for the ear. Then we find out how many decibels above that threshold is the intensity level of the sound. That level is the sensation level. It varies for different sounds and for different ears.

SL = Intensity of Sound – Threshold of Ear

6. LOUDNESS

Loudness is the term used in designating the magnitude of sensation experienced by a listener whose ear is subjected to sound waves. Strictly speaking, loudness is an individual matter and, therefore, not comparable, quantitatively. How do we know, for example, that a tone we both hear and that you say is "loud," has the same loudness for me? Nevertheless, to prevent chaos, audiologists have adopted a *standard reference tone* whose loudness level is accepted, arbitrarily, as being the same as its intensity level.[24] By this means, loudness may be expressed in comparable quantitative terms. Once the reference tone is accepted one may determine the loudness of an unknown tone, *X*, by listening to the reference tone and *X* alternately, and regulating the dial of the testing equipment controlling the loudness of the reference tone until the two tones are heard with what is judged to be equal loudness. The loudness of *X* may then be read directly as the intensity level indicated on the equipment.

Phon is a term used to express a unit of loudness. The loudness level of a tone in phons is equal numerically to its intensity level in decibels.

C. QUALITY

While pure tones are differentiated primarily in terms of pitch and intensity, a complex tone has an additional distinguishing characteristic: quality. An understanding of quality requires an appreciation of the fact that most tones are complex; they consist of combinations of several tones.

It was G. S. Ohm who early observed that the motion of particles in a complex sound wave—i.e., in all sounds except pure tones—is physically and mathematically the sum of the simple periodic motions of its components. The ear has the ability to sort out these individual partial tones and hear their respective pitches.

One might expect that the pitch he would associate with a compound tone would be that of the component having the lowest frequency, and this may be true.[25] By definition, the lowest frequency component of a complex or compound tone is known as the *fundamental tone*. The other components are known as *overtones,* or upper partials. The term *partial* may be used to include the fundamental and the overtones. For example, if the fundamental is 100 d.v./sec. and there are two overtones of 200 d.v./sec. and 300 d.v./sec., respectively, then the fundamental is the first partial; the tone of 200 d.v./sec. is the first overtone, but it is also the

[24] i.e., 10^{-16} microwatts/cm^2 or a corresponding sound wave pressure of 0.0002 dynes/cm^2.

[25] It may be true only because low tones tend to mask or make it difficult to hear high tones. On the other hand, it might not be true; your ear or a spectral analysis of a complex tone may reveal that the greater energy of some other component, of higher frequency, is dominant.

second partial; while the tone of 300 d.v./sec. is the second overtone as well as the third partial. Occasionally, overtones are called harmonics. However, the term *harmonics* should be restricted in use to overtones which have frequencies 2, 3, 4, 5, etc., times that of the fundamental.

Quality (timbre, klangfarbe, tone color, clang) may be defined as that characteristic of the sounds of a voice or of another instrument which distinguishes them from the sounds of other voices or instruments, even though all the sounds may be equal in pitch and loudness. This property of a tone is far more complicated than either pitch or amplitude.

Quality depends upon one or more of these constituents: (1) the particular partials and the number of partials [26] present in the complex sound; (2) the distribution of the partials and their relation to the fundamental and to each other; (3) the intensity of the partials, absolutely, and relative to each other and to the fundamental; (4) the phase relationships of the partials to the fundamental and to each other; (5) transients; (6) vibrato,[27] and, perhaps, (7) subjective tones or aural harmonics.

Due primarily to quality, the voice and speech of each person produces unique and characteristic sound wave patterns; the same is true of different musical instruments. When it is averred that a speaker cannot produce two identical speech sounds, the assertion is based more upon quality parameters than upon pitch or intensity characteristics.

Resonance characteristics play an important role in quality, particularly in speech. Except for the fact that one precedes the other, it is highly debatable whether the various generators of speech sounds or the human resonators contribute the most to speech. Phase characteristics, to which we will devote more time later, are important in quality differentiation.

Usually a sounding body does not vibrate as a unit—i.e., not all of its molecules are in phase. This means, therefore, that as these molecules pass on their energy to the air, the non-phasic relations of the molecules of the air to one another may be infinite. Probably, certain parts of the sounding body will hold such a relationship that the great number of air molecules coming into contact with these parts will make up the bulk of all the air molecules involved in the transmission of sound. One part of the body, for example, might set in motion, in phase, let us say 27 percent of the air molecules; another portion 9 percent; another portion 3 percent. Yet the molecules in each of these three groups are not in phase with those of any other group. We may imagine any number of other groups, likewise out of phase with one another, setting into motion their own small percentage of the total number of molecules. Further, some molecules of the sounding body may be in opposite phase to each other. The part they play in

[26] Harmonics, at least up to the 35th, have been noted in vocal sounds.

[27] This may involve either frequency modulation or amplitude modulation variations. The combination produces periodic alterations of the wave form.

establishing the peculiar pattern of the wave front may be of equal or of greater importance than the part played by the other molecules.

The sound waves which go out as concentric shells from the sonorous body do not present an even or smooth wave front. Further, the angle at which the wave front leaves its center of radius must affect its form. As this jagged wave front strikes against a diaphragm, for example, that portion of the condensation jutting farthest out ahead will move the diaphragm first; but, before the diaphragm is free to return to its neutral position of the resting state, one by one the less advanced portions of the wave will strike it, so that instead of the graphic record of the diaphragm movement looking like *A* in Fig. 87 it might look like *C* in the same figure.

We are justified, therefore, in saying that whereas pitch depends upon frequency, and intensity upon amplitude, quality depends upon the relation of these, one to the other, and to the form of the sound wave front. Graphically, quality is related to the form or shape of the curve produced by the sound being studied.

Of all musical instruments, the human voice offers the most variations in quality. Voice quality varies so greatly among individuals that we may rely upon it as a means of identification when we are unable to see the person who is talking. Moreover, each of the basic speech sounds has its distinct and characteristic quality.

D. Time

Ordinarily, time is not considered in connection with sound except, of course, in relation to frequency (with which, by definition, it is inseparable) and quality, as far as partials are concerned. However, we see time as important in other aspects of the geometry of sound.

Every sound possesses the element or aspect of time; it occupies a definite period of time. From this point of view, a sound is said to have length or duration. Moreover, sound patterns differ not only in the length of the individual sounds which compose them but also in the rate of change, or movement, from one sound to the next throughout the series. Therefore, sound has two time factors: duration and rate.

1. PHASE

One aspect of the time relationship between tones is *phase*.[28] If two or more simple tones of identical frequencies and amplitudes are produced simultaneously, they will be in phase with one another; if they are not produced simultaneously, they will be out of phase. Assume that we have

[28] *Phase* is that fraction of a period which has elapsed since the disturbance passed some reference point when moving in a particular direction. *Period* may be defined as the length of time required for each particle of the sound-conducting medium to execute one complete double vibration.

two curves, exactly like the one in Fig. 88, each representing a pure tone of 500 cycles and the tones having identical intensities. The sounds are in phase; their periods of compression and rarefaction are in exact agreement. If the ear receives both tones simultaneously they will be heard as a single tone but louder than either would be alone. Physically, the amplitude of the combined tones will be double that of either alone.

If the two identical continuous tones were simultaneously traversing the same medium and were exactly one half cycle (180 degrees; ½ period) out of phase, the compression phase of one exactly matching the rarefaction phase of the other, the resultant amplitude would be zero; the ear would hear no tone.

If the two tones of identical frequency and amplitude are out of phase in any other relationship—greater than zero degrees but less than 180 degrees—and continue to be produced, there will come a time when their relationship will be such as to match phase and, hence, they will *reinforce* each other. At another time they will be exactly out of phase and, hence, cancel out each other. This latter effect is known as *interference.*

If three or more tones of the same frequency (e. g., when a violin section or a chorus of voices unite in producing tones of the same frequency) are involved, the complexity of the possible phase relationships increases greatly.

Even more highly involved may be the phase relationships between and among sounds, each of which is itself a complex sound. With only a few sounds the mathematical possibilities are almost infinite. All of these factors must, of course, be considered when one thinks about the quality of sounds.

a. Beats

Beats illustrate an interesting result of phase difference between two sounds differing slightly in frequency. If, for example, tones of 300 cycles and 304 cycles are presented to the ear simultaneously the ear will hear four beats or pulsations each second—the number of beats being equal to the difference, in cycles, between the two frequencies.[29] Because the two tones differ in frequency the compression and rarefaction portions of their sound waves will each be in agreement or in phase four times a second. When the compression phases match, the amplitudes are additive and the ear perceives a sensation of loudness. When the two waves are in exactly opposite phase, or nearly so, the ear will perceive a marked decrease in loudness. Thus, the sensation of beats represents the periodic swelling to maximum peaks of loudness and intervening diminishings of sound pressure to a minimum (zero).[30]

[29] Beats provide a method by which musicians may tune their instruments.

[30] Because of the persistence of hearing it is improbable, if not impossible, under these conditions that the ear would ever perceive actual zero sound or no sound. While, physi-

The ear can hear beats only with a limited range of pulsations; if the two tones presented to the ear differ by too many cycles per second the beats will be produced so rapidly that they will not be perceived by the ear, and the ear may hear two distinct tones.

Or, it may hear three tones. For example, if tones of 1500 cycles and 2000 cycles are produced simultaneously the ear will hear each of these individual tones and, in addition, a tone of 500 cycles, representing the difference between the tones. Physically, this *difference tone* is not present; psychologically, it is.

2. THE VELOCITY OF SOUND

The velocity of sound depends upon two factors: on the elasticity and the density of the conduction medium; it increases when the first increases and when the second diminishes. Velocity $= \sqrt{\dfrac{elasticity}{density}}$. By *elasticity* is meant that constant which is a measurement of the resistance to distortion offered by any substance. To illustrate, we may compare air and steel. The density of steel is greater than that of air, and hence we might expect the velocity of sound to be decreased in steel as compared with air. The elasticity of steel, however, is many times greater than that of air, so that this factor greatly outweighs that of density, and in steel the velocity of sound is much greater than in air. This accounts for our hearing an oncoming train sooner if we put an ear to the rail!

The *velocity of sound* in air at 0° Centigrade (32° Fahrenheit) is about 1100 [31] feet per second. It increases (or decreases) regularly with an increase (or decrease) in temperature—about 2 feet per 1° Centigrade. The rate is independent of intensity or pitch. In liquids or solids the velocity of sound is much greater: in water, approximately 1437 m/sec or 4714 ft/sec at 15° C; in steel, approximately 5000 m/sec or 16400 ft/sec. The velocity of all sound waves is the same in a given homogeneous medium at a given temperature.

3. WAVELENGTH OF SOUNDS

If the molecules of air at a source of sound are disturbed only once a second, the first wave of high pressure will have traveled outward about 1100 feet by the time the second wave begins to follow it. The waves will

cally, the sound waves might actually cancel each other out completely, the fact that this occurs so rapidly and in the midst of otherwise heard sound waves would result, probably, in the ear perceiving a momentary pulsing, a diminution of loudness rather than complete silence. We know that about 1.6 cycles of a sound is the minimum the ear can perceive. It might be argued that in the midst of a continuous sound pattern the ear could not perceive a cessation of the sound lasting less than 1.6 cycles. In the case of beats, the duration of the exactly out-of-phase sound would be only one cycle.

[31] 1088 is a more accurate figure. Or, in meters, between 331 and 332 per second. Velocity changes at the rate of about 0.6 m/sec per degree Centigrade.

be 1100 feet apart—measured from crest to crest or from any point on the wave form to a corresponding point on the next wave form—and will have a wavelength of 1100 feet. If the air is disturbed 100 times a second, the waves will be 100 times closer together—the wavelength will be 11 feet. The wavelength of a sound is determined by dividing 1100 [approximately] by the pitch of the sound.

$$\frac{V \text{ (velocity)}}{N \text{ (pitch)}} = \lambda \text{ (wavelength)}$$

Frequency and wavelength are inversely related; with an increase in frequency there is a corresponding decrease in wavelength.[32]

E. The Reflection and/or Absorption of Sound

As with sunlight reflected from a mirror, so with sound; in general, it may be said that the angle of incidence equals the angle of reflection. Any sound or light wave incident upon any surface is reflected and/or absorbed. The percentage of reflection (or of absorption) depends upon the qualities of the surface (and, at least, upon the frequency, i. e., wavelength, of the sound).

Compared with the absorptive qualities of an open window (absorption factor = 1.0) a surface such as glass, polished steel, marble, or plaster may have an absorption factor for sound of only 0.01 to 0.03, while various felts and draperies may have an absorption factor as high as 0.7 to 0.9.

As far as the reflection or absorption of speech sound waves are concerned, the teeth and hard palate have low factors of absorption in comparison to such surfaces as the uvula, pharyngeal wall, and lungs.

During the production of speech sounds, the sound waves may be reflected several times while traveling from their points of origin to their place of emission into the open air. Once emitted, the sound waves may be subject to numerous reflection patterns from objects and walls, ceilings and floors about the speaker. Every time the sound wave is reflected a portion of its energy is absorbed. Furthermore, as has been pointed out previously, every time the sound wave is reflected resonance factors enter the already complex picture.

THE GRAPHIC REPRESENTATION OF SOUND WAVES

In many books and articles reporting research work on speech sounds there frequently appear curves such as those shown in Fig. 86. They are the graphic representation of what the sound is physically. The curves differ, depending on the duration, pitch, intensity, and quality of the sounds.

[32] Bats use a 90,000~ tone ($\lambda = 1.9$mm) to locate and home on insects.

A pure tone of a given frequency produces a simple wave form like the curve in Fig. 86*A*. Doubling the frequency produces a simple curve showing twice as many waves. (Fig. 86*B*.)

Changes in the intensity of a tone are represented by variations in the height of the wave graph. The pitch of the tones represented in Figs. 86*A* and 86*C* is the same, but the intensity level of the tone represented in *C* is greater than that of the tone represented in *A*.

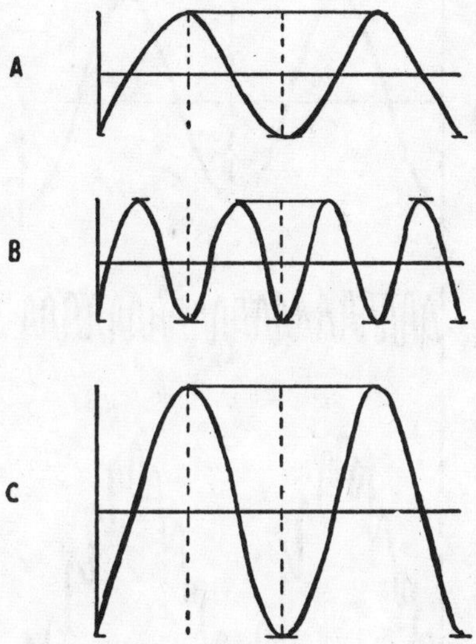

A is a simple curve produced by a pure tone.

B shows the frequency of tone *A* doubled. There are twice as many wave forms per unit of time.

C represents tone *A* with a greater intensity level. Changes in intensity are indicated by the height of the wave graph.

FIG. 86. Graphic Representation of a Sound Wave.

When two or more pure tones are combined, the resultant curve may be quite complex. The form of the curve depends upon the relative frequencies, amplitudes, and initial phases of the combined components. From combining two tones (Fig. 87*A* and 87*B*) the complex wave form of Fig. 87*C* results.

To understand these simple or complex curves and to know how sound waves are represented graphically in research studies on speech, we must learn first some concepts of *simple harmonic motion*.

Essentially, wave motion is produced by a periodic vibration which is maintained at the source and which is passed on from point to point in an elastic medium. These periodic vibrations produce a series of waves which follow each other at regular intervals. Two distinct motions are involved: the individual particles vibrate about their positions of rest and the wave form moves progressively outward. In a simple harmonic vibration—i. e., one producing a pure tone—the pressure [33] changes continu-

[33] The force per unit area which the air or gas would exert upon any containing wall.

ously with the time elapsed; its rate of change is zero at two points—the maximum and minimum values. (See Fig. 88.)

Simple harmonic motion has these properties:

(1) It is motion in a straight line.

(2) It is periodic to-and-fro vibration.

(3) At its two extremes of vibration there are moments of rest.

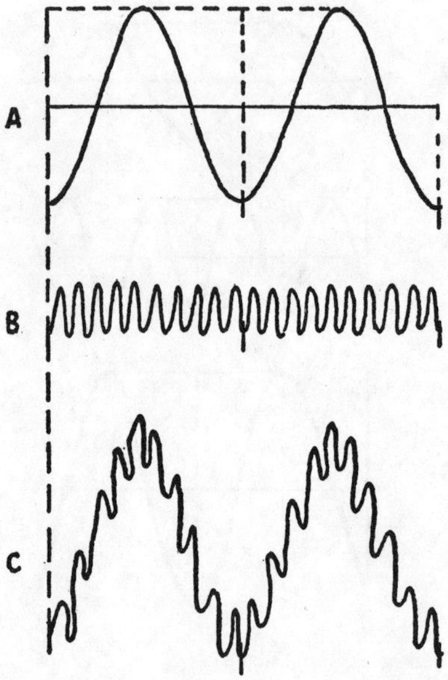

A. The graphic wave form of a pure tone of medium frequency.

B. The graphic wave form of a pure tone of high frequency.

C. The complex wave form resulting when *A* and *B* are combined.

FIG. 87. Pure and Complex Wave Forms.

(4) Its velocity is maximum as it passes through its undisplaced position.

(5) Its instantaneous acceleration is exactly proportional to its displacement.

The following terms are useful in a description of simple harmonic motion:

Frequency—the number of complete (to-and-fro) vibrations per second.

Period—the time required for one complete vibration.

Phase—at any instant, that fraction of a period elapsed since the point last passed through its position of rest in the direction termed *positive*.

When a particle has simple harmonic motion—or another vibratory motion—its *displacement* is its distance from the middle point of its path—or natural position of equilibrium—usually regarded as positive when on one side of the equilibrium position and negative when on the other.

The *amplitude* of a simple harmonic motion means the largest extent of the displacement.

In Fig. 89*A* may be seen the straight line *yz* traced by the pointer on a recording drum when it is not in motion. Most tambour pointers in use will draw an arc rather than a straight line because their point of attachment is fixed. (See Fig. 89*B*.)

At *xo* the pointer is at its neutral position before it begins to move. Once it is set into vibration, it moves between the extremes *y* and *z*, stopping momentarily at each extreme before the reversal of its direction of movement. If the pointer in Fig. 89 be continued in its motion while the recording drum be rotated, the result will be a curved line (Fig. 90) instead of a straight line. This demonstrates that a simple harmonic motion combined with a uniform motion of translation traces a sine curve. It is simple, regular, and symmetrical and is called a *sine curve* because the amplitude is proportional to the trigonometric sine of a uniformly increasing angle. The curves in Fig. 88 and Fig. 90 are examples of simple sine curves.

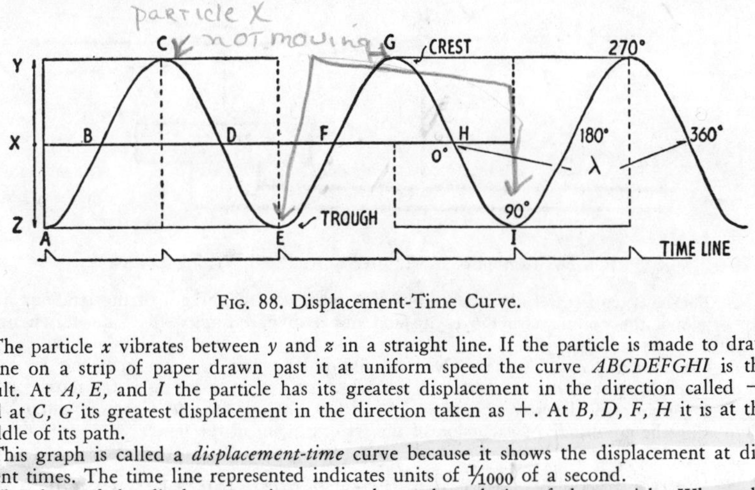

FIG. 88. Displacement-Time Curve.

The particle *x* vibrates between *y* and *z* in a straight line. If the particle is made to draw a line on a strip of paper drawn past it at uniform speed the curve *ABCDEFGHI* is the result. At *A*, *E*, and *I* the particle has its greatest displacement in the direction called −, and at *C*, *G* its greatest displacement in the direction taken as +. At *B*, *D*, *F*, *H* it is at the middle of its path.

This graph is called a *displacement-time* curve because it shows the displacement at different times. The time line represented indicates units of 1/1000 of a second.

The slope of the displacement-time curve shows the velocity of the particle. Where the curve slopes upward toward the right, that particle is moving upward; where it slopes downward toward the right, the particle is moving downward; where the slope is most rapid, the particle is moving most rapidly; and where the curve is horizontal, the particle is not moving. That is, the particle stops momentarily to change its direction at *ACEGI*.

As the vibratory motion of sound waves in the air is longitudinal—i. e., to and fro in the direction of propagation—it is usual to adopt the convention that forward displacements are represented by upward-drawn ordinates and backward displacements by downward-drawn ordinates.

The simplest combination of tones is that produced by two simple tones of identical pitch. The combination of two simple harmonic motions of the same frequency produces a resultant motion which is also simple harmonic; the resultant has the same frequency as the frequency of its components. Inasmuch as the ear performs an analysis[34] similar in nature to that of our graphic recording equipment, it follows, then, that if we hear two or more simple tones of the same pitch at the same time, we will not

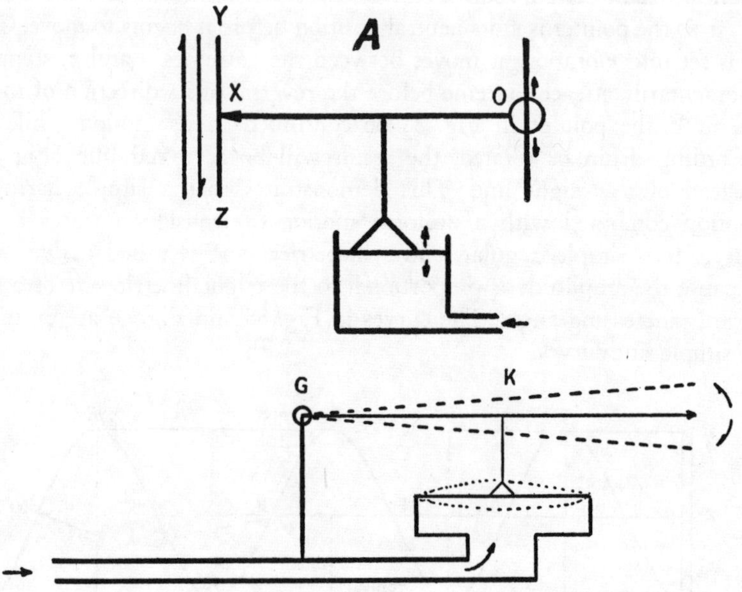

FIG. 89. Tambours and Indirectly Attached Writing Levers.

A. The lever *xo* is carefully balanced so that when the diaphragm of the tambour moves up or down the pointer also moves up and down in its entirety. The line drawn by the pointer is a straight line *yxz*.

B. The lever is pivoted so that only its writing point is free to move when the diaphragm is displaced. The resulting curve drawn by such a lever is an arc. This is the most common type of tambour and lever combination. The distance between *g* and *k* may be altered, thus regulating the amplitude of excursion of the writing point of the lever.

hear the two tones, but instead will hear a single tone of that pitch. It may be louder than either of the original single tones.

If two simple harmonic motions of the same frequency are in phase, the amplitude of the resultant motion is equal to the sum of the amplitudes of the components. If two tones of identical pitch are approximately in phase with each other, the two tones reinforce each other. If they are

[34] George Simon Ohm (1787–1854) set down these observations regarding sound waves: A simple harmonic motion of the air received by the ear gives the impression of a single pitch.

If a more complicated motion of the air stimulates the ear, an impression of hearing a component tone of frequency *N* will result if:

(*a*) It be possible to analyze the complicated wave motion into motions that are either simple harmonic or very nearly so, and

(*b*) one of these simple motions has a frequency of *N*.

in opposite phase, the amplitude of the resultant motion is equal to the difference between the amplitudes of the components. If the two components are opposite in phase the resultant tone will be less loud than the louder of its components and we say that one tone interferes with the other. Where two component simple harmonic motions have not only the same frequency but also the same amplitude and are also just opposite in phase, there is no resultant motion, hence, no sound.

SOUND-WAVE RECORDING EQUIPMENT

The best way to understand graphic sound records is to make some records. First, however, something must be known about the equipment used in making such records. Sound-recording equipment is available in a wide variety of types, from the simplest and most inexpensive do-it-yourself air, air and water, and electrical devices to the most sophisticated and costly console-controlled or programmed electronic marvels. In any case, at one or more steps, the equipment makes use of some kind of diaphragm—operating in a manner similar to that of the eardrum—for the translation of the sound waves into their visible representations.

An ideal diaphragm would be one which would execute the same movements, during the passage of the wave-train, that the air particles themselves execute. Approaching the ideal, perhaps, might be an electron-curtain diaphragm, or a light-ray reflector such as a glycerine-soap film diaphragm.

In practice, the ordinary diaphragm—mounted and confined under pressure at its circumference, and having inertia because of its weight—possesses a characteristic periodicity of its own to which frequency or frequencies it most readily responds. This means that sound waves containing these frequencies may have them accentuated, thus distorting to a greater or lesser degree the true picture of the wave. In general, however, a good diaphragm faithfully preserves the wave-form characteristic with a high degree of accuracy.

The ideal recording device or writing stylus would be one which has no weight, no mechanical parts, no friction and, hence, no inertia; its response would be instantaneous. Approaching the ideal are a ray of light (e. g., writing on a sensitive photographic film) or an electron beam writing on a phosphor screen, such as in a cathode ray oscilloscope.

If not in a laboratory in the department in which this textbook is used, then in some other laboratory [35] surely will be found some kind of equipment which will make it possible for the student to see either transient graphic representations of sound waves or to see the making of perma-

[35] If only a demonstration of the principles involved in graphic representation is sought, the field may be widened by adding to physics, biology, psychology, and engineering laboratories, such other places as radio and television stations, hospitals and clinics (representations of heart sounds via an electric stethoscope, EKG graphs, and basic metabolism

nent pictures or graphs of sound waves with still camera, motion picture camera, electronically, or with a writing stylus tracing an ink or pencil line.

It would be well if the student could have opportunities to work with oscillographic equipment and sound spectrograph equipment or, at least, to see these and other devices demonstrated in the speech and hearing laboratory. In the laboratory, too, it is hoped that high quality microphones, amplifiers, tape recorders, and stereo reproducing equipment will be available for the use of students.

Although we would prefer to concentrate on electrical equipment, we realize from long experience with students that some of them have little or no background knowledge of electricity and circuits. Hence, we shall use as our basic example of recording equipment an air-impinging device that applies the same principles we have been studying in this chapter.

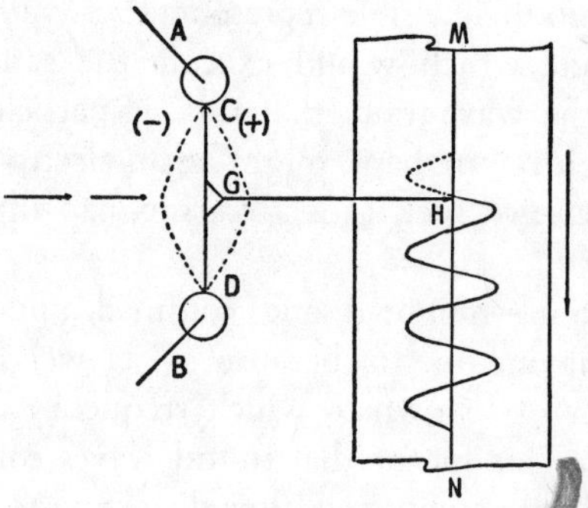

The megaphone shape of the cone *AB* concentrates the sound waves against the diaphragm represented by the solid line extending from *C* to *D*. One end of the writing lever *GH* is fastened to the diaphragm. The other end of the lever is the writing point; it is in light contact with the paper at *H*. If no sound waves strike the diaphragm, the lever point does not move. But, if the paper be moved in the direction indicated by the arrow, a straight line *MN* will be drawn by the writing point. Now if a pure sound wave strikes the diaphragm, the diaphragm moves in the direction of the dotted line (*CD*+) and then rebounds in the opposite direction (dotted line *CD*−). The movement of the writing lever corresponds to that of the diaphragm, and if the paper is moved at uniform rate in the direction of the arrow, a curved line will be drawn on the paper.

FIG. 90. Curve Resulting from Combined Movements of Writing Lever and Paper.

A. Recording Sound Waves by Means of an Air-Impinging System

Fundamentally, the air system of recording provides a means of concentrating sound waves so that they impinge against a diaphragm which actuates, either indirectly or directly, a writing lever. Figures 89 and 90 show a diaphragm in normal position (solid line), bearing indirectly (Fig. 89*B*) or directly (Fig. 90) a writing lever. With mechanical levers, the record may be made on a continuous paper band on a revolving drum which moves past the writing stylus with a constant velocity.

graphs), and such commercial places of business as watch repair and auto repair shops where oscilloscopic observations are made of the sounds of watches or automobile engines. Equipment that utilizes some of the same principles may be found in steam plants, electric utility substations, and many industries having installations of devices for recording temperature or production line variables. Frequently the graphs will be inked lines, often in more than one color.

Sound waves possess momentum; when they strike against a surface, they exert a pressure on it. When a compression wave impinges on the diaphragm, the diaphragm is moved or displaced approximately the distance which air particles in that place would move were the diaphragm not there. (See Fig. 90.) The dotted line, to the right, represents the position taken by the diaphragm during the compression phase of a sound wave. Its movement, of course, brings about a movement of the attached writing lever or, if a diaphragm actuates a mirror, the diaphragm movement swings the reflecting surface through an arc. (See Fig. 91.) The light beam on the mirror is likewise deflected, and at a given distance from the mirror it will make an excursion on the film (or screen if used for demonstration purposes) of any desired amplitude.

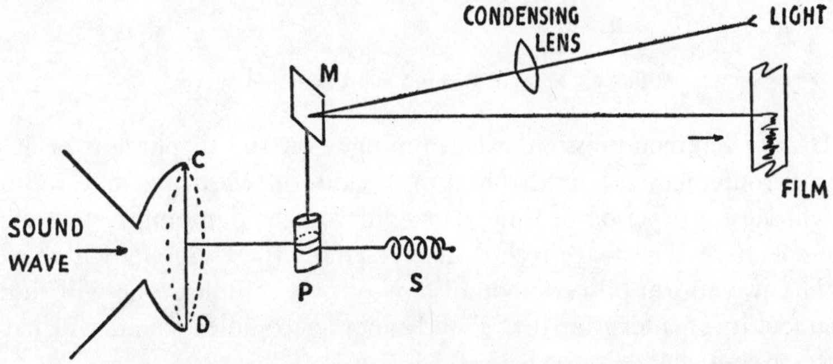

FIG. 91. The Phonodeik.

This is an improved phonautograph, developed by Dayton C. Miller. To the center of a thin glass diaphragm is attached a fine silk or platinum fiber. The fiber passes once around a pulley (*P*) to which is affixed a mirror (*M*), and which ends by being attached to a fine spring (*S*). The spring keeps the fiber and mirror system under tension. A light beam reflected from the mirror on a film is deflected when the diaphragm (*CD*) actuates the mirror.

Immediately following the compression phase is the rarefaction phase of the sound wave. The positive pressure of the condensation phase having expended itself, the diaphragm, because of its elasticity, will tend to return to its normal position, but, like any other elastic body, and like a vibrating air particle, it overshoots the neutral position and goes approximately as far in the negative direction, to the left in the sketch, (—) as it did in the positive direction. (See Fig. 90.) This movement likewise actuates the attached lever. If the stylus were placed on a paper on a stationary drum, the resulting record would be a single line—a straight line or an arc, depending upon the type of tambour. (See Figs. 89*A* and 89*B*.) Now if the drum is rotated, or if the surface upon which the record is to be made moves past the lever, the resultant of these two motions at right angles to each other produces a characteristic graphic wave form. If the sounding body (e.g., a tuning fork) produces a pure tone, the graphic record will be a simple sine wave. This is illustrated in Fig. 88. The up-stroke of the record represents compression; the down-stroke, rarefaction. All the wave crests are identical; all the wave troughs are identical. The area included between the neutral position line (e.g., *B-D-F*) and a crest is equal to that included between the neutral position (zero amplitude) and a trough. The distance between two particles (points) in the same phase is the *wavelength*. For example, one wavelength is represented by *AE, CG, BF,* etc.

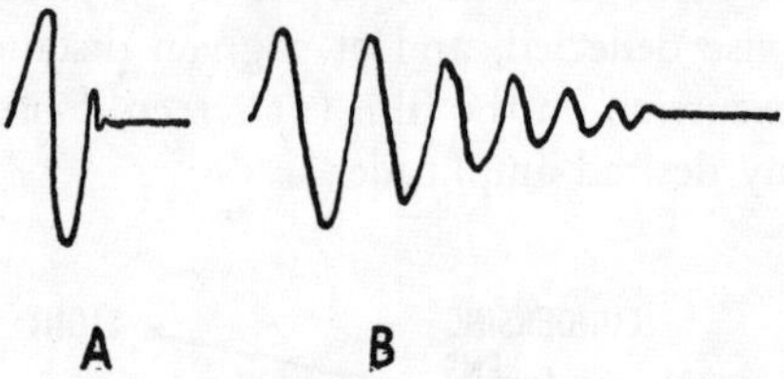

A. Highly damped wave. The oscillations cease almost at once.
B. Intermediately damped wave. The vibrations continue for several cycles.

FIG. 92. Form of Damped and Undamped Waves.

If only one compression wave impinges on the diaphragm or if the sound source ceases, the diaphragm, because of elasticity, may continue to vibrate for a period of time, depending on the damping factors which are operative. The wave record may resemble the forms shown above.

The wave form of a compound tone or of a complex tone will show a characteristic pattern for that sound; another complex sound will have a different but characteristic wave form.

It would seem, therefore, that if sounds have characteristic wave forms we should be able to identify a definite portion of a graphic record as having been made by a given sound. For example, once we know the wave form for the sound [k], it should be a simple matter to find it in any and all records in which it occurs. As a matter of fact, however, because it is generally agreed that no two sounds in speech, except by accident, could ever be identical, if one were presented with a record, and without any other evidence were asked to associate a given wave form with the speech sound which made it, one could only guess. With increased experience the guesses might become highly intelligent and show some degree of accuracy.

The utility of such an electrical device as the sound spectrograph, depends upon making such distinctive visible patterns of speech sounds that instant recognition and complete or almost complete accuracy may be expected of a deaf person trained in the use of the equipment.

B. The Sound Spectrograph

As developed in the Bell Telephone Laboratories during the last quarter of a century or so, the sound spectrograph has grown out of attempts to devise some commercial means of making telephone service available to the deaf by making it possible for them to see the speech they cannot hear. This has given rise to the term *visible speech*.[36]

In simple terms, the BTL equipment consists of a loop of magnetic tape upon which is recorded the speech sample to be analyzed. The length of the loop and the speed of its rotation limit the sample to a duration of 2.4 seconds.[37] It requires 2.5 minutes to complete an analysis.

The tape is played back repeatedly, but each time it is reproduced the variable filter is tuned to pass only a selected band of frequencies. If each band width is but 15 to 50 cycles, for example, a detailed analysis results. If a broader band (e. g., 100, 200, or 300 cycles) is selected, the analysis is not as detailed. However, for some purposes this analysis may be preferable. Also, it speeds up the time required to make an analysis. In the experiments of Potter, Kopp, and Green (1947) the frequencies from 70 ~ to 3500 ~ were analyzed using about two hundred band widths of approximately 15 cycles each.[38]

Each time a speech sound is reproduced from the tape and fed through the variable filter, the output of the filter for the wave band being analyzed actuates a stylus which draws the wave form pattern on a loop of electrically sensitive paper rotating on a drum revolving at exactly the same speed as the loop of magnetic tape. Thus, point for point, in space-time relationships, during each of the hundred or more steps in the analysis, the visible sound spectrogram corresponds to the speech recorded on the loop. Each step in the analysis represents the frequency pattern of the sound component. The intensity of the sound is represented by the relative degree of darkness of the tracing.

THE SYNTHESIS OF SOUND

The analysis of a complex sound can be tested by combining the obtained parts to produce a synthetic sound; if a discriminating ear testifies that the synthetic sound is like the original, the analysis is proved correct. At least as early as Helmholtz such syntheses were made. Since then, numerous experimenters have synthesized speech or music. Today, this field is advancing so rapidly that one cannot keep abreast of it. The sheer number of developments going on, and the fact that so much of the work is classified, either because of commercial expediency or defense secrecy, would prove discouraging. Nevertheless, this same situation exists in

[36] A significant contribution to the field is *Visible Speech* (1947), a book summarizing experimental applications of work with sound spectrographs.

[37] Equipment to handle any length may be designed. Equipment to take longer samples has proved effective.

[38] The pattern, even when the range was extended to 10,000~, was scarcely more informative.

many other fields and is no excuse for the student not to try to read about as many of the new developments as possible.

One soon realizes that in the vast majority of cases, the synthesis of speech or other sounds is done for reasons of practical commercial applicability. Corporations may invest five percent or more of their capital in their research and development programs. Sooner or later such investments must pay dividends in commercially successful products if the company is to remain competitive. In other cases, equipment has been developed as a part of the national defense effort. Almost inevitably, because of the tremendous expenditures involved in reasearch and development, and in manufacturing, only the government, or industry, or both working together, can afford to do much in these areas involving complex communications, guidance, detection, and other defense weaponry systems. Because so much of the research and development in this field has defense implications or competitive corporate potentialities, the result is that there are almost inevitably time lags of varying degrees between the date when the actual research findings are made and the time when public announcement is forthcoming or when the equipment is put on the market.

Some of the journal articles in the *Bibliography* were selected for inclusion for the specific purpose of highlighting the rapid developments in the field of sound analysis and synthesis. We suggest that the student notice the dates of pertinent contributions and that he read a sampling of the articles to see for himself how rapid the pace of research has become.

When the student does consult such materials, and when he learns from his newspapers, magazines, radio, and television about the highly sophisticated and costly communications satellites orbiting the earth, which, together with land-based equipment, can successfully analyze his speech, code it, compress it, transmit it, synthesize it, and relay it to a listening friend a quarter of the distance around the world, he may rightly be amazed and stand in wonder at the black boxes of our scientific age. But, at the same time, he cannot sensibly overlook the fact that while the scientists may know almost everything about their orbiting satellites filled with hardware, out there in space, they still know comparatively little—in some cases, almost nothing—about the normal speech and hearing mechanisms right here on earth; embryology and neurology still remain almost closed books to their inquiring minds.

EXERCISES AND QUESTIONS

1. Statement: Sound waves are refracted if the medium (air) is not homogeneous. For example, in winter, when the ground is snow covered and the temperature is low, sound is refracted toward the earth and carries farther.

(*a*) Is the statement correct? Explain.

2. Make a chart showing the pitch range of human voices, and indicate in each case the wavelength of the sounds.

3. In this chapter we say that "there will be a compression wave flung off by the sounding body in all directions. . . ." Explain then why, if a tuning fork is struck and held before the aperture of the tube of a stethoscope through which you receive the sound, and if it is rotated slowly, there are positions at which no sound is heard. Draw a diagram of the prongs of the fork and show the axes of silence.

4. (*a*) At room temperature, what is the velocity of sound? (*b*) If a sound in a room has a velocity of 1130 feet per second, what is the temperature of the room?

5. The student should look at a simple radio loud-speaker or telephone receiver, observing especially the size of the diaphragm in comparison to the electromagnet. Why is the diaphragm large? Can you illustrate the reason with a vibrating fork held (1) five feet from the ear, and (2) against a table top which is five feet from the ear? Or, is some different principle involved?

6. Obtain a graduated tube about 2 to 4 inches in diameter and from 8 to 24 inches in height. The tube should have a base so that it will stand unsupported. Fill the tube with water to any selected level—e.g., from ⅓ to ⅔ full. Obtain glass tubing about 12 to 30 inches long, about 1 to 2 inches in diameter, and open at both ends. Obtain a tuning fork.

(*a*) Strike the fork and hold it over the graduated tube. Is there any reinforcement due to resonance?

(*b*) Strike the fork and hold it over the upper end of the long tube, immersing the lower end of the tube in the water in the graduated tube. Slowly move the open-ended tube up and down. At what points, if any, is there reinforcement of the fork tone? Explain.

(*c*) If there are several points of reinforcement, make measurements to determine their relationship to each other and to the frequency of the fork. What can you discover about the wavelength of the tone of the fork?

(*d*) Define acoustical resonance.

7. A vocalist has always practiced with an accompanist whose piano is tuned to A = 440 cps. On a concert tour she has to use another accompanist and a piano tuned to A = 435 Hz.

(*a*) How, if at all, will this affect her singing?

(*b*) Will it alter the case if she does or does not have absolute pitch?

8. Statement: The ear cannot distinguish more than about 16 to 20 beats per second.

(*a*) Explain in detail.

(*b*) (After reading the next chapter.) In your opinion, does the length of the basilar membrane or the location of the helicotrema have anything to do with the reasons behind the statement?

9. Based on your knowledge of masking, explain why at a convivial class reunion a semideaf alumnus with a threshold of 55db may be able to hear as well or better than a classmate whose hearing is normal.

10. In high fidelity recording and reproduction of speech and/or music which problem is greater:

(*a*) to reduce (masking) background noise to a minimum?

(*b*) to obtain a maximum of speech (or music) energy?

11. (*a*) When a bass and soprano sing together does one have to sing with greater intensity to overcome the masking effect of the other voice? Explain.

(*b*) Explain how composers of duets usually overcome this conflict of interest.

12. Explain how a violinist may use beats to tune his instrument.

Chapter IX

THE EAR AND HEARING

I. The Anatomy of the Ear
  A. The External Ear
  B. The Middle Ear
  C. The Internal Ear
II. The Nature of Auditory Stimulation
  A. Introductory Statement
  B. Points of View on the Manner of Origins of Auditory Nerve Stimuli
    1. The Physical Point of View
    2. The Chemical Point of View
    3. The Electrical Point of View
      a. Electrophysiology of the Cochlea
  C. Bone Versus Air Conduction in Hearing
III. Theories of Hearing
  A. Introductory Statement
  B. Basic Theories
    1. Displacement Theory
    2. Resonance Theory
    3. Traveling Wave Theory
      a. Eddy Currents
    4. Standing Wave Theory
    5. Telephone Theory
IV. How We Hear—Summary and Surmise
  A. Stage One: The Ear Levels
  B. Stage Two: The Ear and Neuron Levels
  C. Stage Three: The Neurological Levels
    1. Not-This-Not-This-But-This
  D. Stage Four: The Associative-Relational Levels
V. The Neurology of Hearing
VI. Psychology and Physics of Hearing
  A. Characteristics of Sound as Related to Hearing
  B. Duration
    1. The Conscious Present
  C. Determination of the Least Perceptible Change in Pitch

D. Pause
E. Psycho-physical Experiments
VII. Audiometry
Exercises and Questions

THE ANATOMY OF THE EAR

The ear consists of an outer, middle, and inner portion, which are, respectively, the sound-gathering part, the sound-conducting part, and the sound-analyzing and nerve-impulse-originating part.[1]

A. The External Ear

The *external ear,* made up essentially of the auricle and the external acoustic (auditory) meatus, is nothing more or less than a reversed megaphone or funnel for gathering and concentrating sound waves on the tympanic membrane. It is not essential to hearing. The auricle, which projects from the side of the head, represents the large end of the megaphone. The *external acoustic meatus* (meatus acusticus externus), the passage from the auricle to the tympanic membrane, is about 3 cm. long and slightly less than 1 cm. in diameter. It is a tube closed at its inner end by the tympanic membrane.

In the external meatus, hairs and wax-producing glands serve a function of protection against dirt and insects; the wax is known as *cerumen* and when produced in excess may reduce hearing.

Normally, a slight bend in the meatus makes it impossible to see the tympanic membrane without the aid of a *speculum,* the funnel-shaped metal instrument used by otologists. Care should be taken to use a speculum only under competent direction. With its use, and strong illumination, the attachment of the malleus is apparent through the somewhat circular, semitransparent, pearly gray membrane.

The *tympanic membrane* (membrana tympani), a thin cone-shaped semitransparent diaphragm, separates the bottom of the external acoustic meatus from the tympanic cavity of the middle ear.

The eardrum consist of three layers. Békésy notes that the eardrum is about 0.05mm thick in man.[2] Its radial fibers give the eardrum its slightly

[1] As mammals have evolved—i.e. fish adapted to land and air—not all of man's most sensitive organs of perception have made the complete transition; they are still bathed in a fluid having, probably, a chemical composition similar to that of the water of the early seas. Perhaps, evolved from the lateral line organs of fish, the cochlea contains a sea-water-like fluid. This adaptation requires some method of transmitting air vibrations to the cochlear fluid. As a problem of physics, a stretched membrane with a piston centrally attached offers a simple, efficient solution. The different kinds of eardrums among animals indicate that almost any variety will work well enough. Nature, therefore, did not evolve one universal type. Nevertheless, in man the conical shape of the eardrum is about optimal for transmitting air sound pressure to a fluid system of high impedance.

[2] Sometimes, a thickness of 0.1mm may be given.

convex form, causing its conical central portion to protrude into the tympanic cavity. It is along one sector of this cone-apex that the malleus is attached. The conical form of the eardrum assures close coupling between membrane and manubrium. Because of its configuration the eardrum normally acts as a piston, transmitting its pressure changes to the ossicles of the middle ear.

FIG. 93. Cone-shaped Eardrum Showing Slack Edge (*SE*) and Attachment of Malleus.

The natural frequency of the eardrum is well within the speech range, perhaps between 1000 ∼ and 2000 ∼.

Békésy is of the opinion that the eardrum must be readily movable at its peripheral attachments. He points out that, indeed, the cone-shaped

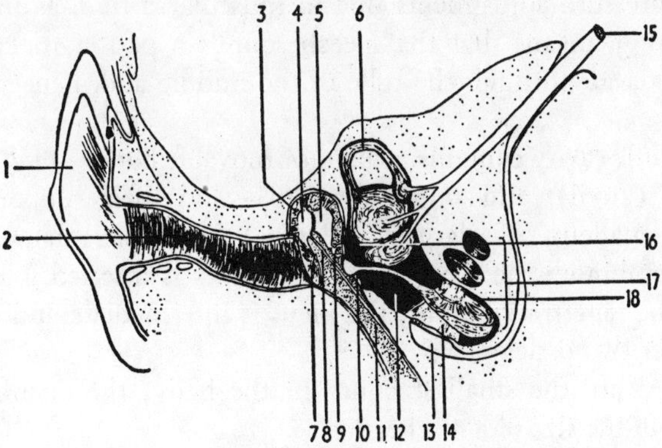

FIG. 94. Diagrammatic Section through Ear.

1. Auricle; 2. external acoustic meatus; 3. tympanic cavity; 4. malleus; 5. incus; 6. semicircular canals; 7. tympanic membrane; 8. tensor tympani muscle; 9. stapes in fenestra vestibuli; 10. fenestra cochleae; 11. Eustachian tube; 12. scala tympani; 13. auditory nerve fibers to cochlea; 14. modiolus at base of cochlea; 15. VIIIth cranial nerve; 16. vestibule; 17. cochlea; 18. scala vestibuli.

eardrum does have a slack edge—as is true of dynamic loudspeaker diaphragms—which may be displaced under pressure without distorting the central area of the membrane.

B. The Middle Ear

The *middle ear* comprises the tympanic cavity, the tympanic antrum, and the auditory tube. We are interested in the *tympanic cavity,* an irregular space within the temporal bone. The cavity is filled with air which is maintained at atmospheric pressure by a connection between the cavity and the external air through the pharyngotympanic (*Eustachian* or auditory) tube.

The volume of the tympanic cavity varies from 1 to 2 cubic centimeters. It is lined with mucous membrane continuous with that of the nasal cavities and with that of the air cells of the mastoid process of the temporal bone. Developmentally, the middle ear (including the auditory tube) is an evagination from the nasopharynx.

The Eustachian tube connects the nasopharynx with the middle ear, providing a means of ventilating the cavity and equalizing its air pressure with that of the outside air.

In diving or in flying, acts requiring equalization of the air in the middle ear, the tube plays a vital role. Were it not for this equalizing effect, high altitude, with less pressure outside the eardrum, would cause the membrane to bulge outward unduly; in diving, the opposite would be true.

The normal closed condition of the Eustachian tube, except when making air-pressure adjustments due to muscular action, as in swallowing or yawning, means that the speech sounds a person makes are not transmitted via air through the tube to the middle and, hence, the inner ear.

The tympanic cavity contains a chain of movable bones—*malleus* (hammer), *incus* (anvil), and *stapes* (stirrup)—and their supporting ligaments. The malleus, the largest (8 mm.) bone, articulates with the tympanic membrane; the footplate of the stapes is inserted into and fills the area of the fenestra vestibuli; the incus is intermediate and articulates with the other two ossicles.

The ossicles are the smallest bones in the body; the opening of the stirrup is about the size of a pin head.

The manner of suspension of the ossicles and the relatively large head of the malleus combine to insure that the center of gravity of the ossicles and the axis of rotation of the axial ligaments are so related that the entire middle-ear mechanism responds easily and precisely to high frequencies. It also provides protection against bone conduction of speech sounds of high intensity.

We are interested in two depressions in the medial (labyrinthine) wall of the tympanic cavity.

(*a*) The fossula fenestrae vestibuli at the bottom of which is the *fenestra* vestibuli (oval window). The window has an area of about 3 sq. mm. and is sealed by a membrane against which is attached the footplate of the stapes.

The seal of the piston at the fluid end is critical; if it is too large pressure will cause it to bulge back like a collar around the piston head. In man, the seal, a narrow annular membrane, is only slightly larger than the footplate and only slightly smaller than the oval window that is sealed. Stretched between the margins of the footplate and the circumference of the window, the membrane seal shows a maximum width of 0.1mm and a minimum width of 0.015mm; it limits the excursion of the footplate to approximately 0.1mm.

Stapedial movements are related to frequency; they decrease proportionately with increases in sound frequencies up to about 2000 ~.

(*b*) The fossula fenestrae cochleae is a deeply recessed bony niche, with steep sloping sides, in the bottom of which is the regular circular *fenestra cochleae* (round window). The window has an area of about 2 sq. mm. and is closed over by the secondary tympanic membrane.

In a prepared skull, the fenestra vestibuli opens into the ***vestibule*** (vestibulum labyrinthi) and the fenestra cochleae opens into the scala tympani of the cochlea.

In the tympanic cavity are found the tensor tympani and the stapedius muscles. Lying in bony canals, only their tendons are actually within the cavity proper.

Each of the muscles of the middle ear is encased throughout its length by a surrounding bony canal. Thus, they can contract and exert pull via their tendons without, at the same time, being out in the air where their mass would be set into vibration and thus contribute subharmonics to the sound wave complex.

Tensor tympani

Origin:	In a bony canal above and paralleling the bony portion of the Eustachian tube is the tensor tympani muscle. It is about 2 cm. in length. Its origin is the cartilaginous portion of the Eustachian tube and the osseous canal in which the muscle lies.
Insertion:	The muscle ends in a tendon which emerges from the canal into the tympanic cavity and bends sharply before being inserted into the manubrium of the malleus.
Innervation:	Mandibular (Vth cranial) nerve.
Action:	Swings handle of malleus inward medially; thus increases tension on and tightens the tympanic membrane.

Stapedius

Origin: Interior of pyramidal eminence. It is the smallest muscle in the body.

Insertion: This muscle ends in a tendon which is inserted into the neck of the stapes.

Innervation: Facial (VIIth cranial) nerve.

Action: Draws base of stapes outward.

The exact functions of the stapedius and tensor tympani muscles are not understood. Some authorities believe that the muscles are antagonists —one serving to force the footplate of the stapes further into the fenestra vestibuli while the other acts to withdraw the footplate. This antagonistic action would permit a regulation of the extent of the thrust of the stapes into the fenestra vestibuli and consequently the regulation of the degree of pressure to be transmitted to the liquor perioticus and finally to the liquor oticus and the structures bathed by this liquid. Because muscle actions in the body are so almost universally antagonistic, this concept appears logical.

Other authorities believe that both muscles function protectively to prevent the inner ear from being assaulted by the impingement of too loud sounds on the eardrum. The louder the sound, the greater is the degree of contraction. Thus, for ordinary sounds the stapedius contracts reflexly to act as a dampener and thus protect the labyrinth from damage; for loud sounds the tensor tympani also functions, reflexly, to further guard the labyrinth from damage.[3]

The tensor tympani and stapedius muscles act with considerable friction upon the middle ear mechanisms; these frictional forces are the main contributing factors acting to control the movements of the ossicles for sounds of the middle range of frequencies.

The combined middle ear mechanisms, plus the inherent loading of the cochlear fluid, add up to a highly damped vibratory system having a natural frequency of approximately 1400 cycles (800 ~ to 1500 ~). The student will recognize the central position 1400 ~ bears to the range of significant speech frequencies, 500 ~ to 2000 ~.

[3] Békésy is of the opinion that ordinarily the muscles of the middle ear play only a minor role in protecting the middle ear against excessive sounds. Instead, he believes that the complex ossicular mechanism itself provides the major protection. The provisions that the ossicles rotate on their axes, and that the vibratory axis of the stapes differs by 20 to 35 degrees from the plane of axes of the other two bones seem to be the effective mechanisms. When the amplitude of movement of the eardrum increases above a certain limit the stapes rotates on its axis (it is fastened by looser ligamental fibers at its posterior than at its anterior margins) so that less pressure is transmitted by the footplate to the fluid in the inner ear. There are significant changes in the operation of the mechanism for different frequency ranges to protect the ear in emergencies. The mechanism is especially effective below 50cps, offering protection from very low frequencies, e.g., in windstorms or in cases of thunder.

Because the density of the cochlear fluid is much greater than that of air, and since the surface of the eardrum is notably greater than that of the footplate of the stapes, the middle ear provides a mechanism for increasing the pressure (in dynes/cm^2) on the footplate significantly. It is estimated that approximately 55mm^2 of the 85mm^2 of the tympanic membrane produce the stiff piston action on the manubrium. 3.2mm^2 represents the approximate area of the stapes footplate. The leverage gain of the ossicles is of a ratio of 1.3 to 1. Combining advantages, therefore, there is an increase in pressure value of 22 times between the tympanic membrane and the footplate.[4]

The sketch is not to scale. However, some dimensions will be helpful. From the center of the footplate to the center of the round window is approximately 4mm. From the oval window to its extremity the basilar membrane is about 30mm long. The footplate has an area of about 3 square mm. The malleus (largest of the ossicles) is 8mm long. The external auditory meatus has a diameter of about 10mm. The tympanic cavity has a volume of 1 or 2 cubic cm. The vestibule measures about 5mm x 5mm x 3mm. The cross-sectional area of each scala is about 1.2 square mm.

Not indicated is the rich blood supply of the cochlea. Blood vessels have a symmetrical distribution on either side of the basilar membrane.

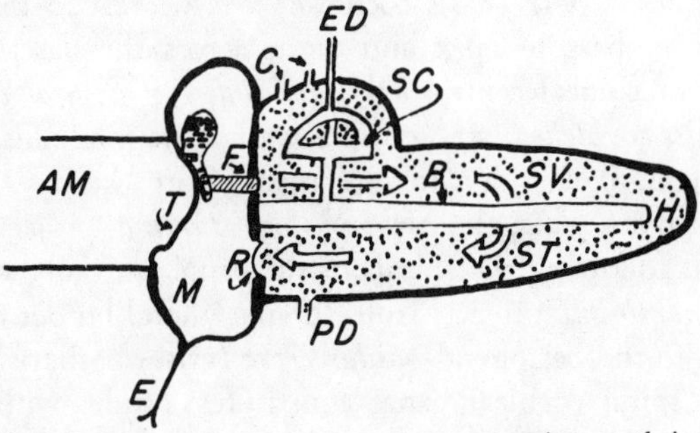

AM External auditory meatus
T Eardrum, showing slack edge
E Eustachian tube (closed)
M Middle ear cavity
F Footplate of stapes and oval window
R Round window
PD Perilymphatic duct
C Capillaries (may give under pressure, or may impart their own pulsations to the fluid)
ED Endolymphatic duct
SC Semicircular canals
SV Scala vestibuli
ST Scala tympani
B Basilar membrane
H Helicotrema

Arrows indicate course of pressure transmission

FIG. 95. Schema Showing Relations of Outer, Middle, and Inner Ear.

C. The Internal Ear

The *internal ear,* the essential organ of hearing, contains the terminations of the nerve fibers of the auditory (acoustic; cochlear) nerve, a part of the VIIIth cranial nerve. Such is the complexity of the internal ear that it was early given the name of labyrinth. There are two parts: the bony labyrinth, a complex series of connected cavities located within the

[4] This represents a gain of about 26db.

petrous portion of the temporal bone, and the membranous labyrinth, a complex system of connecting sacs and ducts contained within the bony labyrinth.

(*a*) The *bony labyrinth* (labyrinthus osseus; periotic labyrinth) is made up of three divisions: the vestibule, the semicircular canals, and the cochlea. We are interested, primarily, in the latter. We mention, however, that in the lateral wall of the vestibule is located the fenestra vestibuli, while the semicircular canals contain the semicircular ducts.

The *vestibule*[5] is a common meeting place for the fluid of the cochlea and of the semicircular canals (through five orifices). In the vestibule are the utricle and saccule. In the bony lateral or tympanic wall of the vestibule is the oval window, normally closed by the base of the stapes and annular ligament. Ovoid in shape, the vestibule has a volume of about 75mm^3; its dimensions are: 5mm from front to back, 5mm from top to bottom, and about 3mm wide.

The bony *cochlea* bears some resemblance to a snail shell, hence its name. Its *apex* (cupola) is directed upward and outward (anteriorly and laterally), while its *base* (basis cochleae) lies nearest to the middle ear. It is 5mm from base to apex and 9mm across the base. It contains a cochlear axis or conical central axis (*modiolus*); a *spiral cochlear canal* (canalis *spiralis cochleae*), whose inner wall is the modiolus, about which it winds in helix-like fashion for 2¾ turns, from the base to the helicotrema; a thin bony plate, the *osseous spiral lamina,* projecting from the modiolus, and following the spirals of the canal, partially subdividing it. The *basilar membrane* projects from the peripheral border of the osseous spiral lamina to the peripheral *basilar crest* (crista basilaris) of the bony cochlea. The spiral cochlear canal constitutes a tube with a length of approximately 30mm. The osseous spiral lamina and the basilar membrane, aided by the cochlear duct which will be described later, serve to divide the spiral cochlear canal into an upper and lower passage, the *scala vestibuli* and the *scala tympani,* respectively. These scalae are continuous through the helicotrema at the apex of the cochlea. The scala vestibuli is open to the vestibule; the scala tympani would be open to the tympanic cavity through the fenestrae cochleae if it were not for the secondary tympanic membrane which seals that window.

Each scala has a cross-sectional area of approximately 1.2mm^2, except that at the round window it is 0.6mm^2 and at the helicotrema it is 0.4mm^2. (Some writers assign a diameter of about 2mm to the scalae throughout their length.)

[5] In spite of the experimental evidence localizing the hearing function in the cochlear mechanism, we are not convinced that the vestibular mechanism may be ruled out of consideration entirely in a study of hearing; anatomically and physiologically it has the proper attributes for playing some role in analyzing what we like to think of as the tri-dimensional-quality aspects of sound.

It has been calculated that the perilymph moving through the scalae —2 x 30mm—would encounter about the same resistance as if it were moving through a capillary tube of that same length and having an inside diameter of about 0.6mm.

The total length of the column of perilymph from oval window to round window (estimating the length of the basilar membrance as 30mm and the distance from the end of the membrane in one scala through the helicotrema and back to the end of the membrane in the other scala as from 5 to 7mm) is approximately 65mm. Only in the case of frequencies below the audible range (e.g., 16 cycles) would pressure patterns be transmitted this full distance through the fluid.

1. THE BASILAR MEMBRANE

The *basilar membrane,*[6] stretching from the osseous spiral lamina to the basilar crest, is of particular importance in most theories of hearing, supporting, as it does, the spiral organ of Corti. According to some observers, the transverse fibers which constitute the membrane are under tension; this tension is greater in that portion of the basilar membrane at the base of the spiral and less in that portion at the apex. Other authorities, however, doubt that there are differences in tension or that if they exist they are important in hearing.

Indeed, anatomically, the basilar membrane shows similar elastic properties in the longitudinal and transverse directions. This independence is due to its structure: a layer of radial or transverse fibers plus an underlying layer (the tympanic lamella) of longitudinal fibers at right angles. It may be characterized as a gelatinous ribbon (or a gelatinous, unstressed, elastic plate) supporting a thin, homogeneous layer of fibers. Its elasticity (not the same as tension) is a direct function of locus, increasing proportionately from the stapes toward the helicotrema; from the one end to the other the increase is on the order of one hundred times.

The basilar membrane forms the roof of the scala tympani. Some idea of the minuteness of the inner ear may be obtained from realizing that the basilar membrane is only about 30mm long; it is widest at the end nearest the *helicotrema*[7] (approximately 0.5mm) and becomes progressively narrower until it reaches the end nearest the stapes (0.25mm to 0.1mm).

[6] In evolutionary development the basilar membrane in mammals has become greatly lengthened and, also, coiled. (There has been little or no change in size or shape of the vestibular organ.) Compare, for example, the ears of turtles, birds, and mammals. In the coiled organ of Corti the bony modiolus gives better protection for the nerve and blood supply. Whether there is a purpose for the coiling (the guinea pig has 4 coils to man's 2¾ turns) and whether it improves hearing are unanswered questions. It is believed that there are advantages to the movements of the tectorial membrane in a curved rather than a straight tube, but the significance of this depends, in part, upon how important a part the tectorial membrane plays in the inner ear mechanism.

[7] The helicotrema in man has a diameter of 0.5mm to 0.8mm.

Except for individual differences, which would have to be taken into account in any case, the student might think that scientists could agree upon an answer to the question: How long is the basilar membrane? However, consider here a matter of interpretation: What do we mean by basilar membrane? Inasmuch as we are interested in the membrane only as it pertains to hearing, are we interested in a length of the membrane on which there rests no organ of Corti? And, by organ of Corti, do we include the tectorial membrane? Or is the tectorial membrane essential for hearing? In either case, there is a section of the basilar membrane on which there is a portion of the organ of Corti but above which there is no tectorial membrane.

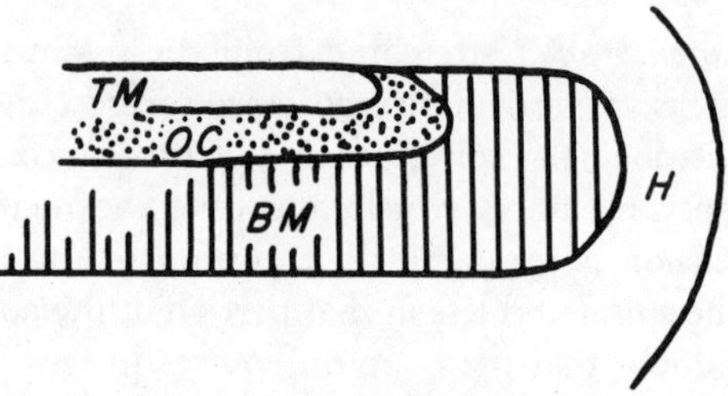

FIG. 96. Structure of Inner Ear Near Helicotrema.

Schema (not to scale) showing that near the Helicotrema (*H*) the Tectorial Membrane (*TM*) is shorter than the organ of Corti (*OC*) which, in turn, is shorter than the Basilar Membrane (*BM*).

Entering the base of the modiolus is the *auditory nerve* whose fibers ascend with the coils of the bony axis, pierce the bony matrix, to be given off all along the turns of the spiral so that their sensitive receptive end organs lie in intimate relation to the numerous cells composing the organ of Corti.

Within the bony labyrinth and separated from it except at certain points is the membranous labyrinth. The space separating the two labyrinths is known as the *periotic* (perilymphatic) *space* and is filled with *liquor perioticus* (perilymypth). This means that the scala vestibuli and the scala tympani, described previously, are filled with liquor perioticus, as are the vestibule and semicircular canals.

(*b*) The *membranous labyrinth* (labyrinthus membraneus; otic labyrinth) is made up of communicating sacs and ducts contained within, and having a shape similar to, the bony labyrinth. They include the three semicircular ducts, saccule and utricle, and the cochlear duct—the latter connected to the others by the ductus reuniens. We are interested, primarily, in the cochlear duct, which, together with the remainder of the membranous labyrinth, forms a closed system filled with *liquor oticus* (endolymph). Some persons interested in the evolution of man from a life in the sea to life on land have suggested that the saline liquids in the ear have the chemical constitution of the ancient seas—a chemistry not identical with that of the modern oceans.

The *cochlear duct* (ductus cochlearis) is the part of the membranous labyrinth within which are located the sensory cells related to hearing. It is a spiral tube lying within the bony spiral canal of the cochlea. In transverse section it is triangular in shape. The floor of the cochlear duct is the basilar membrane, a portion of the periosteum of the outer wall of the cochlear canal, and a part of the osseous spiral lamina. The peripheral wall of the duct is the outer wall of the cochlear canal. The third wall of the duct of the cochlea is made up of the delicate *vestibular membrane* (Reissner's membrane), extending diagonally at about an angle of 45° with the basilar membrane, from the osseous spiral lamina to the outer cochlear wall. It is about 0.0025 mm. thick. The cochlear duct ends as a blind pouch near the helicotrema; its other or basal extremity becomes the ductus reuniens.

The term *cochlear partition* [8] is sometimes used to refer to the total structure which partitions off the tube-like cavity of the cochlea into the two scalae.

The Organ of Corti [9]

In hearing, we are greatly interested in the specialized cells lying on the floor of the cochlear duct; specifically, our interest is in the *spiral organ of Corti* (organon spirale). This aggregation of cells on the basilar membrane is bathed by endolymph, i. e., liquor oticus.

Many different types of epithelial cells make up the spiral organ of Corti. The inner and outer hair cells are closely related to the terminations of the fibers of the auditory nerve. From each hair cell project 12 to 20 cilia into the otic fluid. There are approximately 5000 *inner hair cells* and 12,000 *outer hair cells,* although estimates of as low as 3000 inner,

[8] It consists of the triangular cochlear duct closed above by Reissner's membrane and bounded below by the spiral ligament, the basilar membrane, and the petrous portion of the partition—made up of a bony ledge on the edge toward the axis of the cochlea. (Sometimes in the literature, one gets the impression that the term is being used to refer only to the basilar membrane and the structures it supports.) Man, as well as cows, elephants, mice, and pigeons (to mention only a few of the animals tested) possesses cochlear partitions that are 100 times stiffer near the stapes than near the helicotrema. The difference is partly due to the varying proportions of petrous partition and/or basilar membrane, as well as to the fact that the basilar membrane probably alters its elastic characterisics as its dimensions change.

We must not overlook the fact that a thin, petrous projection of the partition, continuous with the membrane, may have as definite a pattern of vibration as the basilar membrane although it certainly does not vibrate as readily as the basilar membrane. Indeed, the difference would perhaps be only in the degree of amplitude of vibrations.

[9] The organ of Corti is a physically complex structure because its architecture is asymmetrical.

and as high as 20,000 outer hair cells have been given. The outer hair cells are about two-thirds as large as the inner hair cells.

Apparently, man has only one row of inner hair cells (all large) around the modiolus, and three rows of outer hair cells. However, the latter number seems not to be as definite as the former.

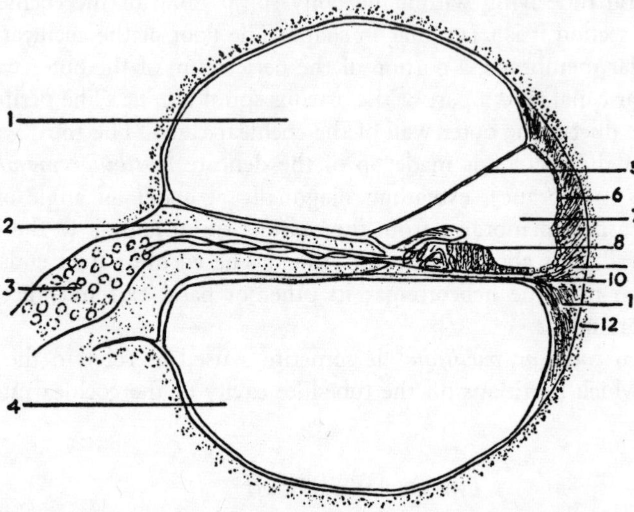

FIG. 97. Section Through Single Spiral of the Cochlear Canal Showing Ductus Cochlearis.

1. Scala vestibuli; 2. osseous spiral lamina; 3. spiral ganglion and fibers of auditory nerve; 4. scala tympani; 5. vestibular membrane; 6. cells of Chambaugh; 7. ductus cochlearis filled with liquor oticus; 8. spiral organ of Corti and overhanging tectorial membrane; 9. sulcus spiralis externus; 10. basilar crest; 11. spiral ligament of cochlea; 12. bony matrix (stippling).

The *reticular membrane,* a stiff covering extension that acts like a net mechanically, has somewhat the appearance of a cantilevered roof plate overhanging the rods of Corti to which it is structurally united; the foot plates of the rods, in turn, are imbedded firmly in the basilar membrane.

One might almost picture the hair cells as fruit hanging from the limb of the reticular membrane.

There are approximately 6000 *outer rods* and 4000 *inner rods* of Corti. The inner and outer rods near the helicotrema are from 1½ to 2 times as long as the rods near the fenestra cochleae.

Early investigators attempted to associate the number of hair cells or the number of rods, or both, or some combination of them, with the possible tones of different pitches that could be heard. Also, the size of the various cells was thought to be a clue to the range of hearing. Again, the width of the rows of cells at various points along the basilar membrane was thought to be of significance. The cross section of the *tunnel of Corti* becomes larger as one proceeds from the region of the fenestra cochleae to the helicotrema. Once one gets the idea that the number or arrangement of the cells in the spiral organ of Corti is determinant of the range of hearing, it is easy to see how hypotheses will spring up.

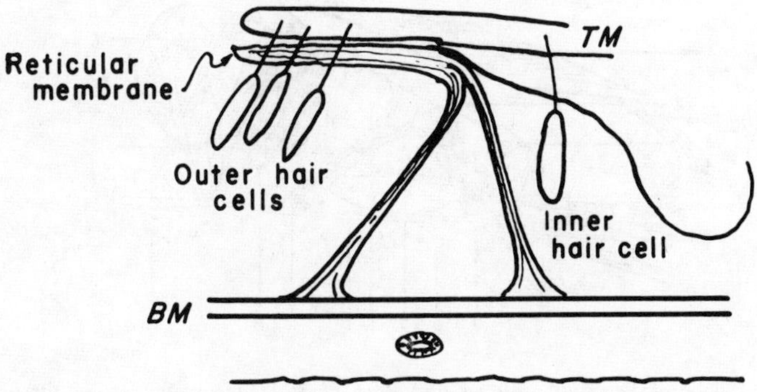

FIG. 98. Enlarged Section of Organ of Corti Showing Reticular Membrane.

Schema showing cantilevered reticular membrane supported by the pillars of Corti resting on the basilar membrane. Apparently suspended from the reticular membrane are the hair cells. The tectorial membrane is superior to the reticular membrane.

Overhanging the spiral organ of Corti is the *tectorial membrane.* Although not all the anatomical details are understood, it is believed that the tectorial membrane, normally, is attached to the superior aspect of the reticular membrane. Or, it may be only that the cilia of the hair cells project through the reticular membrane into the tectorial membrane, providing whatever attachment binds the two membranes together. These same authorities believe that only because of damage by tearing during the preparation of histological sections has the tectorial membrane so often appeared to be free of attachment.

Anatomically, the tectorial membrane is essentially a flat, delicate membranous structure difficult to demonstrate histologically. Actually, it may be a thin-walled tubal protrusion filled with fluid.[10]

The tectorial membrane, Reissner's membrane, and the basilar membrane apparently show displacement in phase when they vibrate. Certainly the tectorial membrane is so tenuous that it must vibrate, if anything does. Later we shall consider what part, if any, the vibrations

[10] When Nature finds a structure effective she utilizes it many times. In this respect it may be instructive to think about the tubes within tubes that combine to make up the cochlea: the initial tube divided into two tubes, the scalae; the cochlear duct dividing the scalae; and, within the cochlear duct, such areas as the tunnel of Corti, the space of Nuel and now, perhaps, the tectorial membrane.

of one or more of these membranes may play in somehow stimulating the hair cells or in other ways originating stimuli in auditory nerve fibers.

In Fig. 99 we represent only one or two of the unmyelinated auditory nerve fibers crossing through the tunnel of Corti en route to termini in or among the outer hair cells. Other dendritic ends of fibers (not shown)

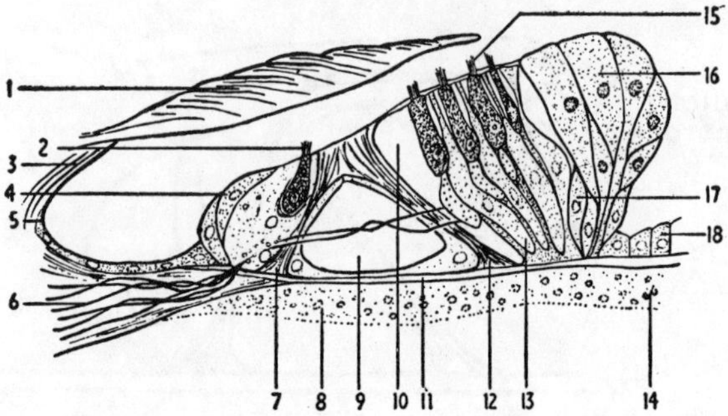

FIG. 99. Floor of Ductus Cochlearis and Roof of Scala Tympani. Section through Spiral Organ of Corti. (After Retzuis.)

1. Tectorial membrane; 2. inner hair cell; 3. vestibular lip; 4. border cells; 5. inner spiral sulcus; 6. auditory nerve fibers emerging from modiolus; 7. inner rod of Corti; 8. zona arcuata; 9. tunnel of Corti; 10. space of Nuel; 11. basilar membrane; 12. outer rod of Corti; 13. cells of Dieters; 14. zona pectinata; 15. outer hair cells; 16. cells of Hensen; 17. cells of Boettcher; 18. cells of Claudius. In terms of our present knowledge, the tectorial membrane would be represented as hanging lower, actually attached to the reticular membrane and/or the cilia of the hair cells.

relate to the inner hair cells and, no doubt, to other cells, tissues or structures of the organ of Corti. With such a rich network of afferent nerve endings supplying the organ of Corti it is easy to understand that anatomically, at least, they are in strategic positions to receive stimuli from their immediate environment.

Most research on the ear, except for a vast fund of clinical investigation, has had to be conducted using lower animals. However, excellent work on the human inner ear has been based on anatomical and histological study of that structure after death.[11] The minuteness of the ear and its relative inaccessibility makes it difficult to obtain data on the normally functioning organ. Therefore, knowledge about it has been slow in accumulating, and there remain many unanswered questions.

THE NATURE OF AUDITORY STIMULATION

A. Introductory Statement

The senses of hearing and touch seem to be related genetically and physiologically. Movements of mass stimulate both. They may be simul-

[11] One may date the modern study of the anatomy and physiology of the ear with G. Breschet (1833).

taneously stimulated, particularly in the range between 50 and 1500 cycles. This may be demonstrated with a tuning fork and resonator. Listen to the fork vibrating in the resonator. Now touch the resonator and feel the vibrations. Probably the inner ear has evolved from a primitive form of tactile organ.

Primitively, then, hearing was probably only a feeling of vibrations. In fish, the lateral line system is some such hearing mechanism by which some vibrations are interpreted as indicative of danger or of conditions beneficial to the animal. As land animals evolved, the ear was developed to detect vibrations of from 30 d.v./sec. to 30,000 d.v./sec. in the medium of air. Such sound waves have wavelengths of from 13 mm. to 12,280 mm.[12]

Somewhat like the question of whether the chicken or the egg was first is that of whether hearing must have preceded the purposive use of sounds. For an animal, the correct interpretation of sounds means life, for itself and the species. Mating calls, sounds indicating the presence of enemies, food, or friends—such sounds are of paramount importance. For human beings it is almost certain that hearing is a precondition of speech. There is no psychological significance in unheard sounds.

In studying hearing, we cannot avoid acknowledging that a composite of related mechanisms is involved. Unfortunately, authorities in the field are not nearly as well informed in some aspects of hearing as they are in others; indeed, in some cases information is almost nonexistent. For example, our knowledge of what goes on within the central nervous system, especially at the cerebral level, is meager. Nevertheless, in addition to what we have already learned about the potential contributions to hearing of the external, middle, and inner ears, we shall now look more specifically at the internal ear, the auditory (VIIIth cranial) nerve, and the auditory cortex. Destruction of the middle ear results in conduction deafness, but not loss of hearing. Partial or complete destruction of certain portions of the internal ear leads to diminution or total loss of hearing. We may eliminate the auditory nerve from the discussion because it serves only to connect the inner ear and the cerebral cortex and is probably similar in all respects to any other nerve.

Hearing, the analysis of sounds and perhaps, to some extent, the interpretation of sounds, are carried on either in the internal ear, in the cerebral cortex, or in both. Most theories of hearing attempt to fix the responsibility of analysis on the internal ear.

The purpose of any such analysis is to translate the sound waves received into properly coded neural impulses in the afferent fibers of the auditory nerve.

Before we consider the several theories of analysis it will help to under-

[12] Bats are known to utilize higher frequencies (50,000~ to 75,000~) and may have expanded their audible spectrum to 100,000~ or 150,000~ for beep homing systems.

stand the manner in which auditory nerve fibers may be stimulated by physical, chemical, and electrical excitation. Excitation may result from direct or indirect causes.

B. Points of View on the Manner of Origins of Auditory Nerve Stimuli

Cells *A* and *B* are two adjacent cells among many located in the organ of Corti on the basilar membrane; they are in a fluid environment of endolymph. They are shown magnified many times their actual size. They may be considered to be cells of any type (e.g., hair cells, cells of Hensen, etc.) because the principle demonstrated is the same. Or, if considered to be even much more highly magnified, they may be thought of as cross-sectional views through one or two dendrites or afferent nerve fiber endings of one of the ramifying nerve fibers of the auditory nerve.

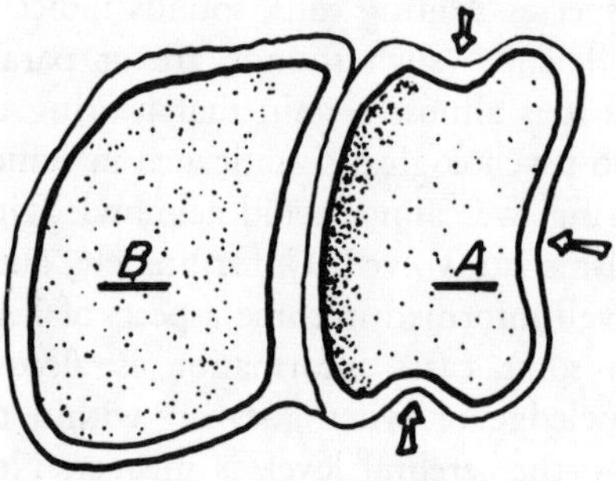

Fig. 100. Schema Illustrating Some Possible Results of Deformations of Cells of the Organ of Corti.

Each cell is surrounded by a semipermeable membrane wall. The chemical composition of the cell is not completely known or understood. Presumably, the exact composition of the contents of a cell may vary depending upon the state of its metabolic activity at the moment.

Due to the vibratory (displacement) movements of the basilar membrane upon which the cells rest, the cell walls are deformed every time the membrane movement bears a certain relationship to the cells, the degree of deformation depending upon the type of movement and the location of the cells in respect to that movement. In some cases there may be no deformation. The wall of a given cell may be forced in from one side or another depending upon the location of the cell in relation to the membrane and to the movement of the membrane at that instant. (The cell is tridimensional and pressure may be from any angle: up, down, top, bottom, right, left, front, back, etc. Furthermore, during a complete vibratory cycle, with the membrane moving from a full positive to a full negative phase relationship, and through all the intermediate positions, the cell wall may also be displaced through a corresponding series of phase relationships.

The hollow arrows represent the gradients of pressure producing some of the possible deformations of the cell wall.

To give the student some idea of the actual magnitude of the vibrations of the basilar membrane some experimental evidence may be noted: an intense tone (between 300 ~ and 1500 ~) whose sound pressure is so great (3×10^3dyne/cm^2) as to be at the pain threshold, produces vibrations of the basilar membrane, whose amplitude is only 3×10^{-3}mm. In other cases, even when magnified 140 times by a microscope the amplitude of vibration approximated only 0.4mm. Even such minute displacements, however, take on their proper significance when compared with the microscopic size of the cells on the basilar membrane.

1. THE PHYSICAL POINT OF VIEW

From a physical point of view any pressure upon cell *A* may, itself, be the force that set off a nerve impulse. If *A* represents the cross section of a nerve fiber the action may be direct and instantaneous. If *A* and *B* represent hair cells or some other type of cells, the pressure on them may, in turn, be passed along to an adjacent nerve fiber which would be stimulated. For example, a dendrite of a nerve fiber might be lodged between cells *A* and *B* or in some such relation to the cells that their physical movements (pinch, pull, stretch, compress, bend, etc.) would excite the fiber and produce a nerve impulse.[13]

2. THE CHEMICAL POINT OF VIEW

The lack of stippling along the right side of cell *B* represents the fluid that has been forced into the cell through its wall from the wall of cell *A;* the heavier stippling at the left of cell *A* represents a concentration of certain chemicals of cell *A* that remain due to the loss of fluid resulting from the pressure on the cell. The semipermeability of the walls prevents some chemicals in the fluid from passing through; the process is selective.[14] Across the walls there is represented a difference in chemical concentration and, hence, of chemical potential. Some of the external pressure upon cell *A* is transmitted to cell *B,* but an increase in osmotic pressure and the inherent forces of elasticity of the cells quickly tend to balance the pressure gradients.

[13] Based on *anatomical evidence* alone, we might conclude that physical deformations of the cells (or tissues made up of cells or cell products) of the organ of Corti produce the excitations in the auditory nerve fibers.

[14] If we assume that the walls of all nerve cells are alike, they have identical characteristics of semipermeability on all sides. An increase in concentration at one place produces the same excitation no matter whether produced by positive or negative action.

The differences in chemical concentration on the two sides of the membranes may be the trigger that excites a single nerve impulse (all or none) or determines the magnitude of excitation—i. e., whether one, two, or more nerve fibers are stimulated.

Another hypothesis explains the stimulation of the nerve fibers as a result of the liberation of some chemical mediator (*acetylcholine* has been suggested), the release of the chemical being due to the mechanical pressure on the cell.

3. THE ELECTRICAL POINT OF VIEW

Assuming that cell *A* has a stored pool of electrical potential (and is bathed in endolymph which constitutes a larger pool of electrical energy to which the cell may contribute energy and/or from which it may take energy), the deformation of the cell wall due to external pressure and/or the alteration in chemical composition of the cell contents could trigger off a release of electrical energy that would, itself, result in the origination of a nerve impulse in one or more fibers.

a. Electrophysiology of the Cochlea

Living cells and tissues display electrical potentials.[15] Cells are biological batteries; they produce constant supplies of electrical energy which

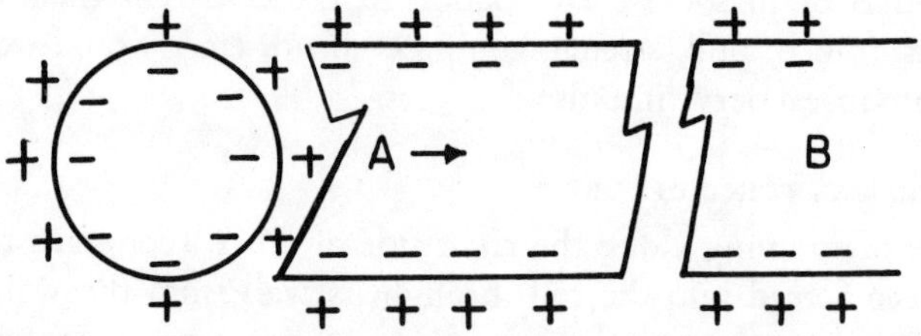

FIG. 101. Schematic Cross Section of Nerve Fiber.

Schema showing positive electrical charges outside cell wall and negative inside. The same sketch may represent the cross section of a nerve fiber. Part of such a nerve is represented between *A* and *B*. As a nerve impulse travels (arrow) along the fiber the electrical phenomena present involve changes in potential moving progressively with the stimulus. It is a fine question whether the electrical phenomena constitute the stimulus wave or are a manifestation of it.

may be stored or which may be utilized when differences of potential occur.

As with the rest of the body, the cochlea represents a dynamic metabolic system displaying creation and building up in some parts and decay

[15] Their origins are incompletely understood. They may originate as a result of the transformation of mechanical energy, inherent metabolic forces, differences in chemical composition and interactions of the contents of the cells, interrelationships of cell membranes, terrestrial and/or cosmic electromagnetic fields, and other factors.

and destruction in others. With such a physiological system, featuring dynamic equilibria, any stimulus alters many or all of the patterns of equilibrium.

The equilibrium of a cell may be altered directly by pressure changes and such pressures may produce a *piezoelectric effect.*

If a quartz crystal is put under pressure, a measurable electric potential-difference may be observed at its surface edges. If the pressure is released and traction (pull opposite to direction in which pressure was applied) applied there will be a reversal of the polarity of the potential-difference. This is called the *piezoelectric effect.* This phenomenon is applicable not only to crystalline structure but to others to which pressure may be applied.

Movements of the basilar membrane probably produce pushes and pulls, or pressure and traction, on the hair cells (or some other cells) of the spiral organ of Corti. If so, reason some observers, a piezoelectric effect will be produced. The internal ear mechanism may then be considered to act as a transducer—that is, it changes the mechanical energy of the sound wave directly to electrical energy.

Presumably, the piezoelectric distortion potentials are originated when there is an up-bulging of the basilar membrane. This occurs when there is an outward movement of the base of the stapes. The up-bulging compresses the hair cells and so alters their polarity. According to this hypothesis the piezo potentials may stimulate the nerve fiber terminations of the auditory nerve, or the stimulation may be due directly to the same mechanical pressure which produces the piezo effect.

Studies are continuing to reveal the electroanatomy [16] of the cochlea so that the complete electrical situation may become known, in addition to the histological-anatomical picture of the region.

There exists in the cochlea, even in the absence of sound stimuli, a constant flow of current producing potential differences (resting potentials).[17] The dc potentials in the perilymph of the scala vestibuli are all positive and generally larger [18] (of the order of $+2mv$) than those of the scala tympani, where near the round window, and for nearly half the length of the basilar membrane, the potentials may be negative (as little as $-1\ mv$).[19]

It seems true that the endolymph is electrically insulated from the perilymph by Reissner's membrane and the basilar membrane,[20] and that

[16] The electrical geometry of the inner ear involves relationships of voltage, resistance, and capacitance patterns in the cochlea.

[17] If there is a constant production of positive potential within the cochlear partition there must also be a continuous consumption of electrical energy in the cochlea.

[18] Although the basilar membrane and Reissner's membrane are said to be equal as insulators of the endolymph, may it be that the thinner Reissner's membrane accounts for the larger potential in the scala vestibuli?

[19] mv = millivolt

[20] Either or both may insulate the organ of Corti chemically, as well as electrically.

in spite of their great differences in structure, as insulators the membranes are apparently equal. This means, then, that the entire organ of Corti and its surrounding endolymph are enclosed within an insulating layer.

First order microphonics originate inside the cochlear partition.

Experiments seem to show that the microphonic voltages in the organ of Corti are proportional to the degree of displacement of the basilar membrane and not to the velocity of its vibrational displacements.

Microphonics may be produced as a result of shearing forces and displacements of the basilar membrane; these affect the cells and tissues adjacent to the membrane.

Some experimenters have surmised that the electrical energy must be due to the transformation of mechanical energy transmitted to the basilar membrane in the form of vibrations. However, studies have not verified the theory that energy in the cochlea is so transformed. But the vibrations may serve to trigger off the mechanism by which an energy pool is tapped. The energy pool appears to be the endolymph with its direct potential of 80mv. If the electrical energy is present and stored in cells, tissues, and/or fluid, it only need be released to become an effective stimulus.

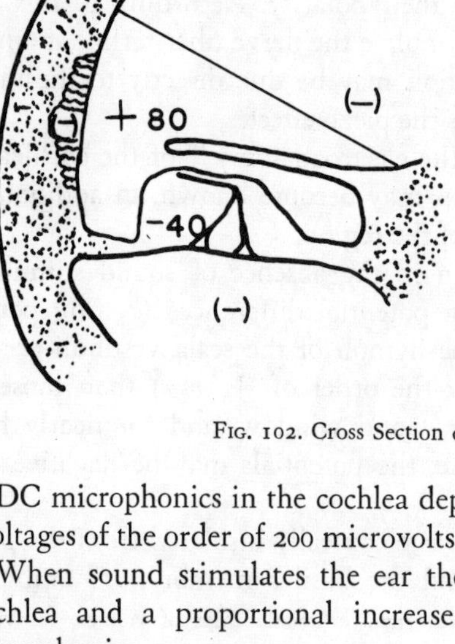

Schema representing cross section of cochlear partition, showing perilymph (negative), endolymph (positive dc potential in mv), and cells (negative).

FIG. 102. Cross Section of Cochlear Partition.

DC microphonics in the cochlea depend upon a reserve pool of energy. Voltages of the order of 200 microvolts (200μv) are found.

When sound stimulates the ear there is a dc fall in potential in the cochlea and a proportional increase (except at high frequencies) in microphonics.

The student should recognize that although we have a substantial background of information about the cochlea, often we do not know whether what we have observed is the cause of something happening or whether it is the resultant by-product of something happening.

With new information and more accurate data coming from the experimental laboratories every month, we are making steady progress in building up our knowledge of the ear and hearing. However, we must never forget the major contributions made by those authorities who pioneered in the field—men who, without the advantages of modern-day sophisticated electronic and optical equipment, nevertheless demonstrated their ability to think clearly and to arrive at the hypotheses, theories, and principles that created the foundation upon which we are still building.

C. Bone Versus Air Conduction in Hearing

At this point we may differentiate two methods of hearing. We hear others by air conduction, but we hear ourselves by both air and bone conduction. Therefore, when we first hear a record of our own speech, the voice does not sound like our own, because for the first time we are hearing it solely by air conduction.

The student may well ask why his own voice does not sound louder because of the added factor of bone conduction. The answer is that the distribution of mass of the bones of the middle ear [21] and/or their attachments are so designed that they reduce the sound reaching the middle ear from the throat.

The intensity with which one hears by air conduction is approximately equal to that with which he hears by bone conduction. By bone conduction, if one hears his own voice whispering it is about 5 db less than his own voice phonating. However, the decrease in loudness is more for vowels requiring a large mouth opening (e. g., [ɑ] as in *father*) and less for those requiring a small mouth opening (e. g., [u] as in *cool*). Presumably, the sound pressures of vibrations in the oral cavity cause the mandible to vibrate, thus aiding in bone conduction.

Bone conduction is like air conduction in that in the end both produce movement of the periotic and otic fluids and of the basilar membrane. With *air conduction,* the vibrations arrive by way of the ossicles of the middle ear. With *bone conduction,* the vibrations of the bones of the skull produce compression waves on the contents of the canals of the internal ear. Because the membrane covering the fenestra cochleae is more elastic than the footplate of the stapes of the fenestra vestibuli, less resistance to compression is produced in the scala tympani than in the scala vestibuli. Another reason for the greater pressure in the scala vestibuli is the immediate connection which it has with the semicircular canals which are also under compression.

[21] The relatively massive head of the malleus is a factor in minimizing rotations of the bones during hearing by bone conduction.

The pattern of vibration for bone and/or air conduction is the same (i. e., in the 100~ to 10,000~ range).

THEORIES OF HEARING

A. Introductory Statement

We must be careful to explain what we mean when we talk about theories of hearing.

Hearing involves (1) what happens to sound waves at the level of the ear—(*a*) outer, (*b*) middle, and (*c*) inner—and (2) what disposition is made of nerve impulse patterns originating in the ear and conducted by fibers of the auditory nerve to (*a*) intermediate neural levels en route to (*b*) the auditory cortex and (*c*) other related brain areas.

Because of the limitations of knowledge about the second area of investigation (i. e., neurological), students of hearing are still forced to confine themselves mainly to the first, the ear.

Thus, when we discuss theories of hearing we almost always mean simply, what are the theories relating to the method by which the ear discriminates pitches? For this reason, theories of hearing deal with the problem, primarily, of the patterns of vibration of the basilar membrane and the sense organs attached to it.

We have previously learned that Reissner's membrane, the tectorial membrane, the organ of Corti, and the basilar membrane vibrate in phase. Measurements of the elasticity of Reissner's membrane (quite uniform throughout its length), the tectorial membrane (quite uniform throughout its extent, except near the stapes), and the basilar membrane (demonstrating marked differences in stiffness showing continuous change along the extent of the cochlear partition) have previously led us to the conclusion that it is the latter membrane that determines the pattern of movement of the cochlear partition and the locus of maximum displacement.[22] Thus, we focus our attention on the vibratory pattern of the basilar membrane.

The Basilar Membrane: Patterns of Displacement. What is the mode of vibration of the basilar membrane? The question has long been a challenge to students of the ear and hearing. Clinical findings, observations of psychological phenomena, and philosophical speculation have produced, perhaps, every conceivable hypothesis about the action of the membrane. Yet a complete and acceptable answer still eludes us.

Because it is accepted that the place of maximum excitation along the

[22] We may state the basic physical characteristic underlying displacement of membrane and of fluid: given a specific change of pressure (increase) in one scala, a correlated volume of fluid per unit (e.g., 1mm) length of the basilar membrane is forced into the other scala, the volume depending, in the main, upon the rigidity of the intervening partition.

basilar membrane varies with and is related to the frequency of the stimulating sound, it becomes almost a requirement to try, first, to understand the vibratory pattern of the basilar membrane before trying to determine the relative merits of the various theories of hearing. Knowledge of the first will assist in reaching a decision as to which theory or theories may be right.

It is usually assumed that the pattern of vibration of the basilar membrane remains the same if the magnitude of the stimulus producing the displacement is halved or reduced even more.

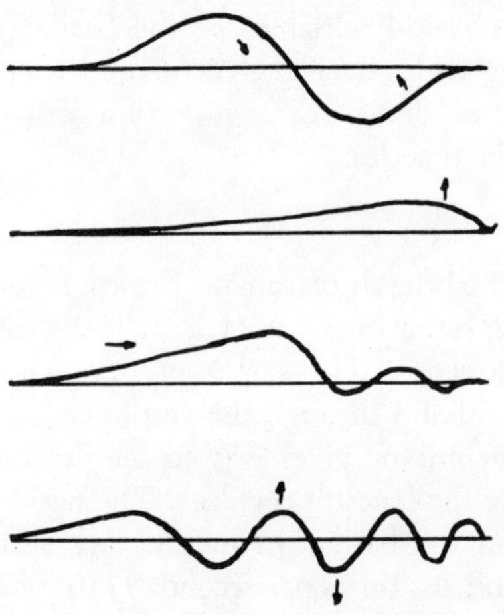

FIG. 103. Patterns of Basilar Membrane Vibrations.

Schema representing the principal wave patterns presumed possible in basilar membrane vibrations.

Use of Models of the Cochlea. To determine the pattern of vibration, Békésy and others have not only developed elaborate and delicate equipment for investigating the cochleae of various animals, but have designed cochlear models [23] which, because of their relatively greater size, make it possible to study their workings more easily. Usually, the dimensions of such models are relative to the length of the basilar membrane; other dimensions are made proportional to this unit. Similarly, such factors as the densities and viscosities of fluids or the elasticity of tissues are compared and constants ascertained. Rechecks are run frequently to be sure that what occurs in the model does or could happen in the cochlea of the animal under study.

[23] There are many properties of the human ear that cannot be reproduced in models. On the other hand, tests show that for some experimental studies a model needs no simulated Reissner's membrane. This last statement of fact should not be interpreted as a commentary on the importance or function of this membrane in the human cochlea.

Although the human cochlea is coiled, a model may be constructed as though the cochlea were straight; this does not invalidate the experiments.[24]

B. Basic Theories

Fortunately, by eliminating the displacement theory, after we discuss it, we may reduce to four the major theories of hearing: Resonance, Traveling Wave, Standing Wave, and Telephone.

As we discuss the theories in order it will help to show how we can relate the theories to one another. Then, as Békésy explains, if we work with two independent physical variables of the basilar membrane—its elasticity and its coupling with attached structures—we can obtain a continuous series of patterns of vibrations, each portion of which is found to support one or more of the theories.

1. DISPLACEMENT THEORY

Max F. Meyer formulated the displacement theory. It considers the basilar membrane as an indifferent mass. Assume that the ear is receiving a sound of 400 cycles frequency. The stapes produces 400 impulses per second on the periotic fluid and through the vestibular membrane on the otic fluid. The basilar membrane gives way to the pressure and the impulses are free to displace the fenestra cochleae. The nerve endings in the spiral organ of Corti on the basilar membrane are stimulated by the vibrating column of liquid 400 times per second. Thus, pitch is explained. A greater intensity of the same sound simply means a greater excursion of the stapes and involves a greater extent of the basilar membrane in displacement. Hence more nerves carry the impulses. This theory assumes that any nerve can carry any or all frequencies; that the more nerve fibers stimulated, the greater the loudness observed by an individual.

2. RESONANCE THEORY

This is one of the *place theories*. The assumption is that pitch discrimination is determined by a certain place along the basilar membrane being set into maximum vibration so as to excite the sensory nerve fibers at that locus. The word "point" is, perhaps, too definite. Later in the chapter we shall have something to say about the neurological interpretations of place and/or point.

Presumably, every particular section (i. e., transverse band, or width of fibers) of the membrane is so tuned (more or less sharply) that its resonance characteristics will correspond to the frequency of some one tone within the audible range; for every tone there is a corresponding tuned

[24] In some animals (e.g., anteater) the cochlea is not coiled, but is a tube only slightly bent.

resonator, and it vibrates at a maximum in resonance to tones of its frequency.

As in resonance systems in general, the pattern of the vibrational curve is sinusoidal; its positive and negative phases mirror each other. The basilar membrane is displaced equally, first in one direction and then in the opposite direction.

Because the characteristics of the resonators vary progressively from one end to the other of the basilar membrane, discrimination of tones of high frequency takes place near the stapes, tones of low pitch near the helicotrema, and places for the discrimination of others are regularly distributed between these extremes.

The force producing the vibration (displacement) is the energy transmitted to the fluid surrounding the membrane by the thrusts of the stapes. The membrane vibrates (maximally) only at the locus of the resonant frequency; for a given tone, other portions along the membrane are not set into (maximal) vibration.

Propounded a little less than a century ago, the resonance or harp theory of Hermann von Helmholtz was a major contribution to the field of hearing because of some of its basically good ideas and, also, because of the productive controversy it has continued to stimulate. The theory assumed that the 24,000 or so transverse fibers which make up the basilar membrane are tuned, somewhat as are the strings of a piano or harp, to different frequencies, and that when sound waves containing those frequencies are received by the ear the appropriate fibers resonate automatically to those pitches, thus stimulating the hair cells of the organ of Corti which rest on those fibers of the membrane. This stimulation produces impulses in the auditory nerve fibers. Because the transverse fibers at the base of the cochlea are short they resonate to high pitches. The longer fibers near the apex resonate to lower pitches.

If the student has performed Exercise 15 in Chapter III, he is prepared to understand the Helmholtz theory of hearing. The ear analyzes complex sounds as does the piano. We must imagine each piano string as connected with a nerve which carries to the brain the particular tone sensation. The basilar membrane corresponds to the piano sounding board and its numerous strings.

Békésy believes that we cannot accept the resonance theory in its total implications because the coupling factors between the basilar membrane and its attached structures are so variable.

3. TRAVELING WAVE THEORY

This is another of the place theories; pitch discrimination is determined when a certain place along the basilar membrane is set into maximum vibration, exciting the sensory nerve fibers at that locus.

The place on the membrane where the nerve endings will be stimulated depends upon where the maximal displacement of the traveling wave occurs. The energy for creating the wave comes from the stapes, but the wave, starting at one end, runs along the length of the membrane gradually waxing until it attains maximal displacement.[25] At that point the wave pattern shows a highly damped decline, disappearing altogether in one or, at most, two more cycles. The pattern of the curve is quite unlike that of a resonant system curve.

Increasing the frequency of the tone moves the place of maximal vibration toward the base of the cochlea; decreasing the frequency moves the place in the direction of the apex.

Fig. 104 helps to explain our ability to distinguish a slight change of pitch in the upper half of the helix, say between 256 cycles and 260

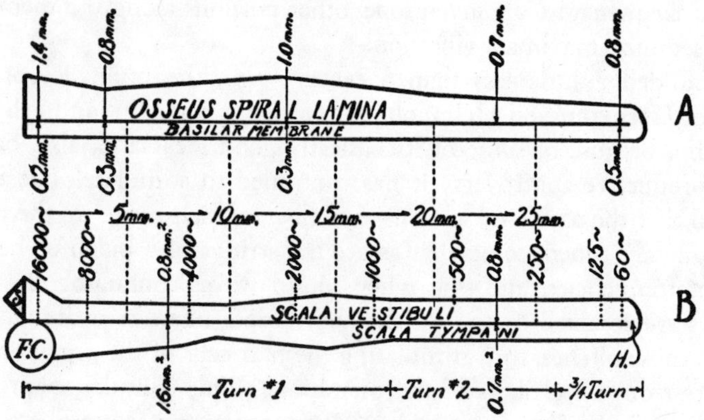

FIG. 104*A*. Diagram Showing Relative Size of Osseous Spiral Lamina and Basilar Membrane.

FIG. 104*B*. Diagram Showing Relative Size of Scala Vestibuli and Scala Tympani.

In each case the 2¾ turns of the canal of the cochlea are represented as stretched out straight. The length, of approximately 30 mm., is marked off into lengths of 2 mm. In *B*, the location of certain areas along the basilar membrane are marked; e.g., 3 mm. from the fenestra vestibuli is the area for pitches of 8000 ~ (cycles); at 25 mm., 250 ~. S = stapes; F.C. = fenestra cochlea; H = helicotrema.

cycles, though we are unable to make such close distinctions between higher frequencies. Because our most useful sounds are in the lower range of frequencies, a cochlea has been developed which favors these ranges. For example, it will be seen in Fig. 104*B* that 10 mm. (from 15 to 25 mm. on the basilar membrane) covers a range of only about 1200 cycles (1500 cycles to 250 cycles); while 3 mm. (from 1 to 4 mm.) covers a range of 8000 or more cycles (16,000 to 8000 cycles).

[25] If one suddenly flips a slack rope, a traveling wave sweeps progressively along its length; the basilar membrane acts like the slack rope when the stapes is displaced. Where the traveling wave causes a bulging of the membrane, auditory nerve endings will be stimulated.

Proof of frequencies having specific loci on the membrane is obtained in various ways. If we know that a person is deaf to certain tones, an autopsy after his death may disclose degeneration of the related area of the spiral organ of Corti. Or experimental animals may be subjected to constant sounding of a tone of a definite frequency. After the animal has been sacrificed, histological study of the spiral organ of Corti shows degeneration depending on the pitch. If the tone was low, the degeneration is near the helicotrema; if the tone was high, the degeneration is near the base of the cochlea.

Authorities who believe that the traveling wave theory is the most satisfactory of the several theories point out that, in any case, it is necessary in explaining the part transients play in speech (or music).[26]

In our sketch of the traveling wave form we showed the wave being damped out almost at once. This rapid damping is believed to be due to the fact that the basilar membrane and Reissner's membrane enclose the cochlear duct, which is filled with a fluid of about the viscosity of honey or glycerine and has a pronounced damping effect on the unison vibrations of the membranes and intermediate structures.

The movements of the basilar membrane may be observed with a microscope and stroboscopic illumination. The membrane shows a vibratory pattern of traveling waves. The waves are propagated continuously toward the helicotrema, rapidly losing their amplitude. A reference to our sketch of the traveling wave shows that from the stapes (at left) to the locus of maximal displacement the membrane is vibrating in phase; at the locus a reversal of phase occurs.

Some day we hope that one of the readers of our book will be able to supply the answers to these questions: If the amplitude of vibration of the basilar membrane[27] at a certain point is responsible for the excitation of the sensory cells at that locus, at what stage of vibration does stimulation of a nerve fiber begin? (*a*) As the amplitude is building from zero to maximum? (*b*) At maximum only? (*c*) During the decrease from maximum to zero? (*d*) Or, is there some other possibility?[28]

a. Eddy Currents

When the perilymph and, hence, the basilar membrane, are subjected to sinusoidal vibrations, the amplitude of vibrations at successive time

[26] Transients, onset and decay, the initiation, connection, and termination of sounds have been discussed in an earlier chapter. Because running speech is made up of continuous changes of frequency and intensity, transients are extremely important for speech recognition. If transients are masked out on a tape recording it is impossible to distinguish between a violin and a flute.

[27] It may be that the stimulation of individual nerve endings while not proportional to the amplitude of vibration of the membrane at their locus is, nevertheless, related in some other manner to amplitude.

[28] Mach's law of contrast seems to support the second possibility. But, our basic question

intervals may be represented by the following curves, number 1 to 6, in order.

The physical movements of the membrane displace the surrounding fluid (solid arrows); at the same time, hydrodynamically, fluid is drawn in (dotted arrows) to replace the displaced quantity. The combined result is the formation of rotational eddy movements in the fluid. The location of any eddy is a function of frequency—i. e., it is related to the frequency resonated. The mid-point of the eddy represents exactly the locus of maximum amplitude of vibration of the basilar membrane.

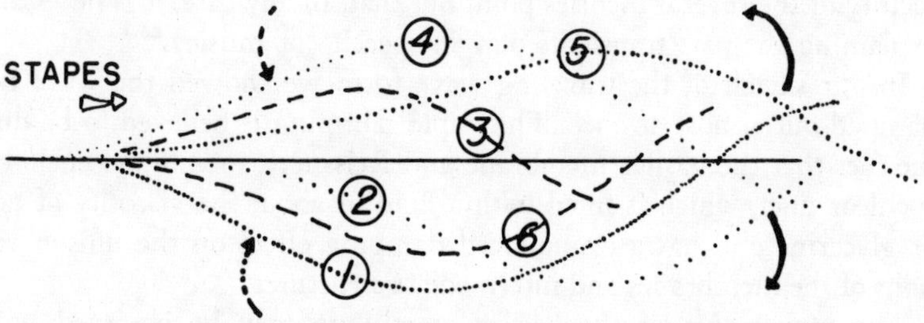

FIG. 105. Displacement of Fluid by Movements of Basilar Membrane.

In explaining the formation of the eddy, Békésy goes back to the resonance theory to the extent of assuming the membrane to be divided into transverse bands equal in width (i. e., as measured from stapes to helicotrema) but differing in length (shorter near the stapes and increasing progressively in length toward the helicotrema). Each band may now be regarded as a resonator; the shortest is in resonance with the highest audible frequency, and the longest is tuned to the lowest audible frequency; the tuning of the intermediate bands, from high to low, is determined by their respective lengths.

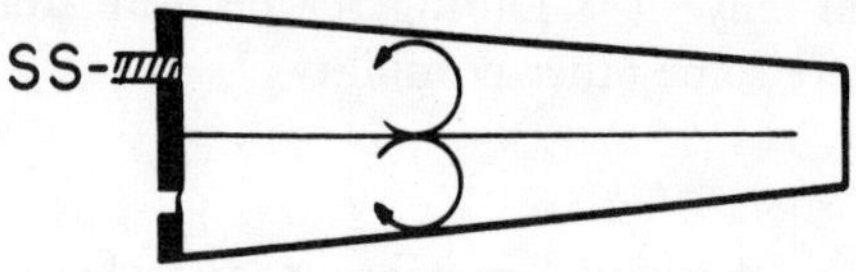

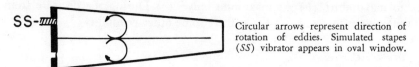

Circular arrows represent direction of rotation of eddies. Simulated stapes (*SS*) vibrator appears in oval window.

FIG. 106. Schema Showing Eddy Currents.

During displacements of the membrane, eddy currents develop above and below the membrane. Their direction of rotation is counterclockwise in the simulated scala vestibuli and clockwise in the other scala. Their diameter depends on the diameter of the scala, being equal to the distance

asks about the *beginning* stage. This is not necessarily the same as the firing, triggering or threshold stage that the all-or-none law leads you to think about!

from membrane to tube wall. Their velocity of rotation is proportional to the amplitude of the displacements of the membrane. Their location along the membrane is determined by the frequency of stapedial vibration, being closer to the helicotrema for low frequencies and closer to the stapes for high frequencies.[29]

In early experiments, Békésy assigned some probability to the view that it is the effect of fluid eddies on the basilar membrane that produces the excitation of the nerve endings, instead of the stimulus resulting from movements of the membrane, directly or indirectly. This is a difficult issue to decide, especially if movements and eddies occur concurrently.

It may be relatively easy to see how any movement (stress, shear, etc.) of the basilar membrane may produce corresponding movements of the cells and other tissue structures located on the membrane or bathed by fluid bounded by the membrane, and how such relative movements may excite the nerve fiber endings. Or, if the physical movement itself is not the direct cause, the movement may bring about the release of chemical and/or electrical energy which, in turn, triggers the nerve impulse.

On the other hand, how do the eddy currents stimulate the nerves? Do the eddies produce movements that, in turn, excite the fibers? Or do the eddies set up forces that produce chemical and/or electrical energy releases that excite the fibers without physical movement playing a part?

Nature does not usually take extra or unnecessary steps in accomplishing an objective. Here, the physical movement or vibration of the membrane is necessary to produce the eddy currents. When the nerve endings can be stimulated directly by the original vibratory movements, or by other resulting movements, or by resulting chemical and/or electrical releases of energy, why should the extra step of the eddy current be essential? On hydrodynamic principles the eddy may be produced by the vibrations of the membrane; the eddy may appear concurrently with the vibration. This is not to say, however, that the eddy is anything more than fortuitous.

For the eddy mechanism to be essential it would seem that it must produce some movement or movements that are different from those produced by the vibrating membrane or that it must, in some way, trigger off some force or store of energy that cannot otherwise be sparked, directly or indirectly, by the vibratory movement. In other words, the eddy must

[29] Békésy photographed eddy currents in his models. To aid in seeing and photographing the rotational movements in the fluid, fine carbon particles and/or gold or aluminum powder were introduced into the liquid. If the particles were evenly distributed along the membrane at first, they were transported rapidly toward the helicotrema when the stapes began vibrating, thus demonstrating the presence of traveling waves moving toward the helicotrema. As soon as pressure variations were equalized along the membrane there was no further movement of the particles that had already accumulated at the helicotrema.

contribute uniquely to the chain of events required in attaining the threshold of excitability of the nerve fibers involved.

4. STANDING WAVE THEORY

Standing waves depend for their vibratory pattern on the formation of nodes and antinodes. Vibrations run the length of the basilar membrane, producing sinusoidal displacements. Increasing the frequency increases the number of nodes, i. e., brings them closer together, or decreases their wave lengths (node to node).

The Ewald hypothesis proceeds along the lines of the Chladni phenomena, treating the basilar membrane as an elastic surface, portions of which become nodal according to the complexity of the sound-wave pattern. This permits cochlear analysis of the sound.

Maximal displacements of the membrane at the nodes stimulate the nerve endings. It is left to the nervous system to utilize the spatial-time relationships of the signals to determine pitch or to combine the various excitations distributed along the membrane into the impression of a sound. Each different vibratory pattern of nodes and internodes is interpreted as a different sound. Inasmuch as we know almost nothing about the action of the nervous system in this respect, we are, for the present, at least, up against a dead end with this theory.

In addition, Békésy rules out the standing wave theory on the grounds that the basilar membrane is too stiff to vibrate to such a pattern.

5. TELEPHONE THEORY

According to this theory a change in frequency need not change the vibratory pattern of displacement of the membrane. An as yet unknown function of the nervous system is instrumental in discriminating among pitches.

The pattern of vibration of the membrane is similar to that of the diaphragm of a telephone. In conformity to the movements of the stapes, the entire membrane vibrates in phase. At about 30cps or below, the traveling wave pattern on the basilar membrane is the same as that shown as the pattern for the telephone theory.

Rutherford and, later, Sir Thomas Wrightson, compared the basilar membrane to the diaphragm of a telephone. Its vibration as a whole produces stimuli which are transmitted to the brain where analysis takes place. This requires rates of impulses in the auditory nerve as high as 20,000 per second. The hypothesis does not explain fatigue to one pitch or islands of deafness. (When an audiometer test is given and a person is found to have a hearing deficiency for a certain pitch but to have no deficiency for other frequencies above and below that pitch, the individual is said to have an island of deafness.)

HOW WE HEAR—SUMMARY AND SURMISE

At the present time it is not possible to make an unqualified statement about how hearing takes place; more facts are needed.

Hearing is so complex that we shall do well to agree that no one simple explanation at hand today will suffice.[30] To explain all of the dimensions of hearing it is probable that several kinds of stimuli are involved to excite the nerve fibers and bring about the total neural pattern required for perception. At best we may summarize our current views, in part, and surmise, in part.

A. Stage One: The Ear Levels

Physical, physiological, and psychological data are in agreement that there is a first-stage (mechanical or hydromechanical) frequency analysis [31] made spatially along the cochlear partition. If space is involved, so is time.

At this stage, particularly, we may summarize some of the facts on which most authorities find themselves in substantial agreement. We know, for example, that sound waves strike the tympanic membrane, causing it to vibrate. To the center of the tympanic membrane is attached the malleus. When the tympanic membrane vibrates, the malleus must vibrate likewise. Furthermore, the other ossicles attached to the malleus vibrate, with the result that the footplate of the stapes vibrates in the fenestra vestibuli and passes the vibrations on to the periotic fluid in the vestibule and thence to the scala vestibuli.

In the case of low frequencies—i. e., less than 16 d.v./sec.—the thrust of the stapes against the fenestra vestibuli and fluid in the scala vestibuli is so slow that the pressure wave has time to travel in the periotic fluid to and through the helicotrema and to the fenestra cochleae which, because the liquid is incompressible, bulges outward into the middle ear to an extent corresponding to the inward displacement at the fenestra vestibuli —and all this before the next thrust of the stapes. Because the pressure wave passes through the helicotrema, the basilar membrane is not disturbed and no sensation of sound is received.

In the case of high frequencies—e. g., 16,000 cycles—the thrusts of the stapes against the fenestra vestibuli occur with such rapidity that the pressure wave in the periotic fluid can travel but a short distance before another thrust occurs. But no second thrust can be given if in the meantime there has been no displacement of the incompressible liquid. If the

[30] How difficult it is to arrive at a firm decision about a theory of hearing is apparent in this statement: In mammals the depth of anesthesia alters the reciprocal inhibition of the nervous system; for every level of anesthesia there may be necessary a different theory of hearing.

[31] Other attributes of sound must be analyzed here (or elsewhere), too.

vibration does not have time to go to the helicotrema and thence to the fenestra cochleae, how can it get to the fenestra cochleae more directly and in less time? The answer is that the pressure thrust on the periotic fluid in the scala vestibuli is transmitted at once to the basilar membrane,

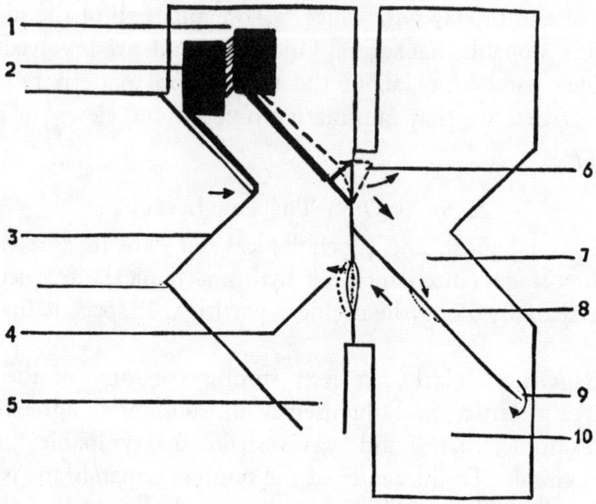

FIG. 107. Highly Schematic Diagram to Represent the Mechanics of Hearing.

1. Incus; 2. malleus; 3. tympanic membrane; 4. fenestra cochleae (solid lines represent normal position; dotted lines represent position after displacement in direction of arrow); 5. Eustachian tube (usually closed; here represented patent to equalize air pressure as in yawning and/or swallowing movements); 6. stapes in fenestra vestibuli (solid lines represent normal position; dotted lines represent position after displacement in direction of arrows); 7. scala vestibuli; 8. basilar membrane (solid line represents normal position; dotted line represents displacement in direction indicated by arrow); 9. helicotrema (arrow indicates continuity of periotic fluid); 10. scala tympani.

causing it to be displaced and to encroach on the scala tympani. The thrust of the basilar membrane into the scala tympani in turn sets up a pressure wave in the periotic fluid therein, which in turn is transmitted to the fenestra cochleae, causing it to bulge outward, thus relieving and equalizing the pressure in the scalae so that the second thrust of the stapes may occur. While this takes place the otic fluid is, of course, concurrently placed under pressure.

Likewise, if the tone received be of 1500 cycles, there will be no time for the pressure in the scala vestibuli to be transmitted through the helicotrema to the scala tympani and to the membrane of the fenestra cochleae. But the thrusts of the stapes are more than ten times less frequent than in the case of the 16,000-cycle tone; therefore, the vibration has time to get part way up the scala vestibuli toward the helicotrema before it passes through the basilar membrane to the scala tympani and, thence, to the fenestra cochleae.

In the case of just audible tones—e. g., 20 cycles—the pressure wave gets almost to the helicotrema before displacing the basilar membrane.

Wherever the basilar membrane bulges to permit the vibration to be transmitted from one scala to the other, the cells of the spiral organ of Corti on that portion of the basilar membrane will be moved in relation to one another and to the nerve endings. The nerve endings there will be stimulated mechanically, chemically, or electrically, and nerve impulses will be transmitted from that area by the auditory nerve to the brain.

The following graph helps summarize what we have been saying; in the graph we have plotted *the locus of maximum excitability along the basilar membrane as a function of frequency.*

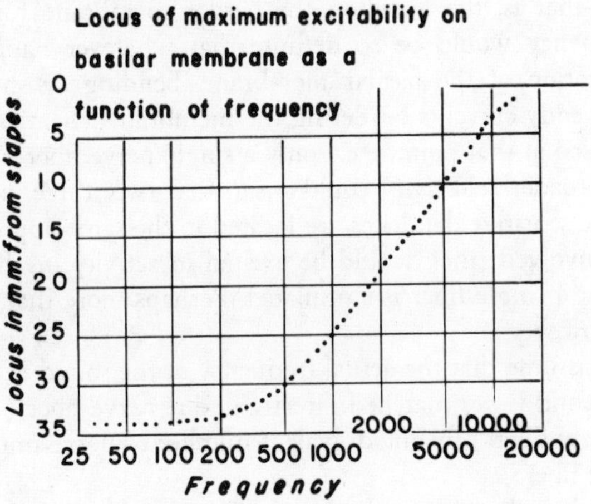

B. Stage Two: The Ear and Neuron Levels

The second stage takes the products of the first-stage analyses and codes them for transmission to the central nervous system. This involves triggering off nerve impulses by some means intimately associated with the first-stage analyses. Previously we have considered physical, chemical, electrical, or other means, or some combination of means.

We stop here to remind the student that when we mention space and time relationships we are not talking about a one- or even two-dimensional linear arrangement of frequencies, intensities, or other attributes of sound, along the basilar membrane from one end to the other. At least three dimensions are always involved in every stage of hearing.[32] If, to

[32] Most of you have played the ancient game, tick-tack-toe, three-in-a-row, on paper, on a single plane. Some of you have played the game in three dimensions, utilizing three

explain it, we have simplified by unwinding the cochlea and making a straight ribbon of the cochlear partition, it still remains its helical self. If we have concentrated on a single locus on the membrane, or a single cell at a given locus, or a single nerve fiber, it has been for the purpose of making understanding easier. There are many loci, cells and fibers; no two fibers occupy the same point in space. The thousands of cells and fibers are separated from one another in space and their relationships to one another are in all dimensions. Stimuli arising from these origins have, at least, all the dimensional-time attributes of their sources.

We can imagine that the ear-neuron mechanisms at this stage demonstrate the highest degree of selectivity or we can assume that they are only broadly selective. We may assume that to convey a nerve impulse corresponding to a given frequency to the brain requires a minimum of one nerve fiber. As far as we know, one fiber would represent the ultimate in selectivity—that is, the locus on the basilar membrane for a tone of a given frequency would be so definite that whatever happened at that point (vibration of the basilar membrane, bending or shearing of the membrane, eddy currents bordering the membrane, chemical or electrical forces released at that point, etc.) only a single nerve fiber would be stimulated. A broader selectivity could mean that two, three, or more nerve fibers whose sensitive dendrites are located in the same approximate locus would be involved; they would be excited to activity in about the same manner that a single fiber is stimulated. Perhaps more than one factor is involved, however.

Shall we assume that the actual frequency of the sound in double vibrations per second is *not* matched directly in one nerve fiber (or divided up among several fibers) by an equivalent number of nerve impulses pulsing through the fiber?

Whatever the degree of selectivity, we have indicated the mechanism by which the inner ear analyzes single frequencies and originates nerve impulses traveling in the direction of the central nervous system. What now of the analysis of a complex sound wave made up of fundamental frequency and twenty or more partials? And what of innumerable differing sound wave patterns that follow it in rapid order as we listen to a symphony orchestra or to a person in conversation? Does the ear break down the complex into its component parts and then put it all back together? Does the ear perform analysis and synthesis? Does the ear analyze the complex into its component parts and leave it to the central nervous system to reconstitute the complex?

---

transparent drawing planes. This is childishly simple compared to the multitudinous possibilities available to the ear and nervous system in hearing. Even the simplest tone, with twenty or thirty overtones, is formidable when compared with only three-in-a-row. A complex sound, involving numerous tones, all with their overtones, might bog down a computer, but the ear and nervous system handle such sounds easily.

And what of intensity? If a single nerve fiber at a given locus on the basilar membrane is excited by a given frequency, what is the mechanism by which the brain perceives the sound as soft, loud, or of some intermediate degree of loudness? Can the single fiber convey this information and also the frequency information? What is the coding mechanism? Is one fiber sufficient to indicate a soft sound and are more and more fibers essential in indicating progressively louder tones? Or may the number of impulses per second, in one fiber or more fibers, be the coded message to the brain signifying intensity to be translated into loudness? Or is some entirely different mechanism involved? And, again, what part of the entire operation is performed by the ear and what part by the central nervous system? At what level or levels?

C. Stage Three: The Neurological Levels

A third-stage screening (neurological and/or electro-chemical) of a more definitive nature is made at various neural levels. Space-time relationships continue to be important.

Synthesis takes place at this stage—if, indeed, synthesis does not also occur in the previous stage.

Even the mere transmission of the coded symbols along nerve fiber paths may add to the tri-dimensional complexity of hearing, because now some of the transmissions cross over to the other side of the central nervous system. The crossings may take place at any of several levels. It may be interesting to consider what could happen in the central nervous system, at one or more levels, if the coded impulses coming from the left ear are mixed with those arriving from the right ear. Are the signals compared? Must they be in agreement before being forwarded? Is further dimension added? Is this where quality or other factors are added to pitch and loudness? Or are all conceivable signals included in the coded symbols even at this stage?

1. NOT-THIS-NOT-THIS-BUT-THIS

In the hearing mechanisms, inhibition plays a vital role. In some cases it may be as important as stimulation. In our view, different types or different degrees of inhibition are the products of different neurological levels.

If we consider the inhibitory qualifications of the nervous system it may help explain why the ear may perform only a preliminary mechanical analysis of frequency that is satisfied with a vibratory pattern of a pure

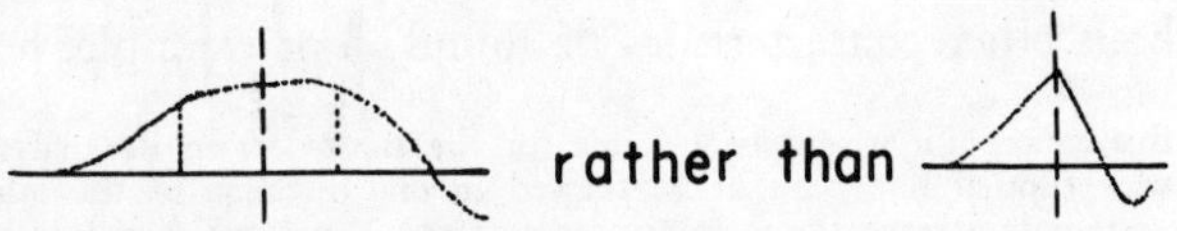

tone that does not have too sharp a maximum, but is, on the contrary, a flat pattern.

This permits the nervous system, by inhibition (not-this-not-this-but-this), to arrive at the sharpest possible localization, and within the time limitations of one to two cycles.

Or, assuming that a simple mathematical relationship of curve-angle and/or steepness-form to area under the curve is involved, the analysis might be pictured somewhat in this fashion.

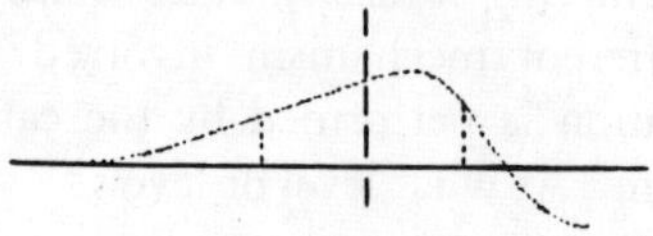

In either case, *the dotted lines at extreme right and left indicate the limits of the area stimulated* (physical analysis), *while the central line* (dashes) *indicates the final analytical decision* (neurological) that is made.[33]

If we say that we are not exactly certain how the cochlea analyzes sound, we can add that we know even less about the part the central nervous system plays in hearing. If the cochlea analyzes a complex sound into harmonic tones and the many individual frequencies are transmitted to the cerebral cortex, does the brain reassemble the simple tones into the original complex?

In lower animals, and probably in man, there is a spatial relation between the various areas which are stimulated along the length of the basilar membrane and the areas of the auditory cortex which are stimulated; the relationship is thought to be point-to-point.

Because frequency is such an important attribute of sound and, perhaps, because it seems to be simpler to deal with, we have devoted much more space to frequency and/or pitch than to intensity and/or loudness, quality, and all the other attributes of sound combined.

The sensation of loudness which we obtain may be due to inner ear and/or middle ear mechanisms. The number of nerves carrying impulses to the brain constitutes an inner ear mechanism. If more fibers are involved, the strength of the tone will be interpreted as greater. If the stapedius and tensor tympani muscles act to protect the ear from the assault of loud sounds, the neuromuscular mechanism regulating their adjustments also may transmit to the brain stimuli which are interpreted as related to the loudness of tones.

What about other characteristics of sound? For example, how do we

[33] Under this concept, it would be possible for the ear to err in its analysis (e.g., the locus boundaries (dotted lines) might be skewed in one direction or the other) and yet have the nervous system reach the right answer as a result of experience (inhibition).

hear and perceive quality? Although they are singing at the same pitch and with approximately the same intensity, how does the ear distinguish between the voice of Helen and the voice of Ruth? Or between the violin and the flute? Or, over the telephone, where frequencies below 300cps for example, have been eliminated, how do we know whether we are talking to a male or a female?

D. Stage Four: The Associative-Relational Levels

A fourth stage (perhaps this should be divided into two stages), which we have called associative-relational, adds to the present instant of hearing the accumulated resources of the past, and the biases of the present, to produce a composite perception. Although you are listening to exactly the same source of speech sounds, what you hear can never be exactly the same as what another listener hears.

In respect to this last stage, we must not think of all transmissions of coded signals as proceeding only upwards or toward higher levels in the central nervous system. Old information stored at higher or lower levels may be mixed with the new incoming information, at higher or lower levels, in ways that are highly significant. For example, consider the normal man who today listens to a tape recording of a speech. Later, having in the meantime suffered from a blow on the head or a growing tumor in the brain, he listens to the same tape. What does he now hear? Or has his interpretation of hearing changed? Or consider a man who has never heard poetry, and a scholar who has spent his life studying poetry. They listen to a poet reading his own works. Do the same sound waves produce the same hearing?

Only when we are careful to specify what we mean by hearing, or what stage of hearing we mean, can we establish any common ground of understanding.

THE NEUROLOGY OF HEARING

There are between 20,000 and 30,000 ganglion cells in the modiolus. Nerve fibers connecting inner hair cells engage only one or two, while fibers going to the outer hair cells may connect with many cells. Each inner hair cell may be innervated by a single fiber, while each outer hair cell may be innervated by numerous fibers.

The bipolar cell-bodies of the neurons of the first order of the auditory nerve are located in the modiolus. Their peripheral processes end in the spiral organ of Corti. Their central processes enter the brain stem at the side of the pons, lateral to the restiform body, and terminate in synaptic relation with secondary neurons in either the *ventral cochlear nucleus* or the *dorsal cochlear nucleus* in the pons.

The cell-bodies of the second order in the ventral and dorsal cochlear nuclei send fibers (about half) across the median plane (in the *trapezoid body*) [34] where some synapse in the *superior olivary complex* (on that side) and some do not until they ascend as the *lateral lemniscus* of the opposite side. About half the fibers from the ventral and dorsal cochlear nuclei do not cross over. They, too, may or may not synapse in the superior olivary complex (of that side) before ascending in the lateral lemniscus of the same side.

While running in the lateral lemnisci some of the fibers synapse in the *nuclei of the lateral lemnisci,* others do not.

At the midbrain level the fibers (some, perhaps, of the second, third, or fourth order) may synapse in the *inferior colliculus* on their respective side. At this level, again, fibers may cross or recross from one side of the brain to the other.

On either side, fibers now continue in the brachia of the inferior colliculi to the *medial geniculate body* [35] of that side, where they synapse. From the medial geniculate body, the acoustic radiation (i. e., radiating distribution of fibers) fans out; its fibers, whose cell bodies are in the medial geniculate body, run in the auditory radiation and sublenticular portion of the internal capsule to end in the receptor center for auditory stimuli in the cerebral cortex. The auditory center is located in the anterior transverse temporal gyrus.[36]

From their distribution linearly along the extent of the spiral organ of Corti, through the intermediate nuclei to the termini in the cerebral cortex, the arrangement of the nerve fibers is quite regular so that there is a linear point-to-point relationship of the spiral organ upon the cortex. The exact significance of this orderly projection is not understood.

PSYCHOLOGY AND PHYSICS OF HEARING

A. Characteristics of Sound as Related to Hearing

Loudness, as opposed to intensity and amplitude, is not strictly a physical term; it is a comparative, psycho-physiological term describing the

[34] Fibers from the ventral cochlear nucleus cross over in the trapezoid body; those from the dorsal cochlear nucleus run in the stria medullares before crossing over to join the others.

[35] Also, some terminate in the inferior colliculus of the corpora quadrigemina which serves as a reflex center.

[36] The temptation to think of nerve fibers as similar to a bundle of wires in an electric cable or a telephone cable, and to think of a point on a map of the basilar membrane as being connected to a corresponding point on a map in the cerebral cortex offer intriguing and simplifying possibilities. In sections of the nervous system this may be the situation; generally, however, it does not fit all the facts. The nervous system is never passive, it never comes to rest. It is active, whether there are sound stimuli or not. This is not true of a telephone system. Against this ever present activity of the nervous system a stimulus may cause an increase or a decrease in activity. The stimulus may alter the present activity. The effects of summation and inhibition must be considered. For example, subliminal stimuli to which other subliminal stimuli contribute may summate to bring them above the threshold.

degree of strength of the sensation which we receive by means of our hearing apparatus. The interpretation of the loudness of a given tone may vary for individuals or for the same individual in different circumstances. We cannot say that if, at a given intensity, two compound tones are judged to be of equal loudness, increasing their intensities equally will result in our again judging the tones to be of equal loudness. The ear may or may not render such a judgment, depending upon the circumstances. If the intensity of a compound sound be increased, its low tones mask its high tones and the ear interprets the low tones as being relatively more prominent.[37]

The sensitiveness of the ear to intensity is remarkable. At the most favorable pitch the ear will detect periodic pressure changes of less than 1/1000 of a dyne per square centimeter. Such a pressure is equivalent to the weight of a human hair one-third as long as its diameter! As the normal pressure of the air is about 1,000,000 dynes per square centimeter, this means that the ear will respond to a periodic change of one billionth part of the value of this pressure. In stimulating the ear the necessary flow of energy is of the same order of magnitude as that necessary for stimulating the retina.

We may arrive at some idea of the extreme delicacy of the hearing mechanism by recalling that in ordinary conversation, the average speech power is approximately 15 microwatts. This amount of power, when transmitted to the air molecules just outside the mouth, means that they will have a vibration amplitude of 1/100 mm. Even this force of ordinary conversation is not too painful if directed almost into a listener's ear, yet it is easily heard for many feet. And it must be remembered that sound energy decreases as the square of the distance.

The equivalent of the power generated by the voices of nearly four million people in conversation or of forty thousand persons all talking as loudly as possible—i. e., 40,000,000 to 60,000,000 microwatts—is required to light a forty to sixty watt electric light bulb.[38]

The ear is even more sensitive to changes of pitch than it is to changes of intensity. A pitch change of about one-fifth of one per cent may be detected, but about a five per cent change in intensity is required before it can be detected. The approximate number of simple tones that can be distinguished as being different, either in pitch or in loudness, may be determined as follows. Starting with the lowest pitch that can be heard at a given intensity, the frequency is raised until a change of pitch can be detected; then the frequency is raised until a further change in pitch is detected, and so on until there be determined the number of steps of

[37] Just as individuals may have a capacity of absolute pitch, so individuals may have or acquire a capacity for absolute loudness.

[38] 1 microwatt = 1/1,000,000 watt (one millionth of a watt).

frequency that can be detected at the given intensity. The experiment may then be carried out at each of many intensities. Further, tests may be made in which the frequency is held constant and the intensity is varied. It is estimated that the normal ear may distinguish approximately half a millon simple tones as different in either intensity or pitch. The number of complex tones which it would be possible to distinguish must be in the millions.

Beats result when two sinusoid wave forms of similar frequency are united. Increasing the frequency of the beats until they occur at least sixteen to twenty times per second causes them to be heard as a *difference tone,* whose frequency is equal to the difference between the two pitches. Although physically there be no third tone, the ear hears one.[39] A *summation tone* may result from the combination of two simultaneous tones.

B. Duration (Quantity)

The duration of a sound is, like frequency, a time relationship. It is the time taken by a sound-wave train to damp out, to be interrupted, or to be terminated so that the ear no longer perceives it. To designate a voice as drawling is to refer to the duration of certain of its sounds. The quantity of a sound determines how it shall be interpreted.

A tone must be produced with successive increases in its duration to be heard as an indefinite sound, a tone, or a tone of definite pitch. 1.6 vibrations of a high-pitch tuning fork may result in a sensation of tone, while for a low tone as many as 5 vibrations may be necessary.

There is a definite time lag between the actual reception of a sound and its conscious recognition. There is a sudden rise of the tone to near its maximum, then a gradual increase to its maximum. Tones of different pitches show different time-lag limits. As a kind of compensating mechanism for the fact that sounds do not instantaneously enter consciousness, is the persistence in consciousness of the sound after the cessation of the external vibrations. In this respect the ear may be likened to the eye. If pictures are moved before the eye at the rate of about sixteen per second they become moving pictures, and the observer does not detect pauses or blanks between pictures. The production of successive sounds easily distinguishable as separated by pauses or periods of silence, holds only within certain limits. If the pauses are made successively shorter there will come a time when the persistence of the tone in consciousness obliterates the pauses, and the interrupted tone will sound like a continuous

[39] Some experiments indicate that difference tones (and overtones) have a mechanical origin due to stapedial vibrations in the middle ear. If the ear hears two tones of 2000∼ and 2260∼ it will hear, also, a difference tone of 260∼. The vibrations will be transmitted to the inner ear and stimulate a locus on the basilar membrane just as is the case with the two higher frequencies. But, it may be noted, the basilar membrane itself can give rise to difference tones of frequencies below 200∼.

one. By reversing the process, that is, starting with a time interval so short that the tone appears to be continuous, and increasing the intervals until the observer can detect the discontinuity, it can be demonstrated that the length of time of the detectable intervals varies for different sounds. For high-pitch tones, the time interval may be as short as $5/1000$ of a second while for low-pitch tones it may increase to $15/1000$ of a second.

I. THE CONSCIOUS PRESENT

One important aspect of time, affecting the choice and structure of our speech, involves what psychologists refer to as *the conscious present.* Training and individual differences aside, in general it is impossible for an individual to follow a continually changing phenomenon for a duration of time longer than approximately 0.8sec. After this interval—the conscious present—there is a momentary lapse of consciousness. In a sense it is an evolutionary throwback in which the highest neurological level abdicates momentarily in rhythm with one of Nature's inexplicable time clocks.

In speech this interval may be a determinant in one's speech pattern and even in the choice of words. Inasmuch as in normal running speech it takes about 0.20sec to produce a syllable, it becomes apparent why so few words exceed four syllables. Words not capable of being enunciated within a time period of 0.8sec are not likely to be apprehended as a whole.

Number of Syllables	*Nouns %*	*Verbs %*
1	18	29
2	45	45
3	22	16
4	11	8
	96%	98%
5 or more	only 4%	only 2%

Because the feedback of speech sounds echoing back to a speaker's ear may upset his speaking rhythm and cause him to make errors in his speech, the reverberation time of a room in which he speaks is important to him. Often this is affected by the location of loud speakers. Reverberation time for many rooms of all sizes and used for speakers, soloists, orchestras, etc., show an acceptable optimal reverberation time of approximately 0.7–0.8sec.

As we might expect, the limited range of consciousness applies to spatial as well as temporal conditions. You may demonstrate easily that you can give attention to (i. e., be conscious of) only a relatively limited portion of auditory space at a given instant. This portion is known as the area of apprehension. If two different sounds are produced in auditory space simultaneously, one on your right and one on your left, you cannot attend to the two different directions at once. You may hear the two sounds as in the same location, or you may apprehend only one sound at a time, the attention jumping to the other sound at the end of each conscious present. If the two sounds are of equal intensity, they may seem to be at a point midway between their actual locations.

C. Determination of the Least Perceptible Change in Pitch

To determine the just perceptible difference (j.p.d.) of pitch between two tones,[40] an oscillator may be used. Often, however, matched tuning forks or a set of graduated forks are used because they are easier to find. Using the matched forks, first one is struck, then the second. The pitch of the second is altered slightly by weighting one of the prongs. The listener reports whether the two tones are the same (*S*) or different (*D*). When the difference is perceptible the two forks are sounded together, and the number of beats gives their frequency difference. In general the j.p.d., in d.v./sec., is smallest for low tones, largest for high tones. The smaller the just perceptible difference, the greater the time required to perceive the difference.

In experiments to determine the least perceptible change in pitch which may be detected by an observer, the changes involve the pitch, its intensity, and the rate of variation of the tone.

Stern (1896) blew a jet of air over a bottle, the bottom of which was in communication with a reservoir of mercury in such a way that the mercury level in the bottle could be raised, thus raising the pitch of the cavity. A tone was produced and gradually altered in pitch by raising or lowering the mercury level. It was altered until detected by the observer. Two types of alterations were made:

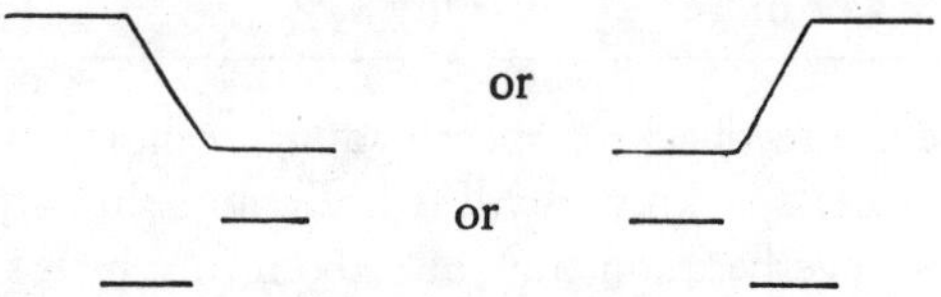

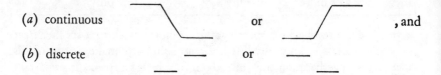

(*a*) continuous or , and

(*b*) discrete or

The results of such experimentation indicate that: (1) continuous changes are more accurately detected; (2) ability to detect pitch change is directly related to the actual extent of change of pitch, and is greater for continuous changes; (3) with continuous changes, rise in pitch is

[40] Normally, the two ears are alike in their threshold sensitivities throughout the audible range of frequencies.

detected more accurately than fall in pitch, a disparity which is not so great in the case of intermittent changes; (4) the accuracy of perception of the similarity of two intermittent tones is less than that of the perception of the constancy of pitch of a continuous tone; (5) the accuracy of the perception of the difference of two successive tones is greater than that perception of the likeness of two successive tones; (6) accuracy of perception increases as the change in pitch becomes slower.

D. Pause

Pause is an actual physical stoppage of sound-wave propagation, magnified or reduced psychologically. Whereas duration is temporally concerned with sound from start to finish, pause has to do with the time interval between the cessation of one sound and the beginning of the succeeding sound. Psychologically, the value of a pause of given duration is highly variable.

E. Psycho-physical Experiments

Most studies of speech sounds involve not only the purely physical approach, but psychological elements as well. For example, we may produce a series of syllables by speaking into a microphone so that a tape recording can be made of the series. The tape may be run by an experimenter in one room while listeners in another room hear the sounds by means of a loudspeaker. First, articulatory norms are established on the number of sounds heard correctly. Then electrical filters are placed in the circuit of the system so that any band of frequencies may be prevented from reaching the loudspeaker and, hence, the listeners. When certain frequencies are removed, the energy of the speech sounds is reduced and, also, the percentage of sounds correctly noted by the listeners decreases. The following table is based on the experiments of Wood:

Frequencies eliminated	*% of energy decrease*	*% of reduction in articulation, i. e., decrease in sounds noted correctly*
All below 500 cycles	60%	2%
All below 1500 cycles	90%	35%
All above 1500 cycles	10%	35%

As a means of distinguishing between the physics of sounds and the psychology of sound, experimental work with electrical equipment in connection with wave or frequency filters gives valuable information. Russell found, for example, that after eliminating all frequencies below 250, in the case of a male voice, the voice sounded natural to listeners. Peculiarly enough, although the physical fundamental was doubled—i.e., raised from its natural frequency of about 128 cycles to approximately 256 cycles—it was not perceived as a higher voice. Even if all frequencies below 500 cycles be eliminated the listener does not get the impression of hearing a female voice. However, the voice does appear to be coming from a great distance. This is because the energy of speech is carried to the extent of 60 per cent by the frequencies below 500 cycles.

In the main, the range of frequencies for speech is from 100 cycles to 6000 cycles per second. Filtering out all frequencies above 5000 cycles leaves the quality of the voice satisfactory. This fact indicates that the intelligibility and quality of speech is carried by those frequencies between 500 and 5000 cycles. In this range, however, some speech sounds are partly eliminated. Filtering out everything above 3500 cycles makes for a mushy throatiness of quality. Eliminating all frequencies above 1500 cycles produces a muffled, lifeless quality of voice. If the filters in this latter range are switched in suddenly, the impression is as though someone had clapped a hand over the mouth of the speaker. Under these conditions, the speech is still understandable. Speech becomes unintelligible, however, when only the frequencies up to 1000 cycles are retained.

In the case of a musically complex sound a listener may perceive its fundamental frequency even if it is not present in the sound actually heard. If the harmonic structure of the sound is received, the ear and/or brain will supply the fundamental.

Let a sound have a fundamental frequency of 250∼. Its harmonics are 500∼, 750∼, 1000∼, 1250∼, etc. Even though all frequencies below 500∼ are filtered out the sound will be perceived as having a fundamental of 250 cycles. The harmonic pattern fits only a complex sound having such a fundamental.

Such phenomena are encountered almost daily in telephone communications. Although telephones carry no frequencies below approximately 300∼ we have no difficulty in distinguishing male (fundamental frequency of about 130∼) or female (fundamental frequency about 230∼) voices.

AUDIOMETRY

An electrical instrument designed for measuring normal hearing (as well as the degree of loss of hearing) is known as an *audiometer*. An *audiogram* [41] is a curve, the graphic representation of the hearing capacity of an individual. It shows the minimum intensity of sound that can be detected at various frequencies. An audiogram shows the hearing ability

[41] An audiogram is the graphic record of a hearing test. Two dimensions of sound are shown by the audiogram: frequency is indicated along the abscissa, and intensity, in decibels, is indicated along the ordinate.

at each of the following pure tone frequencies, 125, 250, 500, 750, 1000, 1500, 2000, 3000, 4000, 6000, 8000, which may be produced at various sensation levels from —20 decibels to +90 decibels. A reduction in hearing between 250 and 2000 cycles is particularly serious in the hearing of speech.[42]

On the audiogram, the horizontal line marked NORMAL, indicates zero decibels. This is the level of the normal threshold of hearing.[43]

In the fields of physiology and psychology, threshold has a commonly accepted definition: *the intensity of stimulus required just barely to elicit a response* or sensation.[44]

The auditory threshold varies greatly with frequency. It is about 10,000 times less for a tone of 1000 cycles than for one of 25 cycles. The ear is most sensitive in the frequency range 1000~ to 4000~. To be equally well heard, sounds of from 250~ to 1000~ and from 4000~ to 8000~ must be produced with more intensity, while sounds below 250~ and above 8000~ must be produced with even greater intensity to be perceived.

With the audiometer one may test minimum audibility (that is, the threshold of audibility) as well as maximum audibility (that is, the amount of sound to which the ear can be subjected without adding the sensation of feeling or pain).

In theory, an audiogram of a person with completely normal hearing would appear as a straight line corresponding to the NORMAL line mentioned above. In practice, however, one expects such a person to demonstrate some hearing loss at the lowest and highest frequencies. He may show normal or even better than normal hearing, or less than normal hearing, in the intervening portions of the chart. This is because, as with many other tests, audiometry is based on averages. The normal range was determined and standardized originally by giving tests to thousands of persons presumed to have normal hearing. Once the norm was determined, it was possible to designate a hearing loss as anything below that norm.

While the development of pure tone audiometry is the result of many years of testing and standardization, speech audiometry is a younger partner. Standards and specifications have been set up for speech audiom-

[42] In audiometric circles the pure tone frequencies of 500, 1000, and 2000 cycles may be spoken of as "the speech frequencies" because there is such a high correlation between hearing loss at these frequencies with speech loss as measured on a speech audiometer.

[43] In talking about an audiogram one must avoid confusing terms. Note that a lowered threshold is represented as higher on the graph; a higher threshold is represented as lower on the audiogram. Above the threshold is represented below the NORMAL line, while below the threshold is represented above that line.

[44] Sensory thresholds do not remain constant; they are not absolutes; they fluctuate as functions of an individual's physical, emotional, and mental states. In spite of this, under laboratory test conditions fairly precise measurements may be obtained, comparable from test to test.

eters by the American Standards Association, which recommends that the equipment output cover at least the range from —10db to +100db. Testing is for the purpose of determining the individual's threshold for speech (i. e., just how loud simple standard speech must be for the individual to understand it). Testing is *not* to determine the threshold of detectability (the point at which the presence of speech can just be detected) but to determine the person's SRT (speech reception threshold or point at which the person can repeat simple words or understand simple connected speech). Called zero SRT, the normal (average) SRT has been standardized at a sound pressure level of approximately 20db above the standard reference pressure, 0.0002 dyne/cm^2.[45]

For testing an individual's speech discrimination ability, lists of phonetically balanced (*PB*) words are read to him. The test is his ability to repeat each word or to write it correctly.

Presbycusis, progressive loss of hearing with increasing age, apparently is normal. We have been successful in increasing the span of life; we have not, concurrently, offset presbycusis.

EXERCISES AND QUESTIONS

1. (No student should be permitted to complete this course without having first made and studied one or more recordings of his own speech.)

Make a record of the voice. Then listen to the recording as follows:

(*a*) By *bone conduction* at least twice. Does it sound like your voice? Explain.

(*b*) By *air conduction.* Does it sound like your voice? Does it sound more or less like your voice in comparison with (*a*)? Explain.

(*c*) Run the tape at various speeds from half regular speed to twice regular speed. Explain the voice changes heard.

(*d*) What is the range of pitch of the voice? Increase the range on a second tape and compare the two recordings.

(*e*) What is the range of intensity of the voice? Increase the range on a second tape and compare the two recordings.

2. Have an audiogram made (both ears) and compare the curves for the two ears with the normal hearing curve.

3. If there were no means of equalizing air pressure in the tympanic cavity with outside air pressure, what would be the effect on hearing

(*a*) if the outside pressure were doubled?

(*b*) if the outside pressure were halved?

4. Given two tones of the same intensity, the one of higher pitch will be perceived as louder. Explain.

[45] Numerous tests are used, but two are in common use. (1) Auditory Tests W-1 and W-2 are spondaic word lists. The two-syllable words, spondees, are pronounced with equal stress of both syllables. (2) The cold running speech test utilizes informative (i.e., cold) not emotional material in connected speech.

5. Up to a certain degree of complexity, the more complex a sound, the louder it will seem to be. Explain.

Beyond that point, however, greater complexity of the sound causes it to be interpreted as less loud. Explain.

6. With paper funnels and tubes of various lengths, artificially increase the length of the external acoustic meatus, each time sounding a tone at the orifice. Vary the pitch of the tones. Is the alteration in the length of the meatus more striking for high or low notes? Explain.

7. As the piano acts as a harmonic analyzer of the voice, so Helmholtz believed that the basilar membrane analyzed the sounds coming to the ear. Is the comparison justified?

8. Explain how hearing takes place. Use a complex tone having these components: 60 cycles, 1024 cycles, and 8000 cycles. Describe the process from the time the sound waves strike the tympanum to the time the nerve impulse has started along the VIIIth cranial nerve.

APPENDIX

ADDITIONAL EXERCISES AND QUESTIONS

CHAPTER I

I-1. Define:

1. External respiration
2. Diffusion
3. Residual air
4. Torque
5. Primary lobule
6. Bifurcation
7. Pleural cavity
8. Pulmone
9. Vital capacity
10. Origin
11. Insertion
12. Pleura
13. Inhalation
14. Exhalation
15. Patent
16. Physiological airway
17. Thorax
18. Alveoli
19. Mediastinum
20. Respiratory center
21. pH
22. Diaphragm
23. Complemental air
24. Supplemental air
25. Spirometer
26. Inhalation phase
27. Auscultation
28. Pneumograph
29. Vesicular murmur
30. Atmospheric pressure

I-2. Make a drawing * of the pertinent parts of the physiological airway involved in normal breathing. Label the parts.

(*a*) Would your drawing be the same if it were to represent the airway during the production of speech sounds? Explain.

I-3. Make a simple sketch of the thorax. Label the parts. Indicate with color its diameters.

I-4. Make a drawing showing the relation of larynx, trachea, and esophagus during normal speech production. Label.

(*a*) Make a sketch to show the relation of the same structures during the production of esophageal speech. Explain the differences, if any.

I-5. Make a drawing of the trachea and lungs. Label.

I-6. Describe the diaphragm and its innervation.

I-7. Explain the part the diaphragm plays in external respiration.

I-8. Describe the mechanism of inhalation during normal respiration and during speaking. Explain the differences, if any.

I-9. Describe the mechanism of exhalation during normal respiration and during speaking. Explain the differences, if any.

I-10. Active and passive factors play a part in exhalation.

(*a*) Explain the part played by active factors.

(*b*) Explain the part played by passive factors.

(*c*) In your opinion, are active factors or passive factors more important? Explain.

(*d*) Could you live without the active factors? Explain.

* The student should use colored inks or pencils where color will make his drawings more understandable.

(*e*) Could you live without the passive factors? Explain.

I-11. In your opinion, what is the relation of vital capacity to normal speech production? Explain.

I-12. Using one or more simple drawings, explain and compare normal quiet breathing and breathing during speech production.

I-13. Using one or more simple graphs, explain and compare normal quiet breathing with breathing during speech production.

I-14. Make an enlarged drawing of a pneumograph. Explain how such equipment could be used (in connection with what other equipment?) in a study of respiration during normal breathing and during speaking.

I-15. In the material dealing with *inhalation,* read the paragraph numbered (5). Holding the nostrils closed and trying not to move the tongue, open the lips with your fingers and breathe through the closed teeth.

(*a*) Can you provide adequate ventilation in this manner?

(*b*) Did you, in fact, move your tongue?

(*c*) Now, what do you think of the first part of the statement in paragraph (5)?

I-16. In the material dealing with *inhalation* you will find this statement: "The musculature of the entire system is in a state of normal tonus. . . ."

(*a*) What is *tonus?*

(*b*) What is the mechanism by which tonus is maintained?

(*c*) Drawing upon your own experience, give examples of bodily conditions demonstrating less than normal tonus.

I-17. The diaphragm has (1) (2) (3) domes. Circle the correct answer.

(*a*) How do you explain the presence of one or more domes?

I-18. Statement: A hiccough is an inspiratory reflex produced by a sudden contraction of the diaphragm.

(*a*) Do you accept or reject the statement? Explain in detail.

I-19. Statement: Extending and shortening a tubular Japanese lantern (or an accordion) somewhat conveys the idea of the lengthening and shortening of the trachea.

(*a*) Analyze and give a critique of the statement.

I-20. Under the section entitled *Control of Volume Varies* some figures are given of the expenditure of air in cc during the production of a vowel sound.

(*a*) Can you find more recent figures on this point? Give your references.

(*b*) Even though the figures were not correct would it be possible for you to show that the ratios were correct (or incorrect)?

(*c*) Explain in detail an experimental method you might follow in securing correct data on this point.

I-21. A girl who is in danger of immediate suffocation because of some blockage of the glottis has an emergency tracheotomy. Now air can get to her lungs and her life is saved. Analyze the following questions from several points of view before answering each fully.

(*a*) Will the girl ever be able to breathe in a normal manner?

(*b*) Will she ever be able to produce normal speech?

(*c*) Will she ever be able to fix her thoracic cage for purposes of lifting a heavy weight?

I-22. A man has a cancerous growth involving the entire larynx. He is told that he is in danger of possible suffocation because of blockage of the glottis. He has a total laryngectomy. Assuming a complete absence of cancer cells after the operation, analyze the following questions from several points of view before answering each fully.

(*a*) Will the man ever be able to breathe in a normal manner?

(*b*) Will he ever be able to produce intelligible speech?

(*c*) Will he ever be able to fix his thoracic cage for the purpose of lifting a heavy weight?

I-23. If you were to add a passive factor (atmospheric pressure acting on the wall of the thorax) to those listed on page 23, where, to be logical, would you insert it? Explain.

CHAPTER II

II-1. Define:

1. Glottis
2. Phonation
3. Sagittal section
4. Laryngoscopy
5. Glottis vocalis
6. Larnygoscope
7. Glottis respiratoria
8. Syrinx
9. Vocal folds
10. Vocal cords
11. Vocal ligaments
12. Hyperglottal
13. Hypoglottal
14. Supraglottal
15. Epiglottis
16. Aditus laryngis
17. Fossa
18. Coronal section
19. Stratified squamous epithelium
20. Antero-posterior diameter
21. Larynx
22. Lamina
23. Cornu
24. Hyaline cartilage
25. Secondary sex characteristic
26. Superior
27. Inferior
28. Apices
29. Ligament
30. Roentgenogram
31. Medial
32. Intrinsic (muscle)
33. Facet
34. Diarthrodial
35. Abduction
36. Vertical axis
37. Approximate
38. Adduction
39. Transverse
40. Margin
41. Vocal process
42. Fasciculus
43. Sphincter
44. Fixed
45. Adjacent
46. Depress
47. Anastomoses
48. Whispering
49. Seebeck siren
50. Bernoulli effect
51. Antagonist
52. Phase
53. Segmental vibration
54. Falsetto
55. Kinesthetic sensation
56. Ventricular folds
57. Artificial larynx
58. Laryngo-periskop
59. Stroboscopy
60. Puff theory

II-2. Read the following statement of *The Bernoulli Effect:* "After the vocal folds have been blown upwards and lateralwards, the very flow of air pressure that blew them apart is instrumental in creating an interesting counterforce acting to assist in drawing the vocal folds downwards and medialward. This is the 'negative' pressure or sucking force demonstrated in the Bernoulli effect. This is in line with aerodynamic principles. If air particles under some pressure are passing through a tube or pipe of a given cross-sectional area and encounter the resistance of a narrowing of the passageway, after which the cross-sectional area again is enlarged, the velocity of the particles at the central core of the air stream flowing through the restricted area increases, but along the outer edges of the air column the velocity is reduced, relatively. These conditions are met in the case of the exhaled air stream discharging from the subglottic tube through the relatively restricted area of the glottal aperture into the supraglottic area."

(*a*) Read what at least two other commentators have to say about this phenomenon.

(*b*) In your opinion, is this an important factor in phonation?

(*c*) Relative to other factors (see pages 65–66) rate this factor in importance. Explain.

(*d*) If you were to include the above statement or a statement of your own among the factors on pages 65–66, where, to be logical, would you insert it?

(*e*) Describe *The Bernoulli* (do you find variant spellings?) *Effect* in your own words.

II-3. Make a drawing of the laryngeal cavity. Use color. Label the parts.

II-4. Draw and label a laryngoscopic view of the laryngeal cavity with the vocal folds separated.

II-5. Identify: V. E. Negus.

(*a*) In two or three paragraphs summarize his contribution to the study of the larynx.

II-6. You know that a female voice tends to be of higher pitch than a male voice.

(*a*) Can you relate this to the information on sex differences of the vocal folds? Explain.

(*b*) Is all of this consistent with a statement that the larynx was not designed primarily for use in speech? Explain.

II-7. If the larynx was not developed in the human being primarily as a voice-producing mechanism, why was it developed? Explain and illustrate.

II-8. (*a*) Explain the statement: the cricoid cartilage may be considered the differentiated upper cartilage of the trachea.

(*b*) After studying Fig. 13, evaluate the statement.

II-9. List the intrinsic muscles of the larynx. Give the origin and insertion of each. Give the innervation of each. Describe the action of each. Tabulate all of your answers in a logical manner.

II-10. Combining your study of respiration and phonation, and what you may have seen of high speed motion pictures of the vocal folds, how do you explain voice production?

II-11. If, on the basis of your knowledge of phonation, you were asked to create an ideal, highly efficient language, what characteristics would distinguish it? Explain, showing how it would differ from English speech.

II-12. Statement: The inferior horns of the thyroid cartilage articulate with the lateral facets on the cricoid cartilage, providing a variety of relational movements: rocking or tipping, sliding or gliding.

(*a*) What method would you suggest for establishing this as fact or not fact?

(*b*) If fact, what effect or effects might such movements have upon voice production?

(*c*) Now, assuming that any or all such movements may occur (and giving consideration, too, to all other possible refinements of movement and adjustment between or among the muscles and/or cartilages of the larynx): (1) are the gliding or rocking movements necessary or essential for phonation? or (2) are such movements only contributory, and if so, to what extent?

II-13. Granted that no one knows the exact mechanism of phonation, what is the most convincing explanation of phonation, in your opinion?

II-14. (*a*) Explain how an artificial larynx works.

(*b*) How does an electrically operated artificial larynx show relationship, if any, to a synthetic speech robot?

II-15. Vogel (1952) suggests that the transverse arytenoid may receive efferent fibers from the superior laryngeal and the inferior laryngeal nerves.

(*a*) If this is true, what explanation may be offered for this exception (is it an exception?) to intrinsic laryngeal muscle innervation?

(*b*) If you were to predict that there might be another exception (or other exceptions), what muscle (or muscles) would you select as logical candidates for dual innervation?

(*c*) If the larynx had been developed primarily as a speech-producing mechanism would there be more or less likelihood of all of the muscles having dual innervation?

(*d*) Assuming that evolution is continuing, do you predict that in the future the laryngeal muscles will have dual innervation? Explain.

II-16. Statement: Most experts in the fields of Speech and Hearing agree that listeners find esophageal speech more intelligible and more pleasing than speech produced with an artificial larynx.

(*a*) Do you agree or disagree with the statement? Present evidence to support your position.

II-17. Statement: Most experts in the fields of Speech and Hearing agree that persons who must use one or the other prefer esophageal speech to speech produced with an artificial larynx.

(*a*) Do you agree or disagree with the statement? Present evidence in support of your position.

II-18. Statements: When a frog vibrates its tongue in croaking (along the longitudinal axis of its body) its entire body vibrates longitudinally. In man, with two symmetrical vocal folds vibrating symmetrically and in a lateral direction, their center of gravity does not change and the laryngeal cartilages transmit a minimum of vibration to the body. However, the passage of the vibrating vertical air stream between the folds produces some vibrations of the laryngeal cartilages in the direction of the exhaled air stream.

(*a*) From your study of high speed motion pictures of the vocal folds during phonation, does it appear that, in the main, their mass vibrates horizontally or laterally, but that their thin glottic lips vibrate vertically? Explain.

II-19. Experiment for from two to four students. Let one student act as subject (*S*) and the others as observers. *S* will practice producing a loud vowel sound.

(*a*) Which vowel does the group agree is best for this purpose? Explain. *S* should attempt to produce the vowel each time with uniform intensity.

(*b*) Each observer will place the stethoscope in the immediate area of the larynx during the production of the vowel. Note the loudness of the tone, designating it as 100. Each observer should make a drawing similar to the sketch on p. 370.

(*c*) On your drawing indicate the relative degrees of loudness of the tone, at the areas designated by *x* in your sketch. The vibrations are carried to these parts of the body by bone and/or tissue conduction and their intensities are reduced the greater the distance from the laryngeal generator.

(*d*) You are listening to a companion speak. He or she is 20 feet, 15 feet, 10 feet, 5 feet, 1 foot away from you. At any of these distances would the phenomena you have just observed have any effect on the speech you hear? Explain.

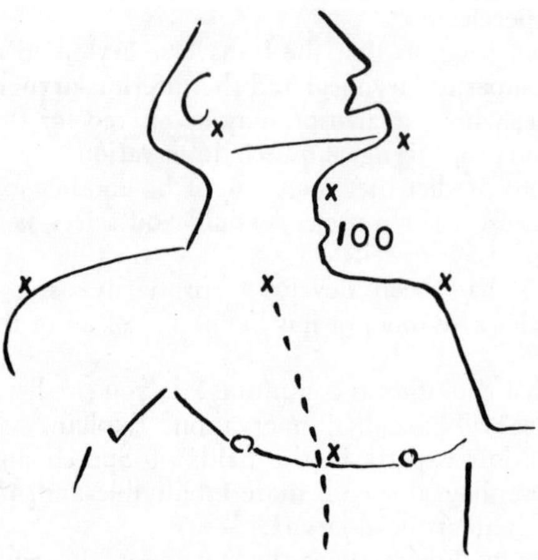

(*e*) If your companion were speaking into a microphone would this make any difference in the speech you hear? Would the quality be changed? (Consider various types of microphones, including one hanging around the neck or fastened to the clothing.)

II-20. After several screenings of high speed motion pictures of the vocal folds in action answer the following questions:

(*a*) What is the exact time order as the folds are separated or blown apart? (1) One end first? (2) If so, which end? (3) How long before (proportionately)? (4) At the center first? (5) Or at some other place between center and either end? (6) If the opening is at or near the center, does the opening progress toward one end? Or toward both ends? (7) Is the opening clean-cut, instantaneous, and total along the entire length?

(*b*) What form does the opening take? Triangular? Oval? Rectangular? Other?

(*c*) What are the open-phase to closed-phase ratios? (1) Is opening more rapid than closing? (2) Are the folds open longer than they are closed?

(*d*) How thick (from inferior to superior levels) do the folds appear to be? Did you think they would be thinner or thicker? Restudy Fig. 13 before and between screenings.

(*e*) Questions (*a*) and (*b*), above, dealt with the appearance of the folds in an anterior-posterior dimension, or a lateral-medial dimension, or in both aspects. Now, consider their appearance in depth (vertical dimension, or inferior-superior dimension) and describe how the folds open. (1) Is the opening instantaneous? (2) Is it from bottom to top in a wave-like motion? (3) How would you describe it?

(*f*) Combining the movements of the folds in all dimensions, describe one complete cycle—from closed to open to closed—of the movements of the vocal folds.

(*g*) If you were able to see them in the film, what relation did the movements or adjustments of other structures surrounding the supra-glottic cavity bear to the movements of the vocal folds?

CHAPTER III

III-1. Define:

1. Generator
2. Resonator
3. Natural period
4. Resonance
5. Sharp
6. Sounding board
7. Sounding body
8. Oscillation
9. Aperture
10. Orifice
11. Neck
12. Surface
13. Sympathetic vibration
14. Helmholtz resonator
15. Tuning
16. Coupling
17. Supra-glottic
18. Septum
19. Symphysis of the mandible
20. Plexus
21. Constrictor
22. Acoustic spectrum
23. Paranasal sinus
24. Ciliated epithelium
25. Relative-pitch theory
26. Cavity-tone theory
27. Damping factor
28. Resting position
29. Free period
30. In tune
31. Incident wave
32. Reflected wave
33. Oropharynx
34. Laryngopharynx
35. Nasopharynx
36. Sinus
37. Hyoid bone
38. Forced vibration
39. Nares
40. Potential resonator
41. Coupled system
42. Infra-glottic
43. Choanae
44. Diaphragm of the mouth
45. Synthetic speech
46. Dilate
47. Ventricular resonance
48. Nasolacrimal duct
49. Harmonic theory
50. Vowel diagram
51. Analogue
52. Rhinoscopy

III-2. Consult one or more books of anatomy to determine what structures, if any, are attached to the trachea or bronchi.

(*a*) If the larynx is raised during speech production is the trachea raised? Lengthened? Raised and lengthened? Explain.

(*b*) If you found structures attached to trachea or bronchi, what damping effect, if any, would you expect them to have upon the resonance characteristics of the trachea? Of the larynx? Explain.

(*c*) Are there structures which, although not attached, could affect the movements of the trachea? Could they affect the damping factor of the trachea? Of the larynx?

III-3. (*a*) Explain what is meant by singly-resonant, doubly-resonant.

(*b*) Can a sound show three, four, or more resonant frequency areas? How many? Explain.

(*c*) To offset misunderstanding, what is the key word to an understanding of the resonance frequency area concept? Explain.

III-4. Number and name the coupled human cavities acting as resonators of normal speech sounds.

III-5. Differentiate between a cavity resonator and a sounding board.

(*a*) Name three of each type that may be involved in resonating speech sounds.

III-6. Does the trachea play a significant role in resonating voice or speech? Explain. Justify your answer.

III-7. Study Fig. 26 and the accompanying explanatory materal. If the ventricular resonance hypothesis were true would it be in accord with (*a*) the relative-pitch theory, (*b*) the cavity-tone theory, (*c*) neither of the above theories?

III-8. Assume that a sustained tone is generated by the periodic puffs of air exhaled through the vocal folds.

(*a*) Will the resulting sound waves be transmitted into the hypoglottal cavity as readily as into the hyperglottal cavity? Give reasons supporting your answer.

(*b*) Explain in detail, *from the point of view of resonance,* whether it makes any difference how you answer (*a*), above.

III-9. Statement: From 50% to 90% of adults have deviated septums.

(*a*) In your opinion, is the statement correct? What proof can you find to support your answer?

(*b*) By analyzing his speech could you prove conclusively that a speaker did or did not have a deviated septum? Explain.

(*c*) In your opinion, can a radio announcer with a deviated septum be a "normal" speaker? Explain.

III-10. Compare and explain the relative-pitch theory of vowel production and the cavity-tone theory of vowel production.

(*a*) Which theory do you prefer? Explain.

(*b*) What other theory might there be? Explain.

III-11. Explain how a knowledge of the production of whispered sounds helps in an understanding of normal vowel production.

III-12. List and explain five modifications of the physiological foodway and airway systems essential in the production of the vowels.

III-13. Differentiate between nasal fossae and nasal sinuses.

III-14. Is the oral cavity a single resonator or coupled multiple resonators? Explain in detail. Give examples of sounds produced.

III-15. The three pharyngeal constrictors (See Figs. 28 and 29) have an interesting overlapping as an anatomical feature.

(*a*) Explain how it is a benefit as far as swallowing is concerned.

(*b*) Would it be better for speech resonance purposes if the overlapping were the opposite of what it is? Explain in detail.

III-16. Obtain a number of whistles of various sizes. Using the same force, blow each whistle. The air, forced through the mouthpiece, produces a weak composite of frictional noises. One component which has the same vibratory frequency as the natural vibratory period of the cavity of the whistle sets the air in the cavity into vibration, producing a sound of considerable intensity. The loudness of the sound is due, chiefly, to resonance.

(*a*) Do you agree? Explain.

(*b*) Why do different whistlcs producc such different results?

(*c*) What, if anything, does your answer to (*b*), above, have to do with your observations that male and female voices differ in frequency, intensity and quality? Explain.

III-17.

APPROXIMATE DIMENSIONS OF NASAL SINUSES

Name of Sinus	*Height*	*Width*	*Depth*
Frontal	3.0cm	2.5cm	2.5cm
Sphenoidal	2.2cm	2.0cm	2.2cm
Maxillary	3.7cm	2.5cm	3.0cm

(*a*) To the above table add information concerning the ethmoidal air cells.

(*b*) Consult a number of references to see if these figures are in fair agreement with others you find. List the references consulted and give the figures found.

(*c*) If you wished to compile a new set of figures based on your own investigations, how would you proceed in order to obtain figures of satisfactory accuracy? What laboratory or experimental methods would you employ?

(*d*) If, after concluding a long and careful series of original research studies, you found that your figures approximated, but did not fully agree with the figures of other experimenters, what conclusions would you draw? Explain in detail, giving your philosophy of research.

CHAPTER IV

IV-1. Define:

1. Articulation
2. Pressure pattern
3. Buccal cavity
4. Mandible
5. Dilator
6. Raphe
7. Soft palate
8. Gingivae
9. Tambour (tongue)
10. Lingual
11. Proprioceptive
12. Caninus
13. Oral orifice
14. Consonant
15. Stop
16. Voiceless analogue
17. Sonant
18. Explosion
19. Plosive
20. Artificial palate
21. Palatogram
22. Articulator
23. Vowel links
24. Fauces
25. Maxilla
26. Vestibule
27. Oral
28. Hard palate
29. Buccae
30. Dorsum
31. Kinesthetic
32. Stereotype expression
33. Caput
34. Orbicularis oris
35. Fricative
36. Continuant
37. Surd
38. Implosion
39. Plosion
40. Nasals
41. Palatography, direct
42. Palatography, indirect

IV-2. Students working in groups of two or more will take turns as (*S*) subject and (*O*) observer. To distinguish examples of feedback, bring into consciousness the proprioceptive sensations matching the auditory stimuli received when producing the sounds [u] and [ʊ].

(*a*) Subject (*S*) will note the kinesthetic sensations or feel the difference in muscular movements and tensions as he produces these pairs: *boot-book, fool-full, lute-look, pool-pull, root-rook, shoot-shook, tool-took*. Repeat each pair several times. Observer (*O*) will check on pronunciation.

(*b*) Practice with other lists of words, using other sounds.

IV-3. Read the reference: Nusbaum (1935).

(*a*) In your own words, what does the experiment demonstrate?

IV-4. Describe a tongue tambour.

(*a*) Devise an experiment in which you could use such equipment.

(*b*) Outline the purposes of the experiment.

IV-5. You have seen the contrasting masks of Comedy and Tragedy.

(*a*) In terms of your knowledge of the muscles discussed in this chapter, explain the significant differences between the masks.

IV-6. Explain *stops,* from lungs to open air outside the mouth. Give examples to illustrate each sound.

IV-7. Explain the production of each of the three "nasal" sounds. Be specific in showing how one of the nasal sounds differs from each of the others.

IV-8. Defend the statement: Consonants are more important than vowels.

IV-9. Defend the statement: Vowels are more important than consonants.

IV-10. In your opinion, are all normal speech sounds produced voluntarily? Explain.

IV-11. Statement: All normal speech sounds are produced voluntarily.

(*a*) Assuming the truth of the statement, could you invent a language that made use of only one stop sound? Explain.

(*b*) What stop sound would you select for your new language?

(*c*) What would be advantages of your language?

(*d*) What would be the disadvantages?

IV-12. If you were required to invent a new language and were told that you could include voiceless *or* voiced continuant fricative consonants, but not both, which would you decide to use? Explain in detail.

IV-13. Depending upon the decision you made in the preceding question, would this force you to make other changes in your new language? For example, would you have to omit some other sounds because you omitted either the voiceless or the voiced continuant fricative consonants? Explain in detail.

IV-14. *Students in groups of three to five.*

(*a*) You have been asked to devise a new language, but one that will make use of only one-half of the phonemes in English speech. The only requirement of the new speech is that it must be of maximum rapidity. Make tests on all the English sounds, alone and in combination (before and after) with the other sounds. On the basis of these tests, make a list of the phonemes to be included in your new rapid speech.

IV-15. The previous questions have stimulated you to do some thinking about developing new languages.

(*a*) How do you explain the great number of languages in the world?

(*b*) How do you explain the difficulties linguists have had in attempting to devise a "universal language"?

(*c*) In your opinion, are the chances for a universal language improving?

CHAPTER V

V-1. Define:

1. Phonetics
2. Vowel
3. Neutral vowel
4. Front vowel
5. Central vowel
6. Back vowel
7. Schwa vowel
8. Vowel glide
9. Semi-vowel
10. Diphthong
11. Consonant
12. Stop plosive
13. Bilabial
14. Continuant fricative
15. Affricate
16. Applied phonetics
17. General linguistics
18. Morphology
19. Etymology
20. Dialect
21. Alphabet
22. Phonetic alphabet
23. "Narrow" system (phonetics)
24. "Broad" system (phonetics)
25. International Phonetic Alphabet
26. Speech sounds
27. Stereotyped sounds
28. Symbols (speech)
29. Imitative speech
30. Sound patterns
31. Phoneme
32. Kinesiologic approach
33. Velar modification
34. Oral modification
35. Fortis
36. Aspirated
37. Glottal-fricative approach
38. Glottal-fricative termination
39. The [h] approach
40. Unstressing

V-2. Write the appropriate phonetic symbols—including, in each case, a representative word—for the following vowels: neutral, front, central, back, schwa.

V-3. List the vowel glides by writing the phonetic symbol for each. Give a key word for each.

V-4. List the stop plosives by writing the phonetic symbol for each. Illustrate with a key word other than the one used in the table of phonetic symbols in the textbook.

V-5. List the continuant fricatives by writing the phonetic symbol for each.

V-6. Differentiate between phonetics proper and applied phonetics.

V-7. Explain the statement: Phonetics may be called the study of symbols.

V-8. Explain the statement: Spoken language is, in reality, a series of auditory symbols.

V-9. How do sound patterns become stereotyped? Explain in your own words, using a number of examples.

V-10. Must spoken language always precede writing?

V-11. Give a brief description of the historical development of the English alphabet.

V-12. Is it possible to have an alphabet which is not a phonetic alphabet? Explain.

V-13. What determines how many phonemes there are in English? Explain in detail.

V-14. Give a detailed explanation, based on phoneme theory, of why an adult foreigner finds it difficult to learn English.

V-15. What are the advantages and disadvantages of the schematic vowel diagram?

(*a*) Draw a diagram that you believe is an improvement over the one in your textbook.

(*b*) How might one construct a diagram other than a "schematic" one?

V-16. Statement: Authorities have not been able to agree upon the number of phonemes in English.

(*a*) If you agree with the statement, explain why this inability to agree is based upon valid scientific grounds.

(*b*) If you agree with the statement, explain why this inability to agree is based upon personal, emotional, and/or other grounds.

(*c*) Taking into consideration the evolutionary nature of language, do you believe it will become (1) easier or (2) more difficult for the authorities to come to an agreement in the future?

V-17. Statement: It is impossible for an individual to produce two identical speech sounds.

(*a*) Do you believe this or just accept it because the text says so? Explain.

(*b*) Could you devise some way of proving that the statement is correct or incorrect?

(*c*) Before a person can accept the statement, he should have in mind some yardstick of comparative measurement. What must be the characteristics of such a yardstick? What specific yardstick can you suggest? Explain.

V-18. By various means, speech may be compressed or expanded. (Read two or three articles on the subject.)

(*a*) Describe one type of equipment that may be used to do one or the other.

(*b*) Explain the benefits to be gained from extending or compressing speech.

V-19. Explain the statement: Speech sounds are produced by seriate muscle movements.

V-20. Statement: Seldom, if ever, do you make use of isolated speech sounds in normal speech. Strictly speaking, it is impossible.

(*a*) List examples of sounds you use that come close to being exceptions to the statement.

V-21. The word *success* is given as an example of one in which the same sound occupies the initial, middle, and final positions.

(*a*) Write five or more words in which the same sound (any sound) occupies these positions. Write the words phonetically.

V-22. Taking care not to confuse regular alphabet and phonetic alphabet, is it true that the same sound occupies the initial, middle, and final positions in these words: *somersaults, divided?*

V-23. In the two previous questions the term *middle position* is used.

(*a*) Does this mean that there are exactly as many phonetic symbols preceding and following the symbol that is termed the middle position? Explain.

(*b*) In (*a*), above, should one say "phonetic symbol?" Or "speech symbol?" Or "symbol?" Or "speech sound?"

(*c*) If there were one or two more symbols preceding (or following) the symbol that is in the middle position than there were following (or preceding) it, would it be accurate to continue to call it the *middle* position?

(*d*) What other term (e.g., *intermediate, central*) might be used in preference to the term *middle?* (Do not select *intermediate* or *central* as your term.)

V-24. Consider everything you know about the position of speech sounds.

(*a*) If you were designing an ideal language what laws, and in what order of importance, would you set down concerning the position of speech sounds? (Limit yourself to discussing *position*.) Tabulate your laws in order of importance.

V-25. Statement: As far as the *p* sound is concerned, the way we spell *apple* does not correspond to the way we pronounce *apple*.

(*a*) Is the statement true or false? Explain.

(*b*) Would you advocate changing the spelling of *apple*? Explain.

V-26. Refer to the devices for initiating, connecting, and/or terminating speech sounds. Consider these possibilities:

(1) Moving from a no-speech-sound state to a speech-sound state.

(2) Moving from a speech-sound state to a no-speech-sound state.

(3) Moving from a speech-sound state to another speech-sound state.

(*a*) In your opinion, which of the possibilities should result in the greatest influence on the sounds produced? Explain.

(*b*) What equipment could be used to prove that the opinion you express is correct?

(*c*) From a philosophical point of view can you establish that no matter what the possibility the influences will be equal? Explain.

V-27. Reread the summary of the kinesiologic-auditory-position approaches with particular attention to the phrase *"will you come here"* used as an example.

(*a*) Choose another phrase of about the same length and write out a similar complete descriptive treatment.

V-28. Can a person think without speaking? (Audibly or at some other level?) Explain.

V-29. Can a person read (silently) without actually speaking the words he reads? Vocally or subvocally? Explain.

V-30. Combining all your information about speech, write a description of the speech people will be using at some future time. (Century? Thousand years? Some other period? Explain why you selected the period you did.)

V-31. (Working in groups of 7.) Spend a minimum of one to three hours listening to speeches on radio or television. Use only public addresses. Do not use newscasts, announcements, commercials, etc.

(*a*) Analyze the speeches to determine what percent of the words were spoken almost automatically by the speaker (i.e., if he says a certain few words he is compelled to say the next words).

(*b*) What percent of the words are redundant?

(*c*) What percent of the words are stereotypes?

(*d*) Pool and write out your ideas about the insight into continuous speech you derived from the experiment.

V-32. (Working in groups of 5.) Work out a method of testing a number of subjects to see if the following statement is true: Persons reading aloud a prose or poetry selection tend to read it with some similarity of pattern.

(*a*) Will you use prose or poetry? Explain.

Make a tape recording of the selection. Use two groups of subjects.

(*b*) Have one group read the selection *after* having listened to the tape. Record their readings on tape and compare with the original.

(*c*) Have the other group read the selection without having heard it read previously. Record the readings on tape. Compare these tapes with the tapes secured in (*b*), above. Explain the results. What do you conclude?

CHAPTER VI

VI-1. Define:

1. Protoplasm
2. Nucleus
3. Irritability
4. Conductivity
5. Segmentation
6. Differentiation
7. Amniotic cavity
8. Entoderm
9. Primitive streak
10. Caudad
11. Somatopleure
12. Primordium
13. Neural groove
14. Dendrite
15. Dorsal root
16. Axon
17. Ganglion
18. Brain
19. Mesencephalon
20. Metencephalon
21. Visceral arch
22. Maxillary process
23. Pulmonary pleura
24. Chrondrification
25. Mandibular process
26. Embryology
27. Inherent characteristics
28. Spermatozoon
29. Germ cell
30. Cell membrane
31. Assimilation
32. Fertilization
33. Embryonic disc
34. Mitosis
35. Ectoderm
36. Mesoderm
37. Cephalad
38. Embryo
39. Diverticulum
40. Neural tube
41. Neuroglia
42. Neuroblast
43. Axonic dendrite
44. Osseous
45. Medulla spinalis
46. Rhombencephalon
47. Myelencephalon
48. Prosencephalon
49. Visceral groove
50. Lung bud
51. Alveoli
52. Fossa
53. Fetus stage
54. Spinal cord
55. Ovum
56. Cell division

VI-2. Invite a teacher of embryology to lecture to the class, showing a series of models of embryos at various stages of development.

(*a*) Be sure to learn how much enlargement each model represents. How do the dimensions compare with those found in the textbook or in reference books you have studied?

VI-3. Follow the procedure of (VI-2), above, but with the teacher lecturing about stages of the fetus.

VI-4. Refer to Fig. 47, and the material on the general development of the nervous system.

(*a*) What forces do you think might operate to make a flat plate into a groove and, eventually, into a tube?

(*b*) Do you know of other instances, in embryology, in which the same principle seems to be applied by nature?

VI-5. Explain, in detail, how a normal face is formed.

VI-6. Explain the step-by-step development of ectoderm, mesoderm, and endoderm from undifferentiated protoplasm.

VI-7. Statement: The study of human embryology is essential for the student of speech and hearing.

(*a*) Do you agree? Explain.

(b) If your answer is in the affirmative, what courses on your campus would you recommend as prerequisites to the study of embryology?

VI-8. Statement: The moment you are born you begin the process of dying.
(*a*) Do you agree or disagree? Why?
(*b*) What does the statement mean?

VI-9. Considering the millions of cells involved and the split-second developmental relations of the many tissues, organs and structures, how do you account for the fact that so many normal babies are born and grow to adulthood?

VI-10. Explain what is meant by the term: *normal human being*.

CHAPTER VII

VII-1. Define:

1. Neurology
2. External stimuli
3. Response
4. Reaction
5. Neural integration
6. Neuron
7. Multipolar
8. Myelin sheath
9. Efferent
10. Central nervous system
11. Nerve
12. Nerve impulse
13. Refractory period
14. All-or-none law
15. Excitability
16. Chronaxy
17. Reflex arc
18. Esodic
19. Cervical vertebrae
20. Anteroposterior
21. Dorsal column
22. Lower motor neuron
23. Reciprocal innervation
24. Encephalon
25. Cranial nerve
26. Decussation
27. Telencephalon
28. Gyri
29. Upper motor neuron
30. Contralateral
31. Conduction
32. Internal stimuli
33. Receptor
34. Stimulus
35. Effector
36. Unipolar
37. Cyton
38. Dendrite
39. Afferent
40. Peripheral nervous system
41. Nerve trunk
42. Latent period
43. Action current
44. Self-contributory
45. Medullated
46. Synapse
47. Exodic
48. Trophic unit
49. Sulci
50. Anterior column
51. Gray commissure
52. Final common pathway
53. Diadochokinesis
54. Cerebellum
55. Spinal nerve
56. Somatic
57. Longitudinal cerebral fissure
58. Cerebral cortex
59. Motor area (cortical area)
60. Motor nuclei

VII-2. What is the difference in neurological control when the vegetative-biological mechanism is used for normal respiration and when it subserves the speech production function? Explain.

VII-3. (*a*) What are proprioceptors?
(*b*) What part do they play in speech production?

(*c*) Is the part they play related to the part hearing plays in speech production? Explain.

(*d*) Assume that your answer to (*c*), above, is in the affirmative. Make a sketch to illustrate the neurological levels involved.

VII-4. Statement: For convenience in referring to various areas of the brain these areas have been assigned numbers.

(*a*) Can you discover who was responsible for this convention?

(*b*) What numbered area or areas would be involved in normal speech?

(*c*) What numbered area or areas would be involved in writing?

(*d*) Considering the chronology of the development of speech and writing, what relation, if any, would you expect to find between or among the areas noted in (*b*) and (*c*), above?

VII-5. Based on the protection they are afforded in the human body, is it your opinion that nature considers spinal nerves or cranial nerves more important?

VII-6. Statement: Some recent experiments might lead one to believe that memory may not be confined to the brain, but may reside in protein-molecular aggregates widely distributed throughout the organism (even in the tail of lower forms).

(*a*) Considering the importance of memory as related to speech, what advantages do you see in such a theory?

VII-7. Read about the chemical-neurological-physical control of respiration, consulting at least two other textbooks or reference articles.

(*a*) Using simple sketches, explain how inhalation and exhalation are regulated and controlled.

VII-8. Combining your knowledge of phonation and neurology, explain how neurological control of the laryngeal muscles permits such fine adjustments of the phonative mechanism.

VII-9. Recall your information about phonation and articulation.

(*a*) In your opinion, is the total neurological involvement in phonation more complex or less complex than the total neurological involvement in articulation? Explain, giving specific illustrations.

VII-10. You may recall the following, or some similar, statement: When a centipede began to "think" about the order in which he moved his "legs" he became so confused that he could not move.

(*a*) Consider your tongue and its intricate musculature and neurological control, efferent and afferent. In your personal experience, do you find that even in normal speaking you make more (or fewer) errors in pronunciation when you focus thought on what you are saying than when you do otherwise? What, if anything, does this tell you about the levels of neurological control of speech mechanisms?

VII-11. Some radio announcers speak much more rapidly than others, but are still clearly understood.

(*a*) Assuming that the more rapid rate is superior, would it be due, in your opinion, to a superior nervous system or to a superior musculature? Give a detailed explanation.

(*b*) Considering only the nervous system, how rapidly could a person talk? Three times as fast? Five times? Ten times? Even faster? Explain in detail how you arrive at your answer.

VII-12. In your opinion, what advantages are there in having some nerve fibers, afferent and/or efferent, crossing over from one side of the body to the other? Answer for (*a*) motor nerves and for (*b*) sensory nerves. Can you think of any possible disadvantages?

VII-13. Statement: Not only does the speaker's speech alter his own respiratory cycle, but his speech also influences and alters the respiratory cycle of the listener.

(*a*) Read the reference (Judson, 1932). Do you agree or disagree with the conclusions expressed?

(*b*) What electrical equipment could you use to perform a similar experiment? Describe the procedure you would follow.

(*c*) Give a detailed account of the neurology involved in the case of the alteration of the cycle of the speaker.

(*d*) Do the same for the cycle of the listener.

(*e*) What implications might this have for mass media communications?

VII-14. If, in certain pattern sequences, electroencephalograms matched speech spectrograms made concurrently, would this provide any grounds for a belief that thought is subvocal speech? Explain in depth.

(*a*) How, in your opinion, are thought and speech related?

VII-15. Combining your knowledge of all areas covered in this textbook, what arguments would you present to prove (*a*) or (*b*)?

(*a*) Any foreign language must be learned during early (how early?) childhood if it is to be mastered.

(*b*) No person can master (define: *master*) a foreign language if he does not begin its study until he reaches adult age.

VII-16. It has been said (1) that a person "overlearns" his native language by adulthood and (2) that for this reason he finds it difficult, if not impossible, to acquire the patterns of a foreign language after becoming an adult.

(*a*) Explain (1) in detail.

(*b*) Do you agree or disagree with (2)? Explain your answer.

VII-17. A normal speaker may be made to speak abnormally—perhaps even be made to stutter—if forced to listen, while speaking, to a delayed auditory feedback of what he is saying.

(*a*) Is the term *stutter* used correctly? Explain.

(*b*) Compile a bibliography of articles dealing with experiments of this type.

(*c*) Assemble the equipment needed to perform such an experiment.

(*d*) Perform such an experiment. Analyze your results and draw your conclusions.

(*e*) Offer a comprehensive explanation in terms of the time factors involved in the patterns of efferent and afferent innervations.

CHAPTER VIII

VIII-1. Define:

1. Visible speech
2. Spectrogram
3. Damping
4. Wave length
5. Ideal diaphragm
6. Sine wave
7. Simple harmonic motion
8. Frequency
9. Period
10. Phase
11. Amplitude
12. Displacement
13. Pure tone
14. Complex tone
15. Reflection of sound
16. Absorption of sound

CHAPTER VIII—*Continued*

17. Absorption factor
18. Velocity of sound
19. Homogeneous medium
20. Difference tone
21. Persistence of hearing
22. Reinforce
23. Interference
24. Beats
25. Quality
26. Vibrato
27. Transients
28. Harmonics
29. Partials
30. Fundamental
31. Modulation
32. Loudness
33. Phon
34. Standard reference tone
35. Decibel
36. Average speech power
37. Doppler effect
38. Standard pitch
39. Intensity
40. Compression wave
41. Rarefaction wave
42. Node
43. Sonorous body
44. ~
45. Masking
46. Noise
47. Continuum
48. Sound

VIII-2. You are a passenger on the *Maid of the Mist* at Niagara Falls. You estimate the loudness level of the roar of falling water at 35, 55, 75, 95, or 115 phons.

(*a*) Which figure would you select, if any?

(*b*) How could you arrive at a correct estimate? (If *correct,* is it an *estimate*?) Explain, giving details of the equipment you would use.

VIII-3. Statement: A group of musicians wishing to tune their instruments ask the pianist to strike A = 440~.

(*a*) What would happen if the piano had been tuned incorrectly so that A = 435 cycles? Explain.

(*b*) If a violinist in the group possesses absolute pitch and can sound an accurate 440-cycle tone on his violin, would it be better for those who were tuning their instruments to follow his lead?

VIII-4. Statement: Scientific Pitch or Philosophical Pitch (Koenig, 1872) takes for octaves successive powers of 2.

(*a*) Do you agree? Explain.

VIII-5. From a solid support (e.g., the lintel of a doorway), and separated from each other by equal distances of 4 to 6 inches, suspend three equal weights, *A, B* and *C,* by threads. The threads supporting *A* and *C* should be of equal length, say, 24 inches. The thread supporting *B* should be shorter or longer, as you desire. (Try it both ways.) Start *A* swinging by barely touching it, periodically, with a shred of tissue paper. Deliver the impulses isochronously—i.e., in time with the natural period of *A*. When *A* is oscillating with considerable amplitude,

(*a*) what effect, if any, do *A*'s oscillations have upon *B* and *C*? Explain.

(*b*) Define *mechanical resonance.*

VIII-6. With a pure tone oscillator generate a tone through various intensity levels from threshold to 90db. Statement: Even though it is a pure tone you may hear a number of overtones at high intensities.

(*a*) In your experience, is the statement true? Explain.

VIII-7. Recalling the part *relative velocity* plays in the Doppler effect, (*a*) Under what conditions of relative velocity would it be possible for you to hear the horn (it generates a 1000-cycle tone) of an automobile traveling at 60mph, and yet experience no Doppler effect?

(*b*) To your ear, what would be the pitch of the horn?

VIII-8. Assume: that a gas cannot sustain a tensile stress; that sound is transmitted through gas by the collisions of the molecules of the gas; that the speed of sound in any gas is proportional to the effective speed (i.e., the square root of the average squared speed) of the molecules in the gas. If the speed of sound is approximately 1290 m/sec in hydrogen, 320 m/sec in oxygen, and 1100 ft/sec in air,

(*a*) What will be the pitch of the voice of a demonstrator after inhaling hydrogen (his normal fundamental pitch is 150cps)? Explain.

(*b*) What will be the pitch of his voice after inhaling helium?

VIII-9. Statement: Normal male and female voices differ.

(*a*) Define: continuum.

(*b*) Do you agree or disagree with the statement? Explain.

(*c*) Assume that in the case of a specific man and woman there are voice differences. Are they due to:

(1) Differences in their phonative mechanisms?
(2) Differences in their resonating mechanisms?
(3) Some other factor?

(*d*) If you assume that the voices differ, are both normal? If so, does this require two differing definitions of *normal* voice?

VIII-10. Sound a pure musical tone and its odd-numbered partials.

(*a*) Is this possible?

(*b*) If so, do you also hear some even-numbered partials?

(*c*) Define *subjective tones.*

(*d*) Define *aural harmonics.*

VIII-11. What is the value and importance of experiments in the production or synthetic speech sounds?

VIII-12. Assume that the trachea has a length of 4 or 5 inches. Assume that it is a tube closed at one end.

(*a*) Can you justify the second assumption?

(*b*) If it is 5 inches long, to what tones will it resonate?

VIII-13. In the production of speech sounds, how many basic methods are used in producing the sounds?

(*a*) Give an example of one speech sound produced by each method.

VIII-14. Statement: The pharynx is a musculo-membranous tube. Assume that it is 11cm long.

(*a*) If it is to serve as a resonator for speech sounds must it be considered (1) a tube closed at one end? (2) a tube open at both ends? (3) a tube closed at both ends?

(*b*) Assign to the tube what in your opinion is a fair absorptive factor as far as reflected sound waves are concerned. Check your figure with the figures chosen by other members of the class. Do you want to change your estimate? Explain.

VIII-15. Statement: In the textbook, the energy expended in public speaking has been compared to that expended in playing tennis.

(*a*) What experimental methods can you suggest that would permit you to prove or disprove the statement?

VIII-16. All other things being equal a tube open at both ends, if equal in length, will have a natural frequency twice that of a tube closed at one end.

(*a*) True or false? Explain.

VIII-17. A complex sound is made up of a composite of simple tones. The analysis of a complex sound consists, essentially, of discovering what are its individual components.

(*a*) Do you agree? Explain.

VIII-18. Statement: Radar, sonar, and sodar (the mechanism used by bats) utilize a beep system to improve transmission-reception capabilities and control. The principle is one of periodicity fluctuations in terms of tone-silence-tone-silence, etc. Although differing in mechanics, the periodicity of fluctuations of the phonated portions of speech waves amounts to an application of the same general principle. The vocal generator emits rapid periodically fluctuating wave patterns, scanning and sampling the slower pattern coordinates of the less rapidly moving multiple-coupled resonators, the whole being under an anatomical-physiological-neurological servo-mechanism control dependent on highly delicate proprioceptive-ear-brain feedback mechanisms.

(*a*) Define: *critique*.

(*b*) Present a critique of the statement.

VIII-19. From your knowledge of the molecular nature of air you know that if an artery pulsates it will set into vibration the adjacent air particles. Consult one or more anatomy books to discover what arterial structures, if any, are closely associated with the bronchi or larynx.

(*a*) If there are such associated structures, what effect, if any, would they have upon the exhaled air stream during phonation? Explain in detail.

CHAPTER IX

IX-1. Define:

1. Meatus
2. Tympanic
3. Auricle
4. Middle ear
5. Eustachian tube
6. Articulate
7. Fenestra cochleae
8. Helicotrema
9. Scala tympani
10. External auditory meatus
11. Vestibule
12. Modiolus
13. Helix
14. Endolymph
15. Locus
16. Tectorial membrane
17. Cochlear partition
18. Hair cells, inner
19. Tunnel of Corti
20. Electrophysiology
21. Electroanatomy
22. DC potential
23. Displacement
24. Place theory
25. Traveling wave
26. Hydrodynamic principle
27. Chladni phenomena
28. Hydromechanical
29. Ventral cochlear nucleus
30. Duration
31. Summation tone
32. Discrete
33. Audiogram
34. Threshold
35. Presbycusis
36. Ear
37. Speculum
38. Eardrum
39. Ossicle
40. Fenestra
41. Fenestra vestibuli
42. Scala vestibuli
43. Basilar membrane
44. Cochlea

CHAPTER IX—*Continued*

45. VIIIth cranial nerve
46. Apex or cupola
47. Spiral cochlear canal
48. Perilymph
49. Spiral organ of Corti
50. Stapes
51. Cochlear duct
52. Hair cells, outer
53. Reticular membrane
54. Stimuli
55. Potential, differences of
56. Microphonics
57. Reissner's membrane
58. Resonance theory
59. Transverse band
60. Eddy currents
61. Standing wave theory
62. Telephone theory
63. Neuron level
64. Loudness
65. Difference tone
66. Conscious present
67. Audiometer
68. Audiometry
69. Zero decibels
70. Bone conduction

IX-2. Describe the basilar membrane.

IX-3. Without prejudice, consider if the 4 coils of the cochlea of the guinea pig represent a stage of development higher than that of a mammal having but 2¾ turns.

(*a*) Present reasons for your decision.

IX-4. Statements: The ear of the chicken represents an early developmental stage. The cochlea is an almost straight tube, but with a slight bend near the stapedial end. It is 5mm long. There is no helicotrema. However, it has been argued that because the tube is so short a helicotrema would only reduce the sensitivity of the ear of a bird.

(*a*) Give reasons for and against such a point of view.

IX-5. Describe the organ of Corti.

IX-6. Differentiate between the scala vestibuli and the scala tympani.

IX-7. Statement: Experiments with models of the inner ear show that simply altering the stiffness of the cochlear partition will produce such different patterns of vibration as to give support to almost any theory of hearing.

(*a*) Circle the two methods one could use to decide among various theories.

(1) Test for just-perceptible limen differences.

(2) Measure the stiffness of the cochlear partition at various points and observe the pattern in a model constructed to have similar properties.

(3) Apply phase-reversal bone-conduction tests.

(4) Make direct observations of the pattern of vibration in the human cochlea.

IX-8. Explain completely, but simply and briefly, the operation of a pure tone audiometer.

IX-9. Consider these three statements: (1) Experiments show that the amplitude of vibrations of the basilar membrane are relatively equal no matter what the frequency of the tone. (2) The basilar membrane becomes less elastic with increasing amplitude of vibration. (3) As amplitude increases, the movement of the cochlear partition is not proportional to the movement of the footplate of the stapes.

(*a*) Is each statement correct or incorrect? Explain each of your answers.

(*b*) How would you relate (1) to (2)? Explain.

(*c*) How would you relate (1) to (3)? Explain.

(*d*) How would you relate (2) to (3)? Explain.

IX-10. Refer to the information about eddy currents. Recall that the basilar membrane and Reissner's membrane vibrate in unison.

(*a*) In addition to the eddy currents on either side of the basilar membrane would you expect to find (1) an eddy on one side of Reissner's membrane (which side)? or (2) eddy currents on both sides of Reissner's membrane?

(*b*) If your answer is "Yes" to either (1) or (2), above, draw a sketch to show the rotational direction of the eddy currents related to the basilar membrane and that of those related to Reissner's membrane.

IX-11. What experimental approach might be used to prove the truth or falsity of this statement: The intensity with which one hears by air conduction is approximately equal to that with which one hears by bone conduction.

IX-12. The statement has been made that eliminating air conduction, and hearing by bone conduction alone, results in an attenuation of 6db.

(*a*) How would you determine that the figure is, indeed, 6db and not some other figure?

IX-13. Closing the auditory meatus with your finger tips raises by about 10db the intensity of bone-conducted sound.

(*a*) Do you agree with the statement, in general?

(*b*) How could you determine that the figure is, indeed, 10db and not 5db, 8db, 12db, 15db, or some other figure?

IX-14. Refer to the drawings and explanations covering the difference between waves in a system of resonators and a traveling wave.

(*a*) Describe each in a few words, but so clearly that another person reading your description could not help but distinguish even a section of either wave if he saw it.

IX-15. Assume that the ear has been fatigued by a tone of 900cps. If you were told that "now a tone lower in frequency (e.g., 750~) will have its pattern of excitation lowered in frequency while a tone of higher frequency (e.g., 1050~) will be raised in frequency," how would you attempt to prove or disprove the statement?

IX-16. Consider the anatomical pathways of the auditory nerve fibers (one side of the brain; crossing at various levels; both sides of the brain) of both ears.

(*a*) Could you experience directional hearing with only one ear? Explain.

(*b*) What effect, if any, do the interconnections of the auditory nerve fibers between the two sides of the brain have upon directional hearing?

(*c*) Is the ability to distinguish direction a function of the ear, only? Of the brain, only? Of both?

(*d*) What factor or factors, (e.g., spatial localization along the basilar membrane? spatial localization in the brain? time sequence? others?) is responsible for your ability in directional hearing?

IX-17. From your knowledge of articulation, hearing, and neurology, explain proprioceptive-hearing feedback-control of speech.

IX-18. Statements: In an ear lacking an eardrum (1) the pressure-flow of fluid and displacement of the basilar membrane will be in opposite phase to that in the normal ear and (2) impairment of hearing will be greater at higher frequencies.

(*a*) Is either statement true? Explain.

(*b*) Are both statements true?

(*c*) What is the relation, if any, between the impairment of hearing and the displacement in opposite phase?

IX-19. Statement: A pure tone of less than 800~ is heard as apparently lower in frequency if its loudness be increased.

(*a*) Using a pure tone audiometer can you verify this statement? Explain exactly the procedure you followed in arriving at your answer.

IX-20. What significance do you see in the fact, if it is a fact, that at the end of the cochlear partition, at their termini at the helicotrema (*H*), the tectorial membrane (*TM*) is shorter than the organ of Corti (*OC*) which, in turn, is shorter than the basilar membrane (*BM*)?

IX-21. Form a group of 5 students. Cooperate in preparing a typewritten, bound report. In simple language, *in outline form,* explain how we hear. Trace the sound from:

(*a*) any generator (name and describe)
(*b*) to the external ear
(*c*) to the middle ear (draw a diagram and label it)
(*d*) to the cochlea (draw a diagram and label it)
(*e*) to the organ of Corti (draw a diagram and label it)
(*f*) to the auditory nerve and brain nerve paths (draw a diagram and label it).

IX-22. Taking into account traveling waves, vibrating membrane, eddy effects, etc., in the ear, does the illustration and explanatory caption on p. 388 have any value in relation to the ear and hearing?

IX-23. Using your knowledge of respiration, phonation, articulation, resonance, neurology, and hearing, explain in outline form:

(*a*) How you carry on a conversation with a friend.

(*b*) How a sleeping person carries on a conversation with a person who is awake.

(*c*) How a person under anesthesia carries on a conversation with the surgeon.

(*d*) From (*a*), (*b*), and (*c*) extract the essential differentiating factors.

IX-24. Why is the stapes footplate in the oval window, on the aspect of the cochlear partition leading to the semicircular canals?

(*a*) Was there some reason in past evolutionary history?
(*b*) Is there still some reason?
(*c*) Would it be better, physically, if Nature had put the stapes in the round window?

IX-25. Circle the number opposite the bone in which you would be most likely to find a cochlea: 1. occipital bone; 2. parietal bone; 3. sphenoid bone; 4. temporal bone; 5. zygomatic bone.

IX-26. The basilar membrane and Reissner's membrane are almost completely transparent.

(*a*) Do you agree with the statement?

(*b*) If you agree, suggest one way in which they could be made visible for photographing.

(*c*) Suggest another way.

IX-27. Statement: Nature has perfected an aperiodic frequency analyzer in the ear, but Man with all his technological achievements has not yet been able to devise such an analyzer.

(*a*) Would you agree with the first part of the statement by Békésy? Explain.

(*b*) Would you agree with the second part of the statement? Explain.

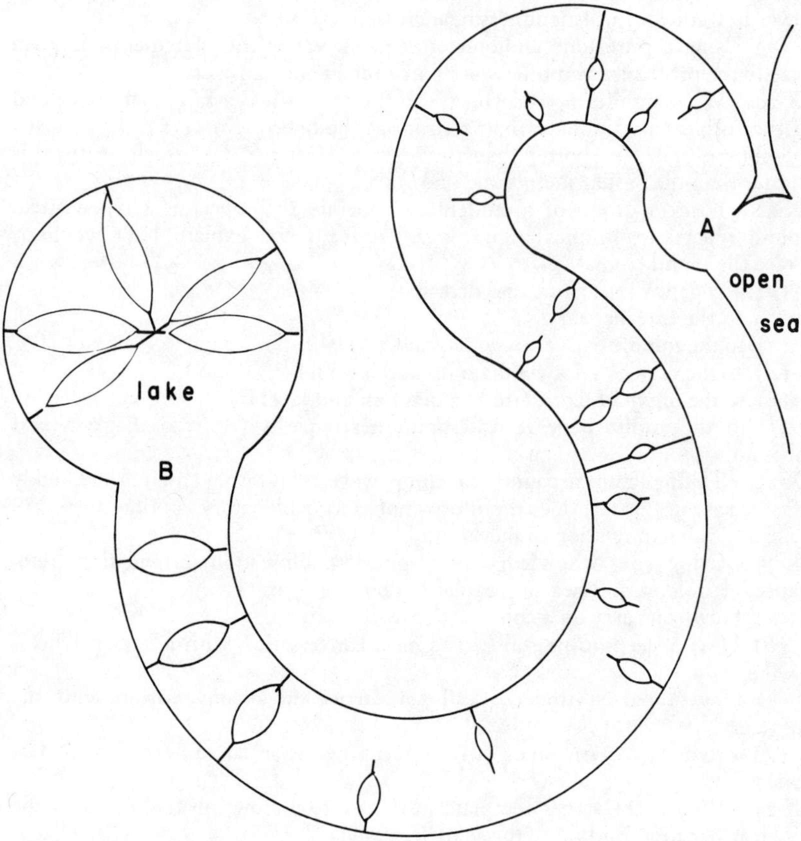

An artificial harbor has numerous rowboats tied and/or anchored within it. The boats are of equal width, but are progressively longer from the entrance *A* to *B*. (Only a few boats are represented in the drawing. You should imagine numerous boats about equally spaced. The moorings differ, in some cases.) A storm in the open sea produces waves that move into the channel at *A* and continue on until dissipating themselves in the lake. It is noted that the boats rise and fall at their moorings in a progressive manner from *A* to *B*. The displacement of each boat causes easily heard sucking noises and observable local eddies as the boats move in ordered sequence.

Form groups of at least five students for the remaining exercises.

IX-28. From a local meat-packing company secure the head of a cow or calf for the purpose of disclosing the cochleas.

(*a*) What are the advantages or disadvantages of a cochlea of 3½ turns (cow) compared with one of 2¾ turns (human)?

(*b*) What are the advantages or disadvantages of a cochlear partition having a length of about 38mm (cow) compared with the shorter one of man?

IX-29. Secure a large live frog. Observe that when it croaks it opens its mouth, producing sound by vibrating the end of its tongue. Observe, also, that when the mouth is open this also opens the Eustachian tube. (The mechanism is somewhat similar in man during yawning.) Look into the tube and see the ossicle attached to the eardrum.

(*a*) Explain, using a simple sketch, how air pressure is equalized on both sides of the eardrum of the frog, thus protecting the frog's ear from the loud noise the frog makes.

IX-30. Arrange to see (or perform) a demonstration showing the structure of the cochlea of the guinea pig.

(*a*) List a number of advantages in selecting the guinea pig as your experimental animal.

(*b*) What can you learn from macroscopic observation?

(*c*) What can you learn from microscopic observation?

(*d*) What sectioning, staining, or other laboratory techniques would it be helpful for the researcher to know if he were doing research on the cochlea of the guinea pig?

IX-31. Study a rooster. Here the protective mechanism is different from that of the frog. The external auditory meatus is surrounded by a cartilaginous ring. This tends to close as the rooster raises its head, as to crow. Thus, the ear is protected (this time from the exterior) against loud crowing noises.

(*a*) Does the presence of this simple mechanism indicate that the rooster never crows unless its head is raised?

IX-32. *This experiment should be conducted only with the cooperation of an otologist or other qualified person.* Cold water on the eardrum cools the fluid in the semicircular canals nearest the eardrum. The cooled fluid sinks, with the result that the head tips in the direction of the eardrum.

Similarly, introducing to the ear an intense tone will produce fluid streaming in the fluid of the cochlea and this, when transmitted to the semicircular canals, also causes the head to tip. When the sound is stopped the head will tip in the opposite direction.

(*a*) Do your experiments indicate that these statements are correct?

(*b*) Work out a sketch to accompany your explanation.

IX-33. Statement: Tones are capable of conveying a sensation of size. For example, a tone of low frequency (50∼) might give the sensation that it "filled the head" of the listener. With sounds of increasing frequency, the listener may report the sound images "growing smaller."

Try listening to clicks of low frequency (large sound image) and to clicks of high frequency (small sound image) to demonstrate the phenomena.

(*a*) Write a report on your observations.

(*b*) How much were you influenced by the manner in which the statement was worded?

IX-34. From various sources compile a list, in chronological order, of fifteen persons whose contributions to our knowledge about the ear and hearing warrant their inclusion.

(*a*) Give a brief statement about each and summarize his contribution.

(*b*) Rearrange the list of names in order of the importance of their contributions.

METRIC EQUIVALENTS

In most scientific publications measurements are given in units based on the metric system. So that the relations between these units, as well as the relation of these units to the units of other systems of measurement, may be more easily understood, the following equivalent values are presented for reference.

Printer's Type Equivalent *	Metric Equivalent		U. S. A. Equivalent
Point	*Millimeter*	*Centimeter*	*Inch*
1 point	0.35278mm	0.035278cm	0.01389 inch
2 points	0.70556mm	0.070556cm	0.02778 inch
3 points	1.05834mm	0.105834cm	0.04167 inch
4 points	1.41112mm	0.141112cm	0.05556 inch
5 points	1.76390mm	0.176390cm	0.06945 inch
10 points	3.5278 mm	0.35278 cm	0.1389 inch
72 points	25.4 mm	2.54 cm	1.0 inch

* The thickness of each line (i.e., from top to bottom) is represented in *points*. Each line is 1 inch or 72 points in width.

MEASUREMENTS OF LENGTH

Metric Equivalents				U.S.A. Equivalents
Millimeter (mm)	*Centimeter* (cm)	*Meter* (m)	*Kilometer* (Km)	*Inch-Foot-Yard-Mile*
1	.1	.001		.03937 inch
5				.19685 inch
10	1.0	.01		.3937 inch

MEASUREMENTS OF LENGTH—*Continued*

Metric Equivalents: *Millimeter* (mm)	*Centimeter* (cm)	*Meter* (m)	*Kilometer* (Km)	U.S.A. Equivalents: *Inch-Foot-Yard-Mile*	
25.4	2.54			1.0	inch
50.0	5.0	.05		1.9685	inches
100.0	10.0	.1		3.937 0.328	inches feet
304.8	30.48	.3048		1.0	foot
914.0	91.4	.914		1.0	yard
1000.0	100.0	1.0	0.001	39.37 3.28 1.0936	inches feet yards
		10.0	0.01	10.936	yards
		1000.0	1.0	.6213	mile
		1609.34	1.6	1.0	mile
		10000.0	10.0	6.213	miles

millionth microns ($\mu\mu$)	*millimicrons* (mμ)	*microns* (μ)	*centimeters* (cm)	*inches*
1	0.001	10^{-6}	10^{-10}	3.937×10^{-11}
100	0.1	10^{-4}	10^{-8}	3.937×10^{-9}
1000	1.0	10^{-3}	10^{-7}	3.937×10^{-8}
10^6	1000.0	1	10^{-4}	3.937×10^{-5}

MEASUREMENTS OF AREA

Square millimeters (mm^2)	*Square centimeters* (cm^2)	*Square meters* (m^2)	*Square inches*
1	0.01	0.000001	0.00155
100	1.0	0.0001	0.155
10000	100.0	0.01	15.5

MEASUREMENTS OF VOLUME

Cubic millimeter (mm^3)	*Cubic centimeter* (cm^3) or (cc)	*Cubic inch*
1	0.001	0.000061
1000	1.0	0.061

MISCELLANEOUS EQUIVALENTS

1 meter/sec	= 3.28 ft/sec
1 foot/sec	= 30.48 cm/sec
1 ounce (oz.) (avoirdupois)	= 28 + grams
1 pound (lb. avdp.)	= 453.6 grams
1 kilogram (kg)	= 2.2045 pounds (avdp.)
1° Centigrade (C)	= 1.8° Fahrenheit (F)
	$= \frac{9^\circ}{5} F$
1° Fahrenheit (F)	= 0.55556° Centigrade (C)
	$= \frac{5^\circ}{9} C$

Atmospheric pressure equivalents: 76 cm mercury (Hg); 29.9 in. Hg; 33.9 feet H_2O; 14.696 lb/in^2; 2116 lb/ft^2; 1033 $grams/cm^2$; 1.01×10^6 $dynes/cm^2$

MISCELLANEOUS ABBREVIATIONS

avoirdupois: avdp
centimeter-gram-second (system): cgs
micron: μ or mu
millimicron: mμ or m mu
micromicron: $\mu\mu$ or mu mu
microvolt: μv
millivolt: mv
microwatt: μw or mu w

THE LABORATORY: ITS USE AND EQUIPMENT

In connection with the classroom meetings, in which this textbook provides the background information for discussion, we recommend a series of correlated laboratory sessions.

MOTION PICTURES

Broadening the term somewhat, we suggest that some of these sessions be devoted to screening a selected group of motion pictures. Helpful films are readily available at university audio-visual instruction centers, from federal government sources, from a limited number of corporations, and from independent film distributors. The films should include those showing the vocal folds in action, and those containing information on the ear, sound, embryology, and the nervous system. A half-dozen or more films are worthy of the consideration of the teacher. A study of the film catalogs available, or inquiries directed to the A–V center, will provide information about films in these and related areas of interest. As A–V personnel will be the first to advise, the effectiveness of the use of any audio-visual teaching aid depends upon its careful integration into the course, its being previewed by the teacher in a conscientious manner, plus some kind of follow-up to determine the value it has had for the students.

REFERENCE MATERIALS

In preparation for laboratory assignments, it is recommended that each teacher compile and supply students with a list of the reference volumes and journals available in the general library or in special college or departmental libraries on the campus. In this same connection, the teacher may wish to make available, for immediate use by students working in the laboratory, a limited number of selected reference volumes, journals, reprints of articles, and manufacturers' brochures or manuals containing directions for the operation of equipment.

WALL CHARTS

Large wall charts, in color, of the anatomy of the human body; of the nervous system; of the head, mouth, larynx, neck and thorax; of the ear; of the respiratory system, nerve tissue, and stages of the embryo, are of great value for use in the classroom and laboratory.

THREE–DIMENSIONAL MODELS

Next, we will suggest materials that will help students overcome one of the major difficulties they encounter in their attempts to understand the normal speech and hearing mechanisms. Every person finds difficulty in visualizing pictures in books or journals, on charts or on the screen, in terms of three dimensions. For demonstration purposes in the classroom, and for individual use by students in the laboratory, three-dimensional models are indispensable. *Handling* the models as well as *seeing* them has value.

Among the models we recommend for use by teacher and student are the following: human skeleton, human figure with musculature, human trunk (with head),* torso, entire head, median section of head,* brain and cranial cavity, brain,* trachea and lungs,* larynx,* ear,* cochlea,* tongue, spinal cord and nerves, development of the human face, development of the human ear, development of the human embryo, semicircular canals and cochlea, and plant mitosis. Many of these models can be dissected and are accompanied by identifying keys. Those starred should, in our opinion, be among the first to be acquired. The teacher may find some of these models in other departments on the campus, or in the offices of local physicians, audiologists, and dentists.

Among the major sources of supply of charts and 3-dimensional equipment we have mentioned may be listed (alphabetically) the following who responded to our requests for information: Denoyer-Geppert Company; General Biological Supply House, Inc.; and Ward's Natural Science Establishment, Inc. There are numerous other suppliers, as the teacher and student will discover by visiting the exhibits at the national Speech and/or Hearing Association conventions, by reading the advertisements in the journals of these organizations, or by studying the catalogs to be found in the office files of Biology, Physics, Psychology and other departments on the campus.

MICROSCOPES AND SLIDES

By figuring out the magnification of what he sees through a microscope, a student learns to appreciate the actual size of some of the cells or tissues he studies. Also, if the tissues are differentially stained, it helps him understand structure and relationships. We recommend slides containing sections of the following: lung tissue; muscle fibers, showing nerve endings; nerve fibers, myelinated and unmyelinated; areas of the brain and of the spinal cord, and types of cartilage.

PRESERVED SPECIMENS AND DISSECTION MATERIAL

Prepared human larynges, in preserving fluid or in plastic mounts so that they may be handled, should be available for comparison with wall charts and models of the larynx. Larynges of sheep or other animals may be obtained from local meat-processing plants and made available for dissection.

GENERAL EQUIPMENT FOR USE IN EXPERIMENTS

Finally, we would suggest that there be included among the laboratory equipment such items as the following: equipment for laryngoscopy (including, light sources, laryngoscopic mirrors, laryngo-periskop, head mirrors); equipment for stroboscopy; equipment for the study of sounds (e.g., oscillograph, spectrograph); kymograph equipment; audiometer; spirometer; physiotachometer; pneumograph equipment; stethoscopes; stop watches; dissecting equipment; sound-recording equipment and tape; sound-generating equipment (e.g., tuning forks, strings, tubes, pure tone generators or other electric oscillators); equipment for experiments in resonance, including resonators of all types; and, for many uses, a variety of experimental equipment, including microphones, amplifiers, meters, headphones, and loudspeakers.

It is not assumed that the equipment is to be used for research. Rather, it is for use for demonstration purposes by the teacher or, better, for use by the student in conducting simple experiments. The equipment has, at least, these two purposes: (1) it will help the student to understand better the phenomena related to the functioning of the normal mechanisms of speech production and hearing and (2) it will introduce him to laboratory equipment, methods, and techniques. These experiences will give him some background to enable him to appreciate experimental work reported in the technical journals. This will be of additional value in case his advanced studies lead him into laboratory research fields.

GLOSSARY

Every scientific field has its own specialized terminology and nomenclature; words which have one meaning for the layman have another strictly delimited meaning for the scientist. The entering wedge in acquainting oneself with a new area of knowledge, quite logically is the learning of its exact vocabulary. The following terms, though by no means exhaustive, have been selected on the basis of their probable usefulness to the student.

abduct: to move away from the axis of the body; away from the mid-line. The posterior cricoarytenoid which aids in opening the glottis is an abductor muscle. The opposite term is *adduct.*

abscissa: one of the reference elements by which a point may be established (i.e., a *fix*) in relation to coordinate axes. In a graph, the horizontal axis or the left-to-right axis. See *ordinate.*

acoustic: relating to the perception of sound, i.e., hearing.

acoustic reflex: the involuntary contraction of the two tympanic muscles (tensor tympani and stapedius) as a protection of the inner ear against intense acoustic stimuli.

acoustic spectrum: refers to the distribution of the intensities of the various frequencies of the components of a sound.

acoustics, "Father" of: Pere Mersenne (1636), French churchman, mathematician, and, perhaps, founder of the French Academy of Sciences. Author: *Harmonie Universelle* (12 vol.).

acuity: the sharpness, clearness, or distinctness with which one is able to hear a sound; hence, usually auditory acuity.

adduct: to move toward the axis of the body, toward the mid-line. Opposite of *abduct.* Because it aids in closing the glottis, the transverse arytenoid muscle is an adductor.

aditus laryngis: the superior aperture of the larynx.

afferent: conducting toward the brain or spinal cord. Used of a nerve conveying impulses from the periphery to the central nervous system; a sensory nerve. Opposite, *efferent.*

agonist: a muscle in a state of contraction in reference to its opposing muscle called the *antagonist.*

air conduction: the normal manner of conducting sound waves through the external auditory meatus; as opposed to *bone conduction.*

ala (pl. alae): wing, or winglike structure.

all-or-none law: a nerve or a muscle fiber will respond either maximally to an appropriate stimulus or will not respond at all. Following one response there is a period of time (refractory period or latent period) during which the fiber is reconstituting its energy; during this brief interval the fiber will not respond to stimuli.

alveolar: relating to a small cavity or cell. For example, the alveolar air cells. Alveolar air is air in the alveolar cells.

amplitude: the range, or extent, of movement of a vibrating body. Directly related to intensity.

analog of human ear, electrical: models the outer, middle, and inner ear. The cochlea is represented by the equivalent of 36 segments, each representing 1 mm of the basilar membrane. Developed by Sensory Systems Group at The Applied Research Laboratory of the University of Arizona.

analogue: one sound which although different is closely related to another sound. For example, [d] is the voiced analogue of [t].

anastomose: to connect or interconnect by anastomosis.

anastomosis: union or intercommunication of systems or networks—e.g., the interconnection of nerve fibers of different nerves to provide dual innervation of an area of the body.

ankylosis: the stiffening of a joint which makes articulation of the bones at the joint difficult or impossible.

anlage: the term applied to the earliest discernible cell aggregation destined to form any organ or part of the embryo.

antagonist: opposing or resisting the action of another; pertaining to muscles. Opposite, *agonist.*

anterior: situated in front of; nearer the head; ventral. Opposite, *posterior.*

anterior-posterior: relating to the front-to-back diameter.

antrum: a cavity or sinus, particularly one with bony walls.

apex: the summit, tip, or extremity of a conical or pyramidal structure.

aphonia; loss of voice; absence of voice.

aponeurosis: a fibrous, sheetlike tendon.

approximate: to come near to; to approach another; to come close together. For example, the vocal folds are approximated; they may only approach one another or they may come together completely.

articulate: to join together; of bones or cartilages meeting at joints; of sounds joined with other sounds.

asynchronous contractions: as opposed to synchronized contractions (which produce tremors), asynchronous contractions of muscle fibers, resulting from asynchronous nerve impulses, combine in their activity to produce the smooth, overall, effective contraction of a muscle.

atlas: first cervical vertebra. Shaped like an oval ring, it receives the dens of the axis, forming the atlanto-axial joint.

attachment: refers to the connection which a muscle has with a bone or cartilage; an origin or insertion of a muscle.

audiogram: a graph expressing the acuity of hearing as measured by an audiometer.

audiology: the study of hearing (and hearing disorders). The identity of the person who coined the term may be unknown; its use dates from about 1945 and the work of Carhart, R. and Canfield, N.

audiometer: an instrument designed to test the hearing of an individual at various frequencies and at various intensities within those frequencies.

auscultation: the act of listening for sounds within the body.

axis: second cervical vertebra. The dens of the axis rotating within the atlas forms the atlanto-axial joint.

axon: the axis-cylinder process of a nerve-cell; usually the largest process of the nerve-cell, as opposed to the dendrites.

bar: unit of pressure 10^6 dyne/cm^2.

basilar membrane: the membrane which supports the organ of Corti and forms the partition between the cochlear duct, of which it forms the floor, and the scala tympani.

beats: perceived pulsations recurring at regular intervals and resulting from summation of two tones differing in frequency by only a few cycles per second. The number of beats per second represents the difference in frequency.

bel: the unit of intensity; a logarithmic unit expressing the ratio of two amounts of power; named in honor of Alexander Graham Bell.

bifurcation: a forking; a division into two branches. The trachea divides into two bronchi.

bilabial: used to describe a consonant formed with the aid of both lips, e.g., [b].

binaural: pertaining to both ears (see monaural).

blast: "blasto," meaning the germ of; that which is to be; that which is to be made (from something indicated by the remaining part of the word). For example, blastoderm, from which (*derm,* skin) come ectoderm, entoderm, and mesoderm.

blastula: the embryo in the stage succeeding the morula stage.

B_n: bandwidth of the nth formant.

B.N.A.: At Basle, Switzerland, an international convention was held in 1895 to agree upon a uniform anatomical terminology which could be used throughout the world. The scientific terminology finally adopted is known as the Basle Nomina Anatomica or B.N.A.

body-section radiography: the production of x-ray images, blurred except on the selected axis, by rotating x-ray tube and film about a chosen axis. Known variously, depending upon the principles involved, as laminagraphy, stratography, and tomography.

bone conduction: the transmission of sound waves through the bones of the head. Opposite, *air conduction.*

Broca's area: the motor speech area on the inferior frontal and pre-central gyri of the left cerebral hemisphere; cortex map area number 44.

bronchus (pl. bronchi): one of the two branches given off from the trachea at its bifurcation.

buccal: relating to the cheek; to the oral cavity bounded by the cheeks.

bulbar: relating to the medulla oblongata.

caput: the head; any expanded or rounded extremity of an organ or anatomical structure. Frequently, the term is applied in discussions of the muscles of the mouth region.

cartilage: (1) hyaline cartilage (e.g., as in nasal cartilage, bronchial rings, parts of trachea, parts of larynx). (2) fibrocartilage (is modified fibrous tissue). (3) elastic cartilage, hyaline cartilage with the addition of elastic fibers, as in external auditory canal, external ear. Hyaline and elastic cartilage undergo ossification.

caudal: toward the tail end; in a posterior direction. Opposite, *cephalic.*

cc. or *c.c.:* abbreviation for cubic centimeter.

cephalic: relating to the head; toward the head; superior; cranial. Opposite, *caudal.*

cerebral: relating to the cerebrum.

cervical: in the region of the neck. *C.* is used as the abbreviation for cervical nerve.

chiloschisis: harelip.

chondrification: from "chondros," meaning cartilage; the laying down of cartilage; conversion into cartilage.

cinefluorography: motion pictures produced with the aid of fluoroscopy.

cineradiography: motion pictures produced with the aid of x-ray equipment.

cm.: abbreviation for centimeter.

cochlear partition: the composite structure which partitions off the tube-like cavity of the cochlea into two scalae, and containing within its extremes (the basilar membrane and Reissner's membrane) the cochlear duct.

compression: the increase in density of a body due to the exertion of external pressure on the body.

conduction deafness: an impairment of hearing due to failure of the mechanics of the middle ear; resulting from the failure of air vibrations to be transmitted to the inner ear.

connective tissue: the general supporting or uniting tissue of the body.

consonant: a voiced or voiceless speech sound which may be used to link vowels together.

continuant: a sound resulting when the air stream, voiced or voiceless, is forced through the resonators of the air tract and escapes into the outer air with or without having encountered some obstruction which produces friction sounds.

continuant fricative: a continuant which does encounter some obstruction, thus producing friction sounds; it may be voiced or voiceless.

contraction of muscle fiber: upon contraction, a muscle fiber may shorten to approximately 57% of its resting length. Several muscle fibers are innervated by the motor end plates at the termini of the processes of an axon (final common pathway) from a single cell body located in the anterior horn of the spinal cord. (The motor end plates tend to be located near the middle of a muscle fiber.) Thus, a nerve impulse (probably) always stimulates a group of muscle fibers to contract. Apparently individual muscle fibers do not contract alone; neither do all of the fibers in a muscle contract at once. There is a systematized rotation of activity; some fibers contract while others are relaxing. The number of muscle fibers in a group innervated by a single efferent nerve fiber constitutes a motor unit. The number of muscle fibers in a group depends upon the muscle involved, being small (2 to 6 muscle fibers) in the case of many of the muscles important for speech and hearing (e.g., stapedius m., tensor tympani m., and the intrinsic muscles of the larynx). This permits the most delicate type of balanced muscular activity and control.

contralateral: relating to the opposite side.

cornu (pl. cornua): a horn; a structure resembling a horn in shape, e.g., the cornua of the thyroid cartilage.

cortex: the outer layer or portion of an organ; the external layer of gray matter of the cerebrum and cerebellum.

coupling: joining together through a common opening, as of resonating cavities united by a common aperture to form one cavity.

cranial: relating to the cranium; toward or associated with the head.

cranial nerve: one of twelve pairs of nerves emerging from the brain or intracranial portion of the central nervous system. We are interested in seven of the twelve pairs: Vth, trigeminal; VIIth, facial; VIIIth, auditory; IXth, glossopharyngeal; Xth, vagus; XIth, accessory; XIIth, hypoglossal.

CVC: consonant vowel consonant. Used in various experiments, CVC syllables are made up with a consonant preceding and a consonant following a vowel.

cycle: a recurrent series of events, or period of time.

cycles per second: abbreviation, cps. An equivalent term: double vibrations per second (dv/sec). An equivalent symbol of notation: $\sim$.

cyton: the body of a nerve cell, as distinguished from its various processes.

damping: the decreasing of the amplitude of vibrations of a sounding body due to the absorption of energy by the surrounding medium.

db.: abbreviation of decibel; one tenth of a bel.

decussation: a crossing of two nerve tracts; the point or area in which the tracts cross like the letter X.

deep: beneath the surface; deeper than superficial.

deglutition: swallowing.

dendrite: one of the branching, treelike, protoplasmic processes of a nerve cell.

dental: relating to the teeth; referring to a consonant formed with the aid of the upper incisor teeth, as [t].

diadochokinesis (Greek *diadochos,* working in turn; *kinesis,* movement): refers to the alternate contraction and relaxation of associated agonists and antagonists; resulting, for example, in the lowering and raising of the mandible rapidly and repeatedly so that the teeth click.

diencephalon: that portion of the prosencephalon which gives rise to the thalamus, metathalamus, and epithalamus.

dilate: to enlarge; to expand.

diphthong: a double vowel in a stereotyped combination.

diplophonia or *diphonia:* double voice; the simultaneous production of two distinct tones during phonation.

diverticulum: a pouch or sac opening out from a cavity; an offshoot; an outpouching cul-de-sac.

Doppler effect: alterations in the apparent frequency of sound waves due to the relative motion of (*a*) the sound source toward or away from the stationary ear, or (*b*) the ear toward or away from the stationary sound source.

dorsal: relating to the back; posterior. Opposite, *ventral.*

dorsum: the upper surface of the tongue.

dsh abstracts: Deafness, speech, and hearing publications abstracted.

d.v.: abbreviation for double vibration; a completed cycle of vibratory movement.

dyne: a unit of force; the force required to produce an acceleration of 1 cm per second per second in a gram mass.

dyne per square centimeter: the unit of measurement of sound pressure.

ear, volume of fluid in inner: the exact amount of fluid (either perilymph or endolymph) in the inner ear is unknown at present. From casts, Bast's figures seem to indicate a total of two drops in the osseous labyrinth. G. von Békésy has recorded "a small drop" in one cochlea.

Echo: a nymph in Greek mythology who for love of Narcissus pined away until nothing remained but her voice!

ectoderm (Greek *ektos,* outside; *derma,* skin): the outer layer of cells formed from the inner cell-mass of the blastoderm and destined to form the nervous system, outer skin covering of the body, etc.

efferent: conducting outward; toward the periphery. Nerve impulses carried from the central nervous system to effectors, i.e., muscles or glands; motor impulses.

electrical potential accompanying muscle fiber contraction: the contraction of a muscle fiber lasts about 1–2msec and is followed by a refractory period or period of relaxation. The contraction is accompanied by the generation of an electrical potential. Because the fibers within a group of muscle fibers contract asynchronously, the sum total of all the times of contractions amounts to about 6–8msec. The total electrical potential amounts to approximately 0.5 millivolts ($500\mu v$).

electromyography: pertaining to muscle action potentials.

embryo: intra-uterine stage of development of the human organism from approximately the third to the ninth week.

embryology: the science of the origin and development of the organism from the ovum to the end of intra-uterine existence.

emg: abbreviation for electromyographic.

EMG: abbreviation for electromyograph and/or electromyogram.

encephalon: brain; that portion of the central nervous system axis contained within the cranium.

entoderm (Greek *entos,* inside; *derma,* skin): the inside or lining layer of cells.

epithelioma: a cancerous growth originating from squamous epithelium; a growth or protuberance on the edge of the vocal fold.

epithelium: the cellular, non-vascular layer covering the free surfaces of the body.

erg: the unit of work in the decimal system; the work done by a force of 1 dyne through a distance of 1 centimeter.

esophageal voice: a post-laryngectomy type of voice in which air is swallowed or gulped and then expelled from the esophagus, setting into vibration the muscular superior opening of the esophagus.

etiology: the demonstration of cause or origin.

evagination: the growth or protrusion outward of a structure or cavity.

EVT: Electrical Vocal Tract (Dunn and Schott, 1950), an electrical analogue of the vocal tract, substituting for coupled resonators variables of capacitance and inductance distributed along coupled systems of transmission lines. *Buzz* and *hiss,* fed into the input, are voice and voiceless equivalents.

explosion (or *break*): the opening of a muscular dam, e.g., the lips, to permit a sudden release of air pressure, e.g., as in the formation of [p]. The phase of sound production following those of implosion and plosion.

extrinsic: referring to muscles which originate outside of the part upon which they act.

extrinsic cue: see secondary cue.

facet: a small smooth area on a bone or cartilage.

falsetto: abnormal voice quality; high-pitched voice.
fascia: the bands or sheets of connective tissue enclosing muscles and groups of muscles and separating their various layers or groups.
fasciculus: a small bundle; referring to a bundle of nerve fibers not large enough to be called a total nerve.
f.c.p.: abbreviation of *final common pathway;* the ultimate or final nerve fiber connection between the nervous system and a gland or muscle.
fertilization: the result of the union of a spermatozoon with an ovum.
fetus: intra-uterine stage of animal after development of the characteristics which make the species distinguishable. In the human it is from about the ninth week until birth.
fissure: a furrow, cleft, or sulcus.
fixate: condition of being fixed; firmly attached or set in position.
fluorescence: conversion of x-rays into rays of visible light and ultraviolet light. (Short wavelength x-rays striking phosphors—e.g., zinc sulphide—produce waves of longer wavelengths.)
fluoroscope: an apparatus for rendering visible the shadows of the x-ray which, after passing through the body, are projected on a fluorescent screen.
fluoroscopic screen: a special intensifying screen which converts x-rays to visible light to permit immediate visualization of the x-ray image.
forced vibration: a vibration imposed and controlled by a force external to the vibrator.
formant: the term, as applied to vowels and resonant consonants, refers to a frequency region in which is concentrated a relatively high degree of acoustic energy. A term variously defined and, hence, loosely used. In a sound spectrogram it indicates a concentration of spectral energy in a characteristic frequency region. Originally used to refer to natural frequency of vocal tract cavities.
formant frequencies: characteristic frequencies due to the influence of the resonators of the vocal tract.
fossa: a cavity or depression, usually below the level of the surface of a part.
Fourier's theorem: any function which, within an interval, is single-valued, finite, and continuous may be represented by a series of sinusoidal functions whose frequencies are in harmonic relation.
frequency: the number of cycles occurring per unit of time; the second is usually taken as the unit of time.
frequency: see, also, cycles per second.
F_n: frequency of nth formant.
F_0: frequency of the fundamental.
fricative: a term used in the description of a speech sound when friction sound waves are a part of the total sound-wave complex.
fundamental: the lowest component frequency of a periodic wave; the principal component of a sound wave; the component having the greatest wavelength.
funiculus: a small bundle of nerve fibers. Smaller than a fasciculus, which may be composed of several funiculi.

generator: the exciting cause which produces the sound wave; the vibrating body from which flows the energy in the form of sound waves.
glossal (Greek *glossa,* tongue): relating to the tongue or to sounds produced with the aid of the tongue.

glottis: the opening or aperture between the vocal folds when they are not approximated. Upon complete approximation of the vocal folds, the glottis ceases to exist.

GSR: galvanic skin response.

guttural mirror: a small mirror on the end of a long handle used for examinations of the throat and laryngeal region.

gyrus (pl. gyri): one of the prominent rounded elevations or convolutions on the surface of the hemispheres of the brain. They are separated from each other by sulci or fissures.

harmonic: a component of a periodic sound wave having a frequency which is an integral multiple of the fundamental pitch. An overtone; an upper partial.

Helmholtz resonator: a brass sphere having a cavity of such volume and with an aperture of such dimension that the air contained within the sphere will vibrate in sympathy with a generator producing a tone of a definite pitch.

hyper-: a prefix denoting "excessive"; that which is above normal.

hypo-: a prefix denoting less than the normal; equivalent to "sub-."

Hz: Hertz. Same as *cycle per second*.

implosion (or *make*): the first step in producing such a sound as [p]; during this phase the air column is suddenly dammed up by the approximation of such structures as the lips.

inferior: meaning lower or below when used in relation to another structure. Opposite, *superior*.

innervation: to furnish with a nerve supply.

insertion: the relatively more movable point of attachment of a muscle. Opposite, *origin*. Many anatomists use the term *attachment* in place of both of the other terms.

intensifying screen: a special cardboard covered with a thin layer of a phosphor (e.g., calcium tungstate) emulsion in a binder. X-rays striking the phosphor are converted (fluorescence) to rays of visible light and ultraviolet light.

intensity: refers to the measure of the magnitude of the pressure, or energy-flow, acting to produce a sound wave.

intensity level: the number of decibels that a given sound is above another sound which is taken as the intensity level.

intercalary: occurring between two others; referring to an intermediate neuron connecting two other neurons, especially if the connection be between an afferent and an efferent neuron.

intereffect: the effect one factor has on another and vice versa. For example, the production of a consonant sound affects the sound of a following vowel, and the vowel affects the sound of the consonant.

intrinsic: denoting muscles whose origins and insertions are contained within the structure, especially the intrinsic muscles of the larynx.

intrinsic cue: see *secondary cue*.

ipsilateral: on the same side.

irritability: a characteristic of protoplasm; the capacity to react to stimuli.

JNA or *INA:* Jena Nomina Anatomica.

JND or *jnd:* just-noticeable-difference (e.g., between two intensities of a tone).

kinesthetic: relating to the sense of perception of movement; the muscular sense.

labial: relating to the lips; to sounds produced with the aid of the lips.
labiodental: relating to the lips and teeth; to sounds articulated by these structures—for example, [f] and [v].
lamina: a thin plate or flat layer.
laminagraph: body-section radiograph.
laryngectomy: excision of the larynx.
laryngo-periskop: a self-illuminating laryngoscopic mirror plus a periscope.
laryngopharynx: that portion of the pharynx extending from the hyoid bone level to the level of the inferior border of the cricoid where it is continuous with the esophagus.
laryngo-reflectoscope: equipment utilizing a transparent mirror to enable a group of observers (including the examinee) to obtain a simultaneous view of the larynx.
laryngoscope: a small round mirror, fixed at an angle on a rodlike handle, so that when held far back in the mouth, it will reflect the image of the interior of the larynx and at the same time reflect light into the larynx.
lateral: to or toward the side; away from the mid-line.
levator: a name applied to a muscle which raises or elevates an organ or structure, e.g., levator palati.
ligament: a sheet or band of fibrous tissue serving to connect two or more bones, cartilages, or other structures; also, serving as a support for muscles or fascia.
lingual: pertaining to the tongue or to sounds produced with the aid of the tongue.
LogEtron: electronic printer that can reproduce pictures from negatives or x-rays in such a way as to show more information than can be seen in the negative.
longitudinal: running lengthwise; that is, in the direction of the long axis of the body or part involved.
loudness: the magnitude of the auditory sensation produced by a sound. The ear's psychological response to the physical quantity intensity. Related to the cube root of intensity.
lower motor neuron: one whose axon ends within the muscle or gland which it activates.
lumen: the cross-section area of the interior of a tubular structure.

macrostomia: a mouth larger than normal.
mandible: the lower jaw.
manometer: an instrument for determining the pressure of gases; in a mercury manometer, the pressures are measured by noting the difference in the heights of a column of mercury.
maxilla: the upper jawbone. Strictly speaking, two fused bones are involved.
maximal: the greatest possible; the highest limit attainable.
medial: relating to the middle or center; median; central, mesal. Opposite, *lateral* or *external.*
mel: unit of pitch.
mesencephalon: the midbrain.
metabolism: the sum total of the effect of the bodily processes of construction

(anabolism or assimilation) and destruction (catabolism or dissimilation); the sum total of the processes of building up protoplasm and destroying it, incidental to life; the sum total of the chemical processes and energy exchanges taking place in the body at a given period.

metencephalon: the hindbrain which gives rise to the cerebellum and the pons.

microbar: one dyne/cm^2.

millisone: 0.001 sone.

mm.: abbreviation of millimeter.

molecule: the smallest unit quantity of matter which can exist independently and yet possess all properties of the substance of which it is a unit.

monaural: pertaining to one ear (binaural, both ears).

morphology: relating to the study of structure.

mucous membrane: the mucus-secreting lining of cavities and passages opening to the exterior.

muscle (Latin *musculus,* a little mouse): so named because the movement of a muscle in contraction reminded an early observer of the movement of a mouse under a piece of cloth!

A muscle is an organ; it can contract or it can relax. The contraction of a muscle depends upon the contraction of its fibers. Contraction produces a decrease in length and an increase in thickness. Muscles are *striated* (striped, skeletal, somatic, or voluntary), e.g., orbicularis oris; or *unstriated* (smooth, organic, or involuntary), e.g., trachealis. We are interested almost exclusively in striated muscles. Muscles are connected with the bones, cartilages, ligaments, and skin either directly or indirectly. If indirectly, then by *tendons* or *aponeuroses.*

Muscles have been named scientifically according to

- their situation or location (e.g., epicranius)
- the direction taken by their fibers (e.g., lingualis transversus)
- their use (e.g., levator veli palatini)
- their shape (e.g., trapezius)
- the number of their divisions (e.g., digastric)
- their points of attachment, i.e., origin and insertion (e.g., cricothyroid)
- some combination of the above (e.g., lateral cricoarytenoid)

Muscles are paired; each has its mirrored homologue on the opposite side of the mid-line of the body. (Exceptions: diaphragm and orbicularis oris.) Three types of paired muscles may be described on the basis of the relations of their origins and insertions to the mid-line:

(1) Paired muscles with a common origin along the mid-line. Their fibers run laterally to separate insertions. (Example, trapezius.)

(2) Paired muscles with a common insertion along the mid-line. Their fibers run in from their separate origins laterally. (Example, levator veli palatini.)

(3) Paired muscles with origins and insertions at points lateral to the mid-line; the muscles running homologous mirrored courses. (Example, digastric.)

Every muscle (agonist) has its antagonist. Contraction of an agonist is associated with relaxation of the antagonist, and vice versa. Normally, contraction is produced by efferent (motor) impulses arriving via the proper nerve supply to the muscle.

Striated muscles vary in the arrangement of the fiber-units of which they are composed. This affects their relative strength and range of movement.

A muscle is made up of a great number of individual muscle fibers. When a muscle contracts, all or any of its fibers may contract, but a single fiber contracts maximally or not at all (all-or-none law). This explains how a muscle may be constantly in a state of partial contraction (tonicity). Not only is it unusual for all of the fibers of a muscle to be called into use at once, but it has been suggested that to prevent the fibers from fatiguing, there is a rotation of the work so that first one group and then another contract, thus leaving some fibers always at rest.

Muscles are never entirely relaxed; when not actively contracted they are always in a state of tonus. Such a provision, together with the mechanism of balanced antagonism, permits a rapidity and smoothness of movement which otherwise could not be obtained.

muscle chart: a summary table of the muscles and nerves involved in the production of speech sounds.

SUMMARY CHART OF MUSCLES AND NERVES INVOLVED IN THE PRODUCTION OF SPEECH SOUNDS

	MUSCLE	INNERVATION [1]
The Muscles of Respiration:		
General:	trachealis	sympathetic, recurrent branch of X.
Quiet inhalation:	diaphragm	C 3, 4, 5.
	external intercostals	T 1–12.
	scalenus anterior	C 5, 6, 7.
	scalenus medius	C 4, 5, 6, 7, 8.
	scalenus posterior	C 7 or 8.
	levatores costarum	C 8; T 1–11.
Forced inhalation, primary:	serratus anterior	C 5, 6, 7.
	serratus posterior superior	T 1, 2, 3, 4.
	serratus posterior inferior	T 9, 10, 11.
	pectoralis major	C 6, 7, 8; T 1.
	pectoralis minor	C 7, 8.
	latissimus dorsi	C 6, 7, 8.
	subclavius	C 5, 6.
	sternocleidomastoid	largely XI.
Forced inhalation, secondary:	trapezius	XI; C 3, 4.
	rhomboideus major	C 5, 6.
	rhomboideus minor	C 5, 6.
	levator scapulae	C 3, 4.
	deltoideus	C 5, 6.
Exhalation:	transversus thoracis	T 2, 3, 4, 5, 6.
	rectus abdominis	T 7, 8, 9, 10, 11.
	transversus abdominis	T 7, 8, 9, 10, 11, 12; L 1.
	obliquus internus abdominis	T 9, 10, 11, 12; L 1.
	obliquus externus abdominis	T 5, 6, 7, 8, 9, 10, 11, 12; L 1.
	subcostals	Related intercostal nerve
	quadratus lumborum	L 1, 2, 3, 4.
	internal intercostals	T 1–12.
	levator ani	S 4.
	coccygeus	S 3, 4.

[1] C = Cervical
T = Thoracic
L = Lumbar
S = Sacral

	MUSCLE	INNERVATION
The Muscles Used in Phonation:		
Intrinsic muscles of the larynx:	cricothyroid	superior laryngeal
	posterior cricoarytenoid	recurrent laryngeal
	lateral cricoarytenoid	recurrent laryngeal
	oblique arytenoid	recurrent laryngeal
	transverse arytenoid	recurrent laryngeal
	thyroarytenoid	recurrent laryngeal
The Infrahyoid Muscles:	sternohyoid	C 1, 2, 3.
	sternothyroid	C 1, 2, 3.
	thyrohyoid	C 1, 2, 3.
	omohyoid	C 1, 2, 3.
The Pharyngeal Region:		
The Suprahyoid Muscles:	digastric, anterior belly	V
	digastric, posterior belly	VII
	stylohyoid	VII
	mylohyoid	V
	geniohyoid	C 1, 2.
The Muscles of the Pharynx:	superior pharyngeal constrictor	pharyngeal plexus.
	middle pharyngeal constrictor	pharyngeal plexus.
	inferior pharyngeal constrictor	pharyngeal plexus and external and recurrent laryngeal.
	stylopharyngeus	IX.
	salpingopharyngeus	pharyngeal plexus.
Oral Cavity:		
The Tongue:		
Extrinsic muscles:	genioglossus	XII
	hyoglossus	XII
	styloglossus	XII
Intrinsic muscles:	longitudinalis superior	XII
	longitudinalis inferior	XII
	transversus linguae	XII
	verticalis linguae	XII
The Muscles of the Palate:	tensor veli palatini	V
	levator veli palatini	XI through pharyngeal plexus
	glossopalatinus	pharyngeal plexus.
	pharyngopalatinus	pharyngeal plexus.
	musculus uvulae	pharyngeal plexus.
The Muscles of Mastication:	masseter	V
	temporalis	V
	external pterygoid	V
	internal pterygoid	V
The Muscles of the Mouth Region:	quadratus labii superioris	VII
	caninus	VII
	zygomaticus	VII
	buccinator	VII
	risorius	VII
	orbicularis oris	VII
	triangularis	VII
	quadratus labii inferioris	VII
	mentalis	VII
	platysma	VII

muscle (striated) fiber: the structural unit of contraction. Fibers may be short or long (as long as 30mm). The width of a fiber is approximately 0.1mm (100μ).

myelencephalon: the posterior division of the rhombencephalon which gives rise to the medulla oblongata.

myelin: the soft, white, fatty material forming the sheath (myelin sheath or medullary sheath) about the axis cylinder of a myelinated (or medullated) nerve fiber.

nasal: a voiced continuant having nasal resonance as its peculiar acoustic property.

nasality: a term used to describe speech sounds when the nasal cavity is being used as a resonator; especially when such resonance produces an abnormal quality.

nasopharynx: the superior portion of the pharynx; it extends from the base of the skull (basilar part of occipital bone) to the level of the soft palate.

neuron: the structural unit of the nervous system, consisting of the nerve-cell body and its various processes.

neuron theory: the theory that the nervous system is composed of neurons (nerve cells and their processes), each of which is a genetic, structural, functional, and trophic unit.

N.K.: abbreviation of Nomenklature Kommission; a commission appointed at Jena in 1935 to propose modifications of the B.N.A. New terms suggested by the commission are designated by the letters N.K.

nucleus: a mass of cell bodies in any part of the brain or spinal cord.

occlude: to close up; to shut off; to fit together.

occlusion: act of occluding—i.e., closing or shutting. Bringing into contact the opposing surfaces of the teeth of the upper and lower jaws.

ontogeny; having to do with the development of the individual, as opposed to *phylogeny,* which deals with the development of the species.

optimum: most favorable; best; most conducive to an objective.

ordinate: one of the reference elements by which a point may be established (i.e., a *fix*) in relation to coordinate axes. In a graph, the vertical axis. See abscissa.

organ of Corti: the specialized group of cells and structures resting on the basilar membrane and, with it, forming the floor of the cochlear duct.

orifice: an aperture or opening.

origin: when applied to a muscle, the term means the relatively fixed or less movable attachment. Opposite, *insertion.* Authorities sometimes disagree on the matter of relative motility. For example, the glossopalatinus muscle is also called the palatoglossus muscle. For just such reasons many anatomists avoid the terms *origin* and *insertion,* using only the term *attachment.*

oropharynx: that portion of the pharnyx extending from the level of the soft palate to the level of the hyoid bone.

osseous: bony.

ossicle: a small bone; one of the ear bones.

ossify: to become bony; to change into bone.

overtone: a partial having a frequency higher than that of the fundamental.

palatogram: a graphic representation of the area of the palate with which the tongue comes into contact in the formation of a given sound.
palatography: the making and study of palatograms.
palpation: touching, feeling, or perceiving by the sense of touch.
parameter: a characteristic; a dimension; an arbitrary constant expressing quantitative values.
partial: a component frequency of a complex tone.
Pascal's law: pressure exerted at any point upon a confined liquid is transmitted undiminished in all directions within the medium.
PAT: Parametric Artificial Talking-Device (Lawrence, 1953). By the manipulation of six controls connected speech may be produced. There are three ways to emphasize a word in a sentence: (1) increase its duration; (2) increase its intensity; (3) increase the frequency of its fundamental.
patent: open or expanded.
perseveration: the tendency of a mental act to continue after the removal of the stimulus.
pH: a symbol used to represent the hydrogen ion concentration of a liquid.
pharynx: the common cavity of the respiratory and digestive tract is somewhat funnel shaped. It extends (approx. 12cm) from the base of the skull to the lower border of the cricoid cartilage. Its greatest breadth (approx. 5cm) is at its attachment to the base of the skull; it tapers to the width (approx. 1.5cm) of the upper esophagus. Its three divisions are: nasopharynx, oropharynx, and laryngopharynx.
phase: that part of a cycle in which, at a given instant, the sound wave is in relation to some arbitrary reference point.
phon: unit of loudness level.
phoneme: a sound family.
phonetics: the study of speech sounds.
phonogram: a symbol designed to represent a sound.
photoelectric kymograph: a photoelectric cell detects variations in the intensity of a beam of light concentrated on a single spot; it photographs the variations on sensitive photographic paper to provide a record of the extent and variety of movements of the surface on which the light is focused.
phylogeny: having to do with the evolutionary development of the species. Opposite, *ontogeny.*
piezoelectricity: the electric polarity produced by pressure on an appropriate body, e.g., quartz.
pitch, standard: physicists at Stuttgart, Germany, in 1834 adopted Scheibler's 440cps as a standard pitch (A_3, or the A above piano middle C is the tone of the second open string of a violin).
plosion (or *stop*): the second phase in the production of such a sound as [p]; during this phase the escape of the air is prevented and the pressure is built up.
pneumatic: relating to air or gas, and hence to respiration.
pneumograph: an instrument for recording the respiratory movements.
posterior: back or dorsal. Opposite, *ventral.*
power ratio (*relation to pressure ratio*): increasing the power of a sound 1,000 times increases it 30db; increasing the pressure of a sound 1,000 times increases it 60db.

Power Ratio	*db*	*Pressure Ratio*	*db*
2 : 1	3	2 : 1	6
10 : 1	10	10 : 1	20
100 : 1	20	100 : 1	40
1,000 : 1	30	1,000 : 1	60
10,000 : 1	40	10,000 : 1	80
100,000 : 1	50	100,000 : 1	100
1,000,000 : 1	60	1,000,000 : 1	120
10,000,000 : 1	70	10,000,000 : 1	140

primordium: term applied to the earliest discernible cell aggregation destined to form any organ or part of the embryo.

probe tube microphone: miniaturized microphone. May be inserted in nasal passages. Even when soft palate is closed, sound pressure changes in the passages during the production of various sounds. In decibels the sound level is not far below that measured at the lips.

proliferation: rapid growth of similar cells by reproduction.

proprioceptor: sense organ (located in muscles, tendons and joints) that initiates afferent impulses which, when brought to consciousness, enable one to determine the relative location or position of a body structure. Functioning at lower neurological levels, proprioceptors enable an individual to perform a multitude of acts without conscious effort—e.g., adjusting fingers and arm muscles so that a spoon can convey food to the mouth, playing a piano, walking, talking, and singing.

prosencephalon: the forebrain.

pseudovoice: voice not produced in the normal manner; usually by the puffs of air released at the upper aperture of the esophagus.

pulmonary: relating to the lungs.

radiography: making of x-ray films.

radiology: a science growing out of the discovery of x-rays by Wilhelm Konrad Röntgen in 1895.

ramus: a branch—e.g., of a nerve. Also, that posterior portion of the mandible that articulates with the temporal bone. Plural, rami. (Note the word *ramification.*)

raphe: a line of union of two contiguous and similar structures.

rarefaction: the second phase in the propagation of a sound wave, following the phase of condensation.

refractory period: the time during which—after a muscle or nerve fiber has responded to a stimulus—the fiber regains its capacity to respond to another stimulus.

Reissner's membrane: the delicate membrane (about 0.0025mm in thickness) which separates the scala vestibuli, filled with perilymph, from the cochlear duct (ductus cochlearis) with its endolymph.

resonance: the phenomenon occurring if the generator is of a frequency equal to that of the natural frequency of a second body which is being set into vibration.

resonator: that body which resonates or responds to a sound generator, and because of whose characteristics certain frequencies of the original sound are intensified. The cavities of the vocal tract or the cavity of a pipe organ tube form resonators in which (due to their size, shape, size of neck, surface, size of aperture) the air molecules are set into vibration by the sound source. The sounding board of a piano acts as a resonator.

reticular membrane: the relatively stiff tissue extension overhanging the rods of Corti, somewhat in the manner of a cantilevered roof.

rhinolalia: nasal speech.

rhinoscopy: examination of the nasal cavity. Anterior rhinoscopy has to do with the inspection of the anterior portion of the nasal cavity; posterior rhinoscopy refers to the inspection of nasopharynx and posterior part of the nasal cavity with the aid of the rhinoscope.

rhombencephalon: hindbrain.

rima glottidis: the true glottis; the opening or interval between the vocal folds.

roentgenogram: a photograph made with roentgen rays or x-rays.

roentgenography: to photograph with x-rays. Named for the discoverer of x-rays, Wilhelm Konrad Röntgen.

rostral: toward or in the direction of the head. Opposite, *caudal.*

sagittal: a plane parallel to the long axis of the body, dividing the body into right and left portions.

secondary cue: an *extrinsic cue* reflects the speech habits of a community. Thus, in some English dialects vowel duration is a distinguishing cue (e.g., *ladder* and *latter, d* and *t* both being flaps).
An *intrinsic cue* reflects the functioning of the (intrinsic) speech mechanisms (e.g., due to anticipatory movements of velar-pharyngeal musculature vowels tend to be nasalized preceding nasal consonants).

semi-permeable membrane: a membrane (e.g., Reissner's membrane, or the membrane of a cell) across which or through which only certain substances —e.g., ions—may pass.

sensation level: of a given sound is described in terms of the number of decibels that sound is above the threshold of audibility.

sensation unit: the smallest change of intensity that can be detected by the normal ear; it is equal to one decibel.

sigma: $1/1000$ of a second.

singer's nodules: singer's nodes, chorditis tuberosa, trachoma of the vocal folds; a condition marked by the appearance of one or more nodules on either or both folds, usually on only one fold.

sinus: a hollow or cavity in bone or other tissue; antrum.

soft palate (*palatum molle*): a mobile fold of muscular and aponeurotic tissue invested with mucous membrane and hanging by its upper border from the posterior margin of the hard palate. Laterally, it is continuous with the pharynx.

somatic: relating to the body or body wall, as opposed to *visceral.*

sonant: with voice; a voiced sound. Opposite, *surd.*

sone: unit of loudness.

sound: the motion of air molecules in regular vibration in a unit of time; an alteration in pressure or particle-velocity propagated in an elastic medium. Sound is also the sensation received through the ear mechanism as a result of the vibrations or disturbances in the air.

sound spectrograph: electrical equipment designed to produce visible speech. The visible speech records show the frequency, intensity, and time elements of the sounds.

sound spectrum: graphic representation of analysis of sound. Shows relationships of frequencies and intensities of components.

speech power: (*a*) instantaneous speech power is the rate of radiation of speech sound energy at any given instant; (*b*) phonetic speech power is the average of the rate of radiation of sound energy during the production of a single vowel or consonant; (*c*) average speech power is the sum total of all of the speech sound energy radiated during a complete speech divided by the elapsed time of the entire speech.

sphincter: an orbicular muscle or combination of muscles which serves to close an orifice when contracted normally.

spirometer: instrument for measuring vital capacity.

SPL: the *sound pressure level* of any sound is the ratio between its pressure and the SRP.

SRI: standard reference intensity. In intensity this reference point is equivalent to a pressure of 0.0002dyne/cm^2 or to a power of 10^{-16}watt/cm^2. The reference point corresponds, for audiological purposes, to zero decibels, the threshold of hearing. The ratio between the reference point and the intensity of any sound is stated in terms of the logarithmic unit, the decibel.

SRP: standard reference pressure (0.0002 dyne/cm^2).

stereoradiography: two radiographs from two tube positions (the separation being in ratio to the interpupillary distance) are made. When viewed in a stereoscope the brain fuses the two views into one and the observer obtains a three-dimensional relationship.

stereoscopy: the three-dimensional impression obtained through stereoradiography.

stop: a speech sound produced when the phonated or non-phonated air stream is blocked, held for a period of time, and then suddenly released.

stratograph: body-section radiograph.

sub-: meaning below or inferior to something that is superior; for example, subcortical level refers to a level of the nervous system below that of the cerebral cortex.

sulcus: one of the fissures or grooves on the surface of the brain, bounding the gyri or convolutions.

superficial: near the outside or at the surface. Opposite, *deep.*

superior: higher than something else; above. Opposite, *inferior.*

surd: without voice; a voiceless sound. Opposite, *sonant.*

synapse: the close approximation of the processes of different neurons; the contiguous relation of the end of an axon and the ends of one or more dendrites.

synergy: the working together of muscles; coordination of action, especially in correct time order.

Tartini's tones: terzi suoni, third tones, the phenomena noted by the Italian violinist, *Tartini,* in 1754, and in 1745 by the German organist, *Sorge.* When two loud tones of different frequencies are listened to simultaneously, a third (or several tones) tone of different pitch is heard. For example: if the loud tones 400~(F_1) and 600~(F_2) are sounded, you may hear some or all of these subjective tones: 200~(F_2–F_1), 800~($2F_1$), 1000~($F_1 + F_2$), 1200~($2F_2$). 800 and 1200 cycle tones are first overtones; 200 cycles is a *difference tone;* 1000 cycles is a *summation tone.*

tectorial membrane: a delicate membranous structure overhanging the organ of Corti and in which, probably, the cilia of the hair cells are imbedded.
telencephalon: that portion of the prosencephalon which gives rise to the cerebral hemispheres.
tendon: a fibrous band or cord connecting a fusiform muscle with its osseous attachment.
threshold of hearing: the minimal value of sound-wave pressure which will produce a sensation of tone for a given frequency.
timbre: quality of a tone.
tomograph: body-section radiograph.
tonus (tonic, tonicity): the state of normal elastic tension of the tissues; a slight, steady contraction of all muscles due to the influence of the cerebellum.
tracheal fistula: a sinus or abnormal passage from the cavity of the trachea to the exterior surface of the body. By inserting a tube the exhaled air stream may be routed through an artificial larynx to produce speech sounds.
tract: an area of greater length than breadth; a pathway. A nerve tract refers to a bundle of nerve fibers; air tract refers to the route followed by the air from the time it enters the mouth or nose until it reaches the lung alveoli, or to the same route used on the passage of the air outwards.
transverse: lying across the axis of the body; crosswise of an organ.
trapezoid body: a group of decussating afferent nerve fibers at the level of the medulla (probably all fibers of the second order neurons whose cell bodies are located in the dorsal or ventral cochlear nuclei) constituting a portion of the ascending fibers of the auditory (VIIIth cranial) nerve.
tympanum: a drum; the ear-drum; the cavity of the middle ear.

upper motor neuron: one whose cell body is located in the motor area of the cerebral cortex. The cell body is one of the giant pyramidal (Betz) cells.
uraniscochasma or *uranoschisis:* cleft palate.
uraniscus: the palate.
uvula: the pendular central portion of the velum.

vallecula: channel, depression or groove. See Fig. 11, number 7, showing the channel between the epiglottis and the base of the tongue.
variable area tract analogue: modified EVT.
vegetative: functioning involuntarily or unconsciously; referring to systems or organs used for vital or life-sustaining processes.
velarpharyngeal mechanism: the pharyngeal and velar musculature involved in closing off the nasopharynx from the oropharynx, or in regulating the degree of openness between the two cavities. Particularly important during acts of swallowing. During the production of speech sounds, the mechanism determines the degree of coupling, if any, of the nasal resonators with those of the mouth, pharynx, and larynx.
velum (*palatine velum*): the lower, free border of the soft palate.
ventral: relating to the belly or abdomen. *Opposite,* dorsal.
ventricle of the larynx (*ventricle of Morgagni*): the cavity, a diverticulum, between the ventricular and vocal folds.
vesicle: a small cavity or sac, usually containing fluid. An air cell or alveolus of the lung.

vesicular murmur: the sound produced by air entering or leaving the lung vesicles or alveoli. (See material on auscultation.)

viscus (pl. viscera): an internal organ, especially an internal abdominal organ.

visible speech: the graphic record produced by a sound spectrograph. Analysis patterns indicate frequencies in one direction and time in another; the contrast (i.e., relation of darker and lighter areas) represents a third quantity, intensity.

vital capacity: the maximum volume of air which may be exhaled following a maximal inhalation.

vocal folds: the pearly white anatomical structures responsible for phonation, but designed primarily to act as a laryngeal valve. The vocal folds may be said to be the thickened upper portion of the conus elasticus. Each fold is made up of an external layer of stratified squamous epithelium covering, with the help of the tissue of the conus elasticus, in order, the vocal ligament, the vocalis muscle, and the thyroarytenoid muscle.

VODER: Voice Operation DEmonstratoR. Perhaps the earliest electrical device to produce complete sentences (1939). *Buzz* supplied phonation; *hiss* provided random frequencies as basis of unvoiced sounds.

vowel: a voiced continuant, dependent for its characteristics upon the resonating cavities of the speaker. Vowels form the basis of spoken language.

vowel glide: a transitory sound produced incidentally during the direct movement of the articulatory structures from one vowel position to another.

Wernicke's area: the auditory center in the posterior portion of the superior temporal convolution. The importance of the convolution (or gyrus) was noted by the German neurologist, K. Wernicke (1848–1905).

x-ray kymograph (multiple slit): the operation is similar to that of the single slit kymograph except that the multiple slits permit recording several areas simultaneously.

x-ray kymograph (single slit): a device consisting of a narrow slit in a lead plate through which x-rays pass to permit making a record of only a single segment of an organ in each of a sequence of movements. The movement of the slit is timed with the exposure and the movement of the organ to produce the sequential record.

x-rays: electromagnetic waves of short wavelength (approx. 1/10,000 the length of visible light waves). Instead of being reflected or absorbed, as are light rays, the short x-rays have the ability to penetrate materials.

zygomatic arch: the bony arch made up (in front) of the zygomatic bone united with the maxillary bone (at side and back) and the zygomatic process of the temporal bone.

zygomatic bone: cheekbone. Malar bone. The prominent bone below the eye and on the side of the face.

zygomatic process: the long narrow process of the temporal bone which unites in helping to form the zygomatic arch.

For definitions, meanings, illustrations, examples or descriptions of many additional terms the student may find help by referring to the *Index*.

BIBLIOGRAPHY AND CHRONICLE

In beginning his study of Voice Science a student should attempt, as soon as possible, to acquaint himself with the leading contributors and the major publications in the field. This bibliography and chronicle is designed to aid the student in these endeavors.

Even a quick glance at the bibliographical references for recent years will indicate to the student that an ever-increasing number of journals must be consulted for material related to the fields of Speech and Hearing. Research in widely diversified areas of science contributes to our knowledge. There are no geographical or departmental limits to research.

KEY TO ABBREVIATIONS USED IN BIBLIOGRAPHY AND CHRONICLE

A.	American	Mém.	Mémorial
Acad.	Academie; Academy	menschl.	menschlichen
Acoust.	Acoustical	Mod.	Modern
Am.	American	Monatschr.	Monatsschrift
Amer.	American	Monog.	Monographs
Anat.	Anatomical; Anatomie; Anatomy	Néerl.	Néerlandaises
		Neurol.	Neurology
		Neurophysiol.	Neurophysiology
Ann.	Annals	N.Y.	New York
Arch.	Archiv; Archives	Ohr.	Ohrenheilkunde
Assn.	Association	Ohrenh.	Ohrenheilkunde
Assoc.	Association	Ophth.	Ophthalmology
Biol.	Biology	Ophthal.	Ophthalmological
Biophys.	Biophysical	Otol.	Otological; Otology
Brit.	British	Otolog.	Otological; Otology
Bros.	Brothers	Otolar.	Otolaryngology
Bull.	Bulletin	Otolaryng.	Otolaryngology
Co.	Company	Otolaryngol.	Oto-Laryngologica; Otolaryngology
Comp.	Comparative		
Compt.	Comptes	Pharm.	Pharmacologia
d.	des	Phil.	Philosophical
Embryol.	Embryology	Phys.	Physical; Physiology
Entw.	Entwicklungs-geschichte	Physiol.	Physiologica; Physiologie; Physiology
Exp.	Experimental		
Exper.	Experimental	Proc.	Proceedings
f.	für	Psychiat.	Psychiatry
Gen.	General	Psychol.	Psychological; Psychology
Heilk.	. . . heilkunde		
Homo.	Homeopathic	Pub.	Publishing
Hosp.	Hospital	Publ.	Publishers
Internat.	Internationales	Public.	Publication
J.	Journal	Q.	Quarterly
Jap.	Japan; Japanese	Quart.	Quarterly
Klin.	klinische	Rad.	Radium
Lab.	Laboratories; Laboratory	Rec.	Record
		Rend.	Rendus
Lang.	Language	Res.	Research
Laryng.	Laryngology	Rev.	Review
Laryngol.	Laryngological; Laryngologie; Laryngology	Rhinol.	Rhinological; Rhinology
		Roentg.	Roentgenology
M.	Medical	Roy.	Royal
Med.	Medical; Medicine	Rundsch.	Rundschau

So.	South	Tr.	Transactions; translated
Soc.	Society	Trans.	Transactions
Sp.	Speech	u.	und
Stud.	Studies	u.s.w.	und so weiter
Suppl.	Supplement: Supplementum	Univ.	University
Tech.	Technical	Zentralbl.	Zentralblatt
Ther.	Therapy	Zschr.	Zeitschrift

SPECIAL COMBINATIONS

Anat.Anz.	Anatomischer Anzeiger	BSTJ	Bell System Technical Journal
AnnOR&L	Annals of Otology, Rhinology, and Laryngology	JASA	Journal Acoustical Society of America
BLR	Bell Laboratories Record	JSD	Journal of Speech Disorders
BME	Bio-Medical Electronics	JSHD	Journal of Speech and Hearing Disorders
		JSHR	Journal of Speech and Hearing Research

BIBLIOGRAPHY AND CHRONICLE

2698 B.C.

Ti, Huang: Editor of *Nei Ching* (Canon of Medicine). The oldest medical work known.

"The thorax and abdomen constitute the city wall, the pericardium the palace of the king. The stomach is the granary and the throat and small intestines the post office. Water and grain enter the oesophagus, and air by the trachea. . . . The mouth and lips are the fan for the voice, the tongue the machine, and the uvula the pass. The larynx divides the air. The breath coming from the lungs is supposed to act on the hyoid bone and tongue in speaking."

From *History of Chinese Medicine*
Wong, K. C., and Lien-teh, Wu.
The Tientsin Press, Tientsin, China. 1932.

130–200 A.D.

Galen, Claudius The most prolific writer and the most painstaking scientist among all of the ancient physicians. Wrote a treatise on the voice. Only fragments are extant. He identifies the cartilages and the muscles of the larynx, classifying the muscles as *extrinsic* and *intrinsic.*

1653

Wallis, John *Tractus grammatico-physicus de loquela.*

1700–1707

Dodart *Mémoires sur la cause de la voix.* Dodart discovered that the pitch of the voice was dependent on the tension of the vocal folds. Originator of the puff theory.

1741

Ferrein, Antoine *De la formation de la voix de l'homme.* Mem. de L'Acad. des Sciences. Paris. Originator of the partials theory. Probably the first experimentalist in voice science. He studied larynges of cadavers and of animals, and constructed models.

1768–1791

von Kempelen, Wolfgang *Mechanismus der menschlichen Sprache.* A Vienna scientist who invented a speaking machine. In order to construct the apparatus he studied the action of the human voice mechanism. He found it easier to produce the consonants than the vowels.

1780

Donders, F. C. *De physiologie der spraakklanken.* The physiology of speech sounds. Discovered that the resonance cavities of the speech mechanism are tuned to different pitches for different vowels.

1806

Dutrochet Mém. de L'Acad. des Sciences. Paris. Compared the vocal folds to the lips of a trumpet blower and believed that the entire thyroarytenoid muscle—not merely the edges—vibrated.

1829

Willis, Wilfred Vowel theory. In 1832 originated the cavity tone theory.

1832

Bell, Sir Charles *On the Organs of the Human Voice.*

1833–36

Breschet, G. *Recherches anatomiques et physiologiques sur l'organe de l'ouïe et sur l'audition dans l'homme et les animaux vertébrés*. Paris. First monograph on anatomy and physiology of the ear. His terminology is still used.

1837

Wheatstone, Sir Charles Vowel theory. Originated the overtone theory.

1840

Müller, Johannes *Von Stimme und Sprache*. In *Handbuch der Physiologie des Menschen*. 2nd volume. Coblentz. Was the first to make extensive scientific experiments with models of the human larynx. He concerned himself especially with pitch, intensity, and registers.

1841

Garcia, Manuel First successful use of laryngoscopic technique. Czermak (1860) is credited, according to Scripture, with the development of the Garcia technique.

1846

Liskovius, K. F. S. *Physiologie der menschlichen Stimme*. Made observations on action of vocal folds at different registers. Found that during phonation the vocal folds, viewed from above, are roof-shaped.

1855

Garcia, Manuel *Observations on the human voice*. Proc. Roy. Soc. 3:399 ff. May, 1855.

1856 or *1864*

Merkel, C. L. *Stimm- und Sprachorgans*. Anat. u. Physiol. d. menschl. 1856.—*Antropophonik*. Leipzig. 1857.—*Die Functionen des menschlichen Schlundes und Kehlkopfes*. Leipzig. 1862.—*Sprache*. Leipzig. 1866.—An early but important worker with the Garcia technique.

Scott Phonautograph—a parabolic megaphone with membrane at small end. Membrane vibrations actuated a writing lever which traced on a smoked drum.

1866

Fournié, Edouard *Physiologie de la voix et de la parole*. Paris. He built and experimented with laryngeal models in which the vocal folds were approximated at an acute angle.

1867

Bell, Alexander Melville Visible speech. Universal phonetic symbols.

1872

Koenig Tuning forks. Manometric flame.

1873

Tyndall, J. *Sound*. D. Appleton. New York.

1874

Barlow Logograph—similar to the phonautograph except that aluminum lever wrote in ink on a paper.

1875

Helmholtz, H. L. F. *Sensations of Tone*. 1st edition. 2nd edition, 1885. Longmans, Green. London

1876

Bell, Alexander Graham Telephone.

Blaserna, P. *Theory of Sound*. D. Appleton. New York.

1877 (Date of patent)

Edison, Thomas Alva Phonograph.

1878

Blake, E. W. Attempted to overcome inertia and friction of recording equipment by using a beam of light as a writing lever. A small mirror was attached to the diaphragm; movements of the diaphragm caused a deflection of the light ray. The light record was written on photographic paper drawn past a slit with constant velocity.

Marey Air tambours.

Oertel, M. J. Applied the stroboscopic method to laryngoscopy.

1880

Seiler, C. *Minute anatomy of the larynx.* Arch. Laryng. 1:27–35; 137–141; 256–260. 1880. 2:50–53. 1881.

1881

Langmaid, S. M. *The treatment of certain forms of vocal disability by the application of the principles of voice-culture.* Arch. Laryng. 2:137–146. —Fix your mind on any given note and then think of any higher note. You will feel movements of the laryngeal, pharyngeal and mouth muscles. Therefore, muscular adjustment and not merely increased air pressure is involved in changes of pitch.

1882

Koenig, R. *Quelques expériences d'acoustique.* Paris.

Morgan, E. C. *Diphthonia or double voice.* Arch. Laryng. 3:48–57.

1883

French, T. R. *On photographing the larynx.* Arch. Laryng. 4:235–243.

Galton, Sir Francis Galton whistle. Used for producing graduated tones of high frequency. Used in testing the upper limits of hearing.

Hooper, F. H. *Experimental researches on the tension of the vocal bands.* Arch. Laryng. 4: Appendix 1–20.

Lander, Brunton, and Cash *The valvular action of the larynx.* J. Anat. and Phys. Vol. 17.

1884

Koschlakoff, D. J. *Die künstliche Reproduction und graphische Darstellung der Stimme und ihrer Anomalien.* Pflüger's Arch. 34:36–67.

1886

Koschlakoff, D. J. *Über die Schwingungstypen der Stimmbänder.* Pflüger's Arch. 38:428–476.

Semon and Horseley *An apparently peripheral and differential action of ether upon the laryngeal muscles.* Brit. Med. J. 2:405.

1888

Hooper, F. H. *Effects of varying rates of stimulation on the action of the recurrent laryngeal nerves.* N.Y. Med. J. 48:485–488.

1889

Delavan, D. B. *Further investigations as to the existence of a cortical motor center for human larynx.* N.Y. Med. J. 49:673–676.

French, T. R. *A photographic study of the laryngeal image during the formation of registers in the singing voice.* N.Y. Med. J. 49:95–98. Tr. Amer. Laryngol. Assoc. N.Y. 10:95–102.

1890

Semon, F. *On the position of the vocal cords in quiet respiration in man and*

on the reflex tonus of their abductor muscles. Proc. Roy. Soc. 48:403 ff.
Sweet, Henry Phonetics.

1891

Howell, W. H., and Huber, G. C. *Physiology of the communicating branch between superior and inferior laryngeal nerves.* J. Physiol. 12:5–11.

1892

Bennett, O. P. *The falsetto voice.* Med. Rec. N.Y. 43:536.

Stuart, T. P. A. *The mode of closure of the larynx.* J. Physiol. Cambridge. 13:59.—*On the mechanism of the closure of the larynx.* Proc. Roy. Soc. 50:323. Lancet. 1:707.

Wilder, H. H. *Studies in the phylogenesis of the larynx.* Anat. Anz. Jena. 7:570–580.

Zahm, J. A. *Sound and Music.* McClurg. Chicago.

1894

Allen, H. *Speech without a larynx.* Med. News. Philadelphia. 54:281–284.

1895

Illingworth, C. R. *Some points in the anatomy and physiology of the larynx.* Brit. Med. J. 11:353.

Rethi, L. *Experimentelle Untersuchungen über den Schwingungstypus und den Mechanismus der Stimmbänder bei der Falsettstimme.* Wiener Klin. Rundsch. Nos. 5 and 6.

Sauberschwartz and Grutzner Utilized laws of interference of sounds in study of vowel quality.

Wilder, H. H. *Studies in the phylogenesis of the larynx.* Med. Record. 47:353.

1896

Donaldson, F. *As to the intrinsic movement of the vocal cords and the treatment of singing voice.* Pacific Med. J. San Francisco. 737–746; 781–783.

Porter, W. *Compensatory arytenoid movement.* Trans. Am. Laryngol. Assoc. N.Y. 17:190–192.

1897

Musehold, A. *Stroboskopische und photographische Studien.* Arch. f. Laryngol. 7:1–21.

Russell, J. S. R. *The influence of the cerebral cortex on the larynx.* Phil. Tr. London. 188:59–81.

Wundt, W. M. *Outlines of Psychology.* Leipzig.

1898

Collins, J. *The Faculty of Speech.* Macmillan. New York.

Ewald, Richard *Physiologie des Kehlkopfes.* In *Handbuch der Laryngologie und Rhinologie.* Vienna.

Marage *Contribution à l'étude des voyelles par la photographie des flammes manométriques.* Arch. Internat. de Laryngol. Paris. 11:3–30.

1899

Makuen, G. Hudson *Falsetto voice in male.* J. Amer. Med. Assoc. 32:474–476.

1901

McDowell, G. W. *Occlusion and strictures of the Eustachian tube.* Trans. Amer. Homo., Ophthal., Otolog., and Laryngol. Soc. 1901:128–135.—Length of Eustachian tube: 34 to 44 mm. Length cartilaginous portion approximately 24 mm.; length osseous portion about 11 mm. Isthmus narrowest part; not over 2 mm. in diameter.

Poulsen *Telegraphone.* Nature. 64:183.

1902
Heisler, J. C. *Textbook of Embryology*. Saunders. Philadelphia.
Scripture, E. W. *The Elements of Experimental Phonetics*. Scribner. New York.
1904
Moeller, J., and Fischer, J. F. *Observations on the action of the cricothyroideus and thyro-arytenoideus internus*. Annals Otol., Rhinol., and Laryngol. 13:42–46.
Wundt, W. M. *Principles of Physiological Psychology*. Vol. I. Macmillan. New York.
1905
Broadhouse, J. *Musical Acoustics*. 4th edition. W. Reeves. London.
Gamble, E. A. McC. *Attention and thoracic breathing*. Am. J. Psychol. 16: 261–292.
Garcia, Manuel *Observations on the human voice*. Laryngoscope. 15:185–194. —In this article the pressure-puff theory is advanced and supported for the first time.
1906
Ingersoll, J. M. *The function of the accessory cavities of the nose*. Ann. Otol., Rhinol., Laryngol. 15:757–774.—In man the sinuses have no function.
Loeb, H. W. *A study of the anatomy of the accessory cavities of the nose by topographic projections*. Ann. Otol., Rhinol., Laryngol. 15:697–756.
1908
Barton, E. H. *Textbook on Sound*. Macmillan. New York.
1909
Hoyt, H. W. *Papilloma of the larynx*. Trans. Amer. Homo., Ophthal., Otol., and Laryngol. Soc. 1909:282–290.—Growths almost always on anterior part of one or both cords. Produces hoarse voice.
Loeb, H. W. *A study of the anatomic relations of the optic nerve to the accessory cavities of the nose*. Ann. Otol., Rhinol., Laryngol. 18:243–276.
Makuen, G. Hudson *The action of the respiratory muscles in the production of voice*. Laryngoscope. 19:671–679.
1910
Bell, Alexander Graham *The Mechanism of Speech*. Funk and Wagnalls. New York.
Johnston, J. B. *The limit between ectoderm and entoderm in the mouth*. Amer. J. Anat. 10:41–68.
Schaeffer, J. P. *The sinus maxillaris and its relations*. Amer. J. Anat. 10:313–368.
Townsend, I. *Deformities of the nasal septum*. Trans. Amer. Homo., Ophthal., Otol., Laryngol. Soc. 1910:167–171.
1911
Berry, R. J. A. *Atlas of Sectional and Topographical Anatomy*. Wm. Wood. New York.
Holmes, E. M. *The examination and treatment of the nasopharynx and Eustachian tube by the nasopharyngoscope*. Ann. Otol., Rhinol., Laryngol. 20:29–40.—Inventor of nasopharyngoscope.
Lisser, H. *Studies on the development of the human larynx*. Amer. J. Anat. 12:27–66.

1912

Mellus, E. L. *The development of the cerebral cortex.* Amer. J. Anat. 14:107-117.

1913

Chevroton, L., and Vlès, F. *Cinématographie des cordes vocales et leurs annexes laryngiennes.* Compt. rend. de l'Acad. des Sciences. 156:949–952.

Hollock, W., and Muckey, F. S. *The result of eighteen years of research on voice production and analysis.* Laryngoscope. 23:5–20.

Mills, W. *Voice Production.* 4th edition. Lippincott. Philadelphia.

Musehold, A. *Allgemeine Akustik und Mechanik des menschlichen Stimmorgans.* Berlin.

Peters, W. E. *A new and accurate method of photographing speech.* Vox. 23:129–134.

Prentiss, C. W. *On the development of the membrana tectoria.* Amer. J. Anat. 14:425–460.

Wycozoikowska, A. *Theoretical and experimental studies in the mechanism of speech.* Psychol. Rev. 20:448–458.

1914

Wright, J. *History of Laryngology and Rhinology.* 12th edition. Lea and Febiger. Philadelphia.

1915

Blanton, Smiley *The voice and the emotions.* Quart. J. Speech. 1:154 ff.

Sano, F. *The cerebral mechanism of speech.* Proc. Roy. Soc. Med. 8:71–74.

Wethlo, F. *Zur Technik der Stroboskopie.* Vox. 25:271–277.

1916

Bell, Alexander Graham *The Mechanism of Speech.* 8th edition. Funk and Wagnalls. New York.

Crane, A. W. *Skiascopy of the respiratory organs.* Amer. J. Roentg. 3:419–430.

Lee, F. D., Guenther, A. E., and Meleney, H. E. *Physiological properties of the diaphragm.* Am. J. Physiol. 40:446–473.

Rothe, K. C. *Beschleunigung der Berussen langer Kymographion Schleifen* Zentralbl. f. Physiol. 31:359–360.—For smoking kymograph records pass the gas through a bottle of benzol before it reaches the burner.

Scripture, E. W. *Speech without using larynx.* J. Physiol. 50:397.

Sluder, G. *The correlated action of the pharynx and soft palate.* Ann. Otol., Rhinol., Laryngol. 25:134–144.

1917

Howell, H. P. *Voice production from the standpoint of the laryngologist.* Ann. Otol., Rhinol., Laryngol. 26:643–655.

Jackson, C. M., and Connor, C. E. *A wax model of the nasal cavity and paranasal sinuses.* Ann. Otol., Rhinol., Laryngol. 26:585–616.

Merry, G. N. *Accessory sinuses and head resonance.* Q. J. Speech. 3:273 ff.

Spencer, F. R. *Transillumination of the larynx and upper trachea.* Ann. Otol., Rhinol., Laryngol. 26:530–536.

1918

Lundsgaard, C., and Van Slyke, D. D. *Studies of lung volume. I. Relation between thorax size and lung volume in normal adults.* J. Exp. Med. 27:65–86.

Streeter, George L. *The histogenesis and growth of the otic capsule and its contained periotic tissue-spaces in the human embryo.* Contributions to Embryology. No. 20. Publication 227. Carnegie Institution, Washington.

1919

Laurens, G. *Oto-Rhino-Laryngology.* Wm. Wood. New York.

Lillie, F. R. *The Development of the Chick.* Holt. New York.

Merry, G. N. *Roentgenological method of measuring the potentiality of voice resonance.* Q. J. Speech. 5:26 ff.

1920

Briscoe, Grace *The muscular mechanism of the diaphragm.* J. Physiol. 54:46–53.

Friedberg, S. A. *Direct laryngoscopy.* Ann. Otol., Rhinol., Laryngol. 29:410–415.

Fritz, C. B. *Construction of the organs of voice and their function in speech production.* Q. J. Speech. 6:1–23.

Hegener, J., and Panconcelli-Calzia, G. *Moving pictures of the vocal cords.* Vox. 30:114.

Lickley, J. D. *The Nervous System.* Longmans, Green. New York.

Lombard, W. P. *Laboratory Work in Physiology.* 3rd edition. George Wahr. Ann Arbor.

Miller, W. S. *A morphological study of the tracheal and bronchial cartilages.* Contributions to Embryol. No. 38. Carnegie Inst. 9:285–298.

Rich, A. R. *The Eustachian tube.* Bull. Johns Hopkins Hosp. 31:206–214.

Schaeffer, J. P. *The Nose, Paranasal Sinuses, Nasolacrimal Passageways, and Olfactory Organ in Man.* Blakiston's. Philadelphia.

Scripture, E. W. *Action of the glottis.* Volta Review. 22:710–713.—*Laryngostroboscope.* Proc. Roy. Soc. Med. 13:127–131.

1921

Browne, L., and Behnke, E. *Voice, Song, and Speech.* 21st edition. Putnam. New York.

Dilworth, T. F. M. *The nerves of the human larynx.* J. Anat. 56:48–52.

Merry, G. N. *Nasal resonance.* Q. J. Speech. 7:171.

Scripture, E. W. *Nature of vowel sounds.* Nature. 106:632–634; 664–666.

Thornton, J. *Human Physiology.* Longmans, Green. New York.

1922

Ingersoll, J. M. *Some points in the comparative anatomy of the nose and the accessory sinuses which account for the variations in these structures in man.* Ann. Otol., Rhinol., Laryngol. 31:1123–28.

Kenyon, E. L. *Significance of the extrinsic musculature of the larynx.* J. Amer. Med. Assn. 79:428–430.

Knock, C. J. *Visual training of the pitch of the voice.* Psychol. Monographs. 31:102–127.

Lange, C. G., and James, W. *The Emotions.* Vol. I. Williams and Wilkins. Baltimore.

Merry, G. N. *Voice inflection in speech.* Psychol. Monographs. 22:205–230.

Miller, D. C. *The Science of Musical Sounds.* Macmillan. New York.

Proetz, A. W. *Observations upon the formation and function of the accessory nasal sinuses and the mastoid cells.* Ann. Otol., Rhinol. Laryngol. 31:1083–1101.

Schoen, M. *An experimental study of the pitch factor in artistic singing.* Psychol. Monographs. 22:231–259.

Wickham, D. E. *Voluntary control of the intensity of sound*. Psychol. Monographs. 22:260–267.

1923

Talvi, W. *Apparatus to demonstrate movements in larynx and pharynx*. J.A.M.A. 80:1496.

1924

Dilling, W. K. *Inexpensive long paper kymograph for students' use*. J. Physiol. 59:11.

Gray, H. *Anatomy of the Human Body*. 21st edition. Lea and Febiger. Philadelphia.

Herrick, C. J. *Introduction to Neurology*. 3rd edition. Saunders. New York.

Simon, C. T. *Puff vs. overtone*. Q. J. Speech. 10:214.

Weaver, A. T. *Experimental studies in vocal expression*. J. Applied Psychol. 8:23–51; 159–186.

1925

Burger, H. *Speech without larynx*. J. Laryngol. and Otol. 40: 789–792.

Clerf, S. H. *Photography of the larynx*. Ann. Otol., Rhinol., Laryngol. 34: 101–121.

Jacobson, E. *Voluntary relaxation of the esophagus*. Am. J. Physiol. 72:387–394.

Sacia, C. F. *Speech power and energy*. Bell System Technical J. October, 1925.

1926

Dodd, L. E. *A method for studying the action of the vocal muscles during phonation*. Laryngoscope. 36:391–406.

Erickson, C. I. *The basic factors in the human voice*. Psychol. Monographs. 36:82–112.

Fletcher, Harvey *Comparison of the results made with two types of audiometers*. Arch. Otolaryngol. 4:51–57.

Forestier, J. *Roentgenological exploration of the bronchial tubes with iodized oil*. Radiology. 6:303–309.

Gault, R. H. *Touch as a substitute for hearing in the interpretation and control of speech*. Arch. Otolaryngol. 3:121–135.

Gray, Giles W. *An experimental study of the vibrato in speech*. Q. J. Speech. 12:296–333.

Jordan, H. E., and Kindred, J. E. *Textbook of Embryology*. Appleton. New York.

Kaiser, L. *Examen phonétique expérimental d'un sujet privé de larynx*. Arch. néerl. de physiol. 10:468–480.

Marifioti, P. M. *Patient who can speak, sing, and hum without use of vocal cords*. Laryngoscope. 36:682–684.

Sacia, C. F., and Beck, C. J. *The power of fundamental speech sounds*. Bell System Technical J. 5:9.

West, Robert *The nature of vocal sounds*. Q. J. Speech. 12:244–295.

1927

Baker, F. C. *How We Hear*. 3rd edition. Winthrop Rogers. London.

Curtis, H. H. *Voice Building and Tone Placing*. 3rd edition. Appleton. New York.

Fletcher, Harvey *Demonstration of the principles of talking and hearing with application to radio*. Ann. Otol., Rhinol., Laryngol. 36:1–22.

Gray, G. W. *Stroboscopic disk for study of vocal pitch*. Q. J. Speech. 13: 326–343.

Heinbecker, P. *A method for the demonstration of caliber changes in the bronchi in normal respiration.* J. Clinical Investigation. 4:459–469.

Kenyon, Elmer L. *Relation of oral articulative movements of speech and of extrinsic laryngeal musculature in general to function of vocal cords.* Arch. Otolaryngol. 5:481–501.

Mosher, H. P. *X-ray study of movements of the tongue, epiglottis, and hyoid bone in swallowing.* Laryngoscope. 37:235–262.

Patten, B. M. *The Embryology of the Pig.* Blakiston. Philadelphia.

Pieron, H. *Thought and the Brain.* Harcourt. New York.

Pohlman, A. G. *Theories of sound analysis and intensity control on the basis of middle and inner ear mechanics.* Ann. Otol., Rhinol., Laryngol. 36:579–603.

Sherrod, V., and Keller, F. *New apparatus for the study of breath control.* Q. J. Speech. 13:135–140.

Simon, C. T. *Approach to the problem of chest resonance.* Q. J. Speech. 13: 432–439.

Stern, H. *Vocal cords and resonance as reciprocal coefficients in voice production.* Monatschr. f. Ohrenh. 61:533–556.

Turner, A. L. (editor) *Diseases of the Nose, Throat, and Ear.* 2nd edition Wm. Wood. New York.

West, Robert *The nature of the laryngeal vibration.* Arch. Otolaryngol. 5:385–393.

1928

Bender, Lauretta *The cerebellar control of the vocal organs.* Arch. Neurol. and Psychiat. 19:796–833.

Brown, S., and Reineke, H. G. *The roentgenological study of the neck.* Amer. J. Roentg. and Rad. Ther. 20:208–212.

Gutzmann, H. *Physiologie der Stimme und Sprache.* 2nd edition, Vieweg. Braunschweig.

Hickey, P. M. *Radiography of the normal larynx.* Radiology. 11:409–411.

Metfessel, Milton *A photographic method of measuring pitch.* Science. 68: 430–432.

Metzger, Wolfgang *The mode of vibration of the vocal cords.* Psychol. Monog. 38:82–152. Whole No. 176. University of Iowa Studies.

Monroe, Alan H. *Effect of bodily action on voice intensity.* (Abstract of M.A. thesis.) Q. J. Speech. 14:472–474.

O'Brien, F. W. *Elevation of the diaphragm.* Radiology. 10:226–233.

Pillsbury, W. B., and Meader, C. L. *The Psychology of Language.* Appleton. New York.

Ridpath, R. *The falsetto voice.* Laryngoscope. 38:469–471.

Russell, G. O. *The Vowel.* Ohio State Univ. Press. Columbus, Ohio.

Stetson, R. H. *A study of speech movements in action.* Arch. neerl. de physiol. 13:175–390.

1929

Brown, S. *Radiology of the thorax.* Radiology. 13:515–525.

Cannon, W. B. *Bodily Changes in Pain, Hunger, Fear, and Rage.* 2nd edition. Appleton. New York.

Drennan, M. R. *The Mechanism of Voice and Speech.* The Mercantile Press. Capetown, So. Africa.

Fletcher, Harvey *Speech and Hearing.* Van Nostrand. New York.

Franz, S. I., and Watson, T. A. *Apparatus for smoking kymograph drum papers.* J. General Psychol. 2:509–513.
Golla, F. L., and Antonovitch, S. *The respiratory rhythm in its relation to the mechanism of thought.* Brain. 52:491–509.
Kiss, F., and Ballon, H. C. *Contribution to the nerve supply of the diaphragm.* Anat. Record. 41:285–298.
Lindsley, C. F. *Objective study of the respiratory processes accompanying speech.* Q. J. Speech. 15:42–58.
McNally, W. J. *The physiology of the ear.* Ann. Otol., Rhinol., Laryngol. 38: 1163–1180.
Pearcy, J. F. *Evidence of functional role of basilar membrane in audition.* Am. J. Physiol. 91:8–13.
Troland, L. T. *The psychophysiology of auditory qualities and attributes.* J. Gen. Psychol. 2:28–58.
Utzinger, Vernon A. *A study of lip movement in speech.* Q. J. Speech. 15: 480–484.

1930

Fletcher, H. *A space-time pattern theory of hearing.* J. Acoustical Soc. 1:311–343.
Hay, Percy D., Jr. *The Neck.* Annals of Roentgenology, Vol. 9. Chap. 2, 3. Hoeber. New York.
Holmes, F. L. D. *The experimental study of individual vocal quality.* Q. J. Speech. 16:344–351.
Negus, V. E. *The Mechanism of the Larynx.* C. V. Mosby. St. Louis, Missouri.
Paget, Sir R. *Human Speech.* Harcourt. New York.
Ridpath, R. F. *The embryology of the larynx.* Trans. Amer. Acad. Ophthalmology and Otolaryngology. 1930:336–342.
Root, A. R. *The pitch factors in speech.* Q. J. Speech. 16:320–341.
Russell, G. O., and Tuttle, C. H. *Color movies of vocal cord action.* Laryngoscope. 40:549–552.
Sante, L. R. *The chest.* Annals of Roentgenology. Vol. 11. Hoeber. New York.
Seashore, R. H. *Phonograph records from the Bell Telephone Laboratories illustrating phenomena of acoustics.* J. Gen. Psychol. 4:416–417.
Starling, E. H. *Principles of Human Physiology.* 5th edition. Lea and Febiger. Philadelphia.
Stewart, G. W., and Lindsay, R. B. *Acoustics.* Van Nostrand. New York.
Wilkinson, G. *Demonstration of a model resonator designed to illustrate the mechanism of the cochlea.* J. Laryngol. and Otol. 45:28–32.
Wood, A. *Sound Waves and Their Uses.* Blackie. London.
Young, I. C., and Stetson, R. H. *Analysis of vowels.* Science. 72:223.

1931

Adrian, E. D. *The microphonic action of the cochlea; an interpretation of Wever and Bray's experiments.* J. Physiol. 71:28–30.
Crowe, S. J., Hughson, W., and Witting, E. G. *Function of the tensor tympani muscle.* Arch. Otolaryngol. 14:575–580.
Felderman, L. *The Human Voice, Its Care and Development.* Holt. New York.
Gray, G. W., and Tomlin, R. D. *Improvement of pitch control in speech.* Q. J. Speech. 17:190–202.
Guggenheim, L. K. *The development of the organ of hearing.* Ann. Otol., Rhinol., Laryngol. 40:812–851.

Heatly, C. A. *Motion-picture studies of the larynx.* Ann. Otol., Rhinol., Laryngol. 40:434–447.
Holmes, F. L. D. *The problem of voice placement.* Q. J. Speech. 17:236–245.
Howell, W. H. *Physiology.* 11th edition. Saunders. Philadelphia.
Krueger, R. G. *An improved system of kymograph recording.* J. Exper. Psychol. 14:176–179.
Metfessel, Milton *Effect of the removal of the fundamental and certain overtones on vocal pitch and quality.* Psychol. Bull. 28:212.
Morrison, W. W. *The production of voice and speech following total laryngectomy. Exercise and practice for the production of pseudovoice.* Arch. Otolaryngol. 14:413–431.
Ranson, S. W. *Anatomy of the Nervous System.* 4th edition. Saunders. Philadelphia.
Russell, G. O. *Speech and Voice.* Macmillan. New York.
Snow, W. B. *Audible frequency ranges of music, speech, and noise.* Bell System Tech. J. 10:616–627.
Travis, Lee Edward *Speech Pathology.* Appleton. New York.
Wegel, R. L. *Nature of stimulation at the organ of Corti in the light of modern physical experimental data.* Laryngoscope. 41:392–393.
Wichart, W. F., Thienes, C. H., and Visscher, M. B. *Two improvements in the technique of kymograph recording.* Science. 73:99–100.
Zoethout, W. D. *A Textbook of Physiology.* 4th edition. C. V. Mosby. St. Louis, Mo.

1932

Carmichael, E. B., and Posey, L. C. *A convenient pneumograph.* Amer. J. Physiol. 101:17. Proceedings.
Davis, H., and Saul, L. J. *The frequency of impulses in the auditory pathways.* Amer. J. Physiol. 101:28–29. Proceedings.
Froschels, E. *Psychological Elements in Speech.* Expression Company. Boston.
Gardiner, A. H. *The Theory of Speech and Language.* Oxford University Press. New York.
Judson, L. S. *Combining the breathing undae of speaker and listener with the dictaphone record of the speech.* Amer. J. Psychol. 44:183–184.
Lemere, Fred *Innervation of the larynx.* Amer. J. Anat. 51:417–437.—Also, Anat. Record. 54:389–407.
McKay, Frederic B. *A study of time control in speaking.* American Schoolmaster. 25:107–115.
Menville, L. J., and Ane, J. N. *A new roentgenologic technic in the study of phonetics.* Proc. Soc. Exp. Biol. 29:825–826.
Meyer, M. F. *Phase difference of pressure between the windows the essence of sound stimulation.* Ann. Otol., Rhinol., Laryngol. 41:323–331.
Sharpey-Shafer, E. *Normal respiration and the influence of the vagi.* J. Physiol. 75:130–135.
Stanley, D., and Watkins, S. *The Science of Voice.* 2nd edition. Carl Fischer. New York.
Tiffin, J. *Phonophotograph apparatus.* Univ. Iowa Studies. Stud. Psychol. Music. 1:118–133.
Trevino, S. N., and Parmenter, C. E. *Vowel positions as shown by x-ray.* Q. J. Speech. 18:351–370.
Troland, L. T. *Psychophysiology.* Van Nostrand. New York. Vol. II, 1930; Vol. III, 1932.

Wise, C. M. *Chest resonance.* Q. J. Speech. 18:446–452.

1933

Barrows, Sarah T., and Pierce, Anne F. *The Voice: How To Use It.* Expression Co. Boston.

Bloomfield, L. *Language.* Holt. New York.

Bronk, D. W., and Ferguson, L. K. *The nervous regulation of the respiratory movements of intercostal muscles.* Amer. J. Physiol. 105:13. Proceedings.

Eijkman, L. P. H. *The internal aspect of the larynx in speech.* Arch. neerlandaises de Phonetique Experimentale. Tome 8–9:122–129.

Gage, F. H., and Shaxby, J. H. *The regions of greatest energy in the production of vowel sounds.* J. Physiol. 77:18. Proceedings.

Hughson, W., and Crowe, S. J., *Experimental investigation of the physiology of the ear.* Acta. Otolaryngol. 18:291–339.

Killing, H. S. *An electric analogue of vowel production.* Science. 77:604–605.

Larsell, O., and Dow, R. S. *The innervation of the human lung.* Amer. J. Anat. 52:125–146.

Law, Frederick M. *Nasal Accessory Sinuses.* Annals of Roentgenology. Vol. 15. Hoeber. New York.

Lemere, F. *Innervation of the larynx.* Arch. Otolaryngol. 18:413–424.

Lewis, Don, and Reger, Scott N. *An experimental study of the role of the tympanic membrane and the ossicles in the hearing of certain subjective tones.* J. Acoust. Soc. America. October: 153–158.

Lorente, de No. R. *The reflex contractions of the muscles of the middle ear as a hearing test in experimental animals.* Trans. Amer. Laryngol., Rhinol. and Otol. Soc. 1933:26–42.

O'Neill, J. M., and Weaver, A. T. *The Elements of Speech.* Revised edition. Longmans, Green. New York.

Osborne, W. A. *Electric symmetry of the thorax.* J. Physiol. 77:31. Proceedings.

Parmenter, C. E., Trevino, S. N., and Bevans, C. A. *The influence of a change in pitch on the articulation of a vowel.* Language. 9:72–81.

Schlosberg, Harold *Cellophane membranes for tambours.* Science. 78:16.

Stewart, G. W. *Introductory Acoustics.* Van Nostrand. New York.

Taylor, H. C. *A conditioned change in vocal pitch.* J. Gen. Psychol. 8:465–467.

Ziegelman, E. F. *Laryngeal nerves. Surgical importance in relation to the thyroid arteries, thyroid gland, and larynx.* Arch. Otolaryngol. 18: 793–805.

1934

Colton, Jack C. *Resonance in soft-walled cylinders.* J. Acoust. Soc. Amer. 5:208–212.

Flemming, Edwin G. *Pleasant voice.* Q. J. Speech. 20:194–199.

Gray, Giles W. *Some persistent questions in vocal theory.* Q. J. Speech. 20: 185–194.

Hallpike, C. S., and Rawdon-Smith, A. F. *The function of the tensor tympani muscle.* J. Physiol. 81:25P–27P.

Hammouda, M., and Wilson, W. H. *Influences which affect the form of the respiratory cycle.* J. Physiol. 80:261–285.

Hay, Rosemary *Correct breathing habits for children's speech.* Q. J. Speech. 20:98–102.

Jackson, C., and Jackson, C. L. *Bronchoscopy, Esophagoscopy, and Gastroscopy.* 3rd edition. Saunders. Philadelphia.

Kallen, L. A. *Vicarious vocal mechanisms. The anatomy, physiology, and development of speech in laryngectomized persons.* Arch. Otolaryngol. 20:460–503.

Kelly, Joseph P. *Studies in nasality.* Arch. of Speech. 1:26–42.

Kelly, Joseph P. and Higby, L. B. *A contribution to the x-ray study of tongue position in certain vowels.* Arch. of Speech. 1:84–95.

Lemere, F. *Innervation of the larynx.* Ann. Otol., Rhinol., Laryngol. 43:525–540.

Lindsley, Charles F. *The psycho-physical determinants of voice quality.* Speech Monographs. 1:79–116.

Lynch, Gladys E. *A phonophotographic study of trained and untrained voices reading factual and dramatic material.* Arch. of Speech. 1:9–25.

McNally, W. J. *Recent advances in the physiology of hearing.* Arch. Otolaryngol. 19:201–215.

Morris, A. R. *A note on the voice inflection of Julia Marlowe.* Q. J. Speech. 20:200–202.

Rioch, J. McK. *The neural mechanism of mastication.* Amer. J. Physiol. 108: 168–176.

Russell, G. Oscar *First preliminary x-ray consonant study.* J. Acoust. Soc. Amer. 5:247–251.

Slattengren, Hattie J. E. *Nasal speech.* Q. J. Speech. 20:542–543.

Steer, M. D., and Tiffin, J. *A photographic study of the use of intensity by superior speakers.* Speech Monographs. 1:72–78.

Steinberg, J. C. *The application of sound-measuring instruments to the study of phonetic problems.* J. Acoust. Soc. Amer. 6:16–24.

Stephens, S. S. *The volume and intensity of tones.* Amer. J. Psychol. 46: 397–408.

Tait, J. *Evolution of vertebrate voice.* Acta Oto-Laryngologica. 20:46–59.

Travis, L. E., Bender, W. R. G., and Buchanan, A. R. *Research contribution to vowel theory.* Speech Monographs. 1:65–71.

Voelker, Charles H. *The function of the epiglottis in speech.* J.A.M.A. 103: 1797.

1935

Culler, E., Finch, G., and Girden, E. *Function of the round window in hearing.* Amer. J. Physiol. 111:416–425.

Curry, R. O. L., and Richardson, E. G. *The application of the cathode-ray oscillograph in speech analysis.* J. Physiol. 87:45–46. Proceedings.

Derbyshire, A. J., and Davis, H. *The probable mechanism for stimulation of the auditory nerve by the organ of Corti.* Am. J. Physiol. 113:35.

Eijkman, L. P. H. *The influence of the subglottal passage and the nasal cavity on non-nasal sounds.* Arch. Néerlandaises de Phonétique Expérimentale. 9:29–38.

Ellis, M. P., and Livingston, A. E. *A method of directly recording changes in the caliber of the bronchi.* J. Physiol. 84:223.

Fray, W. W. *A roentgenological study of pulmonary ventilation.* Amer. J. Roentg. and Rad. Therapy. 33:179–190.

Holmes, F. L. D. *Infra-glottal resonance.* Speech Monog. 2:138–156.—*Resonance.* Q. J. Speech. 21:216–224.

Hudgins, C. V., and Stetson, R. H. *Voicing of consonants by depression of larynx.* Arch. Néerlandaises de Phonétique Expérimentale. 11: 1–28.

Jackson, C., and Jackson, C. L. *Dysphonia plicae ventricularis. Phonation with the ventricular bands*. Arch. Otolaryngol. 21:157–167.

Miller, D. C. *Anecdotal History of Science of Sound to the Beginning of the 20th Century*. Macmillan. New York.

Negus, V. E. *The mechanism of phonation*. Acta Oto-laryngologica. 22:393–419.

Nusbaum, E. A., Foley, Lena, and Wells, Charlotte *Experimental studies of the firmness of the velar-pharyngeal occlusion during the production of the English vowels*. Speech Monog. 2:71–80.

Rinquest, E. H. B. *How to Develop Your Speaking Voice*. Frank J. Wolf. Denver.

Scripture, E. W. *Failure of Fourier analysis applied to vowel vibrations*. Nature. 136:223.—*Macrophonic speech*. J. Exp. Psychol. 18:784–791. —*Puff and profile theory of the vowels*. Nature. 136:435–436.

Shohara, Hide *The genesis of the articulatory movements in speech*. Q. J. Speech. 21:343–348.

Skinner, E. R. *A calibrated recording and analysis of the pitch, force, and quality of vocal tones expressing happiness and sadness*. Speech Monog. 2:81–137.

Strong, L. H. *The mechanism of laryngeal pitch*. Anat. Record. 63:13–28.

Taylor, H. M. *Ossification of the cartilages of the larynx*. Ann. Otol., Rhinol., Laryngol. 44:611–625.

Voelker, Charles H. *Phoniatry in dysphonia ventricularis*. Ann Otol., Rhinol., Laryngol. 44:471–473.

West, R. *A view of the larynx through a new stroboscope*. Q. J. Speech. 21:455–461.—*Speech and hearing*. Q. J. Speech. 21:178–188.

Williamson, Arleigh B. *Two years experience with recording equipment*. Q. J. Speech. 21:195–216.

1936

Barron, D. H. *A note on the proprioceptive fibers of the tongue*. Anat. Record. 66:11–15.

Bloomer, H. H. *A roentgenographic study of the mechanics of respiration*. Speech Monog. 3:118–124.

Colton, J. C. *Syllabic rate: a new concept in the study of speech rate variation*. Speech Monog. 3:112–117.

Cowan, Milton *Pitch and intensity characteristics of stage speech*. Supplement to Archives of Speech. Iowa City, Iowa.

Ellis, M. *The mechanism of the rhythmic changes in the caliber of the bronchi during respiration*. J. Physiol. 87:298–309.

Gesell, R. *Fusillade patterns of inspiratory and expiratory muscles and their mechanical effects on the respiratory act*. Amer. J. Physiol. 116:228–238.—*Individuality of breathing*. Amer. J. Physiol. 115:168–180.

Gesell, R., Bricker, J., and Magee, C. *Structural and functional organization of the central mechanism controlling breathing*. Amer. J. Physiol. 117:423–452.

Gray, G. W. *A speech mechanism hypothesis*. Q. J. Speech. 22:656–660.—*Studies in experimental phonetics*. University of Louisiana Studies. No. 27.

Guild, S. R. *Hearing by bone conduction: the pathways of transmission of sound*. Ann. Otol., Rhinol., Laryngol. 45:736–753.

Hall, A. *On a new method for filming the larynx.* Acta Oto-Laryngologica. 23:113–124.

Henderson, V. E., and Craigie, E. H. *On the respiratory center.* Amer. J. Physiol. 115:520–529.

Iglauer, S. *Artificial larynx.* Ann. Otol., Rhinol., Laryngol. 45:1176–1177.

Krasnoff, Gregory *How To Improve Your Voice.* Dial Press. New York.

Lurie, H. M. *How does the organ of Corti distinguish pitch?* Ann. Otol., Rhinol., Laryngol. 45:339–350.

Moore, Paul *A simple means of studying the relationship between the current and flash in a glow-lamp stroboscope.* Speech Monog. 3:109–111.

Morrison, W., and Fineman, S. *The production of pseudo-voice after total laryngectomy.* Trans. Amer. Acad. Ophth. and Otolar. 1936:631–4.

Raubicheck, L., Davis, E. H., and Carll, L. A. *Voice and Speech Problems.* Prentice-Hall. New York.

Scripture, E. W. *The nature of the vowels.* Q. J. Speech. 22:359–366.

Van Wye, B. C. *The efficient voice in speech.* Q. J. Speech. 22:642–648.

Voelker, Charles H. *The sounding-board function of the hard palate in speech.* Q. J. Speech. 22:23–27.

Warren, Neil *Vocal cord activity and vowel theory.* Q. J. Speech. 22:651–656.

1937

Cotton, Jack C. *Tongue movements and vowel quality.* Speech Monog. 4:38–43.

Drake, Ormond J. *Toward an improved vocal quality.* Q. J. Speech. 23:620–626.

Hallpike, C. S., and Rawdon-Smith, A. F. *The Wever and Bray phenomenon—a summary of the data concerning the origin of the cochlear effect.* Ann. Otol., Rhinol., and Laryngol. 46:976–990.

Holbrook, Richard T. *X-ray studies of speech articulations.* Univ. of California Publications in Modern Philology. XX, No. 4, i–viii and 187–238. November 12, 1937.

Hollister, R. D. T. *Relation between hand and voice impulse movements.* Speech Monog. 4:75–100.

Huyck, E. M., and Allen, K. D. A. *Diaphragmatic action of good and poor speaking voices.* Speech Monog. 4:101–109.

Jerome, Eldon K. *Change of voice in male adolescents.* Q. J. Speech. 23:648–653.

Jones, Arthur Tabor *Sound.* Van Nostrand Co. New York.

Kallen, L. A., and Polin, H. S. *A laryngo-stroboscope and comment upon Dr. West's reference to same.* Q. J. Speech. 23:119–126.

Miller, William Snow *The Lung.* Charles C. Thomas. Springfield, Illinois.

Moore, Paul *A short history of laryngeal investigation.* Q. J. Speech. 23:531–564.—*Vocal fold movement during vocalization.* Speech Monog. 4:44–55.

Ortleb, Ruth *An objective study of emphasis in oral reading of emotional and unemotional material.* Speech Monog. 4:56–74.

Scott, W. G., and Moore, S. *Roentgen kymography of the respiratory movements of the thorax, diaphragm, lungs, bronchi, and mediastinal structures.* Amer. J. Roentg. and Rad. Therapy. 37:721–732.

Tobeck, A. *The mechanism of air-current pressures in the larynx.* Arch. Ohr. u.s.w. Heilk. 118:77–80.

West, R. *Gentlemen: I stand corrected?* Q. J. Speech. 23:402–409.

West, R., Kennedy, Lou, and Carr, A. *The Rehabilitation of Speech*. Harper. New York.

1938

Anonymous *Pedro the Voder, a machine that talks*. Bell Lab. Record. 17: 170–171.

Ansberry, Merle *The effect upon the ability to discriminate between speech sounds by the elimination of frequencies above 4000 cycles*. Q. J. Speech. 23:381–389.

Black, John W. *Vowel quality before and after an operation for an occluded nasal passage*. Speech Monog. 5:62–64.

Carhart, Raymond *Evolution of the speech mechanism*. Q. J. Speech. 23: 557–568.—*Infra-glottal resonance and a cushion pipe*. Speech Monog. 5:65–96.

Covell, W. P. *The peripheral endings of the cochlear nerve*. Ann. Otol., Rhinol., Laryngol. 48:63–67.

Fairbanks, Grant, and Pronovost, Wilbert *Vocal pitch during simulated emotion*. Science. 88:382–383.

Karr, Harrison *Your Speaking Voice*. Griffin-Patterson Pub. Co. Glendale, Calif.

Kobrak, H. G. *Experiments on the conduction of sound in the ear*. Ann. Otol., Rhinol., Laryngol. 48:166–175.

McGregor, Gregor *Comparative anatomy of the tongue*. Ann. Otol., Rhinol., Laryngol. 48:196–211.

Martinelli, Giovanni *Caring for the vocal instrument*. Etude. 56:650, 679, 692.

Moore, Paul *Motion-picture studies of the vocal folds and vocal attack*. J. of Sp. Disorders. 3:235–238.

Orr, F. W. *Voice for Speech*. McGraw-Hill. New York.

Osborn, Loraine *Your Voice Personality*. Putnam. New York.

Pressman, Joel J. *Physiology of the larynx. A résumé and discussion of the literature for 1938*. Laryngoscope. 49: 239–259.

Stevens, Stanley S., and Davis, Hallowell *Hearing—Its Psychology and Physiology*. Wiley. New York.

Tiffin, Joseph, Saetveit, Joseph, and Snidecor, John *An approach to the analysis of the vibration of the vocal cords*. Q. J. Speech. 24:1–11.

Wever, E. G. *The width of the basilar membrane in man*. Ann. Otol., Rhinol., Laryngol. 48:720–723.

Windesheim, Karl A. *The evolution of speech-recording machines*. Q. J. Speech. 23:257–265.

Wise, Harry S. *Speech—"The overlaid function."* Q. J. Speech. 23:11–16.

Young, Barton R. *Soft Tissues of the Air and Food Passages of the Neck. Diagnostic Roentgenology*. Nelson. New York.

1939

Black, John W. *The stability of the vowel*. Q. J. Speech. 24:52–57.

Blewett, John *Laryngocele*. Brit. J. Radiology. 12:163–167.

Critchley, M. *Spastic dysphonia ("Inspiratory Speech")*. Brain. 62:96–103.

Dunn, H. K., and Farnsworth, D. W. *Exploration of pressure field around the human head during speech*. J. Acoust. Soc. Amer. 10:184–199.

Fairbanks, Grant and Pronovost, W. *An experimental study of the pitch characteristics of the voice during the expression of emotion*. Speech Monog. 6:87–104.

Hartung, A., and Grossman, J. W. *Examination of the larynx and adjacent structures with intrapharyngeal films.* Amer. J. Roentg., and Rad. Therapy. 42:481–489.

Le Jeune, Francis F. *A review of the available literature on the pharynx and pharyngeal surgery for 1938.* Laryngoscope. 49:1043–1063.

Lell, William A. *Motion pictures of the human larynx.* Arch. Otolaryngol. 30: 344–351.

Levbarg, John L. *Vocal therapy versus surgery for the eradication of singers' and speakers' nodules.* The Eye, Ear, Nose and Throat Monthly. 18:81–91.

Lynch, Gladys E. *A harmonic analysis of hydrogen tones.* Q. J. Speech. 24: 57–62.

Moore, Wilbur E. *Personality traits and voice quality deficiencies.* J. Speech Disorders. 4:33–36.

Shohara, Hide *An experimental study on the control of pronunciation.* Speech Monog. 6:105–109.

Tiffin, Joseph, and Steer, M. D. *The vibrograph: a combination apparatus for the speech laboratory.* Q. J. Speech. 25:272–278.

Tremble, G. E. *Moving pictures of the larynx with a telephoto lens.* J. of Laryngol. and Otol. 54:664–668.

Wells, Charlotte *A test of pitch discrimination.* Q. J. Speech. 24:665–673.

1940

Brocklehurst, R. J., and Edgeworth, F. H. *The fiber components of the laryngeal nerves of macaca mulatta.* J. Anat. 74:386–389.

Curry, E. T. *The pitch characteristics of the adolescent male voice.* Speech Monographs. 7:48–62.

Curry, Robert *The Mechanism of the Human Voice.* Longmans, Green. New York.

Cushman, R. A. *Audition demonstration.* Bell Lab. Records. 18:273–277.

Davis, Hallowell *The clarification of certain phases of the physiology of hearing.* Laryngoscope. 50:747–755.

Farnsworth, D. W. *High-speed motion pictures of the human vocal cords.* Bell Lab. Records. 18:203–208.

Fletcher, Harvey *Auditory patterns.* Reviews of Modern Physics. 12:47–65.

Froeschels, Emil *Psychology of the laryngeal functions.* Arch. Otolaryngol. 32: 1039–1044.

Gesell, Robert *A neurophysiological interpretation of the respiratory act.* Ergebnisse der Physiologie, biologischen Chemie und experimentellen Pharmakologie. 43:477–639.

Gillespie, H. W. *A short account of radiographic technique as applied to the study of phonetics.* J. Laryngol. and Otol. 60:387.

Goldstein, Max *New concepts of the function of the tongue.* Laryngoscope. 50: 164–188.

Jackson, Chevalier *Myasthenia laryngis. Observations on the larynx as an air-column instrument.* Arch. Otolaryng. 32:434–463.—The length of the air column from the level of the lips to the level of the orifices of the bronchi of the lower lobes of the lungs is 36 cm. In general, persons with high-pitched voices have short necks and people with low voices have long necks.

Jones, F. W. *The nature of the soft palate.* J. Anat. (British). 74:147–170.

Keaster, Jacqueline *Studies on the anatomy and physiology of the tongue.* Laryngoscope. 50:222–258.

Keen, J. A. *The length of the basilar membrane.* J. Anat. 74:524–527.

Levin, N. M. *Teaching the laryngectomized patient to talk.* Arch. Otolaryng. 32:299–314.—Much less air is necessary in the production of pseudovoice than is usually realized.

McMyn, J. K. *The anatomy of the salpingo-pharyngeus muscle.* J. Laryngol. and Otology. 60:1–22.

Pancoast, H. K., Pendergrass, E. P., and Schaeffer, J. P. *The Head and Neck in Roentgen Diagnosis.* Charles C. Thomas. Springfield, Illinois.

Pitts, R. F. *The respiratory center and its descending pathways.* J. Comp. Neurology. 72:605–625.

Pressman, J. J. *Physiology of the larynx. A résumé and discussion of the literature for 1939.* Laryngoscope. 50:277–301.

Pressman, J. J., and Hinman, A. *Further advances in the technique of laryngeal photography.* Laryngoscope. 50:535–546.

Rasmussen, A. T. *Studies of the VIIIth cranial nerve of man.* Laryngoscope. 50:67–83.—Cochlear nerves contain from 23,000 to 40,000 nerve fibers.

Townshend, R. H. *The formation of Passavant's bar.* J. Laryngol. and Otology. 60:154–165.

Wells, Walter *The significance of hoarseness.* Ann. Otol., Rhinol., and Laryngol. 49:99–112.

Young, Barton R. *Recent advances in Roentgen examination of the neck. Body section Roentgenography (Planigraphy) of the larynx.* Am. J. Roentg. and Rad. Therapy. 44:519–529.

1941

Bach, A. C., *et al.* *Senile changes in laryngeal musculature.* Arch. Otolaryng. 34:47–56.

Bennett, G. A., *et al.* *Experimental studies on the movements of the mammalian tongue.* Anat. Rec. 79:39–51.—Believes protrusion due to genioglossus and intrinsic muscles.

Clapp, C. W., *et al.* *The acoustic wattmeter, an instrument for measuring sound energy flow.* JASA 13:124–136.

Clerf, L. H. *Photographic study of the larynx by mirror laryngoscopy.* Arch. Otolaryng. 33:378–383.

Ham, A. W., *et al.* *A histological study of the development of the lung with particular reference to the nature of the alveoli.* Anat. Rec. 81:363–379.

Kobrak, H. G. *A cinematographic study of the conduction of sound in the human ear.* JASA 13:179–181.

Krogh, A. *The Comparative Physiology of Respiratory Mechanisms.* Univ. of Pennsylvania Press. Philadelphia.

Lee, F. C. *Description of a fascia situated between the serratus anterior muscle and the thorax.* Anat. Rec. 81:35–41.—Good schematic drawing of superior and interior posterior serrati.

Moore, S., *et al.* *Use of laminagrams in laryngology.* Arch. Otolaryng. 33:776–794.—Differentiates: *stratigraph* of Vallebona, *tomograph* of Grossman and Chaoul, *planigraph* of Ziedsesdes Plantes, *laminagraph* of Kieffer and Moore, and *biotome* of Bocage.

Moses, P. J. *Is medical phonetics an essential part of otorhinolaryngology?* Arch. Otolaryng. 31:444–450.—Celsus (30 A.D.) made the tongue the center of speech.

Pendergrass, E. P., *et al.* *The roentgen diagnosis of neoplasms of the air and food passages, with particular reference to the larynx.* Radiology. 36:197–211.—Contains detailed description of roentgenologic appearance of the normal pharynx and larynx.

Pressman, J. J. *Sphincter action of the larynx.* Arch. Otolaryng. 33:351–377. —The article and figures may be consulted with profit.

Stanley, D., *et al.* *The Voice, Its Production and Reproduction.* Pitman Pub. Co. New York.

Wood, A. *Acoustics.* Interscience Publishers. New York.

Work, W. P. *Paralyses and pareses of the vocal cords.* Arch. Otolaryng. 34:267–280.

1942

Anderson, V. A. *Training the Speaking Voice.* Oxford University Press. New York.

Beaton, L. E., *et al.* *Variations in the origin of the m. trapezius.* Anat. Rec. 83:41–46.—Except for the pectoralis, the muscle is subject to more deviations from the "normal" than any other.

Carhart, R. *Some aspects of model larynx function.* JASA 14:36–40.

Farnsworth, D. W. *Radiation pattern of the human voice.* BLR 21:298–303. —Spectrum of male speech power: 80% in 250–1000 cycles band; 96% in 125–2000 band; only 0.4% above 4000 cycles.

Hardy, H. C., *et al.* *The velocity of sound in air.* JASA 13:226–233.—Gives the velocity as 331.44 ($\pm$ 0.05) m/sec in dry air at 0° C.

Hunt, R. S. *Damping and selectivity of the inner ear.* JASA 14:50–57.

Judson, Lyman S. and Weaver, Andrew T. *Voice Science.* F. S. Crofts. New York.

Kantner, Claude E. *Phonetics* (pp. 163–186 in *Voice Science* by Judson and Weaver, 1942).

Lachman, E. *A comparison of the posterior boundaries of lungs and pleura as demonstrated on the cadaver and on the roentgenogram of the living.* Anat. Rec. 83:521–542.

Lowy, K. *Cancellation of the electrical cochlear response with air- and bone-conducted sound.* JASA 14:156–158.

No author *American standard acoustical terminology.* JASA 14:84–101.

No author *American standard for noise measurement.* JASA 14:102–110.

Palmer, M. F. *Synchronization of the events of the cardiac cycle with the onsets of respiratory movements.* JSD 7:375–380.

Pepinsky, A. *The laryngeal ventricle considered as an acoustical filter.* JASA 14:32–35.

Pressman, J. J. *Physiology of the vocal cords in phonation and respiration.* Arch. Otolaryng. 35:355–398.

Shohara, H. H. *A contribution to the genesis of speech movements.* JSD 7:29–32.

Woolsey, C. N., *et al.* *Topical projection of nerve fibers from local regions of the cochlea to the cerebral cortex of the cat.* Bull. Johns Hopkins Hosp. 71:315–344.

1943

Galambos, R., *et al.* *The response of single auditory-nerve fibers to acoustic stimulation.* J. Neurophysiol. 6:39–58.

Griesman, B. L. *Mechanism of phonation demonstrated by planigraphy of the larynx.* Arch. Otolaryng. 38:17–26.—Refer to figures.

Hagens, E. W. *Anatomy of the tracheobronchial tree from the bronchoscopic standpoint.* Arch. Otolaryng. 38:469–475.—Gives dimensions of various parts.

Imperatori, C. J. *Bartholomaeus Eustachius: his contribution to the anatomy of the ear, larynx and bronchi.* Laryngoscope 53: 631–652.—Photographs of early publications: Opuscula Anatomica (1564).

Irwin, O. C., *et al.* *Speech sound elements during the first year of life: a review of the literature.* JSD 8:109–121.

Kirikae, I. *The motion of vocal cords and the time relation of the glottis opening during phonation.* J. Oto-Rhino Laryngol. Soc. Jap. 49: 236–246.

Kobrak, H. G. *Direct observations of the acoustic oscillations of the human ear.* JASA 15:54–56.

Noback, C. R. *Some gross structural and quantitative aspects of the developmental anatomy of the human embryonic, fetal and circumnatal skeleton.* Anat. Rec. 87:29–51.

Olson, H. F. *Dynamical Analogies.* Van Nostrand. New York.—Explains analogies between acoustical systems and electrical systems.

Reed, A. F. *The relation of the inferior laryngeal nerve to the inferior thyroid artery.* Anat. Rec. 85:17–23.

Richardson, J. R. *Anatomy and physiology of the ear. Arch. Otolaryng.* 37:567–590.—Summary of the literature.

Simkins, C. S. *Functional anatomy of the Eustachian tube.* Arch. Otolaryng. 38:476–484.

Sokolowsky, R. R. *Effect of the extrinsic laryngeal muscles on voice production.* Arch. Otolaryng. 38:355–364.—Refer to Fig. 2.

1944

Bucy, P. C. ed. *The Precentral Motor Cortex.* Univ. of Illinois Press. Urbana.

Graves, G. O., *et al.* *Epistle on the organs of hearing by Bartholomaeus Eustachius.* Arch. Otolaryn. 40:123–132.—Reproduces some pages of the original.

Graves, G. O., *et al.* *The Eustachian tube: a review of its descriptive, microscopic, topographic and clinical anatomy.* Arch. Otolaryng. 39:359–397.—Recommended.

Griesman, B. *Muscles and cartilages of the nose.* Arch. Otolaryng. 39:334–341.

Harrington, R. *A study of the mechanism of velopharyngeal closure.* JSD 9: 325–345.—Although sphincteric in nature, closure is not due to such simple sphincter action as occurs in the esophagus.

Kellaway, P. *Cochlear microphonics: a critical review.* Arch. Otolaryng. 39:203–210.

Larsell, O., *et al.* *Development of the organ of Corti in relation to the inception of hearing.* Arch. Otolaryng. 40:233–248.

Noback, C. R. *The developmental anatomy of the human osseous skeleton during the embryonic, fetal and circumnatal periods.* Anat. Rec. 88:91–125.—With figures indicates the time sequence of development.

Pressman, J. J. *Effect of the sphincteric action of the larynx on intra-abdominal pressure.* Arch. Otolaryng. 39:14–42.

Rhines, R., *et al.* *An experimental study of factors influencing the course of nerve fibers in the embryonic central nervous system*. Anat. Rec. 90:267–293.—Discusses theories: (1) mechanical; (2) chemotropic; (3) galvanotropism (electrical) or neurobiotaxis.

Sprague, J. M. *The innervation of the pharynx in the rhesus monkey, and the formation of the pharyngeal plexus in primates*. Anat. Rec. 90: 197–208.—Also, discusses innervation in the human.

Simon, E. *Atmospheric pressures in the nasal fossa, the maxillary sinus and the trachea*. Arch. Otolaryng. 39:504–513.

1945

Bomberger, D. C. *Servo-mechanisms*. BLR 23:409–411.—Word "servo" (slave) first used in 1872 by Joseph Farcot, a Frenchman.

Campbell, B. *The distribution of potential fields within the spinal cord*. Anat. Rec. 91:77–88.—Potential gradients within *CNS* are signs, and possible regulators of physiological activity.

Coates-Longerich, M., *et al. German-English speech terminology*. JSD 10: 39–46.—Provides German equivalents of some English terms, together with definitions.

Kellaway, P. *Mechanism of the cochlea*. Arch. Otolaryng. 41:252–260.

MacColl, L. A. *Fundamental Theory of Servomechanisms*. Van Nostrand. New York.

Pike, L. *The Intonation of American English*. Univ. of Michigan Press. Ann Arbor.

Potter, R. K. *Visible patterns of sound*. Science. 102:463–470.

Rayleigh, Lord *The Theory of Sound*. 2 vol. (First published in 1877.) Dover Publications. New York.—Between 1870 and 1919 Rayleigh published 450 articles on physics, including 128 dealing with acoustics.

Reese, A.M. *The laryngeal region of Alligator mississippiensis*. Anat. Rec. 92:273–277.

Waltner, J. G. *Development of the cochlear aqueduct and the round window membrane in the human embryo*. Arch. Otolaryng. 42:239–252.

1946

Bangs, J. L., *et al. Speech after laryngectomy*. JSD 11:171–176.—Describes air-driven and electrically-driven artificial larynges, and esophageal speech. Diagrams show speech mechanism before and after operation.

Baranek, L. L., *et al. The design and construction of anechoic sound chambers*. JASA 18:140–150.

Bassett, D. L., *et al. Terms of position and direction*. Anat. Rec. 94:257–263. —Compares BNA, BR, and NK-INA systems of nomenclature. NK (Nomenklatur Kommission). (Incidentally, in Judson and Weaver the terms ORIGIN and INSERTION are used although there is widespread use of the single term ATTACHMENT.)

Dobson, J. *Anatomical Eponyms*. Bailliere, Tindall & Cox. London.

Dudley, H., *et al. Visible speech translators with external phosphors*. JASA 18:62–73.

Harrington, R. *A note on a lingua-velar relationship*. JSD 11:25.

Howell, W. H. *Textbook of Physiology* (15th edition). Saunders. Philadelphia.

Irwin, O. C., *et al. Infant speech: vowel and consonant frequency*. JSD 11:123–125.—Until he is 2½ years old an infant produces more vowels (5 times as many) than consonants, but at 2½ years they begin to equalize rapidly.

Johnston, T. B. *Anatomical terminology. The British point of view.* Anat. Rec. 94:249–252.—Expresses views on NA (Nomina Anatomica, Jena 1936); BNA (Basle Nomina Anatomica, 1895), and BR (Birmingham Revision, 1933).

Koenig, W., *et al.* *The sound spectrograph.* JASA 18:19–49.

Kopp, G. A., *et al.* *Basic phonetic principles of visible speech.* JASA 18:74–89.

Lachman, E. *Is the concept of the "anatomical position" still tenable? A contribution to the subject of anatomical nomenclature.* Anat. Rec. 95:81–87.—Anatomical terms reflect man's achieving an upright position: e.g., superior, inferior, ascending, anterior and posterior.

Longerich, E. B., *et al.* *French-English speech terminology.* JSD 11:193–196.—Gives French equivalents of English terms, together with some definitions.

Moore, W. E. *Hypnosis in a system of therapy for stutterers.* JSD 11:117–122.—Hypnosis improves speech. Does it alter the bio-chemical or metabolic processes of the body?

Ornston, D. G. *Office study of* (nasal) *cilia.* Arch. Otolaryng. 44:19–23.

Polyak, S. L., *et al.* *The Human Ear in Anatomical Transparencies.* T. H. McKenna. New York.

Potter, R. K. *Visible speech.* BLR 24:7–11.—Describes spectrograph, and spectrograms produced.

Rao, V. V. L. *The Decibel Notation.* Chemical Pub. Co. New York.—Information about decibel, neper, and phon.

Riesz, R. R., *et al.* *Visible speech cathode-ray translator.* JASA 18:50–61.

Rüedi, L., *et al.* *Physics and physiology of acoustic trauma.* JASA 18:409–412.

Steinberg, J. C., *et al.* *The portrayal of visible speech.* JASA 18:4–18.

Wiener, F. M., *et al.* *The pressure distribution in the auditory canal in a progressive sound field.* JASA 18:401–408.—Looks upon the external ear as an effective acoustic amplifier.

1947

Ballenger, C. *Diseases of the Nose, Throat and Ear.* Lea and Febiger. Philadelphia.

Bangs, J. L. *Bibliography: esophageal speech.* JSD 12:339–341.

Bast, T. H., *et al.* *The developmental courses of the human auditory vesicle.* Anat. Rec. 99:55–74.—Rudiment of organ appears at 2mm stage as a plate-like thickening of ectoderm. This primordial auditory placode is depressed to form auditory pit and, with further invagination and closure of the mouth, becomes auditory vesicle at 3mm stage.

de Rosa, L. A. *Theory as to the function of the scala tympani in hearing.* JASA 19:623–628.

Eisenson, J. *The Psychology of Speech.* F. S. Crofts. New York.

French, N. R., *et al.* *Factors governing the intelligibility of speech sounds.* JASA 19:90–119.

Garner, W. R. *The effect of frequency spectrum on temporal integration of energy in the ear.* JASA 19:808–815.

Hauser, Paul *The talking frog of Marion County.* JSD 12:8–10.—An interesting story, T or F, of a man who puts a live frog in his mouth and articulates the croakings of the frog to form recognizable words!

Kobrak, H. G. *Observation of cochlear structure during the process of hearing.* JASA 19:328–331.

Lewis, W. H. *Mechanics of invagination.* Anat. Rec. 97:139–156.—An aid to the student in understanding this common phenomenon in embryological development. Assigns cause to increased contractile tension of superficial gel layers of the cell surfaces bordering concavities.

Mathes, R. C., *et al. Phase effects in monaural perception.* JASA 19:780–797.

Miles, M., *et al. Electromyography during normal voluntary movements.* Anat. Rec. 98:209–218.—Bibliography included.

Munson, W. A. *The growth of auditory sensation.* JASA 19:584–591.—In part, loudness depends upon the duration of the sound, increasing rapidly, at first, then steady, and, finally, decreasing, if extended.

Notes and News *Vocal cord vibrations unaffected by helium gas.* BLR 25:236.—Helium, 1/7th of density of air, raises vocal resonator frequencies by a factor of 2.6; resonators act like cavities ½ their size. Male voice sounds like falsetto. Yet motion pictures (4000 fps) show vocal folds vibrating normally.

Peterson, N. V. *Aerodynamics in the physiology of the upper respiratory tract.* Arch. Otolaryng. 45:117–120.—Contains a simplified account of the Bournelli (1738) theory.

Platt, J. H. *The method of Alexander Graham Bell and A. Melville Bell for studying the mechansim of speech.* JSD 12:377–380.

Potter, R. K., *et al. Visible Speech.* Van Nostrand. New York.—Explains the development of the sound spectrograph; discusses the basic principles of visible speech, illustrating with patterns of speech sounds.

Pronovost, W. *Visual aids to speech improvement.* JSD 12:387–391.—Describes cathode-ray oscilloscope visual pattern of sound wave. Voltmeter indicates intensity. Neon bulb and amplifier serve as detector of nasality.

Samulson, H. *Investigations on acoustic resonators.* JASA 19:191–193.

Sivian, L. J. *On hearing in water vs. hearing in air.* JASA 19:461.

Stevens, S. S., *et al. Methods of measuring speech spectra.* JASA 19:771–780.

Thomas, C. K. *An Introduction to the Phonetics of American English.* Ronald Press. New York.

Tremble, G. E. *Eustachian tube.* Arch. Otolaryng. 46:211–220.—Approximately 35–36mm in length; slanted downward at an angle of about 45 degrees.

von Békésy, G. *The variation of phase along the basilar membrane with sinusoidal vibrations.* JASA 19:452–460.

1948

Brackett, I. P. *The vibrations of the vocal folds at selected frequencies.* Abstract. AnnOR&L 57:556–559.

Brotherton, M. *Making energy talk.* BLR 26:253–257.—Thinks of speech as writing words in the air.

Davis, R. C. *Motor effects of strong auditory stimuli.* J. Exp. Psychol. 38:257–275.

Davis, R. C. *Responses to "meaningful" and "meaningless" sounds.* J. Exp. Psychol. 38:744–756.

Gray, Henry *Anatomy of the Human Body.* 25th edition. Lea and Febiger. Philadelphia.

Hodes, R., *et al. The human electromyogram in response to nerve stimulation and the conduction velocity of motor axons.* Arch. Neurol. and Psychiat. 60:340–365.

Irwin, O. C. *Infant speech: development of vowel sounds.* JSHD 13:31–34.—During first year greater use of front vowels (75%); some use of middle (25%); little use of back vowels.

Kampmeier, O. F., *et al. On the mounting of anatomical museum specimens in transparent plastics.* Anat. Rec. 100:201–231.—Contains bibliography and illustrations.

Kersta, L. G. *Amplitude representation with the sound spectrograph.* JASA 20:796–801.

Kobrak, H. G. *Construction material of the sound conduction system of the human ear.* JASA 20:125–130.

Koenig, W., *et al. Quantitative amplitude representation in sound spectrograms.* JASA 20:787–795.

Miller, G. A. *The perception of short bursts of noise.* JASA 20:160–170.

Mitchinson, A. G., *et al. Changes in the vocal folds in humming low and high notes.* A radiographic study. J. Anat. 82:88–92.

Moses, P. J. *Vocal analysis.* Arch. Otolaryng. 48:171–186.—Biologically, singing and speaking are identical functions. However, whereas in the former each syllable has its individual frequency, in speech one glides through frequencies adjacent. Discusses *melism.*

Potter, R. K., *et al. The representation of vowels and their movements.* JASA 20:528–535.

Richardson, G. S., *et al. The uvula; its structure and function and its importance.* Arch. Otolaryng. 47:379–394.

Rudmose, H. W., *et al. Voice measurements with an audio spectrometer.* JASA 20:503–512.

Schott, L. O. *Playback for visible speech.* BLR 26: 333–339.—Fundamental frequency range for speech: male, 90 to 200 cycles; female, 150–300 cycles. Contains a clear description of how speech becomes visible speech and the reverse.

von Békésy, G. *On the elasticity of the cochlear partition.* JASA 20:227–241.

von Békésy, G. *Vibration of the head in a sound field and its role in hearing by bone conduction.* JASA 20:749–760.

von Békésy, G. *The early history of hearing—observations and theories.* JASA 20:727–748.—The student of hearing should read this. Bibliography.

Wells, W. A. *Bartolommeo Eustachio.* Arch. Otolaryng. 48:58–66.—The intriguing story of the "lost" copper plates and the man who described (1564) the Eustachian tube. (It had been noted earlier by the Greek physician, Alcmaeon, in 500 B.C.) [There are several variations of the spelling of Eustachio's name.]

Wever, Ernest Glen, *et al. The middle ear in sound conduction.* Arch. Otolaryng. 48:19–35.—Dr. Wever is one of the leading contributors in the field of the ear and hearing. Recommended.

1949

Boies, L. *Fundamentals of Otolaryngology*. Saunders. Philadelphia.

Davis, H., *et al.* *Aural microphonics in the cochlea of the guinea pig*. JASA 21:502–510.

Denney-Brown, D. *Interpretation of the electromyogram*. Arch. Neurol. and Psychiat. 61:99–128.

Gruenz, O. O., Jr., *et al.* *Extraction and portrayal of pitch of speech sounds.* JASA 21:487–495.

Henrikson, E. H., *et al.* *Voice recording—some findings and some problems.* JSHD 14:227–233.

Kelemen, G. *Structure and performance in animal language*. Arch. Otolaryng. 50:740–744.

Kelly, J. C., *et al.* *Revised concept of rate*. JSHD 14:222–226.—A study of rate of speaking.

Kobrak, H. G. *Round window membrane of the cochlea*. Arch. Otolaryng. 49:36–47.

Koenig, W. *A new frequency scale for acoustic measurements*. BLR 27:299–301.

Lüscher, E., *et al.* *Adaptation of the ear to sound stimuli*. JASA 21:135–139.

Mathes, R. C., *et al.* *The cathode-ray sound spectroscope*. JASA 21:527–537.

Negus, V. E. *The Comparative Anatomy and Physiology of the Larynx*. Grune and Stratton. New York.

Neil, J. H., *et al.* *Anatomy of the bronchial tree*. Arch. Otolaryng. 50:9–19.

Onchi, Y. *A study of the mechanism of the middle ear*. JASA 21:404–410.

Popper, O. *Hydrodynamics and hearing*. Arch. Otolaryng. 49:335–349.

Potter, R. K. *Objectives for sound portrayal*. JASA 21:1–5.—Explains principle of translating sounds into visible patterns, showing variations in intensity as a function of frequency and time.

Rahn, H., *et al.* *Daily variations of vital capacity, residual air, and expiratory reserve including a study of the residual air method*. J. Applied Physiol. 1:725–736.

Schwartz, R. P., *et al.* *Instrumentation in relation to electromyography: I. Factors influencing recording and interpretation of electromyograms.* Arch. Phys. Med. 30:383–394.

Shannon, C. E., *et al.* *The Mathematical Theory of Communication*. Univ. of Illinois Press. Urbana.

Sullivan, J. A., *et al.* *Effect of differential mobility of the windows of the cochlea on the mechanism of hearing*. Arch. Otolaryng. 49:63–68.—The elasticity of the round window exceeds that of the oval.

Tolhurst, G. C. *Audibility of the voiceless consonants as a function of intensity*. JSHD 14:210–215.

von Békésy, G. *On the resonance curve and the decay period at various points on the cohlear membrane*. JASA 21:245–254.

von Békésy, G. *The structure of the middle ear and the hearing of one's own voice by bone conduction*. JASA 21:217–232.

von Békésy, G. *The vibration of the cochlear partition in anatomical preparations and in models of the inner ear*. JASA 21:233–245.

Watson, L. W., *et al.* *Hearing Tests and Hearing Instruments*. Williams and Wilkins. Baltimore.

Wever, E. G. *Theory and Hearing*. Wiley. New York.

Wever, E. G., *et al.* *The patterns of response in the cochlea.* JASA 21:127–134.

1950

Altmann, F. *Normal development of the ear and its mechanics.* Arch. Otolaryng. 52:725–766.—Read for embryological development. Includes bibliography.

Anderson, B. A. *A photolaryngoscope.* JSHD 15:341–347.

Bavelas, A. *Communication patterns in task-oriented groups.* JASA 22:725–730.

Black, J. W. *The effect of room characteristics upon vocal intensity and rate.* JASA 22:174–176.

Black, J. W. *The pressure component in the production of consonants.* JSHD 15:207–210.—Using such airplane equipment as a Kollsman altimeter or a Hill stall-proximity indicator and Pioneer rate-of-climb indicator, the experimenter found that oral cavity pressures are greater for voiceless consonants (than voiced) and for continuants (than plosives).

Bogert, B. P. *A network to represent the inner ear.* BLR 28:481–485.—The cochlea acts as a frequency analyzer. Contains diagram of cross-section of ear.

Chang, S. H. *Portrayal of some elementary statistics of speech sounds.* JASA 22:768–769.

Corliss, E. L. R., *et al.* *Calibration of audiometers.* JASA 22:837–842.

Dreyfus-Graf, J. *Sonograph and sound machines.* JASA 22:731–739.— Pictures phonetic steno-sonograph.

Dudley, H., *et al.* *The speaking machine of Wolfgang von Kempelen.* JASA 22:151–166.

Dunn, H. K. *The calculation of vowel resonances, and an electrical vocal tract.* JASA 22:740–753.

Edmondson, H. S., *et al.* *Cues for vowel discrimination.* JSHD 15:202–206.—The study throws doubt on the theory that the cue lies in the frequency placement of two or more energy regions.

Fairbanks, G., *et al.* *An experimental study of vowel intensities.* JASA 22:457–459.—The consonantal environment may contribute to the variations.

Fano, R. M. *The information theory point of view in speech communication.* JASA 22:691–696.

Fletcher, H., *et al.* *The perception of speech and its relation to telephony.* JASA 22:89.

Galambos, R. *Neurophysiology of the auditory system.* JASA 22:785–791.

Hawley, M. E., *et al.* *The apparent source of speech in the mouth.* JASA 22:365–369.—The apparent source (distance behind lips) varies with different sounds (from 0.1 to 1.1 inches behind lips) and increases with intensity.

Hirschberg, G. G., *et al.* *Clinical electromyography; physiologic basis, instrumentation, diagnostic value.* Arch. Phys. Med. 31:576–587.

Hirsh, I. J. *Pathology in speech communication.* JASA 22:717–719.—Emphasis on auditory feedback for controlling speech production.

Huggins, W. H. *System-function analysis of speech sounds.* JASA 22:765–767.—The speaker's mouth is part of the listener's ear.

Husson, R. *Étude des phénomènes physiologiques et acoutiques fondamen-*

taux de la voix chantée. Thesis. Paris.—In which his neurochronaxic theory is proposed.

Joos, M. *Description of language design.* JASA 22:701–708.

Kann, J. *A translation of Broca's original article on the location of the speech center.* JSHD 15:16–20.

Katsuki, Y. *The function of the phonatory muscles.* Jap. J. Physiol. 1:29–36. —Cricothyroids contract isotonically; vocalis contracts isometrically. Length of vocal cords: males from 9 to 17 mm (mean length 12.5mm); females from 7 to 15.5mm (mean length 9.4mm).

Kobrak, H. G. *Physiology and pathology of sound conduction in the ear.* Trans. Amer. Acad. Ophth. and Otolar. 54:708–712.

Kuntz, A. *A Text-book of Neuro-Anatomy.* 5th edition. Lea and Febiger. Philadelphia.

Lawrence, M. *Recent investigations in sound conduction. Part I. The normal ear.* AnnOR&L 59:1020–1036.

Lee, B. S. *Effects of delayed speech feedback.* JASA 22:824–826.—The line model of the speech mechanism provokes thought.

Lerche, W. *The Esophagus and Pharynx in Action.* Charles C. Thomas. Springfield, Illinois.

Licklider, J. C. R. *The intelligibility of amplitude-dichotomized, time-quantized speech waves.* JASA 22:820–823.

Lightfoot, C. *Some effects of the common cold on speech.* Arch. Otolaryng. 50:500–513.

Lotz, J. *Speech and language.* JASA 22:712–717.

Lundeen, D. J. *The relationship of diadochokinesis to various speech sounds.* JSHD 15:54–59.—[t], [d], [p], [b] significantly faster than [s], [z], [k], and [g].

Meader, C. I., *et al.* *Handbook of Biolinguistics.* H. C. Weller. Toledo, Ohio.

Menzerath, P. *Typology of languages.* JASA 22:698–701.

Meyer-Eppler, W. *Reversed speech and repetitive systems as means of phonetic research.* JASA 22:804–806.

Miller, G. A. *Language engineering.* JASA 22:720–725.

Miller, G. A., *et al.* (compilers) *A Bibliography in Audition.* 2nd edition. Harvard University Press. Cambridge.

Miller, G. A., *et al.* *The intelligibility of interrupted speech.* JASA 22:167–173.

Morrical, K. C., *et al.* *The electrical and acoustical performance of some commercial audiometers.* JASA 22:843–847.

Munson, W. A., *et al.* *Loudness patterns—a new approach.* JASA 22:177–190.

Penfield, W. and Rasmussen, T. *The Cerebral Cortex of Man.* Macmillan. New York.

Peterson, L. C., *et al.* *A dynamical theory of the cochlea.* JASA 22:369–381.

Potter, R. K., *et al.* *Toward the specification of speech.* JASA 22:807–820.

Renke, O. F. *Theory of operation of the cochlea: a contribution to the hydrodynamics of the cochlea.* JASA 22:772–777.

Rider, J. F., *et al.* *Encyclopedia on Cathode-Ray Oscilloscopes.* John F. Rider Publ. New York.

Schott, L. O. *An electrical vocal system.* BLR 28:549–555.

Stevens, K. N. *Autocorrelation analysis of speech sounds.* JASA 22:769–771. —Recommended.

Stephens, R. W. B. and Bate, A. E. *Wave Motion and Sound.* Edward Arnold and Co. London.

Straus, O. H. *The relation of phonetics and linguistics to communication theory.* JASA 22:709–711.

Vennard, W. *Singing: The Mechanism and the Technique.* Edwards Bros. Ann Arbor.

Verzeano, M. *Time-pattern of speech in normal subjects.* JSHD 15:197–201.

Vilbig, F. *An apparatus for speech compression and expansion and for replaying visible speech records.* JASA 22:754–761.

Wever, E. G. *Recent investigations of sound conduction: Part II. The ear with conductive impairment.* AnnOR&L 59:1037–1061.

Wever, E. G., *et al.* *The acoustic pathways to the cochlea.* JASA 22:460–467.

Wever, E. G., *et al.* *The transmission properties of the middle ear.* AnnOR&L 59:5–18.

Wiener, N. *Speech, language, and learning.* JASA 22:696–697.

Zwislocki, J. *Theory of the acoustical action of the cochlea.* JASA 22:778–784.

1951

Bogert, B. P. *Determination of the effects of dissipation in the cochlear partition by means of a network representing the basilar membrane.* JASA 23:151–154.

Buchanan, A. R. *Functional Neuro-Anatomy.* Lea and Febiger. Philadelphia.

Chang, S. H., *et al.* *The intervalgram as a visual representation of speech sounds.* JASA 23:675–679.

Cremer, Von L. *Über die unglelösten probleme in der theorie der tonempfindungen.* Acustica 1:83–96.

Cunningham, D. J. *Text-book of Anatomy.* 9th edition. Oxford University Press. New York.

Davis, H. *Auditory communication.* JSHD 16:3–8.

Davis, H., *et al.* *Some observations on pitch and frequency.* JASA 23:40–42.

Delattre, P. *The physiological interpretation of sound spectrograms.* Mod. Lang. Assoc. Public. PMLA 66:84–87.

Fletcher, H. *On the dynamics of the cochlea.* JASA 23:637–645.

Guelke, R. *A theory of the action of the cochlear resonators.* JASA 23:717–719.

Hirsh, I. J. *Symposium on audiology: hearing aids: how they work and for whom.* AnnOR&L 60:1032–1038.

Huggins, W. H., *et al.* *Place mechanisms of auditory frequency analysis.* JASA 23:290–299.

Hukuhara, T., *et al.* *On the localization of the respiratory center.* Jap. J. Physiol. 2:44–49.

Jacobson, H. *Information and the human ear.* JASA 23:463–471.

Kallenbach, Von W. *Eine weiterentwicklung des tonkohenschreibers mit anwendungen bei phonetischen untersuchungen.* Acustica 1:AB37–AB42.

Kampmeier, O. F., *et al.* *Mounting of stained serial slices of the brain as wet specimens in transparent plastic.* Anat. Rec. 110:1–15.—Contains a bibliography covering mounting of other kinds of specimens.

Klumpp, R. G., *et al.* *On the correspondence between the intensities of two tones for best beats.* JASA 23:113–114.

Larsell, O. *Anatomy of the Nervous System.* Appleton-Century-Crofts. New York.

Lowy, K. *Physiological demonstration of a property of the inner ear predicted by Békésy's model.* JASA 23:716–717.

McGinnis, C. S., *et al.* *A study of the vowel formants of well-known male operatic singers.* JASA 23:440–446.

Meyer-Eppler, Von W. *Die reliefdarstellung von zeit-frequenz-spiktren durch photographische differentiation.* Acustica 1:AB1–AB3.

Miller, George A. *Language and Communication.* McGraw-Hill. New York.

Morgan, C. T., *et al.* *Pitch and intensity.* JASA 23:658–663.

Pease, D. C., *et al.* *Electron microscopy of nervous tissue.* Anat. Rec. 110:505–529.—Using low magnifications of from 6,500 to 17,500 diameters, the experimenters studied: cytoplasm, axoplasm, neurofibrils, Nissl bodies as precipitates, mitochondria, medullary sheath, nodes of Ranvier, and the neurilemma.

Perlman, H. B. *Mouth of the Eustachian tube: action during swallowing and phonation.* Arch. Otolaryng. 53:353–369.

Perlman, H. B. *Observations on the Eustachian tube.* Arch. Otolaryng. 53:370–385.

Peterson, G. E. *Vocal gestures.* BLR 29:500–503; 510.—Credits Sir Richard Paget with use of term "vocal gesture" as related to movements of articulators: mandible, lips, tongue.

Randall, R. H. *An Introduction to Acoustics.* Addison-Wesley Press. Cambridge, Massachusetts.

Ranke, Von O. F., *et al.* *Cochleaeffekt bei verschluss des runden fensters.* Acustica 1:AB145–AB148.

Rosenblith, W. A., *et al.* *Electrical responses to acoustic clicks.* JASA 23:583–588.

Saltzman, M., *et al.* *Psychophysiology of speech hearing.* Arch. Otolaryng. 53:182–188.

Smith, C. P. *A phoneme detector.* JASA 23:446–451.

Snidecor, J. C. *The pitch and duration characteristics of superior female speakers during oral reading.* JSHD 16:44–52.

Stetson, R. H. *Motor Phonetics, A Study of Speech Movement in Action.* Psychology Department, Oberlin College. Oberlin, Ohio.

Stetson, R. H. *Motor Phonetics.* North-Holland Publishing Co. Amsterdam.

Stevens, S. (editor) *Handbook of Experimental Psychology.* Wiley. New York.

Takagi, K., *et al.* *The significance of the vagus nerve on alternations in respiration.* Jap. J. Physiol. 2:17–26.

Tarnóczy, T. H. *The opening time and opening-quotient of the vocal cords during phonation.* JASA 23:42–44.

Ullman, E. V. *Life of Alfonso Corti.* Arch. Otolaryng. 54:1–28.—An account of the strange life of the man for whom the organ of Corti is named.

Verseano, M. *Time-patterns of speech in normal subjects.* JSHD 16:346–350.

von Békésy, G. *The coarse pattern of the electrical resistance in the cochlea of the guinea pig (Electroanatomy of the cochlea).* JASA 23:18–28.

von Békésy, G. *D.C. potentials and energy balance of the cochlear partition.* JASA 23:576–582.

von Békésy, G. *Microphonics produced by touching the cochlear partition with a vibrating electrode.* JASA 23:29–35.

Warren, J. M., *et al.* *On the accuracy of the method of best beats for determining the intensity of a tone.* JASA 23:111–113.

Weissler, A., *et al.* *The velocity of sound in sea water.* JASA 23:219–223.

Wever, E. G. *Some remarks on the modern status of auditory theory.* JASA 23:287–289.

Zwislocki, J. *Acoustic filters as ear defenders.* JASA 23:35–40.

1952

Ashley, G. T. *The manner of insertion of the pectoralis major muscle in man.* Anat. Rec. 113:301–307.—Clear schematic drawings show the course of the various fibers. Only by dissection of the muscle from its deep aspect can one see clearly the relations of the multilaminar muscle.

Borghesen, E. *Tectorial membrane and organ of Corti considered as a unique anatomic and functional entity.* Acta Oto-Laryngologica 42:473–486.

Cole, I. E. *Magnetic tape editor.* BLR 30:420–421.

Cooper, F. S., *et al.* *Some experiments on the perception of synthetic speech sounds.* JASA 24:597–606.

Davenport, Jr., W. B. *An experimental study of speech-wave probability distributions.* JASA 24:390–399.

Davis, H. *Neuroanatomy and neurophysiology in the cochlea.* Trans. Amer. Acad. Ophth. and Otolar. 56:630–641.

de Vries, H. L. *Brownian motion and the transmission of energy in the cochlea.* JASA 24:527–533.

Fernández, C. *Dimensions of the cochlea (guinea pig).* JASA 24:519–523.

Fischer-Jørgensen, F. *The phonetic basis for identification of phonemic elements.* JASA 24:611–617.

Fletcher, H. *The dynamics of the middle ear and its relation to the acuity of hearing.* JASA 24:129–131.

Franke, E. K., *et al.* *The jaw motions relative to the skull and their influence on hearing by bone conduction.* JASA 24:142–146.—Between 40∼ and 700∼ jaw motions may increase intensity 6 to 10 decibels.

Guelke, R., *et al.* *The anomalous behavior of the threshold of hearing in relation to the equal loudness contours.* JASA 24:317–322.—The possible role of the muscles of the middle ear is discussed.

Harris, J. D. *Pitch discrimination.* JASA 24:750–755.

Huggins, W. H. *A phase principle for complex-frequency analysis and its implications in auditory theory.* JASA 24:582–589.

Hukuhara, T., *et al.* *Further studies on the localization of the respiratory center.* Jap. J. Physiol. 3:138–147.

Hukuhara, T., *et al.* *The mechanism of the nervous regulation of the respiratory movements.* Jap. J. Physiol. 2:316–327.—Refer to work of Hering and Breuer (1868).

Kersta, L. G. *Solid sound.* BLR 30:354–357.—3-dimensional plastic and plaster of paris models show the appearance of sound in space. Each model resembles a mountain range.

Kock, W. E. *The problem of selective voice control.* JASA 24:625–628.

Kock, W. E., *et al.* *Dynamic spectrograms of speech.* JASA 24:783–784.

Lansing, A. T., *et al.* *The structure and chemical characterization of elastic fibers as revealed by elastase and by electron microscopy.* Anat. Rec. 114:555–575.

Lenihan, J. M. A. *The velocity of sound in air.* Acustica 2:205–212.—Summarizes more than 30 attempts (since 1636) to measure the velocity of sound. Gives velocity as 331.45 ± 0.04m/s under certain temperature, pressure and air dryness conditions.

Licklider, J. C. R. *On the process of speech perception.* JASA 24:590–594.

Lotz, J. *Speech and language.* J. Exper. Psychol. 44:712–717.

Martin, D. W. *Do you auralize?* JASA 24:416.—If we say visualize or visualization should we say auralize or auralization? Do such terms as aural, auricle, aurist, etc., have some advantages over audio, audition, audience, auditors, etc.?

Munson, W. A., *et al.* *In search of the missing 6db.* JASA 24:498–501.—When equally loud low frequency tones are presented alternately from a loudspeaker and from an earphone, how explain the 6 to 10 db difference in sound wave pressure in the ear canal?

Patten, B. M. *Overgrowth of the neural tube in young human embryos.* Anat. Rec. 113:381–393.

Peterson, G. E. *The information-bearing elements in speech.* JASA 24:629–637.

Peterson, G. E., *et al.* *Control methods used in a study of the vowels.* JASA 24:175–184.

Pike, K. L. *Operational phonemics in reference to linguistic relativity.* JASA 24:618–625.

Pollack, I. *On the measurement of the loudness of speech.* JASA 24:323–324.—Raises the question of why, although the speech level does vary greatly at the ear of the listener, the continuous speech of a speaker moving about the room does not seem to vary. Nor does the speaker seem to change in size as he moves farther away or comes closer. Suggests that the "size constancy" of vision is matched by a "sound constancy" in hearing.

Read, O. *The Recording and Reproduction of Sound.* Howard Sams and Co. Indianapolis.

Schott, L. O. *Signal translation in hearing.* BLR 30:2–8.

Shuster, B. H., *et al.* *Physiology of the ear.* Arch. Otolaryng. 56:294–312.

Sunderland, S., *et al.* *The intraneural topography of the recurrent laryngeal nerve in man.* Anat. Rec. 114:411–426.—Re-opens question of whether nerve supply of vocal fold abductors is more vulnerable than that of adductors (F. Semon's Law, 1881) as clinical experience indicates.

Tasaki, I., *et al.* *The space-time pattern of the cochlear microphonics (guinea pig), as recorded by differential electrodes.* JASA 24:502–519.

Tobin, C. E. *Methods of preparing and studying human lungs expanded and dried with compressed air.* Anat. Rec. 114:453–465.—Excellent reference.

Tokizane, T., *et al.* *Electromyographic studies on the human respiratory muscles.* Jap. J. Physiol. 2:232–247.—Refer to tabulation showing anti-gravity, normal breathing, and forced breathing functions of principal muscles and accessory muscles of inspiration, and principal muscles and accessory muscles of expiration.

Twaddell, W. F. *Phonemes and allophones in speech analysis.* JASA 24:607–611.

Vogel, P. H. *The innervation of the larynx of man and the dog.* Amer. J. Anat. 90:427–447.

von Békésy, G. *D.C. resting potentials inside the cochlear partition.* JASA

24:72–76.—Without acoustic stimulus the potential between endolymph and organ of Corti may be 100 millivolts.

von Békésy, G. *Gross localization of the place of origin of the cochlear microphonics.* JASA 24:399–409.

Weaver, W. *Information theory: 1. Information theory to 1951—a nontechnical review.* JSHD 17:166–174.

Wever, E. G., *et al.* *Sound conduction in the cochlea.* AnnOR&L 61:824–835. —Discusses theories.

Wolff, D. *Organ of Corti as we see it today, one hundred years after its discovery.* Arch. Otolaryng. 56:588–609. Refers at length to the original work.

Woodburne, R. T., *et al.* *An improved embalming fluid formula.* Anat. Rec. 114:507–514.

Young, R. W. *A Table Relating Frequency to Cents.* C. G. Conn. Elkhart, Indiana.

1953

Aubin, A. *La voix.* Cours international de phonologie et de phoniatrie de paris. Librairie Maloine. Paris.

Belasco, S. *The influence of force of articulation of consonants on vowel duration.* JASA 25:1015–1016.

Beranek, L. L. *Loudspeakers and microphones.* JASA 26:618–629.—Covers the development of such equipment from 1915 to date. Shows pictures of many types. Includes condenser, ribbon, dynamic and crystal microphones.

Black, J. W. *The information of sounds and phonetic diagrams of one- and two-syllable words.* JSHD 19:397–411.

Bloomer, H. *Observations on palatopharyngeal movements in speech and deglutition.* JSHD 10:230–246.

Bogert, B. P. *On the band width formants.* JASA 25:791–792.

Bosma, J. F. *A correlated study of the anatomy and motor activity of the upper pharynx by cadaver dissection and by cinematic study of patients after maxillo-facial surgery.* AnnOR&L 62:51–72.—The key muscle is the levator veli palatini.

Bowen, W. P., *et al.* *Applied Anatomy and Kinesiology* (7th edition revised). Lea and Febiger. Philadelphia.

Davis, H. *Twenty-five acoustical years of speech and hearing.* JASA 26:607–611.

Engström, H., *et al.* *Is there a special nutritive cellular system around the hair cells in the organ of Corti?* AnnOR&L 62:507–512.

Feldman, C. B. *Information theory.* BLR 31:326–332.—Bibliography.

Fletcher, Harvey *Speech and Hearing in Communication.* Van Nostrand. New York.

Geldard, F. A. *The Human Senses.* Wiley. New York.

Hall, W. M. *Logarithmic measure and the decibel.* JASA 26:449–450.—Believes that the term *decibel,* introduced in 1929, is not as good as the term *logit,* or, even, decilog.

Harris, C. M. *A speech synthesizer.* JASA 25:970–975.

Harris, C. M. *A study of the building blocks in speech.* JASA 25:962–969.

Hilding, A. C. *The tectorial membrane in the theory of hearing: the significance of the insertion of the tectorial membrane in the transmission of sound vibrations to the hair cells and a theory of the mechanism of tone location in the cochlea.* AnnOR&L 62:757–769.

House, A. S., *et al.* *The influence of consonant environment upon the secondary acoustical characteristics of vowels.* JASA 25:105–113.

Irwin, J. V., *et al.* *Norms for maximum repetitive rates for certain sounds established with the sylrater.* JSHD 18:149–160.—Describes use of the sound pulse rate meter.

Jones, D. S., *et al.* *An electromyographic study of some muscles of costal respiration in man.* Anat. Rec. 117:17–24.—Sees function of intercostals as keeping ribs at constant distance one from another.

Kanetune, K., *et al.* *Igirisu no Si, Nippon no Si* (English Verse and Japanese Verse). Kokuseido Press. Tokyo.—Assigns an inherent loudness value to each vowel. In poetry, *Ri* (even if stressed) cannot be as loud as *ver,* in *River.* Points out that the duration of a syllable is not constant, that it depends on the word in which it appears—the longer the word, the shorter the duration of the syllable. Believes that psychological speech periodicity has a physiological cause, respiration—actually, expiration is the governing factor.

Kerns, J. L. *An improved technique of embedding specimens in transparent plastic.* Anat. Rec. 117:345–351.

Kietz, Von H. *Das Räumliche hören.* Acustica 3:73–87.—Bibliography. Believes normal hearing person associates a sense of direction and of distance (left-right; in front-behind; above-below; near-far) with each sound perceived.

Krieg, W. J. S. *Functional Neuroanatomy.* 2nd edition. Blakiston. New York.

Kobrak, H. G. *Experimental observations on sound conduction in the middle and inner ear.* AnnOR&L 62:748–756.—Photography with microscopic-stroboscopy.

Low, F. N. *The pulmonary alveolar epithelium of laboratory mammals and man.* Anat. Rec. 117:241–263.—Electron microscopic views at magnifications of from 4000 to 47000 times will give the student an idea of size of capillary and alveolar wall structures. Concludes that pulmonary alveolar wall has epithelium lining.

McLoughlin, R. C., *et al.* *A field meter for sound velocity measurements.* JASA 25:732–734.

Macbeth, R. A., *et al.* *A note on the levator scapulae muscle in man.* Anat. Rec. 115:691–696.

Mezar, J. *Switching systems as mechanized brains.* BLR 31:63–69.—Anything a machine can do is not thinking.

Miller, R. L. *Auditory tests with synthetic vowels.* JASA 25:114–121.

Note *Automatic digit recognizer.* BLR 31:52.—Audrey (AUtomatic Digit REcognizer) understands and reacts to spoken numbers.

Olson, H. F., *et al.* *Electronic sound absorber.* JASA 25:11030–1136.—When a sound wave strikes a surface some of its energy will be reflected and some will be absorbed, the per cent in each case depending upon the nature of the surface and the incident angle of the wave to the surface.

Peterson, G. E. *Basic physical systems for communications between two individuals.* JSHD 18:116–120.

Peterson, G. E. *Design of visible speech devices.* JASA 26:406–413.—One of the leaders in experimentation in the field, this authority suggests improvements in instrumentation of sound spectrography.

Peterson, G. E., *et al.* *The measurement of noise with the sound spectrograph.* JASA 25:1157–1162.

Rambo, J. H. T., *et al.* *A research study of the effect of the autonomic nervous system on the internal ear.* AnnOR&L 62:1149–1173.

Richardson, E. G. *Sound, A Physical Textbook.* 5th edition. Edward Arnold and Co. London.

Robinson, D. W. *The relation between the sone and phon scales of loudness.* Acustica 3:344–358.

Scott, H. H., *et al.* *A compact, versatile filter-type sound analyzer.* JASA 25:727–731.

Simonton, K. M., *et al.* *A laboratory assessment of hearing acuity for voice signals against a background of noise.* AnnOR&L 62:735–747.—0 decibel = 0.0002 dyne/cm². Standard audiometer calibrated so that 0 db has a value of approximately 9 db re 0.0002 dyne/cm² in speech frequencies of 500 to 2000 cycles.

Smith, Jr., P. W. *Precision measurement of the velocity of sound in air.* JASA 25:81–86.—Velocity = 331.45 ± 0.05 m/sec (1000 cycles; 22° C; 810 mm Hg).

Stevens, K. N., *et al.* *An electrical analog of the vocal tract.* JASA 25:734–742.

Tiffany, W. R. *The threshold reliability of recorded sustained vowels.* JSHD 18:379–385.—[i] and [u] differ from other vowels.

Tiffany, W. R. *Vowel recognition as a function of duration, frequency modulation and phonetic context.* JSHD 18:289–301.—Vowel phonemes are relatively unstable. Vowel recognition varies as a function of duration.

Twaddell, W. F. *Stetson's model and the supra-segmental phonemes.* Language 29:415–453.

von Békésy, G. *Description of some mechanical properties of the organ of Corti.* JASA 25:770–785.

von Békésy, G. *Shearing microphonics produced by vibrations near the inner and outer hair cells.* JASA 25:786–790.

Wever, E. G., *et al.* *Physiological Acoustics.* Princeton University Press. Princeton, New Jersey.

Zaliouk, A. *A visual-tactile system of phonetical symbolization.* JSHD 19:190–207.—One cannot produce an isolated speech sound, except by electrical or mechanical (e.g., cutting a tape) means.

Zwislocki, J. *Review of recent mathematical theories of cochlear dynamics.* JASA 25:743–751.—Neither long-wave nor short-wave theories suffice.

Zwislocki, J. *Wave motion in the cochlea caused by bone conduction.* JASA 25:986–989.

1954

Anderson, J. O. *Bibliography on esophageal speech.* JSHD 19:70–72.

Arey, L. B. *Developmental Anatomy: A Textbook and Laboratory Manual of Embryology.* 6th edition. Saunders. Philadelphia.

Black, J. W. *Systematic research in experimental phonetics: 2. Signal recep-*

ception: intelligibility and side-tone. JSHD 19:140–146.—Time of transmission of sound from vocal folds to cochlea: about 0.0003 sec.

Camras, M. *Some recent developments in magnetic recording.* Acustica 4:26–29.

Cherry, E. C., *et al.* *Some further experiments upon the recognition of speech, with one and with two ears.* JASA 26:554–559.—Believes recognition is a multilevel phenomenon: at a low level it is statistical recognition (recognize male or female, English or French); at highest levels recognition involves interpretation and responsive activity.

Cleary, J. A. *On the ary-epiglottic folds.* AnnOR&L 63:960–967.

Curtis, J. F. *Systematic research in experimental phonetics: 3. The case for dynamic analysis in acoustic phonetics.* JSHD 19:147–157.—Questions if, after half century of research, we know what distinguishes one vowel from another.

Cutler, C. C. *A mechanical traveling-wave oscillator.* BLR 32:134–138.

Davis, H. *The excitation of nerve impulses in the cochlea.* AnnOR&L 63:469–480.

Diestel, von H.-G. *Akustische messungen an einem mechanischen modell des innenohres.* Acustica 4:488–499 (printed pagination 420–431).—Describes model of inner ear enlarged 55 times.

Fairbanks, G. *Systematic research in experimental phonetics: 1. A theory of the speech mechanism as a servosystem.* JSHD 19:133–139.

Greenless, A. E. *The Amplification and Distribution of Sound.* Chapman and Hall. London.

Güth, von W. *Kinematographische aufnahmen von wasserdampfblasen.* Acustica 4:445–455.—Motion pictures at 40,000 to 65,000 per second still fall short of the 500,000,000 per second claimed by a Soviet scientist.

Hukuhara, T., *et al.* *Action potentials in the normal respiratory centers and its centrifugal pathways in the medulla oblongata and spinal cord.* Jap. J. Physiol. 4:145–153.

Kallenbach, von W. *Anwendungsmöglichkeiten der schallspektographie bei akustischen untersuchunger.* Acustica 4:403–407.—Uses heterodyne analyser, tape recorder and oscillograph in photographing sound spectrum as a function of time.

Mol, H. *The desired performance of hearing aids.* Acustica 4:168–170.—The material on middle ear mechanics is helpful.

Okamoto, M., *et al.* *Studies of the acoustic reflex. Part II. Experimental studies on the function of the tensor tympani muscle.* AnnOR&L 63:950–959.—Believes the tensor tympani reflex offers incomplete protection against acoustic violence.

O'Neill, J. J. *Contributions of the visual components of oral symbols to speech comprehension.* JSHD 19:429–439.

Peterson, G. E. *Systematic research in experimental phonetics: 4. The evaluation of speech signals.* JSHD 19:158–168.—Believes ear may subtract but not add anything to what it hears before passing it along to the *CNS*. However, memory and association may add signals.

Portmann, M., *et al.* *Efferent nerve fibers of cochlea.* Arch. Otolaryng. 59:543–554.

Pressman, J. L. *Sphincters of the larynx.* Arch. Otolaryng. 59:221–236.—Human larynx is a three-tiered sphincter: (1) vocal folds, (2) ventricular folds, (3) aryepiglottic sphincter. Helpful drawings.

Ptacek, P. H. *An experimental investigation of dichotic word presentation.* JSHD 19:412–422.

Richany, S. F., *et al.* *The development and adult structure of the malleus, incus and stapes.* AnnOR&L 63:394–434.

Rosenblith, W. A. *Electrical responses from the auditory nervous system.* AnnOR&L 63:830–860.—Estimate of number of cells: cochlear nucleus, 90,000; superior olivary complex, 35,000; lateral lemniscus, 40,000; inferior colliculus, 400,000; medial geniculate (parvocellular), 360,000; medial geniculate (magnocellular), 60,000; auditory cortex, 10,000,000. 30,000 fibers in auditory nerve.

Sataloff, J., *et al.* *Audiology: summaries of the bibliographic material in the field of otolaryngology for 1950, 1951, and 1952.* Arch. Otolaryng. 60:80–117.

Skudrzyk, von E. *Betrachtungen zum musikalischen zusammenklang.* Acustica 4:249–253.

Sonninen, A. *Is the length of the vocal cords the same at all different levels of singing?* Acta Oto-Laryngologica Suppl. 118:219–231.—No. They lengthen with increase in frequency (as much as 4 mm).

Swigart, R. H., *et al.* *Electron microscopic observations of pulmonary alveoli.* Anat. Rec. 118:57–71.—(See, also, 1953; Low, F. N.) Study of morphology of alveolar walls, where respiratory capillaries and air spaces are juxtaposed.

Tasaki, I., *et al.* *Exploration of cochlear potentials in guinea pig with a microelectrode.* JASA 26:765–773.—Points out that cochlea produces cochlear microphonic (*CM*) and nerve action potential responses when stimulated by sound. In addition, resting dc potential differences exist between different areas of the cochlea.

Taylor, R. L., *et al.* *"Nerve-type" transmission line.* BLR 32:21–24.—Studies of electrochemical models help explain transmission of nerve stimuli. A clear discussion of synthetic nerves.

Tolhurst, G. C. *Audibility-recognition sound pressure functions of the voiced cognate consonants.* JSHD 19:28–36.

Totsuka, G., *et al.* *Studies of acoustic reflex.* AnnOR&L 63:939–949.—Measures of the total time required, gives an idea of the number of neurons involved.

von Békésy, G. *Some electro-mechanical properties of the organ of Corti.* AnnOR&L 63:448–468.—Good step-by-step account of experimental methods and the development of research equipment.

1955

Bachem, A. *Absolute pitch.* JASA 27:1180–1185.—Absolute pitch is possessed by less than 1/100 of 1% of the population. It is the faculty of recognizing and defining (e.g., by naming, singing, playing) the pitch of a tone without use of a reference tone. Suggests the existence of "laryngeal proprioceptive memory" as an aid in producing a tone of a given frequency.

Batson, O. V. *The cricopharyngeus muscle.* AnnOR&L 64:47–54.—Lower portion of inferior constrictor. Given separate status by Valsalva in 1717.

Bauer, R. W., *et al.* *Lateralization of cerebral functions.* JSHD 20:171–177. —Believes cerebral dominance is unique for the left hemisphere.

Behringer, S. *Die Anordnung der Muskulatur in der menschlichen Stimmlippe und im Gebiet des Conus elasticus.* Zschr. Anat. Entw. 118:324–342.

Black, J. W., *et al.* *Speech: Code, Meaning and Communication.* McGraw-Hill. New York.

Bordley, J. E., *et al.* *The role of the cerebrum in hearing.* AnnOR&L 64:370–382.

Corso, J. F. *Evaluation of operating conditions on a Békésy-type audiometer.* Arch. Otolaryng. 61:649–653.

Delaterre, P. C., *et al.* *Acoustic loci and transitional cues for consonants.* JASA 27:769–773.

Denes, P. *Effect of duration on the perception of voicing.* JASA 27:761–764. —Nonspectral parameters (e.g., duration) may be as important as voicing in providing cues for phoneme recognition.

Dolanský, L. O. *An instantaneous pitch-period indicator.* JASA 27:67–72. —Defines epogram as a two-dimension display of the clipped version of a voice-sound wave form.

Freedman, L. M. *The role of the cricothyroid muscle in tension of the vocal cords.* Arch. Otolaryng. 62:347–353.

Fulton, J. F. *A Textbook of Physiology.* 17th edition. Saunders. Philadelphia.

Furstenberg, A. C., *et al.* *A motor pattern in the nucleus ambiguus: its clinical significance.* AnnOR&L 64:788–793.—See diagram: cells of origin for innervation of certain laryngeal muscles.

Gleason, H. W. *An Introduction to Descriptive Linguistics.* Holt. New York.

Hockett, C. F. *Manual of Phonology.* Indiana Univ. Publications in Anthropology and Linguistics, No. 11. Bloomington, Indiana.—The student will enjoy the author's colorful description of the acoustic elements of speech in terms of Easter eggs (various sizes, various colors), not boiled, carried on a continuous belt through a wringer, smashed and blended together.

Hoople, G. D., *et al.* *A study of voice production in laryngectomized patients.* Arch. Otolaryng. 61:123–124.

House, A. S., *et al.* *Auditory testing of a simplified description of vowel articulation.* JASA 27:882–887.

Hyman, M. *An experimental study of artificial-larynx and esophageal speech.* JSHD 20:291–299.—No difference in intelligibility, but listeners prefer the former.

Lichte, W. H., *et al.* *The influence of overtone structure on the pitch of complex tones.* J. Exper. Psychol. 49:431–435.

Longmore, T. A. *Medical Photography.* 5th edition. Focal Press. New York. (American Photographic Book Publishing Co. New York.)

Meyer, M. F. *Theory for pitches 19, 15, and 11 plus a rumbling resulting from "sin 19x + sin 15x."* JASA 27:749–750.—Applies the graphic method to a hydraulic theory of cochlear mechanics. Rejects the place theory; favors a frequency-analytic theory of hearing. The fluid in the vestibule acts as a hydraulic ram.

Michaelis, A. R. *Research Films in Biology, Anthropology, Psychology, and Medicine.* Academic Press. New York.

Morse, P. M. *Acoustics and basic physics.* JASA 27:213–216.

Moser, H. M., *et al.* *Comparison of hyponasality, hypernasality, and normal voice quality.* JASA 27:872–874.

Moser, H. M., *et al.* *Phonemic confusion vectors.* JASA 27:875–881.—Concludes that the discrimination for front vowels is greater than that for back vowels.

Neff, W. D., *et al.* *Auditory thresholds of the cat.* JASA 27:480–483.—Cats hear up to 60,000 cycles, but are less sensitive than man below 500 cycles.

Olson, H. F., *et al.* *Electronic music synthesizer.* JASA 27:595–612.—Gives a good series of definitions of acoustical terms. Defines a cent as 1/1200 of an octave.

Oyer, H. J. *Relative intelligibility of speech recorded simultaneously at the ear and mouth.* JASA 27:1207–1212.—About the same under conditions of quiet; better at the ear under certain noise conditions.

Pressman, J. J., *et al.* *Physiology of the larynx.* Physiological Reviews 35:506–554.—Bibliography.

Sandel, T. T., *et al.* *Localization of sound from single and paired sources.* JASA 27:842–852.

Schneiderman, N. *A study of the relationship between articulatory ability and language ability.* JSHD 20:359–364.

Shepherd, W. M., *et al.* *Observations on the appearance and ossification of the premaxilla and maxilla in the human embryo.* Anat. Rec. 121:13–28.

Small, Jr., A. M. *Some parameters influencing the pitch of amplitude-modulated signals.* JASA 27:751–760.—Describes experiments with an air siren, during which the ear perceives tones not present physically.

Stevens, K. N., *et al.* *Development of a quantitative description of vowel articulation.* JASA 27:484–493.—Assigns important roles to the position and shape of the tongue and to the cross-sectional areas of the vocal tract in an attempt to set down parameters and work out rules basic to the quantitative description.

Stevens, S. S. *The measurement of loudness.* JASA 27:815–829.—Describes the relation (or lack of relation) between loudness and decibels. Loudness is quantal in nature, and not infinitely divisible. Loudness = 0.06 sone at the threshold of hearing.

Stevens, S. S., *et al.* *Bibliography on Hearing.* Harvard University Press. Cambridge.

Tonndorf, J., *et al.* *Combined effect of sound and oxygen deprivation upon cochlear microphonics in guinea pigs.* AnnOR&L 64:392–405.

van den Berg, J. W. *Calculations on a model of the vocal tract for the vowel /i/ and on the larynx.* JASA 27:332–338.

van den Berg, J. W. *Transmission of the vocal cavities.* JASA 27:161–168. —Transmission curves depend upon the cavity configurations of the vocal tract. 2, 3, or 4 strong formants (below 4000∼) represent major cavity patterns; other, weaker, formants represent other configuration details.

von Békésy, G. *Human skin perception of traveling waves similar to those on the cochlea.* JASA 27:830–841.

von Békésy, G. *Paradoxical direction of wave travel along the cochlear partition.* JASA 27:137–145.

Weibel, E. S. *Vowel synthesis by means of resonant circuits.* JASA 27:858–865.

Wever, E. G., *et al.* *The maximum strength of the tympanic muscles.* AnnOR&L 64:383–391.—Tensions exerted by the tensor tympani (3.5grams) and stapedius (1.6grams) muscles partially oppose each other. Protect inner ear from too great stimulation.

Wever, E. G., *et al.* *Patterns of injury produced by overstimulation of the ear.* JASA 27:853–858.—Intense tones damage the hair cells. The frequency of the sound determines the locus of damage.

Williams, C. R. *Instruments for measuring sound.* Arch. Otolaryng. 62:414–425.—There is no perfect microphone on the market. Describes microphones: crystal (piezo-electric), dynamic, condenser. Discusses noise analysis with electrical filter sets (constant band width or proportional analyzers) and cathode ray oscilloscopes.

Williams, D. E. *Masseter muscle action potentials in stuttered and non-stuttered speech.* JSHD 20:242–261.—There is no neurophysiological difference. Comprehensive bibliography.

Wood, A. B. *A Textbook of Sound* (3rd edition). Macmillan. New York.

Young, R. W. *Why an international standard tuning frequency.* JASA 27:379–380.—Agrees with a standard A = 440 cycles/sec.

1956

Bertsch, W. F., *et al.* *Effects of two message-storage schemes upon communications within a small problem-solving group.* JASA 28:550–553.—The ear can receive and comprehend continuous speech at twice the rate at which speech mechanisms can produce it.

Black, J. W., *et al.* *Intelligibility as related to the path of airborne side-tone.* JSHD 21:173–178.—Side-tone includes sound transmitted via bone or tissue, or by way of air. The cochlea reacts about equally to each. Feedback helps a speaker monitor airborne signals and, thus, determine his vocal level.

Bogert, B. P. *The Vobanc* (VOice BANd Compressor)—A two-to-one speech band-width reduction system. JASA 28:399–404.

Bosma, J. F. *Myology of the pharynx of cat, dog, and monkey with interpretation of the mechanism of swallowing.* AnnOR&L 65:981–992.—Further validates observations of V. E. Negus.

Campbell, C. J., *et al.* *Electrical manifestations of recurrent nerve function.* AnnOR&L 65:747–763.

Chang, S–H. *Two schemes of speech compression system.* JASA 28:565–572.

Chao, Y. R. *Linguistic prerequisites for a speech writer.* JASA 28:1107–1109.—Reveals interesting facts about how we actually use sounds in speech.

Cherry, E. C., *et al.* *"Human 'cross-correlator'"—a technique for measuring certain parameters of speech perception.* JASA 28:889–895.

David, Jr., E. E., *et al.* *Note on pitch-synchronous processing of speech.* JASA 28:1261–1266.

Diehl, C. F., *et al.* *Effect of voice quality on communication.* JSHD 21:233–237.—Pleasant voice quality and effective communication may not be as closely related as might be supposed.

Felker, J. H. *Mechanized memory and logic—what electronics can do.* BLR 34:201–206.

Flanagan, J. L. *Automatic extraction of formant frequencies from continuous speech.* JASA 28:110–118.—Describes electronic equipment used. Shows that formant frequency may be defined in three different ways.

Flanagan, J. L. *Band width and channel capacity necessary to transmit the formant information of speech.* JASA 28:592–596.

Flanagan, J. L. *Development and testing of a formant-coding speech compression system.* JASA 28:1099–1106.—Estimates the vocal tract to have a length of 17cm; its cross-sectional area varies from 0 to 17cm^2.

Flanagan, J. L. *Evaluation of two formant-extracting devices.* JASA 28:118–125.

Galambos, R. *Some recent experiments on the neurophysiology of hearing.* AnnOR&L 65:1053–1059.—Diagrams ascending and descending neurons connecting acoustic cortex and cochlea.

Glorig, A. *A report of two normal hearing studies.* AnnOR&L 67:93–111.

Guild, S. R. *Hearing.* AnnOR&L 65:507–510.—No one, as yet, knows how we hear.

Heilbrunn, L. V. *The Dynamics of Living Protoplasm.* Academic Press. New York.

House, A. S., *et al.* *Analog studies of the nasalization of vowels.* JSHD 21:218–232.—Discusses electrical analogs. Believes nasal cavity has higher damping factor than vocal tract resonators.

Howard, C. R. *Speech analysis-synthesis scheme using continuous parameters.* JASA 28:1091–1098.

Hukuhara, T., *et al.* *Effects of deglutition upon the spike discharges of neurons in the respiratory center.* Jap. J. Physiol. 6:162–166.

Hukuhara, T., *et al.* *On the vagus-respiratory reflex.* Jap. J. Physiol. 6:87–97.

Kock, W. E. *Speech bandwidth compression.* BLR 34:81–85.—Transitions from one sound to another occur slowly (less than 10 per second) in normal speech.

Kryter, K. D. *On predicting the intelligibility of speech from acoustical measures.* JSHD 21:208–217.

Lueders, O. W. *Use of the electrolarynx in speech rehabilitation.* Arch. Otolaryng. 63:133–134.—This battery-powered electronic device (cylindrical: 4 inches long, 1 inch in diameter) is held against the throat. The vibrations produced substitute for phonated sound waves and are articulated as in normal speech. The result is a monotone, but speech is intelligible.

Michels, W. C., *et al.* *International Dictionary of Physics and Electronics.* Van Nostrand. New York.

Moir, J. *High Quality Sound Reproduction.* Chapman & Hall. London.

Neely, K. K. *Effect of visual factors on the intelligibility of speech.* JASA 28:1275–1277.—Even listeners with normal hearing find speech more intelligible when they can see as well as hear the speaker.

Olson, H. F., *et al.* *Phonetic typewriter.* JASA 28:1072–1081.

Pickett, J. M. *Effects of vocal force on the intelligibility of speech sounds.* JASA 28:902–905.—Shouting results in a distortion of the movements of the normal speech-producing mechanisms and the resultant speech is less intelligible.

Pierce, J. R., *et al.* *Man's World of Sound.* Doubleday. New York.

Rayleigh, Lord. *The Theory of Sound.* Paperback edition. Dover Publications. New York.

Sonninen, A. A. *The role of the external laryngeal muscles in length-adjustment of the vocal cords in singing.* Acta Oto-Laryngologica Suppl. 130:1–102.—Bibliography.

Stevens, K. N. *Studies of formant transitions using a vocal tract analog.* JASA 28:578–585.

Strong, L. H. *Muscle fibers of the tongue functional in consonant production.* Anat. Rec. 126:61–79.—See the drawings. Pictures of palatograms of consonants. Recommended for the serious student.

Tarnóczy, T. H. *Determination of the speech spectrum through measurements of superposed samples.* JASA 28:1270–1275.—Suggests that an inertia factor (a hearing time lag of 100 msec to 150 msec) aids the ear mechanisms in analyzing sounds.

Tonndorf, J. *The analogy between fluid motion within the cochlea and formation of surf on sloping beaches and its significance for the mechanism of cochlear stimulation.* AnnOR&L 65:488–506.

van den Berg, J. *Direct and indirect determination of the mean subglottic pressure.* Folia Phoniatrica 8:1–24.

van den Berg, J. *Physiology and physics of voice production.* Acta Physiol. Pharm. Néerl. 5:40–55.

Vilbig, F., *et al.* *Some systems for speech-band compression.* JASA 28:573–577.

Wever, E. G., *et al.* *The control of sound transmission by the middle ear muscles.* AnnOR&L 65:5–14.—Observations in agreement with those of Molinettus and J. B. Morgagni (1764) and J. Müller (1837).

Whatmough, J. *Language: A Modern Synthesis.* St. Martin's Press. New York.—Believes that tongue movements are more important than those of lips and mandible.

Wiren, J., *et al.* *Electronic binary selection system for phoneme classification.* JASA 28:1082–1091.

Yantis, P. A. *Audiologic examination of the inner ear: the aural-overload test.* JSHD 21:303–312.

1957

Black, J. W., *et al.* *The pitch of side-tone.* JSHD 22:339–342.—With what accuracy does a speaker hear his own voice pitch?

Butler, R. A., *et al.* *Factoral analysis of the delayed speech feedback phenomenon.* JASA 29:632–635.—A delay of about 0.18 sec is maximally effective.

Chavasse, P., *et al.* *Contribution à l'étude du zéro absolu des audiomètres.* Acustica 7:132–136.

David, Jr., E. E. *Voice-actuated machines: problems and possibilities.* BLR 35:281–286.—Identification of unit sounds (phones) due to pronunciation or phonetic value, but not to pitch or inflection. Related groups of phones make phoneme. Says there are 40 phonemes in English.

Davis, H. *Biophysics and physiology of the inner ear.* Physiological Reviews 37:1–49.

Davis, H. *Initiation of nerve impulses in cochlear and other mechanoreceptors.* In Bullock, T. H. (editor), *Physiological Triggers,* American Physiological Soc., Washington, D.C.

Dyce, K. M. *The muscles of the pharynx and palate of the dog.* Anat. Rec. 127:497–508.—The dog, cat, and monkey are favorite animals for studies of this kind.

Efron, A. *Sound.* John F. Rider Publ. New York.

Faaborg-Andersen, K. *Electromyographic investigation of intrinsic laryngeal muscles in humans.* Acta Physiologica Scandinavica 41 (Suppl. 140): 1–150.—Bibliography.

Fairbanks, G., *et al.* *Auditory comprehension of repeated high-speed messages.* JSHD 22:20–22.—If listeners score 90% comprehension when a 141wpm message is compressed 50% (282 wpm) what is the best use of the 50% of time saved? Listening to the message a second time? Is ordinary speech inefficient?

Fairbanks, G., *et al.* *Effects of time compression upon the comprehension of connected speech.* JSHD 22:10–19.—Messages were tape recorded at 141 words/min. Time compressions of 0, 30, 50, 60 and 70% resulted in listeners making progressively lower scores. (At 50% compression message rate was 282 wpm.)

Field, E. J., *et al.* *Anatomical Terms: Their Origin and Derivation* (2nd edition). W. Heffer and Sons. Cambridge.

Flanagan, J. L. *Difference limen for formant amplitude.* JSHD 22:205–212. —Psycho-acoustic study. Determined the just-distinguishable differences (3 decibels) for the amplitude of F2 of the synthetic vowel [æ].

Flanagan, J. L. *Estimates of the maximum precision necessary in quantizing certain "dimensions" of vowel sounds.* JASA 29:533–534.

Halle, M., *et al.* *Acoustic properties of stop consonants.* JASA 29:107–116. —Contends that in English voicing is not essential in distinguishing /p/t/k/ from /b/d/g/, but that the pressure pattern (greater in the first group) is.

Harris, C. M. *Handbook of Noise Control.* McGraw-Hill. New York.—The first six of forty chapters contains material on terminology (definitions), propagation of sound, the hearing mechanism, loudness, and audiometric testing.

Hoffman, H. H., *et al.* *Vagus nerve components.* Anat. Rec. 127:551–567. —Differentiates between origin of afferent fibers (nodose ganglion cells) and efferent fibers (cells in brain stem).

House, A. S. *Analog studies of nasal consonants.* JSHD 22:190–204.—The nasal consonants were simulated by electrical analog devices. Studies of the spectral characteristics were reported.

Jones, D. S., *et al.* *Further electromyographic studies of muscles of costal respiration in man.* Anat. Rec. 128:733–746.—Uses 4-channel electrocephalograph adapted for electromyography.

Kaiser, L. *Manual of Phonetics.* North-Holland Publishing Company. Amsterdam.

Ladefoged, P. *Use of palatography.* JSHD 22:764–774.—Direct palatography results are compared with x-ray photographs.

Ladefoged, P., *et al.* *Information conveyed by vowels.* JASA 29:98–104.

Liberman, A. M. *Some results of research on speech perception.* JASA 29:117–123.—Describes pattern playback to convert spectrogram to sound. Raises this question: Do articulatory movements mediate between our reception of an acoustic (speech) stimulus and our perception of it?

Low, F. N., *et al.* *The pulmonary alveolar epithelium.* Anat. Rec. 127:1–63. —Considers its derivation.

McCroskey, Jr., R. L. *Effect of speech on metabolism.* JSHD 22:46–52.—Direct or indirect calorimetry shows that the energy requirements for speaking are high, and the effect continues for some time after. Used Benedict-Roth metabolism apparatus.

Meyer-Eppler, W. *Realization of prosodic features in whispered speech.* JASA 29:104–106.

Myklebust, H. R. *Babbling and echolalia in language theory.* JSHD 22:356–360.

Negus, V. E. *The mechanism of the larynx.* Larnygoscope 67:961–986.

Parkin, P. H. *Loudness of common noises.* Acustica 7:57–58.—Table of phons.

Pierce, J. R., *et al.* *Reading rates and the information rate of a human channel.* BSTJ 36:497–516.—We can articulate from 2.1 to 3.8 words/sec. This is an information rate of only about 30 bits/sec compared with the 50,000,000 bits/sec rate of a television channel.

Pitman, L. K. *Nasolaryngoscope.* Arch. Otolaryng. 65:606–607.—An instrument inserted through the nose for viewing the larynx. Claims advantages over usual (via mouth) laryngoscopic method.

Portmann, G. *The physiology of phonation.* J. Laryngol. and Otol. 71:1–15.

Prestigiacomo, A. J. *Plastic-tape sound spectrograph.* JSHD 22:321–327. —Equipment developed in the Bell Telephone Laboratories was forerunner of commercial Sonograph. Recommended for research-minded students.

Sacerdote, G. G. *Researches on the singing voice.* Acustica 7:61–68.—Delayed speech feedback of 0.15 sec corresponds to about 6.6 cps. Vibrato (produced at larynx) about 6 per second pulsations.

Symposium international sur la fonction phonatoire du laryng. *Larynx et Phonation.* Presses Universitaires de France. Paris.

Tatai, K. *Comparisons of ventilatory capacities among fishing divers, nurses, and telephone operators in Japanese females.* Jap. J. Physiol. 7:37–41. —Female fishing divers work three hours a day, dive to depths of 30 feet and remain under water from 1 to 3 minutes, yet their vital capacity differs but little from that of sedentary telephone operators.

Tolhurst, G. C. *Effects of duration and articulation changes on intelligibility, word reception and listener preference.* JSHD 22:328–334.—If you alter your rate of speaking it affects the degree of intelligibility.

Tonndorf, J. *Fluid motion in cochlear models.* JASA 29:558–568.—Transparent models showed eddy currents, and membrane displacement.

Travis, L. E. (editor) *Handbook of Speech Pathology.* Appleton. New York.

van den Berg, J. A., *et al.* *On the air resistance and the Bernoulli effect of the human larynx.* JASA 29:626–631.

Wise, C. M. *Applied Phonetics.* Prentice-Hall. Englewood Cliffs, New Jersey.

Wise, C. M., *et al.* *Intelligibility of whispering in a tone language.* JSHD 22:335–338.—If you think English is difficult read this about Mandarin Chinese.

1958

Belasco, S. *Variations in vowel duration: phonemically or phonetically conditioned?* JASA 30:1049–1050.—Spanish vowels are of shorter (absolute) duration than English, French or German vowels.

Broadbent, D. E. *Perception and Communication.* Pergamon Press, New York.—Relates the evolution of the hearing mechanism to man's use of language.

Cohen, M. I. *Intrinsic periodicity of the pontile pneumotaxic mechanism.* Amer. J. Physiol. 195:23–27.—Discusses respiratory rhythm.

Cremer, Von L. *Ein mechanisches modell zur demonstration der bewegungen der basilar-membran.* Acustica 8:188–192.—Demonstrates dynamic action of inner ear.

Davis, H. *Mechano-electrical theory of cochlear action.* AnnOR&L 67:789–801.

Davis, H., *et al.* *Summating potentials of the cochlea.* Amer. J. Physiol. 195:251–261.

Dudley, H. *Phonetic pattern recognition vocoder for narrow-band speech transmission.* JASA 30:733–739.—First synthesis of speech from recognized phonetic patterns. Likens speech to a multiparameter telegraph. Good historical background material.

Dudley, H., *et al.* *Automatic recognition of phonetic patterns in speech.* JASA 30:721–732.—Contains historical background material of value.

Dunn, H. K., *et al.* *Artificial speech in phonetics and communications.* JSHR 1:23–39.—Brief history of devices used. Bibliography.

Fairbanks, G., *et al.* *Effects of delayed auditory feedback upon articulation.* JSHR 1:12–22.

Flanagan, J. L. *Some properties of the glottal sound source.* JSHR 1:99–116.

Flanagan, J. L., *et al.* *Pitch discrimination for synthetic vowels.* JASA 30:435–442.

Grant, J. C. B. *A Method of Anatomy: Descriptive and Deductive* (6th edition). Williams and Wilkins. Baltimore.

Gray, G. W., *et al.* *The Bases of Speech.* Harper. New York.

Hagerty, R. F., *et al.* *Posterior pharyngeal wall movement in normals.* JSHR 1:203–210.

Hagerty, R. F., *et al.* *Soft palate movement in normals.* JSHR 1:325–330.

Harbold, G. J. *Pitch ratings of voice and whispered vowels.* JASA 30:600–601.

Harris, K. S., *et al.* *Effect of third-formant transitions on the perception of the voiced stop consonants.* JASA 30:122–126.—These transitions provide the cues in perceiving /w, j, r, l, b, d, g/.

Hattori, S., *et al.* *Nasalization of vowels in relation to nasals.* JASA 30:267–274.

Hoffman, H. S. *Study of some cues in the perception of the voice stop consonants.* JASA 30:1035–1041.

House, A. S., *et al.* *Estimation of formant band widths from measurements of transient response of vocal tract.* JSHR 1:309–315.

McCabe, B. F. *Beethoven's deafness.* AnnOR&L 67:192–206.—A medical detective seeks clues.

Miller, G. A. (Symposium on unsolved problems in acoustics) *Speech and communication.* JASA 30:397–398.

Misrahy, G. A., *et al.* *Changes in cochlear endolymphatic oxygen availability,*

JASA 32:913.—Air pressure blows lips apart for initial [p] and [b] but not for [m].

Gardner, E., *et al.* *Anatomy: A Regional Study of Human Structure.* Saunders. Philadelphia.

Gershuni, S. G. *On the control of neural impulse stream in the auditory system.* Akusticheski (or Akusticheskii) Zhurnal 3:299–306.

Gersteink, G. L., *et al.* *An approach to the quantitative analysis of electrophysiological data from single neurons.* Biophys. J. 1:15–18.

Ingelstedt, S., *et al.* *Aerodynamics with the larynx and trachea.* Acta Oto-Laryngologica Suppl. 158:81–92.

Jesberg, N. *Laryngectomy: past, present and future.* AnnOR&L 69:184–198.

Kaplan, Harold M. *Anatomy and Physiology of Speech.* McGraw-Hill. New York.

Kelemen, G. *Basic anatomy and neurophysiology of speeech and language.* Cerebral Palsy Review 21:8–9.

Kiang, N. Y-S., *et al.* *Components of electrical responses recorded from the cochlea.* AnnOR&L 69:448–458.—Includes: cochlear microphonic potential (*CM*), action potential (*AP*), and summating potential (*SP*). Refers to mechanisms as neural populations.

Langer, S. K. *The origins of speech and its communicative function.* Q. J. Speech 46:121–134.

Peters, R. *Research on Psychological Parameters of Sound.* Mississippi Southern College, Hattiesburg, Mississippi.

Rasmussen, G. L., *et al.* (editors) *Neural Mechanisms of the Auditory and Vestibular Systems.* Charles C Thomas. Springfield, Illinois.

Reger, S. N. *Effect of middle ear muscle action on certain psycho-physical measurements.* AnnOR&L 69:1179–1198.—A few people can contract their middle ear muscles voluntarily and thus attenuate the loudness of sounds.

Roberts, L. *The cerebral cortex and hearing.* AnnOR&L 69:830–848.

Rubin, H. J. *The neurochronaxic theory of voice production—a refutation.* Arch. Otolaryng. 71:913–920.

Rubin, H. J., *et al.* *Human cochlea responses to sound stimuli.* AnnOR&L 69:459–479.

Rubin, H. J., *et al.* *Technique of high-speed photography of the larynx.* AnnOR&L 69:1072–1082.—At 8000 fps a 400-ft roll provides about three seconds effective filming time.

akai, T., *et al.* *New instruments and methods for speech analysis.* JASA 32:441–450.—The sonograph and other devices are described.

chmitt, H. J., *et al.* *Electromagnetic reflection from sound waves.* JASA 32:1660–1667.—A sound wave produces inhomogeneities of density and temperature in the propagating medium.

chour, I. (editor) *Noye's Oral Histology and Embryology* (8th edition). Lea and Febiger. Philadelphia.

onesson, B. *On the anatomy and vibratory pattern of the human vocal folds—with special reference to a photo-electrical method of studying the vibratory movements.* Acta Oto-Laryngologica Suppl. 156. 1960. —Discusses use of high speed camera, synchron-stroboscope. Reviews the extensive literature. Recommended.

evens, K. N. *Toward a model for speech recognition.* JASA 32:47.—

action potential, and microphonics during and following asphyxia, hypoxia, and exposure to loud sounds. JASA 30:701–704.

Misrahy, G. A., *et al.* *Effects of localized hypoxia on the electrophysiological activity of cochlea of the guinea pig.* JASA 30:705–709.

Moore, P. *Laryngeal vibrations: Measurements of the glottic wave. Part I. The normal vibratory cycle.* Arch. Otolaryng. 68:1–19. (Part II appears in 69:438–444. 1959)

Moser, H. M., *et al.* *Relative intensities of sounds at various anatomical locations of the head and neck during phonation of the vowels.* JASA 30:275–277.

Mowrer, O. H. *Hearing and speaking: an analysis of language learning.* JSHD 23:143–152.—Presents autism theory. Infant reproduces word-sound only when it is associated with a good situation; he is autistically rewarded in hearing his own sound.

Newby, H. A. *Audiology: Principles and Practice.* Appleton-Century-Crofts. New York.

Peterson, G. E. *Some observations on speech.* Q. J. Speech 44:402–412.

Peterson, G. E. *Speech and hearing research.* JSHR 1:3–11.

Peterson, G. E., *et al.* *Segmentation techniques in speech synthesis.* JASA 30:739–742.

Rahm, W. E., *et al.* *The stability of the cochlear response through time.* AnnOR&L 67:972–977.

Rosen, G. *Dynamic analog speech synthesizer.* JASA 30:201–209.

Schnitzlein, H. N., *et al.* *The myelinated component of the vagus nerves in man.* Anat. Rec. 131:649–667.—Myelinated fibers mostly are small fibers. Right cervical vagus (approx. 20,000 fibers); left (approx. 16,000). Most of larger myelinated fibers (8μ to 10μ diameter) belong to right recurrent (about 2300) and left recurrent (about 2500).

Thomas, C. K. *An Introduction to the Phonetics of American English.* Ronald Press. New York.

Tonndorf, J. *Harmonic distortion in cochlear models.* JASA 30:929–937.

Tonndorf, J. *The hydrodynamic origin of aural harmonics in the cochlea.* AnnOR&L 67:754–774.

van den Berg, J. *Myoelastic-aerodynamic theory of voice production.* JSHR 1:227–244.

Van Nostrand's *Scientific Encyclopedia.* Van Nostrand. New York.

Van Riper, C., *et al.* *Voice and Articulation.* Prentice-Hall. Englewood Cliffs, New Jersey.

Wang, W. S-Y., *et al.* *Segment inventory for speech synthesis.* JASA 30:743–746.—Believes 43 phonetic units are the minimum needed to synthesize an idiolect of American speech.

1959

Ahmend, R., *et al.* *Effect of sample duration on the articulation of sounds in normal and clipped speech.* JASA 31:1022.—Depending on various factors, speech sounds must be heard for a duration of time if they are to be identified correctly.

Barney, H. L., *et al.* *An experimental transistorized artificial larynx.* BSTJ 38:1337–1356.—Such a device should have these characteristics: (1) Speech volume output equal to normal; (2) Speech quality and pitch inflection output similar to normal; (3) Inconspicuous; (4) Hygienically acceptable; (5) Simple to operate; (6) Reliable; (7) Inexpensive.

Buchthal, F. *Electromyography of intrinsic laryngeal muscles.* Q.J. Exp. Physiol. 44:137–148.

Deatherage, B. H., *et al.* *Latency of action potentials in the cochlea of the guinea pig.* JASA 31:479–486.

Dersch, W. C. *A voice analog.* JASA 31:1563–1564.

Fink, B. R., *et al.* *Observations on the mechanical and acoustical properties of the vocal folds.* Folia Phoniatrica 11:167–172.

Flanagan, J. L. *Estimates of intraglottal pressure during phonation.* JSHR 2:168–172.

Goldstein, Jr., M. H., *et al.* *Responses of the auditory cortex to repetitive acoustic stimuli.* JASA 31:356–364.—Describes two neurophysiological mechanisms of pitch discrimination, one based on the place principle and the other on the time-pattern principle.

Gray, G. and Wise, C. *The Bases of Speech.* Harper. New York.

Harmon, L. D. *Electronic circuit simulates living nerve cell.* BLR 37:113–114.

Hinchcliffe, R. *The threshold of hearing as a function of age.* Acustica 9:303–308.—Hearing tends to grow progressively poorer with increasing age; patterns differ for the sexes.

Katsuki, Y., *et al.* *Interaction of auditory neurons in response to two sound stimuli in cat.* J. Neurophysiol. 22:603–623.

Koch, W. E. *Related experiments with sound waves and electromagnetic waves.* Acustica 9:227–238.

Lehiste, I., *et al.* *Vowel amplitude and phonemic stress in American English.* JASA 31:428–435.

Liberman, A. M., *et al.* *Minimal rules for synthesizing speech.* JASA 31:1490–1499.—The table illustrating the rules should be consulted.

Merritt, H. H. *A Textbook of Neurology* (2nd edition). Lea and Febiger. Philadelphia.

Meschan, I. *An Atlas of Normal Radiographic Anatomy.* Saunders. Philadelphia.—Chapter 1 introduces the student to radiography. Chapter 10 deals with the respiratory system, including the larynx.

Meyer-Eppler, von W. *Zur spektrastruktur der /r/-allophone des deutschen.* Acustica 9:247–250.

Miller, R. L. *Nature of the vocal cord wave.* JASA 31:667–677.—Describes analogs. Believes that fluctuations of amplitude produce secondary resonances.

Nakata, K. *Synthesis and perception of nasal consonants.* JASA 31:661–666. —The lowest resonance is 200–300~. In continuous speech their identification depends greatly upon the second formant locus as observed in the transition of the adjacent vowel.

O'Neill, E. F. *TASI.* BLR 37:83–87.—Time Assignment Speech Interpolation combines freeze-out or clipping (0.5%) of speech (barely perceptible to listener) and rapid shifting of talkspurts to silent (when one person is listening to the other) periods to permit more conversations than there are full-time circuits available.

Penfield, W., *et al.* *Speech and Brain Mechanisms.* Princeton University Press. Princeton, New Jersey.

Peterson, G. E. *Vowel formant measurements.* JSHR 2:173–183.

Rüedi, L. *Some observations on the histology and functi* J. Laryngol. and Otol. 73:1–20.

Sholes, G. N. *Synthesis of final /z/ without voicing.* JAS study emphasizes the American English tendency consonants, particularly in the final position.

Solomon, L. N. *Search for physical correlates to psycholog sounds.* JASA 31:492–497.

Sonesson, B. *A method for studying the vibratory mover cords.* J. Laryngol. and Otol. 73:732–737.

Strong and Elwyn's *Human Neuro-Anatomy.* 4th edition. kins. Baltimore.

Tobias, J. V. *Relative occurrence of phonemes in Americ* 31:631.—40 phonemes are listed whose relative from over 9% [I] and [t] to less than 0.3% [3 attempts to determine relative frequency of phonem

Tonndorf, J. *Beats in cochlear models.* JASA 31:608–61 similar frequency are heard simultaneously, the a single intertone whose pitch is between the two.

Truex, R. C. Strong and Elwyn's *Human Neuro-anat* Wilkins. Baltimore.

von Békésy, G. *Neural funneling along the skin and bet outer hair cells and the cochlea.* JASA 31:12 waves act upon the hair cells so that sounds are se by frequency as well as by intensity.

1960

Allen, G. W., *et al.* *The mechanism of bone conduction.* —Velocity of sound in bone = 3000 m/sec (cal

Blewett, J. E., *et al.* *Anatomy and Physiology for Ra* worth. London.

Bourne, G. H. (editor). *Structure and Function of Mus* Academic Press. New York.

Brewer, D. W., *et al.* *Phonation: clinical testing vers* AnnOR&L 69:781–804.

Cherry, C., *et al.* *Contribution to a study of the "coc* JASA 32:884.—Experiments on ability to separa the same time.

Chusid, J. G., *et al.* *Correlative Neuroanatomy and* (10th edition). Lange Medical Publications.

Davis, H., *et al.* (editors). *Hearing and Deafness.* Holt, New York.

Faaborg-Andersen, K., *et al.* *Phonation: clinical testin raphy.* Acta Oto-Laryngologica. Suppl. 158:200 nique termed Clinical Muscle Activity Assay.

Fant, G. *Acoustic Theory of Speech Production.* H York. (Report No. 10, Royal Inst. Technolo

Felson, B. *Fundamentals of Chest Roentgenology.* S

Flanagan, J. L. *Analog measurements of sound radia* JASA 32:1613–1620.

Flanagan, J. L. *Models for approximating basilar m* BSTJ 39:1163–1191.—Includes a schematic dr

Fujimura, O. *Movement of the lips in the generation*

From the input of speech waves the machine generates an output of phonetic symbols or vice versa.

Stevens, S. S. *The psychophysics of sensory function.* Amer. Scientist. 48: 226–253.

Tonndorf, J. *Shearing motion in scala media of cochlear models.* JASA 32: 238–244.

Virshup, M., *et al.* *Physiology of respiration.* Clinical Physiology 1:40–50.

von Békésy, Georg *Experiments in Hearing.* Translated and edited by E. G. Wever. McGraw-Hill. New York.—Nobel award winner Georg von Békésy is probably the foremost authority on the ear and hearing. His *Experiments* were begun in Budapest in 1924–1946, continued in Stockholm in 1947, and conducted since then at Harvard.

von Hayek, H. *The Human Lung.* Translated by V. E. Krahl. Hafner Publishing Co. New York.

von Leden, H., *et al.* *Laryngeal vibrations: measurements of the glottic wave. Part III.* Arch. Otolaryng. 71:16–35.—Defines open quotient

$$\left(\text{O. Q.} = \frac{\text{fraction of cycle during which glottis is open}}{\text{duration of entire cycle}}\right).$$

Defines speed quotient $\left(\text{S. Q.} = \frac{\text{time of abduction}}{\text{time of adduction}}\right)$.

Weiss, D. A. *Discussion of the neurochronaxic theory (Husson).* Arch. Otolaryng. 70:607–618.

1961

Bell, C. G., *et al.* *Reduction of speech spectra by analysis-by-synthesis techniques.* JASA 33:1725–1736.—States an acoustical theory of speech production.

Bjørklund, A. *Analyses of soprano voices.* JASA 33:575–582.

Brady, P. T., *et al.* *Perception of sounds characterized by a rapidly changing resonant frequency.* JASA 33:1357–1362.

Brosnahan, L. F. *The Sounds of Language.* W. Heffer and Sons. Cambridge.

Bucher, U., *et al.* *Development of the mucus-secreting elements in human lung.* Thorax 16:219–225.—Traces development during foetal ages.

Carbajal, P., *et al.* *Contrast laryngography.* Arch. Otolaryng. 74:537–548.—Frontal and lateral laryngograms show the relationship of parts of the larynx.

DiFiore, M. S. H. *Atlas of Human Histology.* Lea and Febiger. Philadelphia.

Dorland's *Illustrated Medical Dictionary.* 23rd edition. Saunders. Philadelphia.

Dunn, H. K. *Methods of measuring vowel formant bandwidths.* JASA 33: 1737–1746.

Eagles, E. L., *et al.* *Hearing in children: acoustic environment and audiometer performance.* JSHR 4:149–163.—Emphasizes that audiometers may be faulty.

Fairbanks, G., *et al.* *A psychophysical investigation of vowel formants.* JSHR 4:203–219.—Concludes that F_3 is less important than the lower formants (F_1 and F_2) in determining vowelness.

Flanagan, J. L. *Audibility of periodic pulses and a model for the threshold.* JASA 33:1540–1549.—For a tone of 1000 cycles the basilar membrane is displaced 20mm from the stapes.

Foulkes, J. D. *Computer identification of vowel types.* JASA 33:7–11.

Fujimura, O. *Bilabial stop and nasal consonants: a motion picture study and its acoustical implications.* JSHR 4:233–247.—Stroboscopic pictures at 240 fps. Believes that rapid movements of lips (5 to 10 msec) after explosion are in large part responsible for resonant characteristics.

Gacek, R. R., *et al.* *Fiber analysis of the statoacoustic nerve of guinea pig, cat, and monkey.* Anat. Rec. 139:455–463.

Gol'dburt, S. N. *Persistence of auditory processes within microintervals of time.* Biophysics 6:76–81.

Goodstein, L. D. *Intellectual impairment in children with cleft palates.* JSHR 4:287–294.—Children with normal speech have advantage in developing verbal intellectual skills.

Greenwood, D. D. *Critical bandwidth and the frequency coordinates of the basilar membrane.* JASA 33:1344–1356.

Gundy, R. F. *Auditory detection of an unspecified signal.* JASA 33:1008–1012.—Opens up the whole question of hearing by showing that we hear better the things we know we are going to hear. In other words, hearing is not just hearing; it is hearing with or without pre-heard backgrounds of experience.

Heinz, J. M., *et al.* *On the properties of voiceless fricative consonants.* JASA 33:589–596.—Electric model synthesizes surd fricatives.

Hoffman, H. H., *et al.* *The number of nerve fibers in the vagus nerve of man.* Anat. Rec. 139:429–435.—Right mid-cervical vagus (105,375); left (82,379). Each plus or minus about 5%. 80% of fibers not myelinated. Right recurrent laryngeal (8000); left (7496). Each plus or minus 5–10%. Less than 35% of fibers myelinated.

House, A. S. *On vowel duration in English.* JASA 33:1174–1178.—The primary lengthening of vowels is learned; secondary lengthening is inherent in articulation.

Jeffress, L. A., *et al.* *Lateralization vs localization.* JASA 33:482–483.—Sounds heard via earphones are heard as inside the head; sounds heard normally are heard as out there.

Jenkins, R. A. *Perception of pitch, timbre, and loudness.* JASA 33:1550–1557.—Suggests that the shape of the envelope is related to timbre, the area under the envelope is related to loudness, and the repetitive rate of the envelope is related to pitch.

Keele, C. A., *et al.* (revised by) Samson Wright's *Applied Physiology.* 10th edition. Oxford University Press. New York.

Kiang, N. Y–S. *The use of computers in studies of auditory neurophysiology.* Trans. Amer. Acad. Ophth. and Otolar. 65:735–747.

Klumpp, R. G., *et al.* *Intelligibility of time-compressed speech.* JASA 33:265–267.—At 50% compression (a speedup of 2.0) a 1-minute message is heard in ½ minute. A compression of 0.67 results in little loss in intelligibility for numbers and simple phrases.

Kodman, Jr., F. *Controlled reading rate under delayed speech feedback.* J. Auditory Res. 3:186–193.

Konig, W. F., *et al.* *The peripheral nervous system of the human larynx. Part II: The thyroarytenoid (vocalis) muscle.* Arch. Otolaryng. 74:153–163.

Konig, W. F., *et al.* *The peripheral nervous system of the human larynx. Part III. The development.* Arch. Otolaryng. 74:494–500.

Konishi, T., *et al.* *Effect of anoxia on cochlear potentials.* JASA 33:349–356.

LaFollette, A. C. *Special kind of speech noise.* JSHR 4:193.—Combines noise of human speakers for masking purposes.

Lane, H. L., *et al. Voice level: autophonic scale, perceived loudness, and effects of sidetone.* JASA 33:160–167.—In judging your own production of a vowel (i.e., autophonic output) you will depend more upon effort expended than upon your perception of loudness.

Lederer, F. L., *et al. Neurological manifestations in otolaryngology.* Arch. Otolaryng. 74:285–298.—Larynx has two functions: biological and social.

Lehiste, I., *et al. Some basic considerations in the analysis of intonation.* JASA 33:419–425.

Lehiste, I., *et al. Transitions, glides, and diphthongs.* JASA 33:268–277.—Describes 15 syllable nuclei.

Liberman, E. A. *Elementary theory of semipermeable membranes and the "phase" theory of biopotentials.* Biophysics 6:32–38.

Lieberman, P. *Perturbations in vocal pitch.* JASA 33:597–603.—Discusses, quantitatively, the rapid fluctuations occurring in the fundamental pitch of normal speech.

Lintz, L. B., *et al. Phonetic elements and perception of nasality.* JSHR 4:381–396.—Study of influence of vowel quality and consonant environments on nasality.

McCabe, B. F., *et al. Experimental inner ear pressure changes: functional effects.* AnnOR&L 70:541–555.

Mathews, M. V., *et al. Pitch synchronous analysis of voice sounds.* JASA 33:170–186.—Speech formants reflect the resonance characteristics of the vocal tract.

Møller, A. R. *Network model of the middle ear.* JASA 33:168–176.—A contraction of the middle ear muscles produces a change in the acoustic impedance of the ear.

Olson, H. F., *et al. Phonetic typewriter. III.* JASA 33:1610–1615.—The machine transforms speech sounds into phonetic orthography and has a capacity of 100 syllables. (1000 will be required for a practical machine.) Sea, C and See are spelled *See;* I, eye, and aye are spelled *I;* to, too, and two are spelled *to.* A relatively small number of words account for most of our everyday English: 69 words gives us 50% of written English; 155 words yield 80% of conversational speech.

Onchi, Y. *Mechanism of the middle ear.* JASA 33:794–805.—Explains experiments with electrical and mechanical models.

Ostwald, P. F. *Humming, sound and symbol.* J. Auditory Res. 3:224–232. —Discusses the word *hm* and the phoneme /m/.

Owens, E. *Intelligibility of words varying in familiarity.* JSHR 4:113–129.

Peterson, G. E. *Parameters of vowel quality.* JSHR 4:10–29.—Believes fundamental frequency of voice greater than 100 cps bandwidth. Notes whispering and falsetto as two extremes of phonation.

Pike, K. L. *Phonetics: A Critical Analysis of Phonetic Theory and a Technic for the Practical Description of Sounds.* Seventh printing. Univ. of Michigan Press. Ann Arbor.

Pruzansky, S. *Congenital Anomalies of the Face and Associated Structures.* Charles C Thomas. Springfield, Illinois.

Rice, E. A., *et al. Studies on the endolymphatic dc potential of the guinea pig's cochlea.* JASA 33:922–925.

Richardson, A., *et al.* *Ventilation of the paranasal sinuses.* J. Oto-Laryngological Society of Australia 1:17–19.

Rosenblith, W. A. (editor). *Sensory Communications.* Wiley. New York.

Shahrokh, D. K., *et al.* *A teaching device for residents in laryngology.* Arch. Otolaryng. 74:234–235.—Demonstroscope enables laryngologist and a second person to study larynx.

Shelton, Jr., R. L. *Cinefluorographic speech record.* JSHR 4:171.—Equipment used with dynapulse.

Small, Jr., A. M., *et al.* *Pitch shifts of periodic stimuli with changes in sound level.* JASA 33:1022–1027.—Are there two separate mechanisms for the analysis of pitch: peripheral cochlear analysis and central nervous system neuron analysis?

Sommers, R. K., *et al.* *Pitch discrimination and articulation.* JSHR 4:56–60.

Stedman's *Medical Dictionary* (20th edition). Williams and Wilkins. Baltimore.

Stevens, K. N., *et al.* *An acoustical theory of vowel production and some of its implications.* JSHR 4:303–320.

Taber, C. W. *Taber's Cyclopedic Medical Dictionary* (8th edition). F. A. Davis. Philadelphia.

Thompson, P. O., *et al.* *Liveness effects on the intelligibility of noise-masked speech.* JASA 33:604–605.

Tomasch, J., *et al.* *The human nucleus ambiguus: a quantitative study.* Anat. Rec. 141:247–252.—Location: inferior medial reticular formation of medulla. Is not part of reticular formation but is associated with elements of it to form portions of the bulbar centers for deglutition, respiration, and phonation.

Tuttle, W. W., *et al.* *Textbook of Physiology* (14th edition). C. V. Mosby. St. Louis.

von Békésy, G. *Concerning the fundamental component of periodic pulse patterns and modulated vibrations observed on the cochlear model with nerve supply.* JASA 33:888–896.

von Békésy, G. *Pitch sensation and its relation to the periodicity of the stimulus. Hearing and skin vibrations.* JASA 33:341–348.—Periodicity alone is not sufficient to determine pitch sensations.

von Leden, H. *The mechanism of phonation.* Arch. Otolaryng. 74:660–676. —Discusses two theories: myoelastic and neuromuscular.

Wang, W., *et al.* *Intrinsic cues and consonant perception.* JSHR 4:130–136.

Warren, D. W., *et al.* *A cineradiographic study of velopharyngeal closure.* Plastic and Reconstructive Surgery 28:656–669.

Webster, J. C. *Information in simple multidimensional speech message.* JASA 33:940–944.

Welch, P. D., *et al.* *Two multivariate statistical computer programs and their application to the vowel recognition problem.* JASA 33:426–434.

Wendahl, R. W., *et al.* *Identification of stuttering during relatively fluent speech.* JSHR 4:281–286.—All normal speakers show some disfluencies.

Woodburne, R. T. *Essentials of Human Anatomy.* 2nd edition. Oxford University Press. New York.

Zuckerman, S. *A New System of Anatomy.* Oxford University Press. New York.

1962

Abel, J. W. *Syllabic [m, ŋ]*. Amer. Speech 37:106–113.—Discusses authors who include [m̩, ŋ̩]; gives examples of use.

Alcaraz, M., *et al. Changes in acoustic habituation following severance of the intrinsic ear muscles in chronic preparations*. Acta Physiologica Latino Americana 12:1–7.

Andersen, H. C., *et al. Experimental studies on sound transmission in the human ear*. Acta Oto-Laryngologica 56:307–317.

Basmajian, J. V. *Muscles Alive: Their Functions Revealed by Electromyography*. Williams and Wilkins. Baltimore.—Describes electromyographic equipment (high gain amplifiers, cathode-ray oscilloscopes, cameras or other recording devices). Chapters on the *Muscles of Respiration* and *Mouth, Pharynx and Larynx*. The author concludes that almost no emg studies have been made of the muscles of phonation, although he indicates that in phonation the adductor muscles display electric potentials from 0.4 to 0.5 sec *prior* to the actual production of sound waves. Extensive bibliography.

Bennett, G. S. *Remarks on the paper by Montague and Strickland*. JASA 34:347.—Suggests that the ear responds to particle velocity rather than to pressure.

Beil, R. G. *Frequency analysis of vowels produced in a helium-rich atmosphere*. JASA 34:347–349.—Compares the fundamental frequency and the first three formant frequencies of normal and helium vowels.

Bosma, J. F., *et al. Laryngeal and pharyngeal respiratory motions in the rabbit: cinematographic observations*. AnnOR&L 71:341–355.

Briggs, M. H., *et al. The molecular basis of memory and learning*. Psychological Reports 6:537–541.

Cavanaugh, W. J., *et al. Speech privacy in buildings*. JASA 34:475–492.—Reviews speech-intelligibility theory developed in 1947 by the Bell Telephone Laboratories. 200 cycles to 6000 cycles brackets intelligible portion of speech energy. While most of the energy is below 800 cycles, most of the contribution to intelligibility is above that level.

Chase, R. A., *et al. Effect of simultaneous delayed and undelayed auditory feedback on speech*. JSHR 5:144–151.

Davis, Hallowell. *Advances in the neurophysiology and neuroanatomy of the cochlea*. JASA 34:1377–1385.—Should be consulted, especially for its helpful figures.

Desmedt, J. E. *Auditory-evoked potentials from cochlea to cortex as influenced by activation of the efferent olivo-cochlear bundle*. JASA 34:1478–1496.—The inhibitory action of the OCB may decide what signals get to the brain.

Dickson, D. R. *An acoustic study of nasality*. JSHR 5:103–111.—The acoustic characteristics are unique for each person and depend on the variable vocal tract resonators.

Engström, H., *et al. Structure and functions of the sensory hairs of the inner ear*. JASA 34:1356–1363.

Fex, J. *Auditory activity in centrifugal and centripetal cochlear fibers in cat*. Acta Physiologica Scandinavica 55 Suppl. 189:1–68.

Fink, B. R. *Phonatory adaptations in the upper larynx of man*. AnnOR&L 71:356–362.

Fink, B. R. *Tensor mechanism of the vocal folds.* AnnOR&L 71:591–600.

Fisch, U., *et al.* *Electromyographic studies on the human stapedial muscle.* Acta Oto-Laryngologica 56:287–297.

Flanagan, J. L. *Computational model for basilar membrane displacement.* JASA 34:1370–1376.

Flanagan, J. L. *Models for approximating basilar membrane displacement. Part II.* BSTJ 41:959–1009.

Flanagan, J. L., *et al.* *Minimum phase responses for the basilar membrane.* JASA 34:114–118.

Fletcher, S. G. *Speech as an element in organization of a motor response.* JSHR 5:292–300.—Beginning at age one, speech has a regulatory function on a child's actions.

Flock, A., *et al.* *Morphological basis of directional sensitivity of the outer hair cells in the organ of Corti.* JASA 34:1351–1355.

Freud, E. D. *Function and dysfunctions of the ventricular folds.* JSHD 27:334–340.

Friedmann, I. *The cytology of the ear.* Brit. Med. Bull. 18:209–213.—Good description of cells of organ of Corti. One of articles in an issue devoted to electron microscopy.

Fujimura, O. *Analysis of nasal consonants.* JASA 34:1865–1875.—Shows three characteristics of spectra: (1) low (300∼) first formant, (2) high damping factors of formants, and (3) high density of formants in frequency domain.

Fuortes, M. G. F., *et al.* *Interpretation of the repetitive firing of nerve cells.* J. General Physiol. 45:1163–1179.—Since 1848 the view has been held that change of current elicited an impulse in a nerve. It now appears that some myelinated peripheral nerves may discharge in response to a constant current stimulus.

García Ramos, J. *The factors which determine the lung's distensibility.* Acta Physiologica Latino Americana 12:129–138.

Gold, B. *Computer program for pitch extraction.* JASA 34:916–921.

Grant, J. C. B. *An Atlas of Anatomy.* Williams and Wilkins. Baltimore.

Greenwood, D. D. *Approximate calculations of the dimensions of traveling-wave envelopes in four species.* JASA 34:1364–1370.

Groen, J. J. *Inhibitory mechanism of the vestibular system in man in comparison with hearing.* JASA 34:1497.—If the ear be stimulated by a constant sound for about 150 sec loudness is reduced.

Gulick, W. L., *et al.* *The effects of perilymph loss upon the electrical activity of the ear.* AnnOR&L 71:573–584.

Guttman, N., *et al.* *Lower limits of pitch and musical pitch.* JSHR 5:207–214.

Hamilton, W. J., *et al.* *Human Embryology* (3rd edition). Williams and Wilkins. Baltimore.

Hecker, M. H. L. *Studies of nasal consonants with an articulatory speech synthesizer.* JASA 34:179–188.—Utilizes analogs of nasal cavities and of vocal tract.

Hirsh, I. J. *Békésy's audiometer.* JASA 34:1333–1336.

Holbrook, A., *et al.* *Diphthong formants and their movements.* JSHR 5:38–58.

Hollien, H. *Vocal fold thickness and fundamental frequency of phonation.* JSHR 5:237–243.—Use of Keleket Selectoplane laminagraphic x-ray equipment determined that mean thickness of mesial projection of folds decreased as frequency increased (e.g., 9.7 mm to 6.3 mm).

Hollinshead, W. H. *Textbook of Anatomy*. Harper & Row. New York.

Hood, J. D. *Bone conduction: a review of the present position with special reference to the contributions of Dr. Georg von Békésy*. JASA 34:1325–1332.

Hyden, H. *The neuron and its glia—a biochemical and functional unit.* Endeavour 21:144–155.

Iurato, S. *Functional implications of the nature and submicroscopic structure of the tectorial and basilar membranes*. JASA 34:1386–1395.—The membranes were studied with analytical chemistry, x-ray diffraction, electron microscopy, polarized light, and phase contrast.

Jahn, T. L. *The mechanism of ciliary movement. Part II*. J. Cellular and Comparative Physiol. 60:217–228.

Kates, S. L., *et al. Cognitive processes in deaf and hearing adolescents and adults*. Psychol. Monographs 76, No. 32. Pp. 1–34. (Whole No. 551, 1962.)

Keenan, J. S., *et al. Intralaryngeal relationships during pitch and intensity changes*. JSHR 5:173–178.—An opportunity for students to study closely radiograms of the larynx.

Kiang, N. Y–S., *et al. Stimulus coding in the cat's auditory nerve: preliminary report*. AnnOR&L 71:1009–1026.

Krmpotić, J. *L'index neuromusculaire chronométrique en otolaryngologie.* Acta Oto-Laryngologica 56:298–303.—Establishes neuromuscular index indicating instant of arrival of nerve impulses in muscles of mastication, deglutition and phonation.

Lane, H. *Parameters of vowel perception*. JASA 34:743.—An interesting comparison of autophonic scales and reception scales, i.e., what the speaker hears and what the listener hears.

Lane, H. *Psychophysical parameters of vowel perception*. Psychol. Monographs 76, No. 44. Pp. 1–25. (Whole No. 563, 1962.)

Lawrence, M. *The double innervation of the tensor tympani*. AnnOR&L 71:705–718.

Lawrence, M., *et al. Inner ear response to high-level sounds*. JASA 34:102–108.

Moll, K. L. *Velopharyngeal closure on vowels*. JSHR 5:30–37.—Cinefluorographic procedure. Less closure on low than high vowels. Vowels adjacent to /n/ exhibit incomplete closure, less if preceding than following.

Moore, G. P., *et al. Ultra high speed photography in laryngeal physiology.* JSHD 27:165–171.—Describes equipment.

Mountcastle, V. B. (editor) *Interhemispheric Relations and Cerebral Dominance*. Johns Hopkins Press. Baltimore.

O'Leary, J. L. *A litre and a half of brains: contemporary survey in electrophysiology. Part I*. Arch. Neurology 7:487–517.—Includes bibliography of over 500 references.

Olson, H. F. *Printout system for the automatic recording of the spectral analysis of spoken syllables*. JASA 34:166–171.—Automatically records any of a trillion different quantized (spectrum-time-amplitude) analyses of a spoken syllable.

Olson, H. F., *et al. Demonstration of a speech processing system consisting of a speech analyzer, translator, typer, and synthesizer.* JASA 34:1535–1538.—English words spoken into a microphone are analyzed, converted to a syllable code, and synthesized as speech or typed at a rate of 60 syllables a minute.

Parker, D. E. *Vertical organization of the auditory cortex of the cat.* J. Auditory Res. 2:99–124.

Ramaswamy, T. K., *et al.* *Simple laboratory setup for obtaining sound spectrograms.* JASA 34:515–517.

Ruben, R. J., *et al.* *Properties of the eighth nerve action potential.* JASA 34:99–102.—Gives a conduction velocity figure of 25 m/sec.

Ruch, T. C., *et al.* *Neurophysiology.* Saunders. Philadelphia.

Schouten, J. F., *et al.* *Study of time cues in speech perception.* JASA 34:517–518.—Record spoken /s/ on tape. Cutting the tape gives the perception of the /t/ sound.

Sholtz, P. N., *et al.* *Spoken digit recognition using vowel-consonant segmentation.* JASA 34:1–5.—By digital computer simulation 493 words spoken by males (25) and females (25) were identified with 97% accuracy.

Shoup, J. E. *Phoneme selection for studies in automatic speech recognition.* JASA 34:397–403.

Simmons, F. B., *et al.* *The significance of round-window-recorded cochlear potentials in hearing.* AnnOR&L 71:767–800.

Spoendlin, H. H. *Ultrastructural features of the organ of Corti in normal and acoustically stimulated animals.* AnnOR&L 71:657–677.

Tonndorf, J. *Time/frequency analysis along the partition of cochlear models: a modified place concept.* JASA 34:1337–1350.

Tonndorf, J., *et al.* *Permeability of intracochlear membranes to various vital stains.* AnnOR&L 71:801–841.

Tucker, G. F., *et al.* *A histological demonstration of the development of laryngeal connective tissue compartments.* Trans. Amer. Acad. Ophth. and Otolar. 66:308–318.

von Békésy, G. *The Békésy Commemorative Issue on the Occasion of His Nobel Laureateship.* Supplement JASA September 1962.—A series of articles in honor of von Békésy's receiving the Nobel Prize for Physiology or Medicine in 1961.

von Békésy, G. *Comments on the measurements of the relative size of dc potentials and microphonics in the cochlea.* JASA 34:124.

von Békésy, G. *Syncrony between nervous discharges and periodic stimuli in hearing and on the skin.* AnnOR&L 71:678–692.

Weber, R. L. *Films for students of physics, supplement I.* Amer. J. Physics 30:321–327.—220 more films, including 3 on sound. Lists distributors. See same author (1961) in Amer. J. Physics 29:222 (listing 450 films, including 25 on sound), and (1954) in Amer. J. Physics 22:54–59 (lists films for college physics courses, including 16 on sound).

Wever, Ernest Glen. *Development of traveling-wave theories.* JASA 34:1319. —Reviews early theories of Hurst, 1894; Bonnier, 1895; TerKuile, 1900; Watt, 1914; Meyer, 1899 and 1928; Békésy, 1928 and following; Ranke, 1931; Reboul, 1937; Zwislocki, 1946; Peterson and Bogart, 1950; Huggins, 1950; Fletcher, 1951. Believes resonance, telephone, traveling-wave and standing-wave theories constitute stages in a continuum.

Wever, E. G., *et al.* *Hearing in the bat, Myotis Lucifugus, as shown by the cochlear potentials.* J. Auditory Res. 2:158–175.

Whittaker, E. G. *The synapse: biology and morphology.* Brit. Med. Bull. 18:223–229.—Drawings will remove some of the mystery of the synapse.

Youmans, W. B. *Fundamentals of Human Physiology.* Year Book Medical Publishers. Chicago.

Youmans, W. B. *Human Physiology.* Macmillan. New York.

Zwislocki, J. *Analysis of the middle-ear function. Part I: Input impedance.* JASA 34:1514–1523.—Develops a quantitative theory of middle-ear acoustics expressed in terms of an electric analog. The volume of middle-ear cavities varies from about 3 to 18 cc (average about 9 cc).

1963

Agostoni, E. *Diaphragm activity during breath holding: factors related to its onset.* J. Applied Physiol. 18:30–36.

Allison, Jr., R. B. *Using adverbs as multipliers in semantic differentials.* J. Psychol. 56:115–117.—Can adverbs be used as if they were multiplying constants, increasing the value of the words they modify (e.g., extremely = 1.5; very = 1.3)?

Alpiner, J. G. *Audiologic problems of the aged.* Geriatrics 18:19–26.—Presbycusis is progressive. The pattern shows loss of high frequency sensitivity, primarily; low frequencies remain relatively normal.

Angeluscheff, Z. *Decibel vs hearing cell.* JASA 35:810.

Bader, M. E., *et al.* *Changes in lung volumes during breathing negative pressure continuously, during inspiration only, and during expiration only.* J. Lab. and Clinical Med. 62:31–39.—Gives vital capacity figures.

Barrs, J. T. *Voiceless-fricative identification as a function of duration modification.* JASA 35:784.

Bartlett, R. G. *Pulmonary function evaluation in air and space flight.* Industrial Med. and Surgery 32:2–8.—Vital capacity goes into orbit! Describes telemetered pneumotachograph and Servospirometer. Uses velocity-volume loop technique.

Bevan, W., *et al.* *Effect of "subliminal" tones upon the judgment of loudness.* J. Exper. Psychol. 66:23–29.—Discussion of subtle anchor stimuli and their effect upon psychophysical perceptive judgments.

Boehm, G. A. W. *That wonderful machine, the brain.* Fortune, page 125ff. February.—Nuclear physics easier to understand than brain neural theory. At every level the brain is more complex than a computer. Description of neurons (small ones weigh 5/1,000,000,000,000 oz.) and difference potential (70/1000 volt). Believes synapse gap is approximately 2/1,000,000 cm.

Boord, R. L., *et al.* *Projection of the cochlear and lagenar nerves on the cochlear nuclei of the pigeon.* J. Comp. Neurology 120:463–476. —Uses axonal degeneration to demonstrate point to point afferent relation between organ of Corti and primary cochlear nuclei.

Bousfield, W. A., *et al.* *The incidental learning of associated responses to given stimulus words.* J. General Psychol. 68:325–331.

Boyd, W. H., *et al.* *Electromyography of the diaphragm in rabbits.* Amer. J. Physiol. 204:943–948.—The diaphragm functions as a unit.

Buck, L. *Auditory perception of position and speed.* J. Applied Psychol. 47:177–183.—Noise may be helpful in supplying information.

Calearo, C., *et al.* *"Cortical" hearing tests and cerebral dominance.* Acta Oto-Laryngologica 56:17–25.

Campbell, C. J., *et al.* *Laryngeal resistance to air flow.* AnnOR&L 72:5–30.

Cate, R. A., *et al.* *Laminated lung microsections: a new dimension in the study and teaching of pulmonary pathology.* Diseases of the Chest 43:1–7.

Cautela, J. R., *et al.* *A machine capable of being conditioned.* Amer. J. Psychol. 76:128–134.

Chou, J. T. Y. *Respiration of Reissner's membrane of the guinea pig.* J. Laryngol. and Otol. 77:374–380.—Utilizes Cartesian Diver technique. Shows rate higher than that of kidney cortex or brain cortex.

Clarke, E. *Aristotelian concepts of the form and function of the brain.* Bull. History of Medicine 37:1–14.—Aristotle disagreed with his teacher, Plato, in naming heart, not brain, as central organ and seat of soul. He was right that Man's brain is largest, comparatively, but he thought its purpose was to cool the body.

Clements, J. A. *Surface tension in the lungs.* Scientific American 207:121–130. Estimates one square meter of lung surface per 1000 grams of body weight (in an adult, equivalent to the area of a tennis court). Blood and air separated by membrane one micron (0.001 mm) thin.

Corso, J. F. *Age and sex differences in pure-tone thresholds.* Arch. Otolaryng. 77:385–405.—Compares findings on presbycusis with reports by other experimenters. Bibliography.

Crystal, T. H., *et al.* *Computer simulation of a formant-vocoder synthesizer.* JASA 35:805.

Cutt, R. A. *The effects of the local application of middle ear drugs upon the cochlear potentials.* Laryngoscope 73:702–712.

David, Jr., E. E. *Modeling speech for economical communication.* JASA 35:779.

Eblen, Jr., R. E. *Limitations on use of surface electromyography in studies of* speech breathing. JSHR 6:3–18.—Reviews studies in electromyography, employing surface or subsurface electrodes, with special attention to muscle action potentials (*MAP*) from the intercostal muscles. Describes use of pneumotachograph to measure rate of air flow.

Etter, L. E. *Opacification studies of normal and abnormal paranasal sinuses.* Amer. J. Roentg., Rad. Ther. and Nuclear Med. 89:1137–1146.—Refer to pictures.

Fant, C. G. M., *et al.* *Evaluation of various analysis-synthesis speech systems.* JASA 35:804–805.

Focht, L. R. *Dominant formants in phoneme perception.* JASA 35:783.

Fuleihan, F. J. D., *et al.* *Transient responses to CO_2 breathing of human subjects awake and asleep.* J. Applied Physiol. 18:289–294.

Harris, C. M., *et al.* *Display of sound spectrographs in real time.* JASA 35:729.—Pattern is displayed on 12-inch PPI cathode-ray oscilloscope from AN/CPS-1 radar system.

Harris, K. S. *Behavior of the tongue in the production of some alveolar consonants.* JASA 35:784.

Hart, M. C., *et al.* *Relation between anatomic respiratory dead space and body size and lung volume.* J. Applied Physiol. 18:519–522.—The dead space refers to volume of conducting air passages, e.g., mouth, pharynx, larynx, trachea, bronchi, bronchioles.

Heinz, J. M. *Analysis of acoustic speech signals into articulatory parameters.* JASA 35:779.

Holmgren, G. L., *et al.* *Speaker recognition in speech communication.* JASA 35:790.

Howard, C. R. *Vocoder performance on voiceless fricatives.* JASA 35:784.

Indiresan, P. V. *Interrupted speech and the possibility of increasing communication efficiency.* JASA 35:504–508.

Karplus, H. B. *Correlation hypothesis to explain the fine frequency discrimination of the ear.* JASA 35:809.

Kelly, C. M. *Mental ability and personality factors in listening.* Q. J. Speech 49:152–156.

Kerth, J. D., *et al.* *Comparison of the perilymphatic and cerebrospinal fluid pressures.* Arch. Otolaryng. 77:581–585.—Increasing the latter increases the former.

Knight, E. H. *Some considerations regarding the concept "autism."* Diseases of the Nervous System 24:224–229.

Konig, W. F., *et al.* *A three-dimensional reconstruction of a hemilarynx.* Arch. Otolaryng. 77:137–139.—Stained serial sections used in preparing drawings to be covered with wax. See color plate.

Kory, R. C., *et al.* *Evaluation of spirometers used in pulmonary function studies.* Amer. Rev. Respiratory Diseases 87:228–238.—Bibliography.

Kryter, K. D. *Hearing impairment for speech.* Arch. Otolaryng. 77:598–602. —Audiometric zero is 10db higher than it should be. Discusses changing test levels.

Ladefoged, P. *Acoustic correlates of subglottal activity.* JASA 35:778.—Believes activity of internal intercostal muscles may add stress/pitch factor to speech sounds.

Ladefoged, P., *et al.* *Loudness, sound pressure, and subglottal pressure in speech.* JASA 35:454–460.

Lieberman, P. *Laryngeal activity and the analysis and synthesis of speech.* JASA 35:778–779.

Lieberman, P. *Some acoustic measures of the fundamental periodicity of normal and pathologic larynges.* JASA 35:344–353.—Pitch perturbations (absolute value $\geqq$0.5 msec) are small but rapid variations in the fundamental periodicity of normal continuous speech.

Lindblom, B. *Spectrographic study of vowel reduction.* JASA 35:783.

Loewenstein, W. R., *et al.* *The electrical conductance and potential across the membrane of some cell nuclei.* J. Cell Biology 16:421–425.—Deals with cells as small as 30μ.

McCann, G. D., *et al.* *Computers and data processing for nervous system research.* IEEE Transactions on Bio-Medical Electronics. BME 10:48–56.—The journal is a publication of the Professional Technical Group on Bio-Medical Electronics of The Institute of Electrical and Electronic Engineers, Inc.

McCroskey, R. L., *et al.* *The relative intelligibility of esophageal speech and artificial-larynx speech.* JSHD 28:37–41.

MacNeilage, P. F. *Electromyographic and acoustical study of the production of certain final clusters.* JASA 35:461–463.

MacNeilage, P. F. *Electromyographic study of the tongue during vowel production.* JASA 35:783–784.

MacNeilage, P. F. *Motor patterns of speech production.* JASA 35:779.

Mårtensson, A. *Reflex responses and recurrent discharges evoked by stimulation of laryngeal nerves.* Acta Physiologica Scandinavica 57:248–269. —Discusses proprioceptive mechanisms.

Mead, J., *et al. Factors limiting depth of a maximal inspiration in human subjects.* J. Applied Physiol. 18:295–296.

Mitchell, R. A., *et al. Respiratory responses mediated through superficial chemosensitive areas on the medulla.* J. Applied Physiol. 18:523–533. —Includes bibliography.

Molinari, G. A., *et al. The cochleorecurrential reflex.* Arch. Otolaryng. 77:92–100.—Reflex auditory mechanisms control phonation. Shows agreement with Rudolph that feedback mechanism regulates phonation.

Morton, J., *et al. Experiments relating to the perception of formants.* JASA 35:475–480.—The three or four formants (below 3000∼) of speech sounds are indicated by their amplitude peaks in a frequency spectrum. An envelope may be drawn about the line spectrum.

Nixon, C. W., *et al. Speech in vibration environs.* Abstract. Aerospace Medicine 34:262.

O'Leary, J. L. *A litre and a half of brains. Part II.* Arch. Neurology 8:35–49. *Part III.* Arch. Neurology 8:128–144.—Discusses phylogenetic development, a succession of brains operating at different levels. Brain can program varieties of data; encodes and decodes. *Engram* is minimum neurological event capable of memory recall.

Otten, K. W., *et al. On segmentation of speech for automatic speech.* JASA 35:806.

Parker, D. E. *Investigation of speech sounds with an electronic-analog ear.* JASA 35:784.

Parnell, J. E. *High frequency audiometry* (abstract). Aerospace Medicine 34:263.—Does man have latent ability to use echolocation as do bats and whales?

Pong, W., *et al. Nonlinearity of the middle ear as a possible source of subharmonics.* JASA 35:679–681.

Preston, J. B., *et al. A comparison of motor cortex effects on slow and fast muscle innervations in the monkey.* Exper. Neurol. 7:327–341.

Ptacek, P. H., *et al. Maximum duration of phonation.* JSHD 28:171–182. —Low correlation between blowing and phonating.

Radionove, E. A. *Measuring the intensity of a brief sound signal at the first neuron level of the auditory system.* Soviet Physics: Acoustics 8:350–355. (Translation by Amer. Inst. of Physics Translations Advisory Board. Original: Akusticheskii Zhurnal 8:447–453. 1962.)

Ratner, S. C., *et al. The effect of the listener on the speaking interaction.* Psychological Rec. 13:265–268.

Rauch, S., *et al. Arguments for the permeability of Reissner's membrane.* Laryngoscope 73:135–147.—Proportions of electrolytes in perilymph not the same as in endolymph. Endolymph has high potassium level (like nerve interior) but is positive (nerve interior is negative). *K* and *Na* ions pass through the membrane, and because of difference in their concentrations in perilymph and endolymph there exists an ion potential at the membrane. This influences the transformation of mechanical sound waves into energy which stimulates hair cells.

Rosenberg, M. D. *The relative extensibility of cell surfaces.* J. Cell Biology 17:289–297.—Discusses some reasons for distortion of cells. [This journal, formerly The Journal of Biophysical and Biochemical Cytology, is one with which some students will wish to acquaint themselves.]

Rosenzweig, D. Y., *et al. Postmortem lung studies: mechanical and bronchographic properties.* Amer. Rev. Respiratory Diseases 88:6–13.

Ross, J., *et al. Foundations of Anatomy and Physiology.* E. & S. Livingstone. London.

Rossi, G., *et al. Research on the efferent innervation of the inner ear.* J. Laryngol. and Otol. 77:202–233.—Assigns function of selective inhibition to nerves. Bibliography.

Salomon, G., *et al. Electromyography of middle ear muscles in man during motor activities.* Acta Neurologica Scandinavica 39:161–168.—The muscles seem to have non-acoustic functions, contracting during general motor activity, e.g., eye closure, yawning, coughing, and laughing.

Sant'ambrogio, G., *et al. Motor innervation and pattern of activity of cat diaphragm.* J. Applied Physiol. 18:43–46.

Schwartz, M. F. *A study of thresholds of identification for vowels as a function of their duration.* J. Auditory Res. 3:47–52.—As duration increases required mean SPLs decrease.

Sekey, A. *Short-term auditory frequency discrimination.* JASA 35:682–690.

Shelton, R. L., *et al. Filming speed in cinefluorographic speech study.* JSHR 6:19–26.—Lingua-alveolar contacts and patterns of movement during speech production are shown adequately at 24 frames/sec.

Smith, A. C. *A teaching aid in indirect laryngoscopy and posterior rhinoscopy.* J. Laryngol. and Otol. 77:266–268.—Uses principle of automobile rearview mirror on side of car.

Smith, D. L. *Basic concepts in physiology: Francis Gotch and the nerve impulse.* Amer. Biol. Teacher 25:336–341.

Stack, M. V. (editor) *Current papers in oral biology.* Arch. Oral Biol. 8:473–485. Students may wish to consult this and similar listings in issues of the Archives.

Stewart, J. L. *Quantitative laws for sensory perception.* Psychol. Rev. 70:180–192.—Discusses design parameters for electronic analog for hearing. Suggests new Weber Law.

Subcommittee of Committee on Conservation of Hearing. *Listing of audiometers.* Trans. Amer. Acad. Ophth. and Otolar. 67:XLII.—Current listings are made of models meeting A.S.A. specifications.

Sullivan, G. H., *et al. Myoelectric servocontrol* (abstract). Aerospace Medicine 34:267.—If one attempts to move muscles it generates action potentials which act as input to servomechanisms to perform the task for the muscles.

Surivillo, W. W. *The relation of simple response time to brain-wave fre-*

quency and the effects of age. Electroencephalography and Clinical Neurophysiology 15:105–114.—Indicates that the brain wave cycle is the time unit in terms of which the *CNS* programs a response.

Tanaka, M. *Functional role of cortical acoustic areas in the excitatory and inhibitory processes in acoustic conditioned reflex.* Jap. J. Physiol. 13:33–53.

Taylor, I. K. *Phonetic symbolism re-examined.* Psychol. Bull. 60:200–209.—Certain sounds convey meanings other than their conventional ones; for example, *mal* sounds larger than *mil.* Suggests a new theory to account for universality of meaning of sounds.

Valvassori, G. E. *Laminagraphy of the ear: normal roentgenographic anatomy.* Amer. J. Roentg., Rad. Ther. and Nuclear Med. 89:1155–1167.

Vance, J. W. *A bellows-type spirometer for measuring the forced expirogram.* Diseases of the Chest 43:57–61.

Venis, C. G. *A simple laboratory technique for the making of rubber objects.* J. Scientific Instruments 40:331.—Using pre-vulcanized natural latex, objects may be formed for laboratory use.

Virmani, V., *et al. Correlation of electrical activity of brain with metabolic parameters. Part I.* Indian J. Medical Res. 51:75–79.

von Békésy, G. *Hearing theories and complex sounds.* JASA 35:588–601. —So far, theories of hearing are but theories of pitch. Discusses two main theories: place and telephone, with emphasis on the latter, in terms of a periodicity theory.

von Békésy, G. *Three experiments concerned with pitch perception.* JASA 35:602–606.

Wathen-Dunn, W. *Comparison of voicing periodicities and formant frequencies for one speaker in air and in a helium-oxygen mixture at various pressures.* JASA 35:804.

Williams, T. H., *et al. The intrinsic innervation of the soft palate.* J. Anat. 97:259–267.

Wilson, K. V. *Multidimensional analyses of confusions of English consonants.* Amer. J. Psychol. 76:89–95.

Wittenborg, M. H., *et al. Simple roentgenographic demonstration of Eustachian tubes and abnormalities.* Amer. J. Roentg., Rad. Ther. and Nuclear Med. 89:1194–1200.

Wolpert, L., *et al. An electron microscope study of the development of the blastula of the sea urchin embryo and its radial polarity.* Exper. Cell Res. 30:287–300.

Yaggi, Jr., L. A., *et al. Polymodal vocoder; a new approach to versatile and reliable voice communication.* JASA 35:806.

Yanda, R. L., *et al. A comparison of peak expiratory flow rates and normal breathing capacity.* Amer. Rev. Respiratory Diseases 88:92–94.

Yates, A. J. *Delayed auditory feedback.* Psychol. Bull. 60:213–232.—Bibliography.

Zwislocki, J., *et al. Post-mortem acoustic impedance of human ears.* JASA 35:104–107.—Impedance greater than in living ear.

INDEX

INDEX

NOTE. Material in the *Appendix* has not been included in this *Index*. The *Glossary* should be consulted for definitions of a variety of useful terms arranged alphabetically. For references to articles and books or to workers in the field of Voice Science consult the *Bibliography and Chronicle*. Important additional information will be found following many of the references to journal articles.

NOTE. Material in the *Appendix* has not been included in the *Index*. Attention is called to the definitions arranged alphabetically in the *Glossary*. Consult the *Bibliography and Chronicle* for additional information following many of the references to journal articles. See, also, the material in the section on *Metric Equivalents* and in the section on *The Laboratory*.

Chapter 8 - 297 quality

M, W 2:00 - 2:30 211

T 1:30 - 2:30 211